AYURVEDIC MEDICINAL PLANTS OF INDIA

Volume - 2

Dr. Ramesh Kumar Bhutya
Ayurvedacharya
Physician In-charge
Government Ayurvedic Hospital
Bhiya Distt. Bundi (Raj.)

SCIENTIFIC
PUBLISHERS

Dr. Ramesh Kumar Bhutya
3/25, Shiv Vatika Marg,
Keshavrai Patan
(Distt. Bundi) (Rajasthan)
Mobile: 09414538301

Published by:

SCIENTIFIC PUBLISHERS (INDIA)
5A, New Pali Road, P.O. Box 91
Jodhpur 342 001, India
E-mail: info@scientificpub.com
Website: www.scientificpubonline.com

Print: 2026

ISBN: 978-81-7233-735-3 (Vol. 2)
978-81-7233-684-4 (Vol. 1)
978-81-7233-736-0 (Set)
eISBN: 978-93-87307-32-2

Printed in India

Dedicated to
Respected
Dr. Satish Sharma
Range Forest Officer, Udaipur
Famous Zoologist and Botanist,
Critical Researcher, Enthusiastic Scientist

Dr. Satish Kumar Sharma

Range Forest Officer
Forest Research Farm,
Banki (Sisarma) Udaipur,
Rajasthan

Foreword

Dr. R.K. Bhutya, a famous Ayurveda physician of Rajasthan and author of present book had produced a notable volume on Ayurvedic medicinal plants of India in Hindi entitled 'Vanaspati Aushadha Vigyan' in 2007. His Hindi book was well received by the Ayurved experts, teachers, students and public.

There was a constant demand from the Ayurveda experts, teachers, students and public to produce a similar type of book in English language also. Present book is in the massive volume which is an outcome of Dr. Bhutya's dedicated efforts which were intensified after publication of his Hindi book.

Present book is not an English version of his Hindi volume but a separately written independent book having various aspects of medicinal plants, which are well known to Ayurveda. Dr. Bhutya has described 287 plants in first volume and 213 plants in second volume in depth. His descriptions comprising Latin names of plants, their synonyms, classification, detail of vegetative and reproductive organs, phenology, ecology, parts used, dosage, collection period, clinical properties, mode of action and diseases which can be cured. Author has provided many indices at the end of each volume which enhance quality and usability of the book. Colour photographs are strength of the book which will be helpful in easy identification of plants. Most of the photographs were taken by the author himself from various parts of the country.

Dr. Bhutya has thrown sufficient light on classical properties of plants, chemical composition of their various parts and their action on different diseases.

I am sure that this book will prove an asset for Ayurveda experts, teachers, students, nature lovers, medicinal plant growers and common people.

(Dr. Satish Kumar Sharma)

9-5-2010

Preface

In recent years interest in medicinal plants has increased considerably world wide. It has also drawn the attention from common men in general and scholars in the medical streams particular due to sharp rise in problems as a result of adverse/side effects of modern medical science treatments, methods and medicines. In the today's advanced technological era, pharmaceutical companies are launching new medicines every now and then without sound rational and scientific evidence. Their consequences are only known after 10-20 years of their continuous use. By then it may have caused a very serious damage to the public health. This poses a serious threat to the health of the common men, particularly in a country like India, where majority of the people live in villages and lie below poverty line and unable to afford costly medical treatment. For instance, sharp increase in diabetes mellitus among people is observed in recent times and some antibiotics were found responsible for it. Even medical practitioners have started acknowledging the fact now that for most of the diseases the real culprits are either doctors themselves or the medicines they prescribed to the patients. In the light of the above, the curiosity about the sources of the medicines, medicinal plants in most of the cases, has drawn considerable interest among all quarters of the medical science. This further paves the way for the quest for the authentic literature related to the systematic classification of the medicinal plants with the updated information in detail. It won't be out of place to mention here that in spite of availability of a lot of books on medicinal plants in the market, readers are not found them satisfactory as their issues are not adequately addressed and hence, not successfully fulfill their requirements. Some books have focused in detail on a particular aspect of medicinal plants while neglecting the others, whereas, other books are good from botanical perspective but not found appropriate from the point of view of Ayurveda. Even some Ayuverdic books on medicinal plants found contradicting with the ancient classical books on Ayurveda and observed incorrect. Similarly, classic Ayurvedic books have not found acceptability due their lack of botanical coverage. It all leads to chaos and confusion in identification of medicinal plants among academicians, practitioners and research scholars. Author has identified the need for a balanced literature on medicinal plants which may be appropriate for both the people from botany and Ayurveda. This was the major motivation behind writing this book.

In addition, in the absence of proper knowledge related to the identification of medicinal plants, many plants remained either unidentified or wrongly identified. As a result, many important and precious medicinal plants are often considered as weeds and disposed off as waste material. Wrong identification even lead towards more serious repercussions as these may be used wrongly in preparing medicines for which they are not recommended due to different chemical constituents, and hence deprived of their actual uses.

In this book, an attempt is made to fill the above identified gaps. It is my firm belief that this book will be of immense use to Ayurveda experts, teachers, students of post-graduates and under-graduates Ayurvedic courses, researchers, students of botany, scientists, pharmacologists, pharmaceutical organizations, pharmacists, biochemists, medical men and even common men.

However, I have tried to the best of my abilities and knowledge to produce a book containing all major aspects of Ayurvedic medicines and their source plants, even than some gaps and laps may prevail. I will be grateful to the readers for their suggestions and valuable feedback.

Salient features of the book

1. The latest and updated botanical names, synonyms, species, varieties, families, old families and Ayurvedic classical groups are given in this book. Classical names include only those maintained in ancient Ayurvedic literature.
2. English, Sanskrit, Hindi and Local names are also given.
3. Complete botanical identification with habit, root, stem, leaf, flower, fruit and seed with full morphological features and measurement of length, width and height are presented, which would be helpful in tentative identification of the plant in the field.
4. Habitat or distribution of plant in India is meant to give a broad idea of the availability of the species in different eco-climatic zones and altitudes.
5. Flowering and fruiting period of plant is also given, although it is variable due to different geological situation in India.
6. Parts used, dosage and collection period of described plant is presented at appropriate places.
7. Ayurvedic classical properties with purity, its effect on *Vaata, Pitta* and *Kapha*. Grading of effects is also given.
8. Chemical composition of all parts of plant, with action are also given.
9. Action and disease indication of all parts of plant. These are based on ancient as well as recent ayurvedic literature.
10. Clinical uses of different parts of plant, on different disease. Here are, safe, selected, effective, practical and experienced formulae are given.
11. Under formulations, only classical Ayurvedic preparations are included, patent and proprietary items are not included.
12. Determination of doubtful classical Ayurvedic plants with botanical names.
13. Findings related to toxicology and therapeutic evaluation as and where available have been included under respective subheads.
14. For convenience or further readings, list of consulted books and page number of plant is given.
15. Photos of all plants in natural habitat are also given. All photos are original, with quality, distinguishable and taken by author at various places of India. A very little number photos are received from other source.
16. Classification and plant collection of modern style of action are given, which is very valuable chapter of book. Here are 75 groups are described with botanical and Hindi names.
17. For convenience in treatment and practical point of view, there is classification of clinical uses according to various diseases in alphabetical order with serial number of plants.
18. Index of classical formulations with serial numbers of plant, is given.
19. List of Families of described plants is given, here are 87 families are classified.
20. Index of English names of described plants is given with serial numbers.
21. Glossary of Botanical words is given.
22. Glossary of Medical term is also given. For readers convenience, there are simple names of diseases, instead of complicated medical terminology.
23. Meaning of Ayurvedic and Hindi words, used in this book, that translation in English cannot be possible in true sense.
24. Resource plant of various gums is given.
25. Bibliography.
26. List of plants covered in Volume-1.
27. Index of Botanical names, synonyms and species, with serial numbers is also given.
28. Key index of botanical names covered in volume-1 and volume-2.
29. At last, a composite list of Sanskrit, Hindi and Local names is given for readers' convenience.

However, this book should be viewed in the light of following points-

1. Botanical characteristics have not been discussed with deep botanical description. This is merely reported on the basis of visual inspection.
2. Clinical uses are given with utmost care and should be implemented with advice of qualified Ayurvedic doctor. Author will not be held responsible for any complicacy.
3. There is much variation in flowering and fruiting time due to different eco-climatic zones of India.
4. There are compound drugs in the inverted coma.
5. Use clarified butter of cow, by the name of clarified butter.
6. Use oil of *Sesamum orientale,* by the name of oil.
7. Use milk of cow, by the name of milk.
8. Always use roasted seeds of *Cuminum cyminum,* even not described.
9. Always use fried gum of *Ferula narthex,* even not described.
10. Do not take cold water, after the drugs, taken with oil or clarified butter.

A few words of gratitude:

In preparing this book, the help of various sources has been taken. I would like thank all the authorities whose works are consulted during the preparation of this book.

I would like to express my grateful thanks for their valuable guidance and advice. I am indebted to Dr. Satish Sharma, Range Forest Officer, Udaipur, a constant source of inspiration throughout the development of this book for his valuable guidance and timely help. He went out of the way to help me in spite of his very busy schedule and other professional commitments. Further, I am grateful to my colleagues Dr. R.S. Garg, Ayurvedic physician, Baran, Dr. O.P. Chaturvedi, Ay. Physician, Jaipur, Dr. P.S. Solanki, Ay. Physician, Kota, and Dr. Ashok Saxena, Ay. Physician, Bundi, Dr. J.P. Sharma, Ay. Physician, Bundi, Dr. Gopi Nath Pareek, Jaipur, Dr. Shri Krishan Khandal, Professor, N.I.A. Jaipur for their advice and support. I am also thankful to Dr. L.K. Dadhich, Ex. principal, J.D.B. Girls College, Kota, Mr. Dalpat Singh Rajpurohit, Range Forest Officer, Udaipur, for their valuable guidance. My heartfelt thanks are also due to Mr. Satyawan Sharma, Son-in-law, Mrs. Kamini Sharma, daughter, Dushyant Sharma, Son, Mrs. Kirti Sharma, Daughter-in-law, Mr. Milind, Mrs. Kumud Sharma and other family members for their constant support and assistance. Last but not the least; I am extremely grateful to my wife Smt. Manju Sharma for her patience as she almost freed me in discharging my domestic responsibilities during writing this piece of work.

My thanks are also due to Mr. Pawan ji, Mr. Tanay ji and Rajesh ojha, Scientific Publishers (India), Jodhpur.

Dr. Ramesh Kumar Bhutya

3/25, Keshorai Patan, District Bundi, Rajasthan.

E-mail : rameshbhutya@gmail.com

Contents

AYURVEDIC MEDICINAL PLANTS OF INDIA

288. *Macrotyloma uniflorum* Linn.

Family: Papilionaceae; Fabaceae

Synonym: *Dolichos biflorus, Vigna uniquiculata.*

Name: English: Horsegram **Sanskrit:** *Kulattha, Kulatthikaa, Khalva, Vardhipatraka,* **Hindi:** *Kulathi.* **Local:** *Kulathi*

Botanical characteristics: Habit: An annual, much branched sub-erect or trailing herb. **Stem:** Branches downy or glabrescent. **Leaf:** Trifoliate, leaflets 2.5-5 cm, broadly lanceolate or oblong, entire, membranous, downy stipels sublets, stipules oblong, basifixed. **Flower:** Yellow, 1.25-1.85 cm long, 1-3 in the axil of the leaves, one at the base and two placed laterally. **Fruit:** Pods, compressed, sword-shaped, about 3-5 cm long, tipped with the persistent style, 5-6 seeded. **Seed:** Compressed, reniform, grey or reddish-brown.

Flowering and fruiting period: September-October and November-December.

Habitat: Cultivated throughout India, up to 915 m elevation, mostly in Tamilnadu, Karnataka, Maharastra and Andhra Pradesh.

Parts used: Seed. **Dosage:** 3-6 g.

Collection period: November-December.

Ayurvedic properties: ***Ras:*** *kashaaya,* ***Gun:*** *laghu, rukhsa,* ***Veerya:*** *ushna,* ***Vipaka:*** *katu,* ***Tridosha*** **Effect:** alleviates ***Kapha:*** ++, ***Vaata:*** +, aggrevates ***Pitta:*** +.

Chemical constituents: The **Seeds** contain crude protein 20.8, pentosan 10.8 and water soluble gum 2.8, starch 52, oil 2, ash 3.2, phosphoric acid 1%, and urease, haemag-glutinin and a protease inhibitor has been reported, also several common phytosterols including 24-methylene-25-methylcholesterol and 24-alpha-ethyl-5-alpha-cholest-9-en-3-alpha-ol.

Action and disease indications: The **Seeds** are thermogenic, astringent, anaphrodisiac, anthelmintic, diaphoretic, diuretic, emmenogogue, febrifuge, expectorant, ophthalmic and tonic, prescribed for urolithiasis, nephrolithiasis, piles, tumours, obesity, bronchitis, spleenomegaly, asthma, strangury, hiccough, ophthalmopathy and verminosis.

Clinical uses: Renal and vesical calculus: Decoction of seed powder of described plant 6 g, with honey 10 g, **or** seed powder of described plant 6 g, with juice of leaves of *Raphanus sativus* 20 ml, with water three times a day. **Hiccough:** Smoking of seed powder of described plant 10 g, as required. **Mumps:** Local application of paste of seeds of described plant. **Inflammation:** Hot fomentation by seed powder of described plant is beneficial.

Formulations: *Asmarihar kwaatha, Agurvaadi taila, Kulathyaadhya ghrita, Kulatthaadi pralepa.*

Recommended readings

Bhutya, R.K. (2007), Vanaspati Aushadha Vigyana, Scientific Publishers (India), Jodhpur, PP. 70.

Chunekar, K.C. (2004), Bhava Prakash Nighantu, Chaukhambha Bharti Academy, Varanasi, PP. 651.

Dhiman, A.K. (2006), Ayurvedic Drug Plants, Daya Publishing House, Delhi, PP. 220.

Khare, C.P. (2007), Indian Medicinal Plants, Springer (India) P.L. New Delhi, PP. 222.

Kirtikar, K.R. & Basu, B.D. (1998), Indian Medicinal Plants, L.M Basu, Allahabad, Vol. 1, PP. 805.

Misra, B.L. (2005), Dravya Guna Hastamalaka, Publication scheme, Jaipur, PP. 276.

Nair, R. Vasudevan (2007), Indian Medicinal Plants, Orient Longman P.L. Chennai, Vol. 3, PP. 358.

Namjoshi, A.N. (2001), The Ayurvedic Pharmacopoeia of India, Government of India, Department of Indian Systems of Medicine & Homoeopathy, New Delhi, Part-1, Volume- 2, PP. 75.

Prajapati, N.D., Purohit, S.S., Sharma, A.K. & Tarun Kumar (2003), A Hand Book of Medicinal Plants, Agrobios India, Jodhpur, PP. 328.

Sharma, P.V. (1981), Dravya gun vigyana, Chaukhambha Bharti Academy, Varanasi, Vol. 1, PP. 654.

Singh, R.S. (2002), Vanoshadhi Nirdeshika, Uttar Pradesh Hindi Sansthan, Lucknow, PP. 114.

289. *Madhuca longifolia* (Koen.) Macb.

Family: Sapotaceae.

Synonym: *M.indica, Bassia latifolia.*

Other similar plants: *M.neriifolia* Syn. *Bassia neriifolia, M.malabarica.*

Name: English: Mahua Tree, Moha, **Sanskrit:** *Madhooka, Gurpushpa, Madhupushpa, Madhushrvaa, Vaanprastha, Madhusthila,* **Hindi:** *Mahuaa,* **Local:** *Mahuaa.*

Botanical characteristics: Habit: A large evergreen tree, with a dense spreading crown, 20 m high. **Stem:** With dark grey or brownish scaly bark. **Leaf:** Alternate or sub-opposite, thin, often clustered at the end of the branchlets, elliptic or ovate, 7.5-18 by 4-7.5 cm, broad, entire, undulate, shortly acuminate, young leaves densely wooly at beneath, with slender petioles 2.5-3.75 cm long, and 12-15 pairs of main nerves. **Flower:** Pale yellow and fleshy, appearing in dense clusters near the end of branchlets, corolla tubuler, fleshy, pale yellow, sweetish, edible, aromatic and caduceus, pedicel 2.5-3.75 cm long, tomentose and drooping. Flowers looks like the dry fruits of *Vitis vinifera,* when dry. **Fruit:** Berry, 2.5-5 cm long, ovoid, yellow when ripe, edible, 1-3 seeded. **Seed:** Ovoid, ellipsoid, polished, oily, brown.

Flowering and fruiting period: April-May and July-August.

Habitat: Throughout central India, common in Maharastra, Andhra Pradesh and Madhya Pradesh, in mixed deciduous forests.

Parts used: Flower, Fruit, Seed oil, bark, leaves.

Dosage: Flower 10-15 g, Juice 10-20 ml, Fruit 5-10 g, Seed oil 10-20 g, bark, leaves 10-20 g.

Collection period: April-July.

Ayurvedic properties: ***Ras:*** *madhur,* ***Gun:*** *guru, snigdha,* ***Veerya:*** *sheeta* ***Vipaka:*** *madhur* ***Tridosha*** **Effect:** alleviates ***Vaata:*** **+++**, ***Pitta:*** **++**.

Chemical constituents: The **Flowers** contain vitamin A, ascorbic acid, thiamine, riboflavin, niacin, folic acid, pantothenic acid, biotin and inositol and sugars- sucrose, maltose, glucose, fructose, arabinose and rhamnose. The **Fruits** contain triterpenoids including alpha and beta amyrin acetate; *n*-haxacosanol, beta-D-glucoside of beta-sitosterol and free sitosterol. The **seeds** contain saponins-2,3-*di*-O-glucopyranoside of basic acid (Saponin A and B). The **seeds** exhibits spermicidal activity.

Action and disease indications: The **Flowers** are sweet, diuretic, stimulant, demulcent, bechic, refrigerant and anthelmintic, used for verminosis, strangury, haemoptysis and heptomegaly. The **fruits** are sweet, refrigerant, aphrodisiac and tonic, used for dipsia, bronchitis, consumption. The **seed oil** contains emollient, galactagogue, emetic and laxative, used in skin diseases, rheumatism, pneumonia, headache and piles. The **bark** is astringent, anti-rheumatic, emollient, used for tonsillitis, gum troubles, diabetes and ulcers.

Clinical uses: Nervous Debility and Neuralgia: *'Khsira paka'* of flowers of described plant 5 g, two times a day. **Nervous pains and skin diseases:** Massage of seed oil of described plant is beneficial. **Orchitis:** Local application of hot paste of flowers of described plant is very beneficial. **Hemorrhoids:** Local application of fried paste of flowers of described plant is relive pain and inflammation. **Excess and contaminated urination, burning sensation of urine, general debility, Indigestion:** *'Gulkand'* of flower of described plant 10 g, is very beneficial. **Headache, Hypertension:** Juice of flowers of described plant 10 ml, with fruits of *Vitis vinifera* 10 g and sugar candy 5 g, two times a day. **Hiccough:** Juice of flowers of described plant 10 ml, with *Mesua ferrea* 2 g, sugar candy 10 g and honey 10 g, as required. **Nausea and vomiting:** Juice of flowers of described plant 10 ml, honey 10 g and Clarified butter 5 g, as required. **Stiffness:** Local application of hot paste of flowers of described plant with water, is beneficial.

Formulations: *Madhukaasava, Arjunaarista, Kutajaarista, Chandanaasava, Nyagrodhaadi churna, Elaadhya modaka, Madhukaadhyavaleha, Shriparnyaadi Kwaatha.*

Recommended readings

Bhutya, R.K. (2007), Vanaspati Aushadha Vigyana, Scientific Publishers (India), Jodhpur, PP. 173.

Chunekar, K.C. (2004), Bhava Prakash Nighantu, Chaukhambha Bharti Academy, Varanasi, PP. 579 .

Dhiman, A.K. (2006), Ayurvedic Drug Plants, Daya Publishing House, Delhi, PP. 241.

Khare, C.P. (2007), Indian Medicinal Plants, Springer (India) P.L. New Delhi, PP. 392.

Misra, B.L. (2005), Dravya Guna Hastamalaka, Publication scheme, Jaipur, PP. 412.

Nair, R. Vasudevan, (2007), Indian Medicinal Plants, Orient Longman P.L. Chennai, Vol. 3, PP. 362.

Namjoshi, A.N. (2001), The Ayurvedic Pharmacopoeia of India, Government of India, Department of Indian Systems of Medicine & Homoeopathy, New Delhi, Part-1, Volume- 1, PP. 102.

Prajapati, N.D., Purohit, S.S., Sharma, A.K. & Tarun Kumar (2003), A Hand Book of Medicinal Plants, Agrobios India, Jodhpur, PP. 328.

Sharma, P.C., Yelne, MB. & Denis, T.J. (2000), Database on medicinal plants used in ayurveda, Central Council for research in Ayurveda and siddha, Vol. 4, PP. 383.

Sharma, P.V. (1981), Dravya gun vigyana, Chaukhambha Bharti Academy, Varanasi, Vol. 1, PP. 813 .

Singh, R.S. (2002), Vanoshadhi Nirdeshika, Uttar Pradesh Hindi Sansthan, Lucknow, PP. 298.

Swami, K.N. (1985), Gavon Main Aushadh Ratna, Kalera Krishana Gopal, Kalera (Raj.), Vol. 3, PP. 173.

290. *Majorana hortensis* Linn.

Family: Labiatae; Lamiaceae.

Synonym: *Origanum majorana.*

Other similar plants: *Origanum vulgare.*

Name: English: Sweet Majaram, **Sanskrit:** *Marubaka, Maaruta, Maruta, Maru, Fani, Fanijjaka, Prasthapushpa, Samiran, Kharpatra,* **Hindi:** *Maruaa,* **Local:** *Maruaa.*

Botanical characteristics: Habit: An erect, perinnial, aromatic herb, 60-90 cm high. **Stem:** Much branched, more or less hairy. **Leaf:** Stalked, ovate or ovate-lanceolate, 3.5-4.5 cm long, 1,5 - 2.5 cm wide slightly toothed, slightly reddish. **Flower:** Small, white or purplish, in terminal clusters, bracts ovate. **Seed:** Minute, oval, dark brown.

Flowering and fruiting period: June-August and September-November.

Habitat: Throughout India, commonly grown in gardens.

Parts used: Whole plant, oil.

Dosage: Juice 5-10 ml, oil 2-5 drops.

Collection period: November-February.

Ayurvedic properties: ***Ras:*** *katu, tikta,* ***Gun:*** *laghu, rukhsa, Tikhsna,* ***Veerya:*** *ushna,* ***Vipaka:*** *katu,* ***Tridosha*** **Effect:** alleviates ***Kapha:*** ++, ***Vaata:*** + .

Chemical constituents: The **Herb** contains 3% volatile oil, comprising sabinene hydrate, sabinene, linalool, carvacrol, estrogole, eugenol and terpens; flavonoids including luleolin-7-glucoside, diosmetin-7-glucoside, epigenin-7-glucoside; rosmarinic acid, cafeic acid; and triterpenoids as urssolic acid, oleanolic acid and sterols.

Action and disease indications: The **Plant** is emmenogogue, anti-spasmodic, appetizer, carminative, expectorant, anthelmintic, alexipharmic, useful in leucoderma, fevers, pruritis, asthma, cardiac diseases, skin diseases, diaphoretic, heptomegaly, inflammations, constipation, flatulence, and pains.

Clinical uses: Foul ulcers: Local application of paste of leaves of described plant is beneficial. **Sprue:** Juice of described plant 20 ml, with honey 10 g, three times a day. **Cloasma:** Local application of leaves of described plant with seed powder of *Lens culinaris,* with fresh milk of she goat is very beneficial.

Formulations: *Chandrakalaa rasa, Pratisyayahar sharbata, Paardaartihar yoga, Agurvaadi taila.*

Recommended readings

Acharya, B.K. (2008), Ayurveda Jadi-buti Rahasya, Patanjali Yogapitha, Haridwar, PP. 284.

Bhutya, R.K. (2007), Vanaspati Aushadha Vigyana, Scientific Publishers (India), Jodhpur, PP. 175.

Chunekar, K.C. (2004), Bhava Prakash Nighantu, Chaukhambha Bharti Academy, Varanasi, PP. 510.

Khare, C.P. (2007), Indian Medicinal Plants, Springer (India) P.L. New Delhi, PP. 452.

Kirtikar, K.R. & Basu, B.D. (1998), Indian Medicinal Plants, L.M Basu, Allahabad, Vol. 3, PP. 1985.

Prajapati, N.D., Purohit, S.S., Sharma, A.K. & Tarun Kumar (2003), A Hand Book of Medicinal Plants, Agrobios India, Jodhpur, PP. 329.

Sharma, P.V. (1981), Dravya gun vigyana, Chaukhambha Bharti Academy, Varanasi, Vol. 1, PP. 397.

291. *Malaxis acuminata* D.Don.

Family: Orchidaceae.

Synonym: *Microstylis wallichi.*

Ayurvedic Groups: Charak: *Jivaniya, Ashtavarga.*

Name: Sanskrit: *Jivaka, Madhur, shringa, Hrisvanga, Kurchashirshaka,* **Hindi:** *Jivaka,* **Local:** *Jivaka.*

Botanical characteristics: Habit: A terrestrial herb, height 5-30 cm. New plant arising from the side of mother plant which is decaying. **Tuber:** More or less pseudo bulb at the base and fibrous roots. **Stem:** Short. **Leaf:** Simple, alternate, 3-4, sheathing, ovate or lanceolate, acute, 5-15 cm long. **Flower:** Minute, 1 cm in diam., pale yellowish-green, tinged with purple in terminal racemes. Sides of the lip produced upwards into auricles, apex notched.

Flowering and fruiting period: July-August and September-October.

Habitat: Throughout India, Northern Himalayas at altitude of 1500 to 3000 m. Mostly at Meghalaya, Himachal Pradesh, Simala, Chamba, Khajiyar, Deharadun Mausoorie, Chamauli, Ukhimatha, Almora and Ranikheta.

Parts used: Green swollen stem base covered by brown scales.

Dosage: 3-6 g.

Collection period: September-October.

Ayurvedic properties: ***Ras:*** *madhur,* ***Gun:*** *guru, snigdha,* ***Veerya:*** *sheeta* ***Vipaka:*** *madhur*

***Tridosha* Effect:** alleviates ***Vaata:* ++, *Pitta:* ++**, aggrevates ***Kapha:* ++.**

Action and disease indications: The **Plant** is Sweet, refrigerant, aphrodisiac, febrifuge and tonic, used for seminal weakness, hematemesis, fevers, burning sensation, dipsia, emaciation, tuberculosis and general debility.

Clinical uses: Seminal weakness, general debility, necrospermia, oligogalactia, sexual debility: Stem base of described plant 3 g, Stem base of *Malaxis muscifera* 3 g, *Withania somnifera* 2 g, *Asparagus racemosus* 2 g, root of *Argyreia nervosa* 2 g, with milk, two times a day. **Burning sensation, fever, epistaxis:** Stem base of described plant 2 g, *Glycyrhiza glabra* 1 g, *Asparagus racemosus* 3 g, with water, two times a day.

Formulations: *Chyavanpraasha, Ashok ghrita, Mahaa sudarsana churna.*

Recommended readings

Acharya, B.K. (2005), Jivani Shakti Vardhaka Astavarga Padapa, Patanjali Yogapitha, Haridwar, PP. 34.

Bhutya, R.K. (2007), Vanaspati Aushadha Vigyana, Scientific Publishers (India), Jodhpur, PP. 110.

Chunekar, K.C. (2004), Bhava Prakash Nighantu, Chaukhambha Bharti Academy, Varanasi, PP. 61.

Khare, C.P. (2007), Indian Medicinal Plants, Springer (India) P.L. New Delhi, PP. 414.

Nair, R.Vasudevan, (2007), Indian Medicinal Plants, Orient Longman P.L. Chennai, Vol. 3, PP. 367.

Prajapati, N.D., Purohit, S.S., Sharma, A.K. & Tarun Kumar (2003), A Hand Book of Medicinal Plants, Agrobios India, Jodhpur, PP. 330.

292. *Malaxis muscifera* (Lindley) Kuntz.

Family: Orchidaceae.

Synonym: *Microstylis musifera.*

Ayurvedic Groups:Charak: *Jivaniya, Ashtavarga.*

Name: Sanskrit: *Rishabha, Vrishabha, Dhira, Vishaani, Drakhsa.* **Hindi:** *Rishabhaka,* **Local:** *Rishabhaka.*

Botanical characteristics: Habit: A terrestrial herb, height 10-40 cm. **Tuber:** Small ovoid pseudo bulb at the base and fibrous roots. **Stem:** Short. **Leaf:** 3-5, unequal, short-petioled, oblong or ovate, acuminate, 3-10 by 2.5-3 cm. **Flower:** pale yellowish-green, in terminal racemes, 10-25 mm long, lip fleshy, broadly ovate, 4 mm long, basal portion excavated, obscurely angled on either side of the base, apex acuminate.

Flowering and fruiting period: July-August and September-October.

Habitat: Throughout India, in Northern Himalayas at altitude of 1500 to 4000 m, mostly at Simala, Pithoragarh, Almora, Chakarata, Chamouli, Vasukital, Rambaaraa, Harsil, flower's valley, Hemkund and Uttarkaasi.

Parts used: Green swollen stem base covered with brown scales. **Dosage:** 3-6 g.

Collection period: September-October.

Ayurvedic properties: ***Ras:*** *madhur,* ***Gun:*** *guru, snigdha,* ***Veerya:*** *sheeta* ***Vipaka:*** *madhur* ***Tridosha* Effect:** alleviates ***Vaata:* ++, *Pitta:* ++**, aggrevates ***Kapha:* ++ .**

Action and disease indications: The **Plant** is sweet, refrigerant, aphrodisiac, anti-dysenteric, styptic, febrifuge and tonic, used for seminal weakness, sterility, hemorrhage, dysentery, burning sensation, fevers, emaciation and general debility.

Clinical uses: Seminal weakness, general debility, necrospermia, excess and contaminated urination, oligogalactia, sexual debility: Stem base of described plant 3 g, Stem base of *Malaxis acuminata* 3 g, *Withania somnifera* 2 g, *Asparagus racemosus* 2 g, root of *Argyreia nervosa* 2 g, with milk, two times a day. **Burning sensation, fever, dispesis, epistaxis:** Stem base of described plant 2 g, *Glycyrhiza glabra* 1 g, *Asparagus racemosus* 3 g, with water, two times a day.

Formulations: *Chyavanpraasha, Mahaa sudarshan churna.*

Recommended readings

Acharya, B.K. (2005), Jivani Shakti Vardhaka Astavarga Padapa, Patanjali Yogapitha, Haridwar, PP. 36.

Bhutya, R.K. (2007), Vanaspati Aushadha Vigyana, Scientific Publishers (India), Jodhpur, PP. 37.

Chunekar, K.C. (2004), Bhava Prakash Nighantu, Chaukhambha Bharti Academy, Varanasi, PP. 61.

Khare, C.P. (2007), Indian Medicinal Plants, Springer (India) P.L. New Delhi, PP. 414.

Nair, R. Vasudevan, (2007), Indian Medicinal Plants, Orient Longman P.L. Chennai, Vol. 3, PP. 371.

Prajapati, N.D., Purohit, S.S., Sharma, A.K. & Tarun Kumar (2003), A Hand Book of Medicinal Plants, Agrobios India, Jodhpur, PP. 330.

293. *Mallotus philipensis* Muell.-Arg.

Family: Euphorbiaceae.

Ayurvedic Groups: Charak: *Virechan,* **Sushruta:** *Adhobhagahar, Shyamaadi gana.*

Name: English: Kamala Tree, Monkey Face Tree **Sanskrit:** *Kaampilla, Karkasha, Chandra, Raktaanga, Rochana.* **Hindi:** *Kampillaka,* **Local:** *Kabilaa.*

Botanical characteristics: Habit: A small tree, height 5-9 m. **Stem:** Much branched, girth 1-1.35 m, bark grey or pale brown, rough, with irregular fissures, branchlets young leaves and inflorescence tawny or rusty pubescent. **Leaf:** Alternate, variable, ovate or ovate-lanceolate, 7.5-20 by 3-7.5 cm, three ribbed at the base, acuminate, entire or shortly serrate, glabrous above, pubescent and with numerous orbicular red glands beneath, base rounded or acute, petioles 2.5-5 cm long, cylindrical, fulvous-pubescent, with 2 small sessile glands one on each side. Shape like leaves of *Ficus racemosa.* **Flower:** Dioecious, small in spikes, the males clustered sessile or very shortly pedicellate in erect long terminal spikes, usually several together and often longer than the leaves; the females nearly sessile, in short spikes. **Fruit:** Capsules, globose, 3-lobed, 8-10 mm in diam., covered over with dense bright reddish brown glandular pubescent powder. **Seed:** One seed in each lobe, 3-4 mm diam., sub-globose, black and smooth.

Flowering and Fruiting period: September-November and February-May.

Habitat: Throughout tropical regions of India, in evergreen and deciduous forests up to 1500 m in the outer Himalaya.

Parts used: Glandular hairs of fruit. **Dosage:** 1-3 g.

Collection period: February-May.

Ayurvedic properties: ***Ras:*** *katu,* ***Gun:*** *laghu, rukhsa,,* ***Veerya:*** *ushna,* ***Vipaka:*** *katu,* ***Tridosha*** **Effect:** alleviates ***Kapha:*** **++.** ***Vata:*** **++.**

Chemical constituents: The **Capsule hairs and glands** contain phloroglucinol derivatives; rottlerin, isorottlerin, iso-allorottlerin and menthylene-*bis*-methyl-phloroacetophenone, kamalins 1 and 2.

Action and disease indications: The **glands and hairs of fruits** are thermogenic, purgative, anthelmintic, digestive, lithontriptic, depurative, styptic and alexipharmic, used for the treatment of scabies, pruritis, ringworm, herpes, tapeworm infestation, constipation, flatulence, wounds ulcers, cough, renal and vesical calculi, haemorrhage and parasitic skin diseases.

Clinical uses: Skin diseases, pruritis, scabies: Tropical use of powder of described plant 50 g, sulphur 6 g, gum of *Shorea robusta* 6 g, leaves of *Lowsonia inermis* 2 g, root of *Zizyphus nummularia* 2 g, leaves of *Azadirachta indica* 2 g, Blue vitriol 3 g, in *'Shatadhota ghrit'* or seed oil of *Brassica campestris* is very beneficial. **Tape worm, round worm and tread worm infestation:** Powder of described plant 3-6 g, raw sugar 15 g, with hot water, or distillate of *Trachyspermum ammi* 20 ml, at night, weekly. **Verminosis:** Mix powder of described plant, *Embelia ribes, Terminalia chebula,* Nitrate of potash, Rock salt, 4-8 g, with whey, at night, give purgation by Castor oil 20 ml, with hot milk, at morning, **Or** Mix powder of described plant, *Embelia ribes,* seed powder of *Butea monosperma, Hyoscymus niger, Operculina terpenthum,* 2-4 g, with raw sugar 10 g, with whey, two times a day, is very beneficial. **Ulcer and burn:** Local application of paste of powder of described plant, with seed oil of *Pongamia pinnata.* **Alopecia:** Local application of paste of described plant and *'Shatadhota ghrita'.*

Formulations: *Paamaahar lepa, Krimighatini vatikaa, Aditha malham, Paaradaadi malaham.*

Recommended readings

Bhutya, R.K. (2007), Vanaspati Aushadha Vigyana, Scientific Publishers (India), Jodhpur, PP. 51.

Brahmavarchas (2003), Ayurved Ka Pran Vanoshadhi Vigyan, Shanti Kunj, Haridwar, PP. 281.

Chunekar, K.C. (2004), Bhava Prakash Nighantu, Chaukhambha Bharti Academy, Varanasi, PP. 66.

Dhiman, A.K. (2006), Ayurvedic Drug Plants, Daya Publishing House, Delhi, PP. 190.

Khare, C.P. (2007), Indian Medicinal Plants, Springer (India) P.L. New Delhi, PP. 393.

Kirtikar, K.R. & Basu, B.D. (1998), Indian Medicinal Plants, L.M Basu, Allahabad, Vol. 3, PP. 2267.

Misra, B.L. (2005), Dravya Guna Hastamalaka, Publication scheme, Jaipur, PP. 344.

Nair, R.Vasudevan, (2007), Indian Medicinal Plants, Orient Longman P.L. Chennai, Vol. 3, PP. 375.

Namjoshi, A.N. (2001), The Ayurvedic Pharmacopoeia of India, Government of India, Department of Indian Systems of Medicine & Homoeopathy, New Delhi, Part-1, Volume- 2, PP. 55.

Pareek, G.N. (2005), Sudhanidhi, Vanoshadhi Ratnakar, Dhanvantari Karyalaya, Aligarh, Vol. 9, PP. 184.

Prajapati, N.D., Purohit, S.S., Sharma, A.K. & Tarun Kumar (2003), A Hand Book of Medicinal Plants, Agrobios India, Jodhpur, PP. 330.

Sharma, P.C., Yelne, MB. & Denis, T.J. (2000), Database on medicinal plants used in ayurveda, Central Council for research in Ayurveda and siddha, Vol. 5, PP. 101.

Sharma, P.V. (1981), Dravya gun vigyana, Chaukhambha Bharti Academy, Varanasi, Vol. 1, PP. 521.

Singh, R.S. (2002), Vanoshadhi Nirdeshika, Uttar Pradesh Hindi Sansthan, Lucknow, PP. 78.

Swami, K.N. (1985), Gavon Main Aushadh Ratna, Kalera Krishana Gopal, Kalera (Raj.), Vol. 1, PP. 147.

294. *Malus pumila* Mill.

Family: Rosaceae.

Synonym: *M.domestica, M.sylvestris, Pyrus malus.*

Name: English: Apple, **Sanskrit:** *Sinchitikaa, Sivitikaa, Mushtipramaana badar.* **Hindi:** *Seb,* **Local:** *Seb.*

Botanical characteristics: Habit: A deciduous tree, height 15-20 m. **Stem:** Erect, young shoots, underside of leaves and inflorescence clothed with thin white tomentum. **Leaf:** Ovate, acuminate, obtusely serrate, clustered on branchlets, 5-10.5 cm long, petioles usually half the length of leaf or shorter. **Flower:** White, tinged with red, clustered. **Fruit:** Drupe, on a short pedicle, fleshy, large, greenish-yellow or red-brown, glabrous, edible, globose intruded at both ends, crowned by the persistent calyx-lobes. **Seed:** Small, ovate, black-brown.

Flowering and fruiting period: May-June and July-August.

Habitat: Largely cultivated in Himachal Pradesh, Kashmir, Kulu, Kumaon, Assam and in Neelgiris.

Parts used: Fruit, root, bark.

Dosage: Fruit juice 50-100 ml, root, bark 5-10 g.

Collection period: August-September.

Ayurvedic properties: ***Ras:*** *madhur, kashaaya,* ***Gun:*** *guru, snigdha,* ***Veerya:*** *sheeta* ***Vipaka:*** *madhur,* ***Tridosha*** **Effect:** alleviates ***Vaata:*** ++, ***Pitta:*** ++ , aggrevates ***Kapha:*** + .

Chemical constituents: The **Fruits** contain malic acid, citric acid, lactic acid and succinic acid; caffeic acid derivatives, pectins, minearls and vitamins. Fresh apple contains thiamin 0.12, riboflavin 0.03, niacin 0.2 and ascorbic acid 2 mg/100 g. The ascorbic acid content varies widely and values up to 40 mg/100 g. Sugar constitute about 80% of the total carbohydrates of ripe fruits-fructose 60%, glucose 25%, sucrose 15%. The pectin content of the edible portion varies from 0.14 to 0.96% (as calcium pectate). Uronic acid content of apple pectin varies from 0.5-15%. The astringent principles of apple include tannins, tannin derivatives, and flavones. The browning of apple slices on exposure to air is due to enzymic oxidation of tannin compounds. Fresh juice contains 0.2-0.8 malic acid, 11.6 total sugars and 0.021-0.08% tannin.

Action and disease indications: The **Fruits** are refrigerant, fattening, aphrodisiac, constipating, good for heart, brain, liver and stomach, seminiferous, useful in biliousness, seminal weakness, amoebic and bacillary dysentery chronic constipation and general debility.

Clinical uses: Amoebic and basillary dysentery: Jam of fruits of described plant 50 g, three times a day. **Chronic constipation:** Jam of fruits of described plant 25-50 g, at night for 3 months, is very beneficial. **Fever:** Decoction of stem bark of described plant 10 g, with honey 10 g, two times a day. **Helminthiasis, burning sensation, insomnia:** Powder of root bark 5 g, with distil water of *Foeniculum vulgare* 20 ml, two times a day.

Formulations: *Kaamaratnaakaraarka, Maajoon nukaraa.*

Recommended readings:

Bhutya, R.K. (2007), Vanaspati Aushadha Vigyana, Scientific Publishers (India), Jodhpur, PP. 230.

Chunekar, K.C. (2004), Bhava Prakash Nighantu, Chaukhambha Bharti Academy, Varanasi, PP. 589.

Khare, C.P. (2007), Indian Medicinal Plants, Springer (India) P.L. New Delhi, PP. 394.

Kirtikar, K.R. & Basu, B.D. (1998), Indian Medicinal Plants, L.M Basu, Allahabad, Vol. 3, PP. 987.

Sharma, P.V. (1981), Dravya gun vigyana, Chaukhambha Bharti Academy, Varanasi, Vol. 2, PP. 234.

Swami, K.N. (1985), Gavon Main Aushadh Ratna, Kalera Krishana Gopal, Kalera (Raj.), Vol. 3, PP. 365.

295. *Malva sylvestris* Linn.

Family: Malvaceae.

Similar plant: *M. rotundifolia, M. coromandeliana, M. malvestrum.*

Name: English: Common mallow, Blue mallow.

Sanskrit: *Bhustani.* **Hindi:** *Khubbaaji,* **Local:** *Khubbaaji. Gul-kheru.*

Botanical characteristics: Habit: Herb, erect, aerial, branched, biennial or perennial, 30-120 cm high. **Stem:** Herbaceous, aerial, erect, cylindrical, branched, solid, hairy and green. **Leaf:** Cauline and ramal, alternate, stipulate, simple, petiolate, cordate, crenate, obtuse, upper surface glabrous and lower hairy, multicostate reticulate, 3-7 lobed, on long stalk. **Flower:** Bracteate, bracteolate, Bracteols-3, pedicillate, complete, actinomorphic, hermaphrodite, pentamerous, hypogynous, cyclic and purple. **Fruit:** Capsule, smooth. **Seed:** Reniform.

Flowering and fruiting period: April-June.

Habitat: Temperate Himalaya, Kashmir to Kumaun, up to 2400 m and Bihar, Maharastra, Karnataka and Tamilnadu.

Parts used: Flowers, unripe fruits.

Dosage: 4-6 g, for decoction 10 g.

Collection period: May-June.

Ayurvedic properties: Ayurvedic properties: ***Ras:*** *tikta, kashaaya,* ***Gun:*** *laghu, snigdha,* ***Veerya:*** *sheet,* ***Vipaka:*** *katu,* ***Tridosha*** **Effect:** alleviates ***Vaata:*** ++, ***Pitta:*** +, ***Kapha:*** +.

Chemical constituents: The **herb** contain sulphated flavonol, glycosides, mucilage and tannins. Flowers contain malvin, malvidin diglucoside, tannins, carotene and ascorbic acid.

Action and disease indications: Emollient, laxative, mucilaginous, pectoral, antibacterial. It is useful to cure cough colds, bronchitis, pulmonary disorders, cystitis, and whooping cough.

Clinical uses: Whooping cough: Flowers and unripe fruits powder 5g, with honey 15g, 4 times a day. **Bronchitis, cough and cystitis:** Flower powder 4 g, 4 times, with water. **Boils, abscess**: Topical use of unripe fruits pulp.

Recommended readings:

Bhutya, R.K. (2007), Vanaspati Aushadha Vigyana, Scientific publishers, Jodhapur, PP. 80.

Chunekar, K.C. (2004), Bhava Prakash Nighantu, Chaukhambha Bharati Academy, Varanasi, PP. 820.

Khare, C.P. (2007), Indian medicinal plants, Springer (India) P.L.New Delhi, PP. 395.

Kirtikar, K.R. & Basu, B.D. (1998), Indian Medicinal plants, L.M.Basu, Allahabad, Vol. 1, PP. 300.

Pareek, G.N. (2007), Sudhanidhi, Vanoshadhi Ratnakar, Dhanvantari Karyalaya, Aligarh, Vol. 9, PP. 301.

Prajapati, N.D., Purohit, S.S., Sharma, A.K. & Tarun Kumar (2003), A Hand Book of Medicinal Plants, Agrobios India, Jodhapur, PP. 331.

Singh, R.S. (2002), Vanoshadhi Nirdeshika, Uttar Pradesh Hindi Sansathan, Lakhanow, PP. 121.

296. *Mangifera indica* Linn.

Family: Anacardiaceae.

Other similar Plant: *M. coromandeliana* Or *malvastrum.*

Name: English: Mango, **Sanskrit:** *Aamra, rasaala, Sahakaara, Atisorabha, Kaamaanga, Madhudoota, Maakanda, Pikavallabha,* **Hindi:** *Aam,* **Local:** *Aam.*

Botanical characteristics: Habit: A large evergreen spreading tree, height 10-45 m, with a heavy doom shaped crown. **Stem:** Straight, stout clear bole and thick, rough, dark grey bark. **Leaf:** Simple, alternate, crowded at the end of branches, linear-oblong, or elliptic-lanceolate, 12.5-30 by 3.75-7.5 cm, acute, acuminate or subobtuse, entire, coriaceous, dark green, glabrous, margin wavy, base narrowed, petiole 1.2-3.8 cm long, swollen at the base, young leaves soft, pink, specific smell in crushed leaves, bracts ovate concave. **Flower:** Small, 5 mm long, specific sweet odorous, reddish-white or yellowish-green, in large many-flowered pubescent panicles, about 25 cm long, longer than the leaves, male and bisexual flowers are present at the same panicle. **Fruit:** Drupes, fleshy, green, orange, yellow or red in colour, vary in shape, usually 5-20 cm long, obliquely pyriform or subovoid, laterally subcompressed, protuberance at apex, sweet-sour in taste. **Seed:** Solitary, encased in a hard compressed, fibrous endocarp, with plano-convex cotyledons.

Flowering and fruiting period: March-April and May-June.

Habitat: Throughout India, in forests up to 1200 m, also widely cultivated, mostly in Uttar Pradesh, Punjab, Maharastra, Andhra Pradesh, Tamilnadu and West Bengal.

Parts used: Fruit, seed, flower, bark.

Dosage: Fruit juice 50-100 ml, seed 3-6 g, flower 1-3 g, bark 5-10 g.

Collection period: March-June.

Ayurvedic properties: Ripe fruit: ***Ras:*** *madhur,* ***Gun:*** *guru, snigdha,* ***Veerya:*** *ushna,* ***Vipaka:*** *madhur* ***Tridosha*** **Effect:** alleviates ***Vaata:*** **+++,** aggrevates ***Kapha:*** **+,** ***Pitta:*** **+.**

Seed: ***Ras:*** *madhur,* ***Gun:*** *laghu,rukhsa,* ***Veerya:*** *sheeta* ***Vipaka:*** *katu,* ***Tridosha*** **Effect:** alleviates ***Kapha:*** **++,** ***Pitta:*** **+.**

Chemical constituents: The **fruits** contain sugars 9.5-18.6, citric acid 0.12-0.34, ascorbic acid 10.8 mg/100 g, carotenoids as beta-carotene 2000-17000 mcg/100 g, also phenolic compounds (m-digallic acid, gallotannin, phloroglucinol, protocatechuic acid); flavonoids (1,2,3,4-tetrahydroxy benzene, kaempferol and myricetin). The **leaves** contain a pentacyclic triterpene alcohol, besides taraxone, taraxerol, friedelin, lupeol and beta-sitosterol, also several sugars, free malic and citric acids and amino acids. Some esters of benzophenone C-glucosides and kinic and shikmic acids and mangiferin. The **seed** kernel contains alpha and beta amyrins, gallotannin, glucogallin and several sterols. All parts contain phenolic acid (ellagic acid, gallic acid, ethyl gallate); flavonoids (catechin), and xanthones (mangiferin).

Action and disease indications: The **ripe fruits** are thermogenic, sweet, invigorating, emollient, laxative, aphrodisiac, cardio tonic, haemostatic and tonic, used in seminal weakness, anorexia, dyspepsia, cardiopathy, heat apoplexy, haemorrhage, haemoptysis, emaciation, anaemia and general debility. The **Seed kernel** is astringent, refrigerant, anti-inflammatory, anti-bacterial, anti-fungal, anti-spasmodic, anti-scorbutic, anthelmintic, constipating, haemostatic, vulnerary and uterine tonic, prescribed for chronic diarrhea, dysentery, helminthiasis, haemorrhage, haemoptysis, piles, ulcers, bruises, diabetes mellitus, leucorrhea, menorrhagia and menstrual disorder, heart burn, nausea and vomiting. The **unripe fruits** are astringent, refrigerant, digestive, antiscorbutic and carminative, used for gastropathy, dyspepsia, pharyngitis, ulcers, dysentery, urethrorrhea and vaginopathy. The **Root** and **bark** are refrigerant, styptic, vulnerary, anti-emetic, anti-inflammatory, constipating, used for metrorrhegia, leucorrhea, syphilis, wounds, ulcers, vomiting, uteritis, diarrhea, dysentery and rheumatism. The **flowers** are refrigerant, styptic, vulnerary, constipating and hematinic, used for hemorrhage, hemoptysis, wounds, ulcers, anorexia, dyspepsia, gleet, diarrhea, chronic dysentery and anemia.

Clinical uses: Diarrhea, dysentery: Seed powder of described plant 3 g, with cold water, three times a day. **Bleeding piles, menorrhagia, metrorrhagia:** Seed powder of described plant 2 g, *Mesua ferrea* 2 g, *Justisia adhatoda* 1 g, with distil water of *Foeniculum vulgare* 15 ml, or water, three times a day, is very beneficial. **Spleen enlargement:** Juice of ripe fruit of described plant 50-100 g, with honey 20 g, two times a day, for 21 days. **Epistaxis:** Nasal drops of juice of seed of described plant 4-4 drops, as required. **Hiccough:** Smoking of dry and crushed leaves of described plant is very beneficial. **Dysentery:** Mix powder of seed powder of described plant and *Syzygium cumini*, gum of *Bombax ceiba,* root of *Vetiveria zizanoiodes, Symplocos racemosa, Terminalia chebula,* seeds of *Holarrhena antidysentrica,* make pills by decoction of stem bark of *Holarrhena antidysentrica,* of 250 mg. Dose 2-4 pills, three times a day, is very beneficial.

Formulations: *Pushyaanuga churna, Chandana-asava, Ashokaarista, Chandanaadi churna, Visuchikaahar vati, Vridhaa gangadhara churna, Khandaabhrakam, Jaatiphala rasa, Mehamihir taila, Madhukaadhyavaleha.*

Recommended readings:

Acharya, B.K. (2008), Ayurveda Jadi-buti Rahasya, Patanjali Yogapitha, Haridwar, PP. 12.

Bhutya, R.K. (2007), Vanaspati Aushadha Vigyana, Scientific Publishers (India), Jodhpur, PP. 24.

Brahmavarchas (2003), Ayurved Ka Pran Vanoshadhi Vigyan, Shanti Kunj, Haridwar, PP. 282.

Chunekar, K.C. (2004), Bhava Prakash Nighantu, Chaukhambha Bharti Academy, Varanasi, PP. 552.

Dhiman, A.K. (2006), Ayurvedic Drug Plants, Daya Publishing House, Delhi, PP. 33.

Khare, C.P. (2007), Indian Medicinal Plants, Springer (India) P.L. New Delhi, PP. 396.

Kirtikar, K.R. & Basu, B.D. (1998), Indian Medicinal Plants, L.M Basu, Allahabad, Vol. 1, PP. 652.

Nair, R.Vasudevan, (2007), Indian Medicinal Plants, Orient Longman P.L. Chennai, Vol. 3, PP. 380.

Namjoshi, A.N. (2001), The Ayurvedic Pharmacopoeia of India, Government of India, Department of Indian Systems of Medicine & Homoeopathy, New Delhi, Part-1, Volume- 3, PP. 9.

Pareek, G.N. (2005), Sudhanidhi, Vanoshadhi Ratnakar, Dhanvantari Karyalaya, Aligarh, Vol. 1, PP. 325.

Prajapati, N.D., Purohit, S.S., Sharma, A.K. & Tarun Kumar (2003), A Hand Book of Medicinal Plants, Agrobios India, Jodhpur, PP. 332.

Sharma, P.C., Yelne, MB. & Denis, T.J. (2000), Database on medicinal plants used in ayurveda, Central Council for research in Ayurveda and siddha, Vol. 2, PP. 8.

Sharma, P.V. (1981), Dravya gun vigyana, Chaukhambha Bharti Academy, Varanasi, Vol. 1, PP. 661.

Singh, R.S. (2002), Vanoshadhi Nirdeshika, Uttar Pradesh Hindi Sansthan, Lucknow, PP. 34.

Swami, K.N. (1985), Gavon Main Aushadh Ratna, Kalera Krishana Gopal, Kalera (Raj.), Vol. 2, PP. 92.

297. *Manilkara hexandra* (Roxb.) Dubard.

Family: Sapotaceae.

Synonym: *Mimusops hexandra.*

Other similar plants: *Manilkara kauki.*

Name: English: Kauki, **Sanskrit:** *Raajaadan, Phalaadhyakhsa, Rajanyaa, Khsirikaa,* **Hindi:** *Khirani* **Local:** *Reni.*

Botanical characteristics: Habit: A medium sized to large glabrous evergreen tree, height 15-20 m. **Stem:** Clear bole up to 5 m, girth 4 m, bark blackish grey, deeply furrowed. **Leaf:** Simple, alternate, 5-15 cm by 2.5-5 cm, elliptic-obovate or oblong, coriaceous, rounded or emarginated at the apex, dark green and polished above, light green beneath, glabrous on both sides, main nerves 12-20 pairs, petioles 1.25 cm long, channeled above, glabrous. **Flower:** White or pale-yellow, small, odorous, axillary, solitary or in 2-6 flowered fascicles, pedicels 6-13 mm long, glabrous or nearly so. **Fruit:** Berries, ovoid or ellipsoid, milky, one seeded, rarely two, 1.25 cm long, green when unripe, reddish-yellow when ripe, shape like the fruit of *Azadirachta* *indica.* **Seed:** Ovoid, 1 cm long, brownish-black, shining, with white testa.

Flowering and fruiting period: March-April and May-June.

Habitat: Throughout India, in evergreen forests, also cultivated.

Parts used: Fruit, seed, seed oil, bark.

Dosage: Fruit 25-50 g, seed 5-10 g, seed oil 5-10 drops, bark 10-20 g.

Collection period: April-May.

Ayurvedic properties: ***Ras:*** *madhur,* ***Gun:*** *guru, snigdha,* ***Veerya:*** *sheeta* ***Vipaka:*** *madhur* ***Tridosha*** **Effect:** alleviates ***Vaata:*** **+++,** ***Pitta:*** **++,** aggravates ***Kapha:*** **++.**

Chemical constituents: The **fruits** contain sugars, proteins, fats, carbohydrates, calcium, iron, phosphorus, Vitamins A,B,C.

Action and disease indications: The **fruits** are refrigerant, aphrodisiac, appetizer, galactagogue, emollient, and tonic, used for anorexia, dipsia, nervous weakness, bronchitis, spermatorrhea, consumption, hallucinations, unconsciousness. The **bark** is astringent, refrigerant, aphrodisiac, alexipharmic, stomachic and anthelmintic, used for fever, flatulence, colic, dyspepsia, helminthiasis, hyperdipsia and burning sensation.

Clinical uses: Epilepsy: Juice of glands of stem of described plant 20 ml, *Piper longum* 500 mg, honey 10 g, two times a day, for 2 months. **Cloasma:** Local application of paste of leaves of described plant, with fresh milk, is beneficial. **Dentalgia:** Apply latex of described plant, as required. **Menorrhagia, metrorrhagia:** Fried (in clarified butter) leaves powder of described plant, 10-20 g, water, two times a day. **Scorpion sting:** Local application of seed paste of described plant is good for relive pain. **Skin diseases, cloasma, acne vulgaris, black spot on face:** Local application of paste of unripe fruits of described plant, is very beneficial. **Erectile dysfunction of penis, for gaining body weight:** Seed oil of described plant 10 drops, sugar candy 10 g, with cream of milk 15 g, two times a day. **Oligogalactia, nervous weakness:** Fruits of described plant 100 g, two times a day.

Formulations: *Vrihat Narikel khanda.*

Recommended readings

Bhutya, R.K. (2007), Vanaspati Aushadha Vigyana, Scientific Publishers (India), Jodhpur, PP. 79.

Chunekar, K.C. (2004), Bhava Prakash Nighantu, Chaukhambha Bharti Academy, Varanasi, PP. 576.

Khare, C.P. (2007), Indian Medicinal Plants, Springer (India) P.L. New Delhi, PP. 397.

Kirtikar, K.R. & Basu, B.D. (1998), Indian Medicinal Plants, L.M Basu, Allahabad, Vol. , PP. .

Nair, R.Vasudevan, (2007), Indian Medicinal Plants, Orient Longman P.L. Chennai, Vol. 3, PP. 393.

Pareek, G.N. (2005), Sudhanidhi, Vanoshadhi Ratnakar, Dhanvantari Karyalaya, Aligarh, Vol. 9, PP. 299.

Prajapati, N.D., Purohit, S.S., Sharma, A.K. & Tarun Kumar (2003), A Hand Book of Medicinal Plants, Agrobios India, Jodhpur, PP. 334.

Sharma, P.V. (1981), Dravya gun vigyana, Chaukhambha Bharti Academy, Varanasi, Vol. 2, PP. 260.

Swami, K.N. (1985), Gavon Main Aushadh Ratna, Kalera Krishana Gopal, Kalera (Raj.), Vol. 2, PP. 235.

298. *Marsdenia tenacissima* Wight & Arn.

Family: Asclepiadaceae.

Synonym: *Asclepias tenacissima, A.tomentosa, Gymnema tenacissima.*

Other similar plants: *M.hamiltoni, M.royli, Magia volubilis, Sansevierea roxburghiana.*

Different opinion: By the name of *'Moorvaa'* many plants are being used in India. 1. *Marsdenia tenacissima.* 2. *Sanssevieria roxburghiana-Naagadaman,* found at coromandel coast. 3. *Bauhinia vahlii- Yugmapatra-* Found in Haridwar, Deharadoon. 4. *Maerua arenaria-Piluparni, Murhari,* (Capparidaceae), found in Punjab, Sindha, Gujaraat. 5. *Clamatis gouriana-Churnahaar* (Ranunculaceae), found in West Himalaya. 6. *Helicteres isora- Marorphali* (Capparidaceae), found in West and Central india.

Ayurvedic Groups: Charak: *Triptighna, Stanyashodhana, Tiktaskandha,* **Sushruta:** *patoladi, Pittasanshamana.*

Name: English: White Turpeth, **Sanskrit:** *Murvaa, Madhurasaa, Devi, morataa, Tejani, shruvaa, Madhulikaa, Gokarni, Piluparni,* **Hindi:** *Murvaa,* **Local:** *Jartor, Chinhaar.*

Botanical characteristics: Habit: A Large stout woody twining or climbing shrub. **Stem:** cylindrical, young branches tomentose, bark grey or pale-brown, corky, deeply furrowed. **Leaf:** Simple, opposite, 5-20 by 6-15 cm, broadly ovate, acuminate, base cordate with deep sinus, and rounded lobes, tomentose on both sides, petiole 5 cm long. **Flower:** Greenish-yellow, in dense much branched compound cymes, bisexual. **Fruit:** Follicles paired, velvety, tomentose, 7.5-15 cm long, ovoid, lanceolate, prominently marginal, glabrous, smooth and wrinkled on drying. **Seed:** Flattened, ovate-oblong, 1-1.3 cm long.

Flowering and fruiting period: April-July and January-March.

Habitat: Himalayas from Kumaon to Assam, up to an altitude of 1500 m, Madhya Pradesh, Bihar and Deccan Peninsula.

Parts used: Root.

Dosage: Powder 3-6 g, for decoction 10-20 g.

Collection period: April-May.

Ayurvedic properties: ***Ras:*** *madhur, tikta,* ***Gun:*** *rukhsa, guru,* ***Veerya:*** *ushna* ***Vipaka:*** *katu,* ***Tridosha*** **Effect:** alleviates ***Vaata:*** **++,** ***Kapha:*** +, ***Pitta:*** +.

Chemical constituents: The **roots** rich in pregnane glycosides of 2-deoxysugars, which on hydrolysis gave genins and sugars.

Action and disease indications: The **roots** are purgative, thermogenic, anti-spasmodic, mild CNS depressant, used for colic, diabetes, cardiac diseases, pruritis, skin diseases, fever, acidosis, constipation, jaundice and intestinal worms infestation.

Clinical uses: Skin diseases: Local application of paste of root powder of described plant is beneficial. **Malaria, fevers:** Root powder of described plant 10 g, three times a day.

Formulations: *Lakhsaadi taila, Chandanaadi taila, Mahaa sudarshana churna, Vrihat manjisthaadi kwaatha, Chandanbalaalaakhsaadi churna, Mahaa yogaraaja guggulu, Mahaa tikta ghrita, Madhuparnyaadi taila, Mahaa panchagavya ghrita, Mahaa laakhsaadi taila.*

Recommended readings:

Bhutya, R.K. (2007), Vanaspati Aushadha Vigyana, Scientific Publishers (India), Jodhpur, PP. 183.

Chunekar, K.C. (2004), Bhava Prakash Nighantu, Chaukhambha Bharti Academy, Varanasi, PP. 435.

Khare, C.P. (2007), Indian Medicinal Plants, Springer (India) P.L. New Delhi, PP. 399.

Misra, B.L. (2005), Dravya Guna Hastamalaka, Publication scheme, Jaipur, PP. 488.

Namjoshi, A.N. (2001), The Ayurvedic Pharmacopoeia of India, Government of India, Department of Indian Systems of Medicine & Homoeopathy, New Delhi, Part-1, Volume- 1, PP. 116.

Sharma, P.C., Yelne, MB. & Denis, T.J. (2000), Database on medicinal plants used in ayurveda, Central Council for research in Ayurveda and siddha, Vol. 8, PP. 272.

Sharma, P.V. (1981), Dravya gun vigyana, Chaukhambha Bharti Academy, Varanasi, Vol. 1, PP. 699.

Singh, R.S. (2002), Vanoshadhi Nirdeshika, Uttar Pradesh Hindi Sansthan, Lucknow, PP. 315.

Swami, K.N. (1985), Gavon Main Aushadh Ratna, Kalera Krishana Gopal, Kalera (Raj.), Vol. 3, PP. 208.

299. *Marsilea minuta* Linn.

Family: Marsileaceae.

Other similar plant: *M.quadrifolia, Oxalis corniculata-Changeri.*

Name: Sanskrit: *Shitivaar, Shitivaar, Swastika, Sunishnaka, Shreevaaraka, Suchipatra, Parnaka, Kukkutaka, Shikhi,* **Hindi:** *Chopatiyaa,* **Local:** *Chopatiyaa.*

Botanical characteristics: Habit: A creeping perennial herb, height 5-10 cm, with slender long dichotomously branching rhizome rooting at the nodes. **Stem:** Horizontal, thready. **Leaf:** Quadrifoliate, circinate when young, cuneately-obovate, petioles long, 15-25 cm long, slender, flexible, lamina divided into four leaflets, leaflets 0.25-0.5 cm. Shape like the leaf of *Oxalis corniculata.* **Fruit:** Sporocarps bean-like, born on short or long stalks inserted a short distance above the base of the petioles. **Seed:** Small, flattened.

Flowering and fruiting period: November-January.

Habitat: Throughout India, as a weed in marshy places along the banks of canals and rivers.

Parts used: Whole plant.

Dosage: Powder 2-5 g, Juice 10-20 ml.

Collection period: December-January.

Ayurvedic properties: ***Ras:*** *kashaaya, madhur,* ***Gun:*** *laghu, rukhsa,* ***Veerya:*** *sheeta* ***Vipaka:*** *katu,* ***Tridosha*** **Effect:** alleviates ***Vaata:*** **++,** ***Kapha:*** **++,** aggravates ***Pitta:*** **+** .

Chemical constituents: The **plant** contain a most active anti-epileptic principle is marsilin (1-tricontol cerotate).

Action and disease indications: The **plant** is refrigerant, emollient, anodyne, sedative, hypnotic, ophthalmic, diuretic, constipating, expectorant, aphrodisiac, depurative and febrifuge, prescribed for epilepsy, behavioral disorders, psychopathy, ophthalmia, strangury, diarrhea, cough, bronchitis, skin diseases, piles, dyspepsia, fever and insomnia.

Clinical uses: Insomnia, allergic bronchitis, asthma: Juice 20 ml or Powder 5 g, of described plant, with honey 10 g and sugar 5 g, three times a day is very beneficial. **Hemorrhoids, anorexia, sprue, diarrhea, dysentery, prolepse rectum, dysurea:** Medicated clarified butter 10 g, made from juice of described plant and *Oxalis corniculata*, with milk, two times a day. **Dysurea, anurea:** Seed powder of described plant 2 g, with whey, three times a day. **Renal and vesical calculus:** Seed powder of described plant 2 g, sugar candy powder 5 g, with water, three times a day. **Epistaxis:** Leaves powder of described plant 5, fruit powder of *Phylanthus emblica* 3 g, with juice of *Punica grantum* 25 ml, three times a day.

Formulations: *Sunishnaka chaangeri ghrita.*

Recommended readings:

Bhutya, R.K. (2007), Vanaspati Aushadha Vigyana, Scientific Publishers (India), Jodhpur, PP. 99.

Chunekar, K.C. (2004), Bhava Prakash Nighantu, Chaukhambha Bharti Academy, Varanasi, PP. 674.

Khare, C.P. (2007), Indian Medicinal Plants, Springer (India) P.L. New Delhi, PP. 399.

Nair, R.Vasudevan, (2007), Indian Medicinal Plants, Orient Longman P.L. Chennai, Vol. 4, PP. 5.

Pareek, G.N. (2005), Sudhanidhi, Vanoshadhi Ratnakar, Dhanvantari Karyalaya, Aligarh, Vol. 10, PP. 154.

Prajapati, N.D., Purohit, S.S., Sharma, A.K. & Tarun Kumar (2003), A Hand Book of Medicinal Plants, Agrobios India, Jodhpur, PP. 335.

Sharma, P.V. (1981), Dravya gun vigyana, Chaukhambha Bharti Academy, Varanasi, Vol. 1, PP. 535.

Singh, R.S. (2002), Vanoshadhi Nirdeshika, Uttar Pradesh Hindi Sansthan, Lucknow, PP. 379.

Swami, K.N. (1985), Gavon Main Aushadh Ratna, Kalera Krishana Gopal, Kalera (Raj.), Vol. 2, PP. 287.

300. *Martynia annua* Linn.

Family: Martyniaceae.

Synonym: *M.diandra*

Other similar plants: *Asclepias curassavica.*

Name: English: Devil's Claw, Tiger's Claw, **Sanskrit:** *Kaakanaasaa,* **Hindi:** *Kaakanaasaa,* **Local:** *Bichuraa, Kauvaathodi.*

Botanical characteristics: Habit: A handsome, stout, clammy-pubescent sticky, herb, height 0.9-1.2 m. **Stem:** Erect herbaceous. **Leaf:** Large, 15-23 cm, opposite, cordate, sinuately lobed and minutely dentate, often covered with a glutinous dew-like substance. **Flower:** Pink or dark purple, drooping, 3-6 cm long, foxglove shaped, in short racemes terminal and from the forks of the branches, ill-smelling, corolla glandular-hairy with very oblique mouth. **Fruit:** Obliquely ovoid drupaceous with the pericarp finally dehiscent and falling, endocarp with 2 sharp curved apical spines and a central channel opening between the spines.

Flowering and fruiting period: August-September and October-November.

Habitat: Throughout India, in waste places.

Parts used: fruit. **Dosage:** 1-3 g.

Collection period: November-December.

Ayurvedic properties: ***Ras:*** *kashaaya, katu, tikta,* ***Gun:*** *laghu,rukhsa,* ***Veerya:*** *ushna,* ***Vipaka:*** *katu,* ***Tridosha*** **Effect:** alleviates ***Kapha:*** **++.** ***Vata:*** **++**, aggravates **+**.

Chemical constituents: The **flowers** contain several flavonoids including apigenin, luteolin, apigenin-7-O-beta-D-glucoronide, luteolin-7-O-beta-D-glucoronide, pellargonidin-3-5-diglucoside, cyaniding-3-galactoside.

Action and disease indications: The **fruits** are alexitericand anti-inflammatory, used for inflammations, piles, leucoderma, eczema and skin diseases.

Clinical uses: Scorpion sting: Local application of paste of fruit of described plant is beneficial. **Skin diseases, pruritis, scabies:** Local application of seed oil of described plant. **Epilepsy:** Leaves powder of described plant 3 g, with water, two times a day. **Scrofula, Glandular enlargement:** Local application of paste of leaves of described plant is beneficial.

Formulations: *Chyavanpraasha, Mandalkusthahar lepa.*

Recommended readings:

Bhutya, R.K. (2007), Vanaspati Aushadha Vigyana, Scientific Publishers (India), Jodhpur, PP. 57.

Chunekar, K.C. (2004), Bhava Prakash Nighantu, Chaukhambha Bharti Academy, Varanasi, PP. 439.

Khare, C.P. (2007), Indian Medicinal Plants, Springer (India) P.L. New Delhi, PP. 399.

Kirtikar, K.R. & Basu, B.D. (1998), Indian Medicinal Plants, L.M Basu, Allahabad, Vol. 3, PP. 1855.

301. *Matricaria chamomilla* Linn.

Family: Compositae; Asteraceae.

Name: English: German Chamomile, Chamomile, **Hindi:** *Babunaa,* **Local:** *Babunaa.*

Botanical characteristics: Habit: A glabrous aromatic herb, height about 30 cm. **Stem:** Much branched. **Leaf:** 2-3 pinnatisect; segments almost filiform. **Flower:** Heads solitary, long penducled, 1.3-2 cm diam., involucral bracts oblong, margins white, receptacle conic, alongating, during fruiting, ligules white, much longer than the bracts, deflexed after flowering or 0. **Fruit:** Achenes with slender white ribs on the ventral face only.

Flowering and fruiting period: May-June and July-August.

Habitat: Grown in Jammu & Kashmir, Himachal Pradesh and Uttar Pradesh.

Parts used: Flower. **Dosage:** 1-4 g.

Collection period: May-June.

Ayurvedic properties: ***Ras:*** *tikta, kashaaya,* ***Gun:*** *laghu, snigdha,* ***Veerya:*** *ushna,* ***Vipaka:*** *katu,* ***Tridosha*** **Effect:** alleviates ***Vaata:*** **++,** ***Kapha:*** **+,** ***Pitta:*** **+.**

Chemical constituents: The **flowers** contain volatile oil about 2%, also alpha-bisabolol up to 50%, azulenes including chamozulene, guiazuline and matricine; flavonoids including apigenin and luteolin and their glycosides, patuletin and quercetin; spiroethers; coumarins; polysaccharides.

Action and disease indications: The **flowers** are carminative, sedative, anti-convulsant, antispasmodic, analgesic, anti-inflammatory and antiseptic, Used for inflammations, colic, flatulence, cough, cold, inflammatory diseases of gastro-intestinal tract and gastro-intestinal spasm. Externally bacterial skin diseases, anogenital inflammations.

Clinical uses: Rheumatism, arthritis: Local massage of oil of described plant is beneficial. **General debility, hysteria, indigestion, flatulence:** Cold infusion of flowers of described plant, 4 g, with honey 10 g, two times a day, is useful.

Recommended readings:

Chunekar, K.C. (2004), Bhava Prakash Nighantu, Chaukhambha Bharti Academy, Varanasi, PP. 832.

Khare, C.P. (2007), Indian Medicinal Plants, Springer (India) P.L. New Delhi, PP. 400.

Kirtikar, K.R. & Basu, B.D. (1998), Indian Medicinal Plants, L.M Basu, Allahabad, Vol. 2, PP. 1383.

302. *Melaleuca leucadendron* Linn.

Family: Myrtaceae.

Name: English: Cajeput tree, Bottle brush, Swamp Tea tree, White Tea tree, **Sanskrit:** *Kayaaputi,* **Hindi:** *Kaayaputi,* **Local:** *Kaajuputi.*

Botanical characteristics: Habit: An evergreen tree about 15 m high. **Stem:** Bark papery whitish, peeling off in layers, 2.5 cm thick. **Leaf:** Oblong-elliptic, acuminate, sub-acute, nerves vertical, 5-7, glabrous, 3.8-12.5 cm by 5-25 mm, petioles shorts. **Flower:** Pinkish-white, in whorls, numerous, rachis silky, end of a branch with axillary flowers. **Fruit:** Capsule, dehiscing by 3valves, sessile, 4 mm across, cylindric, short.

Seed: Numerous, minute, cuneate.

Flowering and fruiting period: September-October and February-March.

Habitat: Punjab, Maharastra, Tamilnadu, Bihar, Bangal, cultivated in gardens and parks throughout India.

Parts used: Flower, flower oil.

Dosage: Oil 1-3 drops, sprit 5-30 drops.

Collection period: September-October.

Ayurvedic properties: ***Ras:*** *tikta,* ***Gun:*** *laghu, tikhsna,* ***Veerya:*** *ushna,* ***Vipaka:*** *katu,* ***Tridosha*** **Effect:** alleviates ***Vaata:*** **++,** ***Kapha:*** **++,** aggravates ***Pitta:*** **+.**

Chemical constituents: The **oil** contains terpenoids, 1, 8-cineole (40-65%) as major component, with alpha-pinene, alpha-terpineolnerolidol, limonene, benzaldehyde, valeraldehyde, dipentene and various sesquiterpenes; 3, 5-dimrthyle-4,6,di-o-methylphloroacetophenone.

Action and disease indications: The **oil** is expectorant, anthelmintic, diaphoretic, stimulant, anti-convulsant, carminative, used for chronic laryngitis and bronchitis, round worm infestation, fevers, malaria, rheumatism, sprain, neuralgia, migraine, cold, asthma, bronchitis and influenza.

Clinical uses: Bronchitis, pneumonia, pains, arthralgia: Local massage of oil of flowers, with seed oil of *Brassica campestris,* in ratio of 1:10, is beneficial. **Flatulence, abdominal pain, convolsions:** Sprit Kajuputi 10-20 drops, with distil water of *Trachyspermum ammi* 20 ml, three times a day.

Recommended readings

Bhutya, R.K. (2007), Vanaspati Aushadha Vigyana, Scientific Publishers (India), Jodhpur, PP. 61.

Khare, C.P. (2007), Indian Medicinal Plants, Springer (India) P.L. New Delhi, PP. 402.

Kirtikar, K.R. & Basu, B.D. (1998), Indian Medicinal Plants, L.M Basu, Allahabad, Vol. 2, PP. 1042.

Prajapati, N.D., Purohit, S.S., Sharma, A.K. & Tarun Kumar (2003), A Hand Book of Medicinal Plants, Agrobios India, Jodhpur, PP. 336.

Swami, K.N. (1985), Gavon Main Aushadh Ratna, Kalera Krishana Gopal, Kalera (Raj.), Vol. 2, PP. 176.

303. *Melia azedarach* Linn.

Family: Meliaceae.

Other similar plant: *M.composita.*

Name: English: Bead tree, Persian lilac, Pride of India, **Sanskrit:** *Ramyaka, Tek, Vismustika, Keshmusti, Nimbaka, Akhsiva, Dreka,*

Kaarmuka, Keshamushti, **Hindi:** *Mahaanimba,* **Local:** *Bakaayan, Ghoraa nimba.*

Ayurvedic groups: Sushruta: *Adhobhaagahara, Pippalyadi gana.*

Botanical characteristics: Habit: A moderate sized, deciduous tree, 9-14m in height. **Stem:** Cylindrical, solid, branched, bark dark grey having shallow longitudinal furrows. **Leaf:** 22-40 cm long, leaflets are 3-12 in number and 2.5-7.5 cm long and 1.25-3 cm broad, alternate, compound bipinnate or tripinnate and imperipinnate, pinnae ovate or lanceonate, coarsely serrate or entire, glabrous. **Flower:** Lilec, fragrant, white tinged with violet, 7 mm long, in axillary panical cyme **Fruit:** Drupe, round shaped, 1.50 cm diameter, 5-celled and 5-seeded, green when unripe and yellow when ripe and attached long time on tree. **Seed:** Long, grey and very hard.

Flowering and fruiting period: February-March and October-December.

Habitat: Throughout India, wild in sub-Himalayan tract, up to 1800 m, Deharadoon and Saharanpur.

Parts used: Stem bark, leaves and root.

Dosage: 3-5 g.

Collection period: March-April.

Ayurvedic properties: ***Ras:*** *tikta, kashaaya,* ***Gun:*** *laghu,rukhsa,* ***Veerya:*** *ushna,* ***Vipaka:*** *katu,* ***Tridosha*** **Effect:** alleviates ***Kapha:*** ++, ***Pitta:*** +.

Chemical constituents: Pericarp contains bakayanin, azaridin (margosine), sterols and tannins. The **heartwood** also yielded bakayanin and a lactone, bakalectone. Leaves gave quercitrin, rutin, tetranortriter penoids, salanin and vilocinin. **Fruits** contain melianoninol, melianol, melianone, meliandiol, vanillin and vanillic acid.

Action and disease indications: Seeds are bitter, anthelmintic, expectorant and aphrodisiac and beneficial to cure helminthiasis, typhoid fever, pain in the pelvic region, leprosy, uropathy and scrofula. **Seeds oil** is laxative, anthelmintic, depurative, maturant and tonic. Useful to helminthiasis, otalgia, piles, spleenomegaly, heptopathy, inflammations, leprosy and skin diseases. **Flowers** are astringent, refrigerant, anodyne, stomachic, vermifuge, diuretic, emmenogogue, deobstruant. Useful to cure celphalgia, gastropathy, verminosis, strangury, dysmenorrhea and rheumatoid arthritis. **Leaves** are bitter, astringent, vermicidal, expectorant, antilithic, diuretic, emmenogogue and stomachic. Useful to cure hysteria, leprosy, scrofula, spleenomegaly, urolithiasis, heart diseases, strangury, amenorrhea, verminosis, cough, bronchitis, inflammations and scabies. **Roots** are acrid, bitter, astringent, anodyne, depurative, vulnerary, anti-septic, anthelmintic, constipating, expectorant, febrifuge, anti-periodic, emmenogogue and tonic. Useful for sciatica, lumbago, cephalgia, leprosy, leucoderma, skin diseases, ulcers, wounds, piles tape worm, cough, asthma, amenorrhea, dysmenorrhea, vomiting, fevers, burning sensation and vertigo.

Clinical uses: Sciatica: Root powder of the described plant 2 g, 2 times a day, with *'Mahaa raasnaadi kwatha'* 10-15 g, at morning, for 1-2 months. **Headache:** Topical use of paste of flowers and leaves powder of the described plant is beneficial. **Skin diseases, baldness:** Local application of paste of leaves and stem bark of the described plant is useful. **Piles:** Seed powder of the described plant 2 g, aqua's extract of *Berberis ariststa* 500 mg, fruit bark of *Terminalia chebula* 2 g, 2 times a day, with plant juice of *Blumia lacera* 10 ml, for 10 days. **Hysteria:** Decoction of leaves of described plant 10 ml, 2 times a day, for 4 months. **Urinary bladder calculi:** Leaves juice of the described plant 10 ml, with Nitrate of potash 500 mg, 2 times a day. **Psoriasis:** Tropical use of flower and Leaves juice or paste of the plant is beneficial.

Formulations: *Arogyavardhani vati, Raktashodhakaarista, Agurvaadi taila, Arshoghni vati, Habbebavaashir, Mehavajra rasa, Mahaa bhallatakguda, Vrihata manjisthaadi kwaatha.*

Recommended readings:

Acharya, B.K. (2008), Ayurveda Jadi-buti Rahasya, Patanjali Yogapitha, Haridwar, PP. 121.

Bhutya, R.K. (2007), Vanaspati Aushadha Vigyana, Scientific Publishers (India), Jodhpur, PP. 175.

Brahmavarchas (2003), Ayurved Ka Pran Vanoshadhi Vigyan, Shanti Kunj, Haridwar, PP. 284.

Chunekar, K.C. (2004), Bhava Prakash Nighantu, Chaukhambha Bharti Academy, Varanasi, PP. 331.

Dhiman, A.K. (2006), Ayurvedic Drug Plants, Daya Publishing House, Delhi, PP. 245.

Khare, C.P. (2007), Indian Medicinal Plants, Springer (India) P.L. New Delhi, PP. 403.

Kirtikar, K.R. & Basu, B.D. (1998), Indian Medicinal Plants, L.M Basu, Allahabad, Vol. 1, PP. 542.

Nair, R.Vasudevan, (2007), Indian Medicinal Plants, Orient Longman P.L. Chennai, Vol. 4, PP. 10.

Pareek, G.N. (2005), Sudhanidhi, Vanoshadhi Ratnakar, Dhanvantari Karyalaya, Aligarh, Vol. 5, PP. 187.

Prajapati, N.D., Purohit, S.S., Sharma, A.K. & Tarun Kumar (2003), A Hand Book of Medicinal Plants, Agrobios India, Jodhpur, PP. 337.

Sharma, P.C., Yelne, MB. & Denis, T.J. (2000), Database on medicinal plants used in ayurveda, Central Council for research in Ayurveda and siddha, Vol. 2, PP. 389.

Sharma, P.V. (1981), Dravya gun vigyana, Chaukhambha Bharti Academy, Varanasi, Vol. 1, PP. 528.

Singh, R.S. (2002), Vanoshadhi Nirdeshika, Uttar Pradesh Hindi Sansthan, Lucknow, PP. 257.

Swami, K.N. (1985), Gavon Main Aushadh Ratna, Kalera Krishana Gopal, Kalera (Raj.), Vol. 3, PP. 47.

304. *Mentha piperata* Linn.

Family: Labiatae; Lamiaceae.

Name: English: Peppermint, Brandy Mint, **Hindi:** *Piparment,* **Local:** *Piparment, Vilayati Pudinaa.*

Botanical characteristics: Habit: A perennial glabrous strong scented herb. **Leaf:** Ovate or oblong-lanceolate, 2.5-10 cm long, dark green, opposite, upper smaller, sometimes bracteiform, acute or obtuse at base, coarsely serrete, smooth above, rarely sparingly hairy on the nerve below, petioled. **Flower:** Small, white or light blue, glabrous, or very sparingly hispid, calyx often red, in whorls in terminal spikes, spikes cylindric, interrupted below.

Flowering and fruiting period: Almost throughout year, chiefly during August-October.

Habitat: Cultivated in Punjab, Kashmir, Uttar Pradesh and Maharastra.

Parts used: Leaves, flower, extract, oil.

Dosage: Extract 125-250 mg, Flower 2 g, oil 1-2 drops.

Collection period: March-April.

Ayurvedic properties: ***Ras:*** *katu,* ***Gun:*** *laghu, rukhsa, tikhsna,* ***Veerya:*** *ushna,* ***Vipaka:*** *katu,* ***Tridosha*** **Effect:** alleviates ***Kapha:*** ++, ***Kapha:*** + .

Chemical constituents: The **essential oil** contains menthol, menthone, pulegone, menthofuran, 1,8-cineole, menthyl acetate, isomenthone. The **leaves** contain flavonoid glycosides, eriocitrin, luteolin 7-O-rutinoside, hesperidin, isorhoifolin, diosmin, eriodictyol 7-O-glocoside and narirutin, besides rosmarinic acid, azulenes, cholene and carotenes.

Action and disease indications: The **leaves** are appetizer, digestive, carminative, anti-emetic, anti-septic, anti-viral, anesthetic and diaphoretic, used for nausea, vomiting, cough, cold, spastic complains of gastro-intestinal tract, gall bladder and bile ducts, dyspepsia, flatulence, intestinal colic. The **essential oil** is chloretic, digestive, carminative, anti-spasmodic, diuretic, anti-emetic, mild sedative, anti-septic, anti-viral, diaphoretic, used for indigestion, colic, cough, cold, irritable bowel syndrome, spastic discomfort of the upper gastro-intestinal tract and bile ducts and inflammations of oral mucosa. Externally for neuralgia and myalgia, cough, cold, rheumatic complaints, urticaria and irritable skin diseases.

Clinical uses: Dentalgia, rheumatism, neuralgia, headache: Local application of oil, is beneficial. **Rhinitis:** Smelling of extract of described plant 125 mg, is beneficial. **Bronchitis, fever:** Cold infusion of described plant 3 g, with honey 10 g, three times a day.

Formulations: *Karpoordhara, Visuchikaahar vati.*

Recommended readings:

Bhutya, R.K. (2007), Vanaspati Aushadha Vigyana, Scientific Publishers (India), Jodhpur, PP. 152.

Brahmavarchas (2003), Ayurved Ka Pran Vanoshadhi Vigyan, Shanti Kunj, Haridwar, PP. 285.

Chunekar, K.C. (2004), Bhava Prakash Nighantu, Chaukhambha Bharti Academy, Varanasi, PP. 829.

Khare, C.P. (2007), Indian Medicinal Plants, Springer (India) P.L. New Delhi, PP. 409.

Kirtikar, K.R. & Basu, B.D. (1998), Indian Medicinal Plants, L.M Basu, Allahabad, Vol. 3, PP. 1980.

Prajapati, N.D., Purohit, S.S., Sharma, A.K. & Tarun Kumar (2003), A Hand Book of Medicinal Plants, Agrobios India, Jodhpur, PP. 339.

305. *Mentha spicata* Linn. emend. Nathh.

Family: Labiatae; Lamiaceae.

Synonym: *M.viridis.*

Name: English: Spearmint, Garden Mint, **Sanskrit:** *Putihaa, Rochani, Podinaka,* **Hindi:** *Pudinaa,* **Local:** *Podinaa.*

Botanical characteristics: Habit: A herbaceous perennial, with a pungent smell, 0.3-0.9 m high, with aerial leafy stolons. **Leaf:** A Smooth, sessile, lanceolate to oblong, acute, coarsely dentate, smooth above, glandular beneath. **Flower:** Lilac, purple, in loose, cylindrical, slender spikes, which are interrupted, with distant whorls; bracts awl-like. **Fruit:** Nutlets, smooth. **Seed:** Minute, mucilaginous.

Flowering and fruiting period: Almost throughout year, chiefly during August-October.

Habitat: Cultivated in Punjab, Uttar Pradesh and Maharastra.

Parts used: Leaves, oil.

Dosage: Leaves powder 1-3 g, juice 5-10 ml, oil 1-3 drops.

Collection period: March-April.

Ayurvedic properties: ***Ras:*** *katu,* ***Gun:*** *laghu, rukhsa, tikhsna,* ***Veerya:*** *sheeta* ***Vipaka:*** *katu,* ***Tridosha*** **Effect:** alleviates ***Kapha:*** ++, ***Vaata:*** +.

Chemical constituents: The **leaves** contain flavonoids, diosmin and diosmetin. The **essential oil** contains carvone 55-75%, limonene 21.4%, caffeic acid derivatives include rosmarinic acid.

Action and disease indications: The **leaves** are aromatic, thermogenic, stimulant, anodyne, deodorant, vulnerary, carminative, anti-septic, stomachic, expectorant, anti-emetic, cardio-tonic, depurative, sudorofic, dentifrice, febrifuge, appetizer, digestive, anti-spasmodic, diuretic, emmenogogue, anthelmintic and contraceptive, used for indigestion, nausea, vomiting, colic, flatulence, fever, intestinal worms, dyspepsia, peptic ulcer, diarrhea, cough, asthma, bronchitis, strangury, skin diseases, arthralgia, halitosis, ulcers, wounds, cuts, cardiac debility, amenorrhea, dysmenorrhea, dental carries, jaundice, headache, liver and spleen diseases, fever and general debility.

Clinical uses: Anorexia, indigestion, sunstroke: Paste of leaves of described plant 10-20 g with rock salt 1 g, is very beneficial. **Dysmenorrhea, amenorrhea:** Juice of leaves of described plant 5-10 ml, two times a day. **Ozostomia:** Gargles of decoction of described plant, is beneficial. **Malaria, fevers:** Leaves juice of described plant 5 ml, fresh juice of *Zingiber officinalis* 5 ml, with honey 10 g, three times a day. **Abdominal pain:** Leaves juice of described plant 5 ml, fresh juice of *Zingiber officinalis* 5 ml, with rock salt 500 mg, three times a day. **Rhinitis:** Nasal drops of leaves juice 4-4 drops. **Ring worm:** Local application of juice of described plant is beneficial. **Urticaria:** Leaves juice of described plant 10 ml, rose water 20 ml, with sugar candy 10 g, three times a day. **Colic, diarrhea:** Leaves juice 5 ml, juice of *Punica grantum* 25 ml, with honey 10 g, two times a day.

Formulations: *Arka podinaa, Antravridhihar churna, Labooba kabira.*

Recommended readings:

Bhutya, R.K. (2007), Vanaspati Aushadha Vigyana, Scientific Publishers (India), Jodhpur, PP. 154.

Brahmavarchas (2003), Ayurved Ka Pran Vanoshadhi Vigyan, Shanti Kunj, Haridwar, PP. 286.

Chunekar, K.C. (2004), Bhava Prakash Nighantu, Chaukhambha Bharti Academy, Varanasi, PP. 830.

Dhiman, A.K. (2006), Ayurvedic Drug Plants, Daya Publishing House, Delhi, PP. 318.

Khare, C.P. (2007), Indian Medicinal Plants, Springer (India) P.L. New Delhi, PP. 409.

Kirtikar, K.R. & Basu, B.D. (1998), Indian Medicinal Plants, L.M Basu, Allahabad, Vol. 3, PP. 1979.

Misra, B.L. (2005), Dravya Guna Hastamalaka, Publication scheme, Jaipur, PP. 367.

Nair, R.Vasudevan, (2007), Indian Medicinal Plants, Orient Longman P.L. Chennai, Vol. 4, PP. 15.

Prajapati, N.D., Purohit, S.S., Sharma, A.K. & Tarun Kumar (2003), A Hand Book of Medicinal Plants, Agrobios India, Jodhpur, PP. 340.

Sharma, P.V. (1981), Dravya gun vigyana, Chaukhambha Bharti Academy, Varanasi, Vol. 1, PP. 395.

Singh, R.S. (2002), Vanoshadhi Nirdeshika, Uttar Pradesh Hindi Sansthan, Lucknow, PP. 249.

306. *Merremia gangetica* Linn. Cufod.

Family: Convolvulaceae.

Synonym: *M.emarginata, Ipomoea reniformis.*

Other similar plants: *Centella asiatica.*

Name: Sanskrit: *Aakhukarni, Aakhuparni, Parnikaa, Mooshikakarni, Bhudaribhavaa,* **Hindi:** *Mushaakarni,* **Local:** *Mushakani, Chuhaakaani.*

Botanical characteristics: Habit: A perennial, creeping herb. **Stem:** Numerous, filiform, rooting at the nodes, not twining, clothed with scattered long soft hairs. **Leaf:** Simple, reniform or ovate-cordate, 1.3-2.5 cm broad, usually broader than long, obtuse, crenate, glabrous, petioles 6-25 mm long, hairy. **Flower:** Yellow, bell-shaped, axillary, solitary or few (2-3) together on a very short penducle; bracts small, ovate, acute, hairy, pedicels short. **Fruit:** Capsule, 4-5 mm diam., sub-globose, smooth, surrounded by the slightly enlarged ciliate sepals. **Seed:** 2-4, glabrous, light brown.

Flowering and fruiting period: September-October and November-December.

Habitat: Found in Upper Gangetic plains, Bihar, Bengal and Peninsular India, in damp places and hills up to 900 m.

Parts used: Whole Plant.

Dosage: Power 2-4 g, Juice 10-20 ml.

Collection period: November-December.

Ayurvedic properties: ***Ras:*** *katu, tikta, kashaaya,* ***Gun:*** *laghu, rukhsa,* ***Veerya:*** *sheeta* ***Vipaka:*** *katu,* ***Tridosha*** **Effect:** alleviates ***Kapha:*** ++, ***Pitta:*** +.

Action and disease indications: The **plant** is refrigerant, diuretic, deobstruent, alterant, anthelmintic, rejuvenating, carminative and digestive, used for fever, anemia, leucoderma, strangury, otalgia, cephalgia, intestinal worms, skin diseases, fistula, tumours, kidney and bladder diseases, uterus diseases and pains.

Clinical uses: Skin diseases: Local application of leaves paste of described plant is profitable. **Dysmenorrhea:** Vaginal wash by decoction of described plant 10 g. **Otorrhea:** Hot juice of leaves 4 drops is beneficial. **Skin diseases:** Cold infusion of described plant 10 g, *Hemidesmus indicus* 10 g, two times a day. **Neuralgia, headache:** Leaves juice of described plant 10-20 ml, two times a day is beneficial.

Formulations: *Krimikuthaar rasa.*

Recommended readings:

Bhutya, R.K. (2007), Vanaspati Aushadha Vigyana, Scientific Publishers (India), Jodhpur, PP. 184.

Chunekar, K.C. (2004), Bhava Prakash Nighantu, Chaukhambha Bharti Academy, Varanasi, PP. 476.

Khare, C.P. (2007), Indian Medicinal Plants, Springer (India) P.L. New Delhi, PP. 335.

Kirtikar, K.R. & Basu, B.D. (1998), Indian Medicinal Plants, L.M Basu, Allahabad, Vol. 3, PP. 1720.

Nair, R.Vasudevan, (2007), Indian Medicinal Plants, Orient Longman P.L. Chennai, Vol. 4, PP. 18.

Pareek, G.N. (2005), Sudhanidhi, Vanoshadhi Ratnakar, Dhanvantari Karyalaya, Aligarh, Vol. 9, PP. 77.

Prajapati, N.D., Purohit, S.S., Sharma, A.K. & Tarun Kumar (2003), A Hand Book of Medicinal Plants, Agrobios India, Jodhpur, PP. 341.

Sharma, P.V. (1981), Dravya gun vigyana, Chaukhambha Bharti Academy, Varanasi, Vol. 1, PP. 525.

Swami, K.N. (1985), Gavon Main Aushadh Ratna, Kalera Krishana Gopal, Kalera (Raj.), Vol. 3, PP. 219.

307. *Mesua ferrea* Linn.

Family: Guttiferae; Clusiaceae.

Synonym: *M.nagassarium.*

Ayurvedic Groups: Sushruta: *Elaadi, Priyangvaadi, Anjanaadi gana.*

Name: English: Iron Wood, Mesu, Cobra's Saffron, **Sanskrit:** *Naagakeshara, Naagapushpa, Naaga, Chaampeya, Kaanchan,* **Hindi:** *Naagkesar,* **Local:** *Naagkesar.*

Botanical characteristics: Habit: A medium to large sized, handsome, glabrous, evergreen tree, height 18-30 m. **Stem:** Straight, erect, bark reddish-brown, smooth, which peels off in thin flakes, young branches twiggy, slender. **Leaf:** 7.5-12.5 by 2.5-3.8 cm, simple, opposite, thick, coriaceous, oblong-lanceolate, acute or acuminate, covered with waxy bloom underneath, red when young, afterwards shining above, glaucous and pruinose beneath, rounded or acute at the base, nerves close, inconspicuous; petioles 6-8 mm long. **Flower:** Large, 2.5-7.5 cm diam., white, very fragrant, axillary or terminal, solitary or in pairs, subsessile, stamens very numerous, golden yellow. **Fruit:** O2.5-5 cm long, ovoid, with a conical point, surrounded by the enlarged sepals, 2-valved. **Seed:** Angular, 1-4, smooth, dark brown, pulp oily and with fleshy cotyledons.

Flowering and fruiting period: February-March and September-October.

Habitat: Eastern Himalaya, Assam, West Bengal, Western Ghats, Travancore and Andaman Islands, ascending up to an altitude of 1500 m.

Parts used: Stamens. **Dosage:** 1-3 g.

Collection period: March-April.

Ayurvedic properties: ***Ras:*** *kashaaya, tikta,* ***Gun:*** *laghu, rukhsa,* ***Veerya:*** *ushna,* ***Vipaka:*** *katu,* ***Tridosha*** **Effect:** alleviates ***Kapha:*** +++, ***Pitta:*** ++.

Chemical constituents: The **stamens** contain alpha and beta-amyrin, beta-sitosterol, biflavonoids, mesuaferrons A and B, and mesuanic acid.

Action and disease indications: The **stamens** are astringent, mildly thermogenic, haemostatic, anti-dysenteric, anti-inflammatory, anodyne, sudorofic, digestive, carminative, constipating, anthelmintic, diuretic, alexipharmic, expectorant, aphrodisiac, febrifuge, cardio-tonic, stomachic, used in uterine bleeding and renal diseases, bleeding piles, metrorrhagia, haemorrhagic disorders, and diseases of urinary bladder, asthma, cough, hiccough, halitosis, scabies, pruritis, skin diseases, vomiting, burning sensation of the feet, dipsia, erectile dysfunction, leucorrhea, haemoptysis, strangury, gout, cephalgia, fever and cardiac debility. The essential **oil** from stamens is anti-bacterial and anti-fungal.

Clinical uses: Bleeding piles: Powder of described plant 2 g, sugar candy 5 g, with butter, three times a day and local application of paste of described plant, with *'Shatadhot ghrita'*, is very beneficial. **Somatalgia, arthralgia, pruritis, scabies, skin diseases:** Local application of oil of described plant. **Burning sensation of sole:** Local application of paste of described plant, with *"Shatadhot ghrita',* is very beneficial. **Hyperhydrosis:** Dusting of fine powder of described plant is good. **Phlegmatic bronchitis:** decoction of stem bark and root bark of described plant 10 g, with honey 10 g, three times a day. **Nausea and vomiting:** Mix powder of described plant, *Elettaria cardamomum, Hedychium spicatum,* sugar candy, 3 g, with honey 10 g, as required. **Diabetes inspidus:** Powder of described plant 2 g, with whey, two times a day. With this drug, give rice with whey in diet. **Incomplete or threatened abortion:** Mix powder of described plant, gum of *Bambusa arundinacea,* sugar candy, 2-4 g, with fresh milk of cow, two times a day, is very beneficial.

Formulations: *Chyavanpraasha, Naagkeshar Churna, Pushyaanuga churna.*

Recommended readings:

Bhutya, R.K. (2007), Vanaspati Aushadha Vigyana, Scientific Publishers (India), Jodhpur.

Brahmavarchas (2003), Ayurved Ka Pran Vanoshadhi Vigyan, Shanti Kunj, Haridwar, PP. 288.

Chunekar, K.C. (2004), Bhava Prakash Nighantu, Chaukhambha Bharti Academy, Varanasi, PP. 230.

Dhiman, A.K. (2006), Ayurvedic Drug Plants, Daya Publishing House, Delhi, PP. 272.

Khare, C.P. (2007), Indian Medicinal Plants, Springer (India) P.L. New Delhi, PP. 411.

Kirtikar, K.R. & Basu, B.D. (1998), Indian Medicinal Plants, L.M Basu, Allahabad, Vol. 1, PP. 274.

Misra, B.L. (2005), Dravya Guna Hastamalaka, Publication scheme, Jaipur, PP. 434.

Nair, R.Vasudevan, (2007), Indian Medicinal Plants, Orient Longman P.L. Chennai, Vol. 4, PP. 27.

Namjoshi, A.N. (2001), The Ayurvedic Pharmacopoeia of India, Government of India, Department of Indian Systems of Medicine & Homoeopathy, New Delhi, Part-1, Volume- 1, PP. 118.

Pareek, G.N. (2005), Sudhanidhi, Vanoshadhi Ratnakar, Dhanvantari Karyalaya, Aligarh, Vol. 5, PP. 128.

Prajapati, N.D., Purohit, S.S., Sharma, A.K. & Tarun Kumar (2003), A Hand Book of Medicinal Plants, Agrobios India, Jodhpur, PP. 342.
Scientific Publishers (India), Jodhpur, PP. 133.

Sharma, P.C., Yelne, MB. & Denis, T.J. (2000), Database on medicinal plants used in ayurveda, Central Council for research in Ayurveda and siddha, Vol. 1, PP. 280.

Sharma, P.V. (1981), Dravya gun vigyana, Chaukhambha Bharti Academy, Varanasi, Vol. 1, PP. 783.

Singh, R.S. (2002), Vanoshadhi Nirdeshika, Uttar Pradesh Hindi Sansthan, Lucknow, PP. 206.

Swami, K.N. (1985), Gavon Main Aushadh Ratna, Kalera Krishana Gopal, Kalera (Raj.), Vol. 1, PP. 236.

308. *Michelia champaka* Linn.

Family: Magnoliaceae.

Other species: 1. *M. montana* Blume.- Eastern Himalayas and hills of Assam, it bears white and fragrant flowers, used as a bitter tonic in fevers. Contain an essential oil. Flowers contain 75% safrole and latter 76% sarisan. 2. *M. nilgirica* zenk. -Western ghats, is known as *Kattu-Sambagam* in Tamilnadu, the yellow flowered variety of champa. The bark and leaves are febrifuge, aerial parts exhibit diuretic and spasmolytic activities.

Name: English: Golden Champa, Champaka, **Sanskrit:** *Chaampeya, Hempuspa, Swarna champaa, Champaka, Peetpushpa,* **Hindi:** *Champaa.* **Local name:** *Champaa.*

Botanical characteristics:

Habit: Tree, height up to 30 m and 50-80 cm in diam. **Stem:** Herbaceous, lower portion woody, aerial, erect, cylindrical, branched, solid. It is a tall handsome evergreen tree, bark smooth grey or brown, inner part reddish. **Leaf:** 20-30 cm long, 5-10 cm wide, glabrous above, shiny, cauline and ramal, alternate, exstipulate, simple, petiolate, ovate, entire, acute, unicostate, reticulate, oblong-lanceolate or lanceolate, sub coriaceous. **Flower:** Yellowish to orange, very fragrant, 5 cm in diam, bracteate, pedicilate, actinomorphic, hermaphrodite, hypogynous, and acyclic. **Fruit:** Etaerio of follicals, 5-10cm, ovoid or ellipsoid capsules, dark brown, opening on the back by two valves, valves woody, covered with white warty excrescences. **Seed:** 1-12, brown rounded on the back with pink fleshy aril.

Flowering and fruiting period: April-May and July-August.

Habitat: Throughout India, in evergreen forests, also cultivated, Eastern Himalayas, lower hills of Assam, hills of South India up to 1000 m.

Parts used: Bark, flowers and buds.

Dosage: Bark for decoction 3-5 g, flowers and buds 1-3 g.

Collection period: May to July.

Ayurvedic properties: ***Ras:*** *katu, tikta ,kashaaya,* ***Gun:*** *laghu, rukhasa,****Veerya:*** *sheet,* ***Vipaka:*** *katu,* ***Tridosh*** **effect:** allevates ***Kapha:*** ++, ***Vaata:*** +. ***Pitta:*** +.

Chemical constituents: **Stem bark and roots** yield an alkaloid liriadenine. **Root bark** yield sesquiterpene lactones and parthoneloid and micheliolide. **Leaves** gave apolyisoprenoid, beta-sitosterol and liriodenine. Mono-and sesquiterpenes occur in **essential oils**, isolated from the flowers, leaf and fruits rings.

Action and diseases indications: Root and root bark are purgative and emmenagogue. It is beneficial in abscesses, constipation, inflammation, amenorrhea and dysmenorrhea. **Stem bark** is astringent, diuretic, stimulant, febrifuge, and expectorant and useful in fever toxic condition, gastritis, strangury, cough, bronchitis and cardiac debility, gout, skin diseases, dysuria, anthelmintic, utero stimulant and tonic. **Flowers and flowerbuds** are bitter, astringent, acrid, refrigerant, haemostatic, carminative, digestive, vulnerary, depurative, anthelmintic, diuretic, diaphoretic, expectorant, antispasmodic, antipyretic. They are useful in burning sensation, hemoptysis, dyspepsia, nausea, skin diseases, leprosy, ulcer, wounds, anorexia, colic, flatulence, helminthiasis, vertigo, neuropathy, gout, cough, bronchitis, amenorrhea, dysmenorrhea and malarial fever. **Seeds and fruits** are useful in the treatment of psoriasis.

Clinical uses: Malaria: 3 hours before when fever comes, give 30 ml cold infusion of root bark of *M. champaka* 3 g, *Tinospora cordifolia* 5 g, *Swertia chiryata* 3 g, added *Aconitum heterophyllum* 500 mg, *Piper longum* 500 mg, Nitrate of potash 500 mg and sugar 10 g, is very beneficial. **Amenorrhoea:** Cold infusion of root bark of *M. champaka* 3 g, with clarified butter 6 g, 2 times a day. **Polyurea:** 20 ml cold infusion of root bark of *M. champaka* 3 g, with honey 10 g, 2-3 times a day. **Skin diseases, ringworm, scabies, eczema**: Powder of bark 3 g, or flower powder of *M. champaca* 5 g, with water, 3 times a day, is very beneficial.

Formulations: *Champak taila, Chandanbalaa laakshaadi taila, Mahaa laxminaaraayana taila, Elaadi taila.*

309. *Mimosa pudica* Linn.

Family: Mimosaceae.

Similar plant: *M. hispida, M. tetrandra, M. unijuja, Biophytum sensitivum.*

Name: English: Sensitive plant, Humble plant. **Sanskrit**: *Lajjaalu, Shamipatra, Namaskaari, Khadirkaa, Samangaa, Jalkaaraka, Raktapadi, Lajjaavanti, Sankochini, Jalkarika..* **Hindi**: *Lajjaavanti.* **Local:** *Lajjaalu, Chuimui.* **Ayurvedic group: Charaka**: *sandhaaniya, purisha sangrhaniya,* **Sushruta**: *priyangwaadi, ambasthaadi gana.*

Botanical characteristics: Habit: A diffuse prickly under shrub, height 50-90 cm. **Root:** Tapering, reddish-brown, cylindrical, tenacious, sour, bitter in taste. **Stem:** Herbaceous, lower portion woody, diffuse, aerial, cylindrical, branched, hairy. **Leaf:** Cauline and ramal, alternate, stipulate, free lateral, compound, bipnnate, pinnae 2-4, digitately arranged with 10-20 pairs of leaflets, petiolate, leaf base pulvinus, oblong, entire, acute, hairy, unicostate, reticulate, sensitive to touch, rachis clothed with ascending bristles. **Flower:** Braceate, sessile, complete, actinomorphic, hermaphrodite, tetramerous, hygynous and cyclic. Pink Colour In globos heads, penduncles prickly, usually in axillary pairs, all along the branches. **Fruit**: Lomentum, bristly pods, flat, straw coloured, 1.25 -1.90 cm long, consisting of 3-5, one seeded segment. **Seed:** Black, round, shiny, flat.

Flowering and fruiting period: July-August and October-November.

Habitat: Naturalized in tropical and subtropical regions of India. Common in disturbed open places, especially cultivated lands, roadsides and waste areas. **Parts used**: Roots and leaves.

Dosage: Root 500 mg, leaves powder 2-4 g, leaves juice 10-20 ml.

Collection period: October to November.

Ayurvedic properties: ***Ras:*** *tikta, kashaaya,* ***Gun:*** *laghu, rukhsa,* ***Veerya:*** *sheet,* ***Vipaka:*** *katu,* ***Tridosha*** effect: alleviates ***Kapha:*** ++, ***Pitta:*** +.

Chemical constituents: The **plant** contains mimosine and turgorin.The **aerial parts** of plant contains C-glycosylflavones, 2 -O-rhamnosylorientin and 2-Orhmnosylisoorientin. **Diseases indications**: **Roots** are bitter, astringent, acrid, vulnerary, cooling, alexipharmic, resolvent, antispasmodic, emetic, diuretic, constipating and febrifuge. Useful in leucoderma, asthma, gravel and urinary complaints, vaginopathy, ulcer, dysentery, burning sensation, piles, jaundice, fistula, fevers, insect bite and nervousness. **Leaves** bitter, sudorofic, antiseptic, styptic, astringent. It is useful in epistaxis, hemorrhoids, fistula, scrofula, conjunctivitis wounds, cuts, diarrhea, hemorrhages, leucorrhoea, morbid condition of vagina, hydrocele and glandular swelling. The **whole plant** is used internally for vesicle calculi and externally for edema, rheumatism, myalgia and tumors of uterus. **Seeds** are aphrodisiac.

Contra indication: Over dose of roots may be toxic. Do not give over 2 g.

Clinical uses: **Penile dysfunction**: Seed powder of *M. pudica* 2 g, with milk or water diluted honey 20 g, 2 times a day is very useful. **Lithuria**: Decoction of roots of *M. pudica* 20 ml, with honey 20 g, 2 times a day, is beneficial. **Diarrhea, dysentery, bleeding piles, anuria:** Decoction of *M. pudica* 20 ml, should be given at morning. **Bleeding piles:** Leaves powder of *M. pudica* 2 g, with juice of *Punica grantum* 30 ml. Repeat it 3-4 hourly. **Hernia**: Local application of warm poultice of leaves of *M. pudica* and then after make it warm for some time. **Vaginal and rectal prolapse:** Douche by leaves juice of *M. pudica*, 20 ml, and put some cotton and tie a bandage for one hour. **Pterygium**: Apply 2-2 drops of leaves juice of *M.pudica*.

Other scholar's opinion: *Biophytum sensitivum* Linn. syn. *Oxalis sensitiva* Linn. (oxalidaceae), *Lajjalu, Lakjan*, Height up to 50 cm, flower yellow, petiole hairy. Due to sleep movement both leaflets joins at night. It is cooling, bitter astringent, and alleviates *Kapha*. It is useful in epistaxis, diarrhea and vaginal discharges. **Uses: Renal and bladder stone and gonorrhea**: Decoction of roots of *B. sensitivum* 30 ml, with honey 20 g, 2 times a day. **Whooping cough**: Root powder of *B. sensitivum* 1 g, with honey 10 g, twice a day. **Piles and hydrocele:** Local application of paste of leaves of *B. sensitivum* is beneficial.

Formulations: *Ashrigdharhar kwaatha, Chandanaadi churna, Baalmitra churna, Kutajaavaleha, Grahanimihir taila, Lavangaadi churna, Arimedaadi taila, Piyushavalli rasa, Chandanaadi churna, Khadirvatikaa.*

Recommended readings:

Acharya, B.K. (2008), Ayurveda Jadi-buti Rahasya, Patanjali Yogapitha, Haridwar, PP. 270.

Bhutya, R.K. (2007), Vanaspati Aushadha Vigyana, Scientific Publishers (India), Jodhpur, PP. 195.

Brahmavarchas (2003), Ayurved Ka Pran Vanoshadhi Vigyan, Shanti Kunj, Haridwar, PP. 291.

Chunekar, K.C. (2004), Bhava Prakash Nighantu, Chaukhambha Bharti Academy, Varanasi, PP. 456.

Khare, C.P. (2007), Indian Medicinal Plants, Springer (India) P.L. New Delhi, PP. 416.

Kirtikar, K.R. & Basu, B.D. (1998), Indian Medicinal Plants, L.M Basu, Allahabad, Vol. 2, PP. 915.

Misra, B.L. (2005), Dravya Guna Hastamalaka, Publication scheme, Jaipur, PP. 285.

Nair, R.Vasudevan, (2007), Indian Medicinal Plants, Orient Longman P.L. Chennai, Vol. 4, PP. 36.

Namjoshi, A.N. (2001), The Ayurvedic Pharmacopoeia of India, Government of India, Department of Indian Systems of Medicine & Homoeopathy, New Delhi, Part-1, Volume- 1, PP. 98.

Prajapati, N.D., Purohit, S.S., Sharma, A.K. & Tarun Kumar (2003), A Hand Book of Medicinal Plants, Agrobios India, Jodhpur, PP. 345.

Sharma, P.C., Yelne, MB. & Denis, T.J. (2000), Database on medicinal plants used in ayurveda, Central Council for research in Ayurveda and siddha, Vol. 3, PP. 369.

Sharma, P.V. (1981), Dravya gun vigyana, Chaukhambha Bharti Academy, Varanasi, Vol. 1, PP. 749.

Swami, K.N. (1985), Gavon Main Aushadh Ratna, Kalera Krishana Gopal, Kalera (Raj.), Vol. 3, PP. 254.

310. *Mimusops elengi* Linn.

Family: Sapotaceae.

Name: English: Spanish Cherry, West Indian Medlar, Bullet Wood, **Sanskrit:** *Bakula, Madhugandha, Singhakesharaka, Shivamalli, Paashupata, Chirpushpa, Sthirapushpa,* **Hindi:** *Maulashree,* **Local:** *Molshree, Morchadi.*

Botanical characteristics: Habit: A small to large, glabrous evergreen Tree, height up to 12-15 m. **Stem:** Short erect trunk, bark dark grey fissured and dense spreading crown. **Leaf:** Variable, oblong, elliptic or oblaceolate, 6.25-10 by 3.1-5 cm, acute, base acute or rounded, glabrous, leathery with wavy margins, petioles 1.2-2.5 cm long. **Flower:** White, fragrant, nearly 2.5 cm across, star shaped, axillary, solitary or in fascicles of 2-6, pedicel 6.25-20 mm long. **Fruit:** Berry, ovoid or ellipsoid, 2.5 cm long, yellow when ripe, 1-2 seeded. **Seed:** Solitary, ovoid, compressed, brown, shiny.

Flowering and fruiting period: April-May and July-August.

Habitat: Throughout south India, Western Peninsula and Andaman islands in evergreen forests, cultivated throughout India as an avenue or shade tree.

Parts used: Bark, flower, fruit.

Dosage: Bark 10-20 g, flower 1-2 g, Fruit 2-4 g.

Collection period: April-May.

Ayurvedic properties: ***Ras:*** *katu, tikta, kashayaa,* ***Gun:*** *guru,* ***Veerya:*** *ushna,* ***Vipaka:*** *katu,* ***Tridosha*** **Effect:** alleviates ***Kapha:*** ++, ***Pitta:*** +.

Chemical constituents: The **bark** contains taraxerone, taraxerol, betulinic acid, alpha-spinasterol and mixtures of saponins. The **fruits** and **seeds** contain quercitol, ursolic acid, glucose, a triterpene alcohol, quercetin, hydroquercetin and beta-sitosterol glucosides. The **flowers** contain D-manitol, betasitosterol, its glucoside and essential oil.

Action and disease indications: The **Bark, flowers** and **fruits** are astringent, refrigerant and anthelmintic. The **bark** is tonic and febrifuge, used as gargle for odontopathy, ulitis and ulemorrhagia, dipsia, burning sensation, skin diseases, inflammations, leucoderma and intestinal worms. The **flowers** are brain tonic, used for wounds and ulcers and headache.

Clinical uses: Gingivitis, stomatitis : Gargles of decoction of stem bark or unripe fruits of described plant 10 g, is beneficial. **Chronic bacillary dysentery:** Ripe fruit powder of described plant 5 g, with water, three times a day. **Inflammations:** Cold infusion of mix powder of Bark of described plant, *Terminalia chebula,* roots of *Boerhavia diffusa,* 6 g, with honey 10 g, two times a day. **Bronchitis of children:** Cold infusion of flower powder of described plant 2-4 g, with honey 10 g, three or four times a day, is very beneficial. **Burning sensation of urine, hematuria:** Ripe fruit powder of described plant 10 g, or cold infusion of described plant 10 g, with sugar 10 g, with water, three times a day. **Migrain, headache:** Snuff of flower powder of described plant 500-500 mg is beneficial. **Acute menorrhagia, metrorrhagia:** *'Maha gandhaka rasa'* or *'Sarvanga sundar rasa'* 250 mg, *Mesua ferrea, Justisia adhatoda* 2-2 g, with decoction of stem bark of described plant 10 g, with honey 10 g, three times a day, is very useful. **Gingivitis, pyorrhea and as a dental powder:** Powder of stem bark powder of described plant 10 g, *Quercus infectoria* 5 g, black ash of *Quercus infectoria* 5 g, use as tooth powder, two times a day. **Gingivitis, pyorrhea:** Gargles of decoction of stem barks of, described plant, *Phylanthus emblica, Acacia catechu,* 20 g, is very beneficial.

Formulations: *Bakulaadhya taila, Bakulkaanti manjan.*

Recommended readings:

Acharya, B.K. (2008), Ayurveda Jadi-buti Rahasya, Patanjali Yogapitha, Haridwar, PP. 292.

Bhutya, R.K. (2007), Vanaspati Aushadha Vigyana, Scientific Publishers (India), Jodhpur, PP. 188.

Brahmavarchas (2003), Ayurved Ka Pran Vanoshadhi Vigyan, Shanti Kunj, Haridwar, PP. 292.

Chunekar, K.C. (2004), Bhava Prakash Nighantu, Chaukhambha Bharti Academy, Varanasi, PP. 494.

Khare, C.P. (2007), Indian Medicinal Plants, Springer (India) P.L. New Delhi, PP. 416.

Kirtikar, K.R. & Basu, B.D. (1998), Indian Medicinal Plants, L.M Basu, Allahabad, Vol. 2, PP. 1494.

Nair, R.Vasudevan, (2007), Indian Medicinal Plants, Orient Longman P.L. Chennai, Vol. 4, PP. 40.

Pareek, G.N. (2005), Sudhanidhi, Vanoshadhi Ratnakar, Dhanvantari Karyalaya, Aligarh, Vol. 6, PP. 106.

Prajapati, N.D., Purohit, S.S., Sharma, A.K. & Tarun Kumar (2003), A Hand Book of Medicinal Plants, Agrobios India, Jodhpur, PP. 345.

Sharma, P.C., Yelne, MB. & Denis, T.J. (2000), Database on medicinal plants used in ayurveda, Central Council for research in Ayurveda and siddha, Vol. 1, PP. 65.

Sharma, P.V. (1981), Dravya gun vigyana, Chaukhambha Bharti Academy, Varanasi, Vol. 1, PP. 329.

Singh, R.S. (2002), Vanoshadhi Nirdeshika, Uttar Pradesh Hindi Sansthan, Lucknow, PP. 322.

Swami, K.N. (1985), Gavon Main Aushadh Ratna, Kalera Krishana Gopal, Kalera (Raj.), Vol. 3, PP. 234.

311. *Mitragyna parvifolia* (Roxb.) Korth.

Family: Rubiaceae.

Name: English: Kaim, **Sanskrit:** *Dhuli Kadamba, Giri Kadamba,* **Hindi:** *Kalam,* **Local:** *Kalam.*

Botanical characteristics: Habit: A medium to large sized deciduous and evergreen tree, glabrous or pubescent. **Stem:** With rounded crown and light grey smooth bark, exfoliating in small scales. **Leaf:** Simple, opposite, variable in size and shape, 5-12.5 by 3.8-7.5 cm, elliptic, suborbicular, or obovate, rounded, acute or bluntly acuminate at the apex, glabrous on both sides, base rounded or acute, sometimes cordate, main nerves 6-8 pairs, oblique, petiole 1-2 cm long, stipule 13 by 5.8 mm, oblong-spathulate, obtuse, parallel-nerved, pink. **Flower:** Greenish-yellow, fragrant, pendUcles solitary terminal, short, each carrying a globose head of flowers 2-2.5 cm in diam. **Fruit:** Capsules, oblong, with blunt rounded tops and 10 blunt ribs. **Seed:** Globose, hirsuit.

Flowering and fruiting period: May-June and June-July.

Habitat: All over India, in deciduous and evergreen forests, up to 1200 m in outer Himalaya.

Parts used: Root, bark, leaves.

Dosage: Root, bark, leaves 3-6g.

Collection period: May-June.

Ayurvedic properties: ***Ras:*** *tikta, kashaaya,* ***Gun:*** *laghu, rukhsa,* ***Veerya:*** *ushna,* ***Vipaka:*** *katu,* ***Tridosha*** **Effect:** alleviates ***Pitta:*** ++, aggravates ***Kapha:*** ++, ***Vata:*** +.

Chemical constituents: The **plant** contains indole and oxindole alkaloids. The main indole alkaloid is akuammigine and oxindole alkaloid is mitraphylline, isomitraphylline, speciophylline and uncarine F.

Action and disease indications: The **Plant** is thermogenic, stomachic, anti-inflammatory and febrifuge, used for gastropathy, colic, haemorrhage, ulcers, flatulence, dipsia, inflammations, myalgia, erysipelas, skin diseases and fever.

Clinical uses: Internal and external hemorrhage, inflammations, myalgia, erysipelas: Decoction of bark of described plant 10 g, with honey 10 g, two times a day.

Recommended readings:

Bhutya, R.K. (2007), Vanaspati Aushadha Vigyana, Scientific Publishers (India), Jodhpur, PP. 54.

Khare, C.P. (2007), Indian Medicinal Plants, Springer (India) P.L. New Delhi, PP. 417.

Kirtikar, K.R. & Basu, B.D. (1998), Indian Medicinal Plants, L.M Basu, Allahabad, Vol. 2, PP. 1256.

Nair, R.Vasudevan, (2007), Indian Medicinal Plants, Orient Longman P.L. Chennai, Vol. 4, PP. 45.

Prajapati, N.D., Purohit, S.S., Sharma, A.K. & Tarun Kumar (2003), A Hand Book of Medicinal Plants, Agrobios India, Jodhpur, PP. 346.

312. *Momordica charantia* Linn.

Family: Cucurbitaceae.

Ayurvedic Groups: Charak: *Tiktaskandha.*

Name: English: Bitter Gourd, Blsam Pear,Carilla, **Sanskrit:** *Kaarvellaka, Kathilla,* **Hindi:** *Karelaa,* **Local:** *Karelaa.*

Botanical characteristics: Habit: A monoecious climbing annual. **Stem:** Long, much branched, angled and grooved, more or less pubescent or hairy, tendrils simple, slender, elongated, pubescent. **Leaf:** Simple, orbicular in out line, 5-12.5 cm diam., pubescent or subglabrous on both sides, cordate at the base, deeply divided in to 5-7 lobes, the lobes acute or subacute, apiculate, coarsely spinous-dentate, constricted at the base; petioles 2.5-5 cm long, channeled, pubescent. **Flower:** Yellow, monoecious, unisexual, on 5-10 cm long penduncles. **Fruit:** Capsules, 5-15 cm long, bright green when unripe and yellow when ripe, pendulous, fusiform or oblong-ellipsoid, ribbed and beaked bearing numerous triangular, tubercles, giving it the appearance of a crocodile's back, 3-valved at the apex when mature. **Seed:** Numerous, dull white, 8-13 mm long, enclosed in red aril in ripe fruit, compressed, quadrate, corrugate on the margin, shining sculptured on both faces.

Flowering and fruiting period: August-September and September-October.

Habitat: Cultivated throughout India, up to an altitude of 1500 m.

Parts used: Immature fruit.

Dosage: Power 1-3 g, juice 10-15 ml.

Collection period: September-October.

Ayurvedic properties: ***Ras:*** *tikta,* ***Gun:*** *laghu, rukhsa,* ***Veerya:*** *sheeta* ***Vipaka:*** *katu,* ***Tridosha*** **Effect:** alleviates ***Pitta:*** **++,** ***Kapha:*** **++,** Aggrevates ***Vaata:*** **+.**

Chemical constituents: The **Immature fruits** contain several non-bitter and bitter momordicosides, a polypeptide containing 17 types of amino acids, 5-hydroxytryptamine, charantin (a steroidal glucoside), diosgenin, cholesterol, lanosterol and beta-sitosterol. Bitter principles are cucurbitacin glycosides. The fruits and seeds yielded a polypeptide, *p*-insulin, which was considered similar to bovine insulin. Researchers have warned that the fruit extract leads to a false negative test for sugar in the urine.

Action and disease indications: The **fruits** are refrigerant, stimulant, depurative, vulnerary, purgative, appetizer, anti-diabetic, carminative, stomachic, anthelmintic, anti-bilious, anti-inflammatory, emmenogogue, febrifuge and tonic, prescribed for cough, diabetes, skin diseases, urticaria, ulcers, leprosy, wounds, burning sensation, constipation, anorexia, flatulence, colic, helminthiasis, gout, rheumatism, heptomegaly, spleenomegaly, asthma, piles, inflammations, dysmenorrhea, impurities of breast milk, fever and general debility.

Clinical uses: Malaria with spleen enlargement and ascites, helminthiasis: Leaves juice of described plant 20 ml, with honey 10 g, two times a day. **Spleen enlargement:** Fruit juice of described plant 15 ml, common salt 1 g, *Brassica juncea* 1 g, two times a day. **Pneumonitis, bronchitis:** Leaves juice of described plant 15 ml, *Acorus calamus* 500 mg, with honey 10 g, two or three times a day is beneficial. **Chronic skin diseases:** Tropical use of juice or paste of described plant is useful. **Diabetes mellitus, hypercholesteromia:** Mix powder of unripe fruit of described plant, seed powder of *Trigonella foenum-gracum,* leaves of *Azadirachta indica, Cinamomum tamala, Gymnema sylvestre* and *Aegle marmelos,* seed powder of *Syzygium cumini,* 5 g, three times a day, **or** fruit juice of described plant 15 ml, and *Phylanthus emblica,* leaves juice of *Azadirachta indica* 5 ml, three times a day, is very beneficial. **Piles:** Leaves powder of described plant 20 ml, with fresh curd of cow milk 100 g, two times a day, and local application of paste of root of described plant, is beneficial. **Bleeding piles:** Fruit juice of described plant 15 ml, sugar 10 g, three times a day.

Formulations: *Achintyashkti rasa, Mallaadi vati.*

Recommended readings:

Acharya, B.K. (2008), Ayurveda Jadi-buti Rahasya, Patanjali Yogapitha, Haridwar, PP. 261.

Bhutya, R.K. (2007), Vanaspati Aushadha Vigyana, Scientific Publishers (India), Jodhpur, PP. 52.

Brahmavarchas (2003), Ayurved Ka Pran Vanoshadhi Vigyan, Shanti Kunj, Haridwar, PP. 295.

Chunekar, K.C. (2004), Bhava Prakash Nighantu, Chaukhambha Bharti Academy, Varanasi, PP. 684.

Khare, C.P. (2007), Indian Medicinal Plants, Springer (India) P.L. New Delhi, PP. 418.

Kirtikar, K.R. & Basu, B.D. (1998), Indian Medicinal Plants, L.M Basu, Allahabad, Vol. 2, PP. 1130.

Misra, B.L. (2005), Dravya Guna Hastamalaka, Publication scheme, Jaipur, PP. 487.

Nair, R.Vasudevan, (2007), Indian Medicinal Plants, Orient Longman P.L. Chennai, Vol. 4, PP. 48.

Namjoshi, A.N. (2001), The Ayurvedic Pharmacopoeia of India, Government of India, Department of Indian Systems of Medicine & Homoeopathy, New Delhi, Part-1, Volume- 1, PP. 43.

Pareek, G.N. (2005), Sudhanidhi, Vanoshadhi Ratnakar, Dhanvantari Karyalaya, Aligarh, Vol. 9, PP. 187.

Prajapati, N.D., Purohit, S.S., Sharma, A.K. & Tarun Kumar (2003), A Hand Book of Medicinal Plants, Agrobios India, Jodhpur, PP. 346.

Sharma, P.C., Yelne, MB. & Denis, T.J. (2000), Database on medicinal plants used in ayurveda, Central Council for research in Ayurveda and siddha, Vol. 4, PP. 288.

Sharma, P.V. (1981), Dravya gun vigyana, Chaukhambha Bharti Academy, Varanasi, Vol. 1, PP. 684.

Singh, R.S. (2002), Vanoshadhi Nirdeshika, Uttar Pradesh Hindi Sansthan, Lucknow, PP. 84.

Swami, K.N. (1985), Gavon Main Aushadh Ratna, Kalera Krishana Gopal, Kalera (Raj.), Vol. 1, PP. 124.

313. *Momordica dioica* Roxb. ex Willd.

Family: Cucurbitaceae.

Name: English: Small Bitter Gourd, Bur Cucumber, **Sanskrit:** *Karkotaki, Peetapushpaa, Mahaajali, Karkoti,* **Hindi:** *Kakoraa,* **Local:** *Kakoraa, Khekhasaa.*

Botanical characteristics: Habit: A dioecious climbing perennial. **Rhizome:** Perennial, long, yellowish-white, astringent in taste. **Stem:** With tuberous roots, slender, branched, furrowed, glabrous and shining. Tendrils simple, elongate, striate, glabrous. **Leaf:** 3.8-10 by 3.2-8 cm, broadly ovate in outline, variable, membranous, cordate at the base, glabrous, minutely punctuate, entire and more or less deeply 3-5 lobed, the lobes triangular, ovate, or oblong, distantly denticulate, petioles 1.3-4.5 cm long, channeled above, pubescent, glandular. **Flower:** Yellow, penduncle solitary, 3.8-12.5 cm long, slender, angled, glabrous. **Fruit:** 2.5-6.3 cm long, ellipsoid, shortly beaked, densely echinate with soft spines. **Seed:** Numerous, 1 cm long, broadly ellipsoid, pale white, turning black at ripen, slightly compressed, slightly and irregularly corrugated, enclosed in a red pulp. This plant has another variety, called *'Baanjha Kakoraa' or 'Vandhyaa Karkotaki'.* It has only male flowers, so there are no fruiting. It's root is very useful as contraceptive medicine.

Flowering and fruiting period: August-September and September-October.

Habitat: Throughout India, up to 1500 m in Himalaya.

Parts used: Fruit, tuber.

Dosage: Fruit 5-10 g, tuber 4-6 g.

Collection period: September-October.

Ayurvedic properties: ***Ras:*** *tikta,* ***Gun:*** *laghu, rukhsa,* ***Veerya:*** *ushna,* ***Vipaka:*** *katu,* ***Tridosha*** **Effect:** alleviates ***Kapha:*** **++**, aggravates ***Vaata:*** **+**, ***Pitta:*** **+**.

Chemical constituents: The **fruits** contain protein 3.1, carbohydrate 7.7, fibers 2.97, fat 0.97%, also have vitamin C. The **root** extract exhibited significant anti-allergic activity comparable with standard drugs used against allergy and bronchial asthma.

Action and disease indications: The **fruits** are thermogenic, alexiteric, stomachic, laxative, appetizer, haemostatic, used for skin diseases, nausea, biliousness, tumours, urinary discharges, excessive salivation, cardiac diseases, anorexia, bronchitis, asthma and fever.

Clinical uses: Diabetes melitus: Tuber of described plant 5 g, *'Vanga Bhasma'* 125 mg, with old honey water 10 g, two times a day. **Bleeding piles:** Powder of tuber of described plant 5 g, sugar 5 g, with cold infusion of flowers and leaves of *Hibiscus rosa-sinensis*water 10 g, or water, three times a day. **Gland in breast:** Tropical use of paste of tuber of described plant is beneficial. Give *'Kaishor guggulu'* Tablets 1-1 g, three times a day. **Erysipelas, Skin diseases:** Unripe fruit powder of described plant 10 g, or vegetable of described plant 50-100 g, two times a day. **Renal and vesical calculus:** Tuber powder or paste of described plant, 5 g, with milk. two times a day. **Amenorrhea, dysmenorrhea:** Decoction of tuber of described plant 10 g, with honey 10 g, two times a day. **Hemicrania:** Nasal drops of medicated clarified butter, 4-4 drops, two times a day is beneficial. **Abscess:** Poultice of paste of tuber or leaves, on affected part, is beneficial. **Asthma, bronchitis:**

Black ash of tuber of described plant 250-500 mg, with juice of fresh tuber of *Zingiber officinalis* 5 ml and honey 10 g, three times a day, is very beneficial.

Formulations: *Karkotaki lepa.*

Recommended readings:

Bhutya, R.K. (2007), Vanaspati Aushadha Vigyana, Scientific Publishers (India), Jodhpur, PP. 44.

Brahmavarchas (2003), Ayurved Ka Pran Vanoshadhi Vigyan, Shanti Kunj, Haridwar, PP. 297.

Chunekar, K.C. (2004), Bhava Prakash Nighantu, Chaukhambha Bharti Academy, Varanasi, PP. 691.

Khare, C.P. (2007), Indian Medicinal Plants, Springer (India) P.L. New Delhi, PP. 420.

Kirtikar, K.R. & Basu, B.D. (1998), Indian Medicinal Plants, L.M Basu, Allahabad, Vol. 2, PP. 1133.

Pareek, G.N. (2005), Sudhanidhi, Vanoshadhi Ratnakar, Dhanvantari Karyalaya, Aligarh, Vol. 9, PP. 145.

Sharma, P.V. (1981), Dravya gun vigyana, Chaukhambha Bharti Academy, Varanasi, Vol. 2, PP. 111.

Singh, R.S. (2002), Vanoshadhi Nirdeshika, Uttar Pradesh Hindi Sansthan, Lucknow, PP. 60.

Swami, K.N. (1985), Gavon Main Aushadh Ratna, Kalera Krishana Gopal, Kalera (Raj.), Vol. 1, PP. 93.

314. *Moringa oleifera* Lam.

Family: Moringaceae.

Synonym: *M. pterigosperma.*

Other similar plant: *M.concanensis.*

Ayurvedic Groups: Charak: *Swedopaga, Krimighana, Shirovirechana, Katuskandha, Haritaki varga,* **Sushruta:** *Varunaadi gana.*

Name: English: Dumstick, Horse-Radish, **Sanskrit:** *Shigru, Shobhaanjan, Teekhsnagandhaka, Akhsiva, Mochaka, Sweta Maricha* (Seed) **Hindi:** *Shobhaanjan,* **Local:** *Sahinjanaa.*

Botanical characteristics: Habit: A small or medium sized unarmed graceful tree, height 10 m. **Stem:** Bark grey corky, wood soft, branches easily breakable branches. **Leaf:** usually tripinnate,. Rachis slender, thickened and articulated at the base, pinna and pinnules opposite, deciduous, their rachides very slender, articulated and with a gland at the articulations; ultimate leaflets 1.2-2 by 6-10 cm, the lateral eliptic, the terminal obovate and slightly longer, nerves obscure, petiolules of the lateral leaflets 1.5-2.5 mm, those of the terminal 3-6 mm long. **Flower:** White, fragrant, in large puberlous axillary panicles. **Fruit:** Pods, 45 cm long, pendulous, greenish, triangular, 9-ribbed. **Seed:** Trigonous, the angles winged.

Flowering and fruiting period: January-March and April-June.

Habitat: Indigenous in the sub Himalayan tracts, from Chenab to Sarda, also in Oudh forests, cultivated all over the plains of India.

Parts used: Root bark, fruit, seed, gum, flower, tender leaves.

Dosage: Root bark 4-8 g, fruit 25-50 g, seed 1-3 g, gum 2-4 g, flower 1-3 g, tender leaves 50-100 g.

Collection period: May-June.

Ayurvedic properties: ***Ras:*** *katu, tikta, madhur,* ***Gun:*** *laghu, rukhsa,* ***Veerya:*** *ushna,* ***Vipaka:*** *katu,* ***Tridosha*** **Effect:** alleviates ***Kapha:*** ***++,*** ***Vaata:*** ***++.***

Chemical constituents: The **plant** contains 4-hydroxymellein, vanillin, moringine, moringinine, barrenol, indole acetic acid, indole acetonitrile, benzylisothiocyanate, pterigospermin, cartotene, flavanoids, polysaccharide, protein components, various essential amino acids, minerals and vitamins, fatty acids, spirochin and pterygospermin.

Action and disease indications: The **roots** are digestive, thermogenic, anthelmintic, carminative, constipating, anodyne, anti-inflammatory, emmenogogue, sudorofic, diuretic, ophthalmic, rubefacient, expectorant, haematinic, antilithic, alexipharmic, stimulant, and vesicant, used for anorexia, dyspepsia, diarrhea, colic, verminosis, flatulence, otalgia, paralysis, inflammations, dysmenorrhea, amenorrhea, fever, strangury, renal and vesical calculi, ascitis, cough, asthma, bronchitis, ophthalmopathy, spleenomegaly, epilepsy, hysteria, cardiopathy, abscess and pharyingodynia. The **stem bark** is thermogenic, abortifacient, anti-fungal and cardiac and circulatory stimulant, used for ascitis, and ringworm. The **leaves** are anodyne, anti-inflammatory, anthelmintic, ophthelmic and rich in vitamin A and C, used for scurvy, inflammations, helminthiasis, wounds and tumours. The **Seeds** are anodyne, anti-inflammatory, purgative, antpyretic and ophthalmic, used for inflammations, neuralgia, intermittent fever and ophthalmopathy.

Clinical uses: Abscess, inflammations, boils, calculus, epilepsy, hysteria: Decoction of root bark of described plant 10 g, with rock salt 1 g, and fried gum of *Ferula foetida* 125 mg, two times a day. **Coma, vertigo, nervous debility, flatulence, spasmodic pain of abdomen:** Alcoholic extract of described plant, rind of *Citrus reticulata, Myristica franrance,* root powder of described plant, 10-20 drops, with water, two times a day. **Wounds,**

inflammations, boils: Local application of paste of stem bark of described plant is useful. **Osteo arthritis, rheumetoid arthritis, gout:** Massage of seed oil of described plant, is beneficial. **Gingivitis, dentalgia, dental carries:** Gargles of Bark of decoction of described plant 10 g, with roasted seeds of *Cuminum cyminum* 2 g, or use dental powder of bark of described plant 1o g, and roasted seed powder of *Cuminum cyminum* 2 g, is useful. **Dandruff:** Local application of leaves juice of described plant, and wash with cold infusion of fruits of *Sapindus mukorossi*, is beneficial. **Ascitis, inflammation of liver and spleen, renal and vesical calculus:** Decoction of root bark of described plant 5 g, with honey 10 g, two times a day, is useful. **Renal colic:** Decoction of bark of described plant, 5 g, *Zingiber officinale* 1 g, with honey 10 g, two times a day, is useful. **Renal and vesical calculus:** Decoction of mix powder of bark of described plant, *Crataeva magna, Tribulus terrestris, Solanum nigrum, Boerhavia diffusa, Zingiber officinale, Cassia fistula,* 20 g, with honey 10 g, two times a day, is useful. **Colic:** Gum of described plant, 3 g, with warm water, two times a day, is beneficial. **Sciatica, rheumatism, paralysis:** Decoction of root bark of described plant, 10 g, with *Trachy spermumammi* 500 mg, *Zingiber officinale* 500 mg, *Ferula narthex* 125 mg, two times a day, is beneficial.

Formulations: *Shobhanjanaadi lepa, Shyaamaadi lepa, Maanikya rasa, Kaalkoota rasa, Shyamaadi churna.*

Recommended readings:

Acharya, B.K. (2008), Ayurveda Jadi-buti Rahasya, Patanjali Yogapitha, Haridwar, PP. 365.

Bhutya, R.K. (2007), Vanaspati Aushadha Vigyana, Scientific Publishers (India), Jodhpur, PP. 218.

Brahmavarchas (2003), Ayurved Ka Pran Vanoshadhi Vigyan, Shanti Kunj, Haridwar, PP. 298.

Chunekar, K.C. (2004), Bhava Prakash Nighantu, Chaukhambha Bharti Academy, Varanasi, PP. 339.

Dhiman, A.K. (2006), Ayurvedic Drug Plants, Daya Publishing House, Delhi, PP. 357.

Khare, C.P. (2007), Indian Medicinal Plants, Springer (India) P.L. New Delhi, PP. 422.

Kirtikar, K.R. & Basu, B.D. (1998), Indian Medicinal Plants, L.M Basu, Allahabad, Vol. 1, PP. 677.

Misra, B.L. (2005), Dravya Guna Hastamalaka, Publication scheme, Jaipur, PP. 464.

Nair, R.Vasudevan, (2007), Indian Medicinal Plants, Orient Longman P.L. Chennai, Vol. 4, PP. 59.

Namjoshi, A.N. (2001), The Ayurvedic Pharmacopoeia of India, Government of India, Department of Indian Systems of Medicine & Homoeopathy, New Delhi, Part-1, Volume- 1, PP. 155.

Pareek, G.N. (2005), Sudhanidhi, Vanoshadhi Ratnakar, Dhanvantari Karyalaya, Aligarh, Vol. 8, PP. 204.

Prajapati, N.D., Purohit, S.S., Sharma, A.K. & Tarun Kumar (2003), A Hand Book of Medicinal Plants, Agrobios India, Jodhpur, PP. 350.

Sharma, P.C., Yelne, MB. & Denis, T.J. (2000), Database on medicinal plants used in ayurveda, Central Council for research in Ayurveda and siddha, Vol. 1, PP. 431.

Sharma, P.V. (1981), Dravya gun vigyana, Chaukhambha Bharti Academy, Varanasi, Vol. 1, PP. 111.

Singh, R.S. (2002), Vanoshadhi Nirdeshika, Uttar Pradesh Hindi Sansthan, Lucknow, PP. 368.

Swami, K.N. (1985), Gavon Main Aushadh Ratna, Kalera Krishana Gopal, Kalera (Raj.), Vol. 3, PP. 337.

315. *Morus alba* Linn.

Family: Moraceae.

Variety: *M.nigra-* black var. found in Kashmir and Darjiling, *M.acidosa M.australis M.indica.*

Name: English: White mulberry, **Sanskrit:** *Tuda, Tula, Tuta, Brahmadaru, Kramuka, Brahmakastha,* **Hindi:** *Sahatuta,* **Local:** *Shahatuta, Tuta.*

Botanical characteristics: Habit: A medium sized tree, height up to 7 m. **Stem:** Upper portion herbaceous, lower portion woody, erect, cylindrical, solid, bark dark grayish- brown, rough, having vertical fissure. **Leaf:** Alternate, variable in size and shape, usually ovate or broadly ovate, serete or crenate-serete, often densely lobed, acute, glabrous, size 5-12.75 by 5-7.5 cm. **Flower:** Bisexual, greenish, inconspicuous, male catkins broadly cylindrical, or ovoid; female catkins ovoid, pedunclulate. **Fruit:** Syncarp of many drupes, white to pinkish white or dark purple, 5.5 cm long.

Flowering and fruiting period: January-February and June-July.

Habitat: Throughout India, also cultivated.

Parts used: Fruits, leaves, root bark.

Dosage: Fruit juice 25-50 ml.

Collection period: April-August.

Ayurvedic properties: ***Ras:*** *madhur* ***Gun:*** *guru, snigdha* ***Veerya:*** *sheet,* ***Vipaka:*** *madhur* **:** ***Tridosha*** **Effect:** alleviates ***Vaata:*** +++, ***Pitta:*** +++, aggravates ***Kapha:*** **++.**

Chemical constituents: The **plant** is rich in pheolics, **Leaves** contain flavonoids, including rutin, morecetin, anthocyanins, including cynidin and delphinidin-glucosides, artocarpin, cycloartocarpin andanalogues. The **root bark**

contains flavonoids, kuwunons, sangennons, mulberrosides and mulberrofurans.

Action and disease indications: The **roots** are hypoglycemic, astringent, anthelmintic and purgative. The **leaves** are diaphoretic, emollient, anti bacterial, and expectorant. Useful to cure pharngodynia, scabies, hoarseness, hypertension, inflammations. **Fruits** are cooling, aphrodisiac, laxative, roborant, diuretic, anthelmintic and brain tonic, used for burning sensation, small pox, lumbago, phyryngopathy, dyspepsia, diarrhea, ulcerated intestine, strangury, heptomagaly, spleenomagaly and melancholia. An aqua's methanol extract of the **root bark** significantly reduced plasma sugar level and anti inflammatory and anti pyretic activity in exudative, porliferative and chronic phases of Inflammation, alkali extract of **leaves and stem** are active against gram positive bacteria and yeast.

Clinical uses: Pyrexia: Syrup of ripe fruits of plant 20 ml, 3 times a day. **Intestinal worms, constipation:** Powder of stem bark 10 g, with warm water, at night. **Hoarseness:** Gargles of decoction of leaves of described plant 50 g, 3 times a day.

Formulations: *Sahatoot sarbata.*

Recommended readings:

Bhutya, R.K. (2007), Vanaspati Aushadha Vigyana, Scientific Publishers (India), Jodhpur, PP. 213.

Brahmavarchas (2003), Ayurved Ka Pran Vanoshadhi Vigyan, Shanti Kunj, Haridwar, PP. 300.

Chunekar, K.C. (2004), Bhava Prakash Nighantu, Chaukhambha Bharti Academy, Varanasi, PP. 581.

Khare, C.P. (2007), Indian Medicinal Plants, Springer (India) P.L. New Delhi, PP. 423.

Kirtikar, K.R. & Basu, B.D. (1998), Indian Medicinal Plants, L.M Basu, Allahabad, Vol. 3, PP. 2308.

Misra, B.L. (2005), Dravya Guna Hastamalaka, Publication scheme, Jaipur, PP. 389.

Nair, R.Vasudevan, (2007), Indian Medicinal Plants, Orient Longman P.L. Chennai, Vol. 4, PP. 65.

Prajapati, N.D., Purohit, S.S., Sharma, A.K. & Tarun Kumar (2003), A Hand Book of Medicinal Plants, Agrobios India, Jodhpur, PP. 351.

Sharma, P.V. (1981), Dravya gun vigyana, Chaukhambha Bharti Academy, Varanasi, Vol. 2, PP. 228.

316. *Mucana pruriens* (Linn.) DC.

Family: Papilionaceae; Fabaceae.

Synonym: *M.prurita.*

Varieties: White, black and mix. Wild and cultivated. For medicinal purpose, wild var. should be used.

Name: English: Cowhage, Horse-eye Bean, **Sanskrit:** *Kapikachhu, Aatmaguptaa, Vrisya, Markati, Ajadaa, Kanduraa, Duhsparshaa, Langali, Shookashimbi,* **Hindi:** *Kavaancha,* **Local:** *Koncha.*

Botanical characteristics: Habit: A herbaceous, twining, climbing, slender annuals. **Stem:** Branches slender, more or less hairy. **Leaf:** Trifoliate, leaflets broadly ovate, elliptic or rhomboid ovate, membranous, 7.5-12.5 by 5-7.5 cm, sub-acute, unequal at base, mucronate, pubescent above, densely clothed with silvery-grey hairs beneath, petioles 6.3-11.3 cm long, apperessedly silky; stipules lanceolate, 5 mm long. **Flower:** Purple, in axillary, pendulous, 6-30 flowered racemes 15-30 cm long; the flowers solitary or 2-3 together along a slender silky rachies; pediceles 3-6 mm long, hairy; bracts 1.2 cm long, lanceolate, hairy, caduceus; bracteoles 8 mm long, hairy, caduceus. **Fruit:** Pods, 5-10 by 1.2 cm, turgid, longitudinally ribbed, falcately curved on both ends, somewhat like the letter S, densely clothed with persistent irritant pale brown or grey, turning steel grey bristles, 4-6 seeded. **Seed:** Ovoid, black or dull black or white with faint brown specks, inner portion white.

Flowering and fruiting period: November-December and February-March.

Habitat: Throughout India, including Andaman and Nikobar Islands, up to 1000 m in Himalaya.

Parts used: Seed, root, fruit hairs.

Dosage: Seed 3-6 g, root 3-6 g, hairs 15-25 mg.

Collection period: February-March.

Ayurvedic properties: ***Ras:*** *madhur, tikta,* ***Gun:*** *guru, snigdha,* ***Veerya:*** *ushna,* ***Vipaka:*** *madhur,* ***Tridosha*** **Effect:** alleviates ***Vaata:*** **++++,** ***Kapha:*** **+,** ***Pitta:*** **+.**

Chemical constituents: The **seeds** contain the alkaloids, mucunine, mucunadine, mucunadinine, prurieninine, pruriedine and nicotine, besides beta-sitosterol, gluthine, lecithin, vernilic and gallic acid, also contain a number of bioactive sub-stances includingtryptamine, alkylamines, steroids, flavonoids, coumarins and cardenolides. L-DOPA is present in the seed as well as in the stem, leaves and roots. The **hairs** contain amines such as 5-hydroxy-tryptamine (serotonin), and a proteolytic enzyme mucuanain. The **seed oil** contains stearic, palmitic, myristic, arachidic, oleic, linoleic acids and sterol.

Action and disease indications: The **seeds** are thermogenic, stimulant, nervine tonic, laxative, anthelmintic, aphrodisiac, alexipharmic, spermatogenic, tonic and somatotrofic, used for sterility, impotence, spermatorrhea, urinary troubles, leucorrhea, depressive neurosis, gonorrhea, consumption and general debility. The **root** is thermogenic, emollient, stimulant, purgative, aphrodisiac, diuretic,, emmenogogue, anthelmintic, febrifuge and tonic, used for strangury, constipation, nephropathy, dysmenorrhea, amenorrhea, elephantiasis, dropsy, neuropathy, consumption, ulcers, helminthiasis, fever and delirium. The **hairs** of fruits are vermifuge, mild vesicant, used for liver and gall bladder diseases and intestinal worms.

Clinical uses: Intestinal worms: Make tablet of hairs of pods 125 mg, with raw sugar, one tablet, at night, with any purgative drug, as *'Panchasakaar churna'* 6 g, with warm water. **Amenorrhea, dysmenorrhea:** Decoction of root of described plant, 10 g, with fried gum of *Ferula foetida* 125 mg, two times a day. **Nervous debility, facial paralysis, neuritis:** Decoction of root of described plant, 10 g, with clarified butter 5 g, two times a day. **Diarrhea, diarrhea with bleeding:** Sauce of root of descbried plant 10 g, two times a day. **Seminal weakness, erectile dysfunction of penis:** (1) Mix powder of seeds of described plant, roots of *Asparagus racemosus,* root and seeds of *Tribulus etrrestris,* roots of *Grewia tanax,* Seeds of *Sida cordifolia,* seeds of *Hygrophila auriculata,* 5 g, **or** seeds of described plant, roots of *Asparagus adscendens, Cucurligo orchioides, Asparagus racemosus, Elettaria cardamomum,* Gum of *Bambusa orundinacea,* Extract of *Tinospora cordifolia,* 5 g. (2) Seeds and root of described plant, root bark of *Cinamomum verum,* root of *Glycyrrhiza glabra,* roots of *Withania somnifera,* fruit of *Myristica fragrance,* root of *Anacyclus pyrenthrum,* 5 g, with milk, two times a day. (3) Mix powder of seeds of described plant, seeds of *Hygrophila auriculata,* with milk, two times a day. **Vaginal Laxity:** Use tablet of root powder of described plant, as vaginal tablet, at night. **Chorea:** Local massage of medicated oil, made by root of described plant, is beneficial. **Albuminurea:** Mix powder of Seed powder of described plant, roots of *Asparagus adscendens, Asparagus racemosus, Phylanthus emblica, Curcuma longa, Saussurea costus,* sugar, 5 g, with water mixed cold milk, two times a day.

Formulations: *Koncha paaka, Vaanari gutikaa, Mashabalaadi paachan, Krimibhaskar vati, Manmatha rasa, Shatavaryaadi churna, Mushali paka, Dhaatupaushtika churna.*

Recommended readings:

Bhutya, R.K. (2007), Vanaspati Aushadha Vigyana, Scientific Publishers (India), Jodhpur, PP. 48.

Brahmavarchas (2003), Ayurved Ka Pran Vanoshadhi Vigyan, Shanti Kunj, Haridwar, PP. 301.

Chunekar, K.C. (2004), Bhava Prakash Nighantu, Chaukhambha Bharti Academy, Varanasi, PP. 357.

Khare, C.P. (2007), Indian Medicinal Plants, Springer (India) P.L. New Delhi, PP. 424.

Kirtikar, K.R. & Basu, B.D. (1998), Indian Medicinal Plants, L.M Basu, Allahabad, Vol. 1, PP. 777.

Misra, B.L. (2005), Dravya Guna Hastamalaka, Publication scheme, Jaipur, PP. 274.

Nair, R.Vasudevan, (2007), Indian Medicinal Plants, Orient Longman P.L. Chennai, Vol. 4, PP. 68.

Namjoshi, A.N. (2001), The Ayurvedic Pharmacopoeia of India, Government of India, Department of Indian Systems of Medicine & Homoeopathy, New Delhi, Part-1, Volume- 3, PP. 23.

Pareek, G.N. (2005), Sudhanidhi, Vanoshadhi Ratnakar, Dhanvantari Karyalaya, Aligarh, Vol. 2, PP. 243.

Prajapati, N.D., Purohit, S.S., Sharma, A.K. & Tarun Kumar (2003), A Hand Book of Medicinal Plants, Agrobios India, Jodhpur, PP. 352.

Sharma, P.C., Yelne, MB. & Denis, T.J. (2000), Database on medicinal plants used in ayurveda, Central Council for research in Ayurveda and siddha, Vol. 1, PP. 200.

Sharma, P.V. (1981), Dravya gun vigyana, Chaukhambha Bharti Academy, Varanasi, Vol. 1, PP. 569.

Singh, R.S. (2002), Vanoshadhi Nirdeshika, Uttar Pradesh Hindi Sansthan, Lucknow, PP. 102.

317. *Murraya koenigii* (Linn.) Spreng.

Family: Rutaceae.

Name: English: Curry leaf tree, **Sanskrit:** *Giri nimba, Vatnimba, Kalsakah, Kaidaryah,* **Hindi** : *Mista nimba.* **Local name:** *Meethaa neem, Kari patta, Barsang.*

Botanical characteristics: Habit: Small tree, aromatic, unarmed. **Stem:** Cylindrical, branched, solid, bark dark grey and closely crowded spreading dark green foliage. **Leaf:** Alternate, compound, unipinnate, ovate, entire, glabrous, gland dotted and strongly aromatic, 2.5-7.5 cm. long, petiole 12-4. cm. long. **Flower:** White, fragrant in panicle cyme, diam. 1.25 cm., petals-5, gland dotted, stamens-10. **Fruit:** Berry, round or ovate, 1 cm. long, sub-globose or ellipsoid, purplish-black when ripe, 2-seeded.

Flowering and fruiting period July-August.

Habitat: Wild throughout India, up to 900 m. Konkan, Western Ghats, Travankor, Gujarat, Maharastra.

Parts used: Leaves, roots, bark.

Dosage: Leaves bark-5-10 g. roots 3 g.

Collection period: March-April.

Ayurvedic properties: ***Ras:*** *tikta, madhur,* ***Gun:*** *laghu, tikhsna,* ***Veerya:*** *usna,* ***Vipaka:*** *katu,* ***Tridosha prabhava:*** allevates ***Kapha:*** ++, ***Pitta***: ++, ***Vaata*** +.

Chemical constituents: The major aroma constituents in the **oil** are b-caryophyllene, b-gurjunene, b-elemene and b-phellandrene. All part of plant, mostly **leaves** are rich in carbazole alkaloids, also gave a coumarin glucoside, scopolin.

Action and disease indications: The **root, bark** and **leaves** are bitter, acrid, astringent, aromatic, cooling demulcent, depurative, anthelmintic, febrifuge, stomachic, appetizing, carminative, anodyne, constipating, anti-inflammatory, anti-septic and tonic. Use full to cure hyperdipsia, burning sensation, leprosy, skin diseases, anorexia, helminthiasis, leucoderma, dyspepsia, colic, flatulence, diarrhea, dysentery, vomiting, inflammations and foul ulcer. **Leaves** are anti-fungal and insecticide and useful to cure diabetes mellitus.

Clinical uses: Bleeding diathesis, ulcerative colitis, bleeding piles, hemoptysis: Juice of leaves of described plant 10 ml, 3 times a day. **Insect stings, pruritis, skin diseases:** Paste or poultice of leaves of plant on effected area, is beneficial. **Dysuria:** Root powder 3 g, leaves juice 20 ml, with seed powder of *Elettaria cardamomum,* 1 g, 2-3 times a day, is very useful.

Recommended readings:

Bhutya, R.K. (2007), Vanaspati Aushadha Vigyana, Scientific Publishers (India), Jodhpur, PP. 180.

Brahmavarchas (2003), Ayurved Ka Pran Vanoshadhi Vigyan, Shanti Kunj, Haridwar, PP. 302.

Chunekar, K.C. (2004), Bhava Prakash Nighantu, Chaukhambha Bharti Academy, Varanasi, PP. 332.

Khare, C.P. (2007), Indian Medicinal Plants, Springer (India) P.L. New Delhi, PP. 425.

Kirtikar, K.R. & Basu, B.D. (1998), Indian Medicinal Plants, L.M Basu, Allahabad, Vol. 1, PP. 472.

Nair, R.Vasudevan, (2007), Indian Medicinal Plants, Orient Longman P.L. Chennai, Vol. 4, PP. 75.

Prajapati, N.D., Purohit, S.S., Sharma, A.K. & Tarun Kumar (2003), A Hand Book of Medicinal Plants, Agrobios India, Jodhpur, PP. 352.

Swami, K.N. (1985), Gavon Main Aushadh Ratna, Kalera Krishana Gopal, Kalera (Raj.), Vol. 3, PP. 47. 2-401

318. *Musa paradisiaca* Linn.

Family: Musaceae.

Synonym: *M.sapientum.*

Name: English: Banana, Plantain, **Sanskrit:** *Kadali, Rambhaa, Vaarana, Maanya, Ambrasaraa, Ansumati phalaa, Mochaa, Shakrat phala,* **Hindi:** *Kelaa, Kadali,* **Local:** *Kelaa.*

Botanical characteristics: Habit: A tall stout, perinnial stoloniferous herb, 2-8 m, height. **Stem:** Aerial, under ground rhizome, pseudo stem dying after flowering, **Leaf:** Oblong, size 1-3 by 0.2-0.3 m, suddenly truncate at both ends, alternate, entire, obtuse, glabrous, dark green, yellow vein in middle of leaf, acuminate or emerginate; petioles 0.5-1 m on long sheaths forming pseudostems. **Flower:** Brownish red, truncate at base, unisexual, drooping, females at the bottom and males at the top, in a cymose inflorescence subtended by a large bract and all partial inflorescence arranged spirally on a long, drooping stout axis. **Fruit:** Elongated berries, in several clusters, oblong to fusiform, generally 15-25 cm long, fleshy, triangular, green when unripe and golden yellow on ripening, pulp white and sweet.

Flowering and fruiting period: All most throughout year.

Habitat: Cultivated throughout India, up to 1600m, mostly in Maharastra, Andhra Pradesh, Bihar, Gujarat, Assam, Bengal, Kerala and Tamilnadu.

Parts used: Fruits, roots, rhizome, Flowers.

Dosage: Fruit 50-100 g, dried powder 10-20 g, root 5-10 g, rhizome juice 10-20 ml.

Collection period: All most throughout year.

Ayurvedic properties: ***Ras:*** *madhur* ***Gun:*** *guru, snigdha,* ***Veerya:*** *sheet,* ***Vipaka:*** *madhur* ***Tridosha* Effect:** alleviates ***Vaata:*** +++, ***Pitta:*** ++, aggravates ***Kapha:*** +++.

Chemical constituents: Fruit is a good source of carbohydrates, minerals and vitamins, mostly B. The principle proteins of the banana are albumin and a globulin, glutelin, prolamines and proteoses, cystine, lysine, histidine, arginine, serine, glycine, aspartic acid, threonine, glutamic acid, alanine, y-aminobutyric acid, tyrosine, methionine, valine, phenylanine, leucine and isoleucine.

Action and disease indications: Roots are anthelmintic, anti scorbutic, depurative, and tonic, used for dysuria, polyuria, menstrual disordres, veneral diseases, helminthiasis, scabies, leprosy, skin diseases and general debility. **Tender Leaves** are good for scabies, inflammations, opthalmopathy, blisters and burns. **Fruits** are emollient, cooling, anthelmintic, aphrodisiac, anti scorbutic, demulcent, and tonic, it increase semen and flesh quantity, promotes physical health, used for loss of appetite, dipsesis, opthalmopathy and excessive urination, dipsia, helminthiasis, scabies, pruritis, bronchitis, pharyngodynia, nephropathy, strangury and general debility. **Unripe fruits** have antiatherogenic effect, keep low level of cholesterol in serum and LDL cholesterol. **Flowers** are good for asthma, bleeding disorders, vaginal discharges, leucorrhoea, dysentery, hyperglycemia, diabetes, ascitis and dropsy. **Inflorescence axis** (stem) is very specific for renal and vesicle calculi. **Ashes** of plant are anti scorbutic, anthelmintic, stomachic, used for hyperacidity, heart burn, colic and verminosis. The benzene extract of the **root** exhibited significant anti bacterial and anti fungal activity. Pith of the **stem** is significant hypolipidimic and hypoglycemic activity, used for cholesteromia, diabetes, epilepsy and hysteria.

Clinical uses: Epilepsy, hysteria: Stem juice of plant 10-20 ml, 2 times a day. **Bronchitis:** Syrup of fruit pulp 50 ml, 3 times a day. **Epistaxis, Diabetes mellitus**: Flower powder of plant 20 g, 2 times a day, with water. **Diabetes mellitus**: Unripe fruit powder 20 g, with water, 2 times a day. **Somasthenia:** Fruit pulp 100 g, with milk, 2 times a day. **Hyperorexia:** Ripe fruit pulp 250 g, with clarified butter 20 g, 2 times a day. **Diabetes inspidus:** Ripe fruit pulp of described plant 100 g, with powder of *Phylanthus emblica* 3 g, two times a day, is beneficial. **Or** Ripe fruit pulp of described plant 100 g, *Asparagus racemosus* 2 g, *Pueraria tuberosa* 2 g, with milk, two times a day, is beneficial. **Burn:** Local application of paste of fruit pulp of described plant, is beneficial. **Leucorrhea:** Ripe fruit pulp of described plant 100 g, clarified butter 10 g, sugar candy powder 10 g, *Amomum subulatum* 3 g, two times a day, is beneficial. **Menorrhagia, metrorrhagia:** Ripe fruit pulp of described plant 100 g, clarified butter 10 g, sugar candy powder 10 g, *Cuminum cyminum* 5 g, two times a day, is beneficial. **Or** Juice of flowers of described plant, 20 ml, with curd, two times a day, is beneficial. **Headache:** Ripe fruit pulp of described plant 100 g, *Zingiber officinale* 1 g, with milk, two times a day, is beneficial. **Asthma, bronchitis, hiccough:** Black ash of leaves of described plant 1 g, with honey 10 g, two times a day, is useful.

Contraindication: (1) Do not take water after taking fruit of described plant. (2) Do not take fruit before meal. (3) Take fruits of described plant, according to appetite. It takes more time to digestion. Do not take fruits in excess quantity. If feel indigestion, take seeds of *Elettaria cardamomum* 3 g, honey, common salt, warm water, *Solanum nigrum* 500 mg or *Zingiber officinale* 1 g. (4) Do not take fruits with curd or whey.

Formulations: *Vasantkusumaakar rasa, Hemnatha rasa, Kadalpoli, Chandanadi taila, Mochagarbha khanda.*

Recommended readings:

Bhutya, R.K. (2007), Vanaspati Aushadha Vigyana, Scientific Publishers (India), Jodhpur, PP. 46.

Brahmavarchas (2003), Ayurved Ka Pran Vanoshadhi Vigyan, Shanti Kunj, Haridwar, PP. 304.

Chunekar, K.C. (2004), Bhava Prakash Nighantu, Chaukhambha Bharti Academy, Varanasi, PP. 557.

Dhiman, A.K. (2006), Ayurvedic Drug Plants, Daya Publishing House, Delhi, PP. 181.

Khare, C.P. (2007), Indian Medicinal Plants, Springer (India) P.L. New Delhi, PP. 426.

Kirtikar, K.R. & Basu, B.D. (1998), Indian Medicinal Plants, L.M Basu, Allahabad, Vol. 4, PP. 2452.

Misra, B.L. (2005), Dravya Guna Hastamalaka, Publication scheme, Jaipur, PP. 298.

Nair, R.Vasudevan, (2007), Indian Medicinal Plants, Orient Longman P.L. Chennai, Vol. 4, PP. 78.

Namjoshi, A.N. (2001), The Ayurvedic Pharmacopoeia of India, Government of India, Department of Indian Systems of Medicine & Homoeopathy, New Delhi, Part-1, Volume- 3, PP. 73.

Pareek, G.N. (2005), Sudhanidhi, Vanoshadhi Ratnakar, Dhanvantari Karyalaya, Aligarh, Vol. 9, PP. 270.

Prajapati, N.D., Purohit, S.S., Sharma, A.K. & Tarun Kumar (2003), A Hand Book of Medicinal Plants, Agrobios India, Jodhpur, PP. 353.

Sharma, P.C., Yelne, MB. & Denis, T.J. (2000), Database on medicinal plants used in ayurveda, Central Council for research in Ayurveda and siddha, Vol. 5, PP. 78.

Sharma, P.V. (1981), Dravya gun vigyana, Chaukhambha Bharti Academy, Varanasi, Vol. 2, PP. 224.

319. *Myrica nagi* Hook. f. non-Thumb.

Family: Myricaceae.

Synonym: *M. esculenta.*

Ayurvedic Groups: Charak: *Sukrashodhan, Sandhaaniya, Vedanaanaasaka,* **Sushruta:** *Lodhraadi, Surasaadi gana.*

Name: English: Box Myrtle, **Sanskrit:** *Katphala, Somvalka, Kaitarya, Kumbhikaa, Shreeparnikaa,* **Hindi:** *Kaayaphala,* **Local:** *Kaayaphala.*

Botanical characteristics: Habit: A small evergreen dioecious tree, height 3-15 m. **Stem:** Bark rough, grey or brownish-grey, with deep vertical wrinkles, young shoots, petioles, and inflorescence tomentose. **Leaf:** Simple, crowded at the terminal ends of the branches, 7.5-12.5 by 2.5-5 cm, narrowly oblong or oblong-lanceolate, narrowed at both ends, entire, glabrous when mature, coriaceous, the lower surface pale or rust colour, minutely dotted with resinous glands, aromatic, petioles 7.5-15 mm long. **Flower:** Male spikes 7.5 mm long, arranged racemosely on a common axillary stalk 2.5-7.5 cm long; bracts orbicular, often with 2-3 smaller lateral ones; female spikes axillary, erect, 1.3-2.5 cm long. **Fruit:** Drupes, sessile, scaly, 10 mm long, ellipsoid or globose or ovoid, succulent, reddish or cheese colour when ripe, composed of spindle-shaped fleshy fibres radiating from the rugose stone. **Seed:** Wrinkled and pitted.

Flowering and fruiting period: February-March and April-May.

Habitat: Subtropical or outer Himalaya, from Punjab to Assam and eastwards, at altitude of 900-2100 m, also in Khasii hills.

Parts used: Stem bark. **Dosage:** 3-5 g.

Collection period: April-May.

Ayurvedic properties: ***Ras:*** *katu, kashaaya, tikta,* ***Gun:*** *laghu, rukhsa, tikhsna,* ***Veerya:*** *ushna,* ***Vipaka:*** *katu,* ***Tridosha*** **Effect:** alleviates ***Kapha:*** **+++,** ***Vaata:*** **+,** aggravates ***Pitta:*** **+++.**

Chemical constituents: The **bark** contains myricanol, proanthocyanidin. The **root bark** contains beta-sitosterols, taraxerol and myricadiol

Action and disease indications: The **stem bark** and **root bark** are carminative, analgic, spasmolytic, hypotensive, anti-septic and anti-rheumatic, used for fever, cough, asthma, piles, gleet, chronic bronchitis, ulcers, inflammations, anorexia, throat infections, catarrh with headache, anaemia, polyuria and toothache.

Clinical uses: Rhinitis, Hoarseness of voice, bronchial asthma, amebic dysentery, bleeding diarrhea, sprue, sciatica: Decoction of fruit of described plant 4 g, *Cinamomum verum,* 1 g, *Zinziber officinalis* 500 mg, two times a day, is useful. **Piles:** Local application of paste of fruit of described plant 10 g, extract of *Acacia catechu* 1 g, fried gum of *Ferula foetida* 125 mg, *Cinnamomum camphora* 1 g, with clarified butter, is beneficial. **Dysmenorrhea:** (1) Powder of fruits of described plant 3 g, *Crosus sativus* 1 g, black seeds of *Sesamum orientale* 10 g, *Cassia senna* 2 g, raw sugar 10 g, two times a day, for 3 days before mestrual time and during menstrual period. (2) Local use of tablet of fruit of described plant, 2 g, as vaginal tablet, at night. (3) Fruit powder of described plant and *Baringtonia acutangula,* 5 g, with warm water, two times a day, for seven days, before menstrual period. **Coryza, vertigo, headache, epilepsy:** Snuff of powder of fruit of described plant, 500 mg and powder of *Centipeda orbicularis* 125 mg, is beneficial. **Scrofula, foliculitis:** Local application of paste of fruits of described plant, with cow urine, is beneficial. **Piles:** Local application of paste of fruit of described plant, 10 parts, *Ferula narthex, Cinamomum camphora* 1-1 part, is beneficial. **Sprain, inflammation, pain:** Local application of warm paste of fruit of described plant is beneficial. **Hiccough:** Mix powder of fruit of described plant, *Inula racemosa, Zingiber officinale, Piper nigrum,* root of *Piper longum, Nigella sativa,* 5 g, with honey, as required. **Diabetes inspidus:** Decoction of fruits of described plant, *Cyperus scarissus, Symplocos racemosa, Terminalia chebula,* 6 g, with honey 10 g, is beneficial. **Chronic headache, migraine, hemicrenia:** Fried (in clarified butter of cow) 100 g, fruit powder of *Cocos nusifera,* 250 g, fried fruit powder of described plant 25 g, *Crosus sativus* 3 g (diluted in 10 ml rose water), *Prunus amyadalus* 125 g, sugar 250 g, mix all medicines. Dose 20 g, with milk, two times a day, first dose at before sunrise and second at night, is very beneficial. **Urticaria:** Local massage by medicated oil of *Sesamum orientale,* made by paste of fruit powder of described plant, is very beneficial. **Sciatica:** Local massage by medicated oil of *Brassica campestris,* made by paste of fruit powder of described plant, is very beneficial. Use *'Yogaraaj guggulu'* 1 g, two times a day, with water, with this drug. Result occurs within 3 or 4 days.

Formulations: *Kataphala nasya, Punarnavaa mandoora, Pralaapahara lepa.*

Recommended readings:

Bhutya, R.K. (2007), Vanaspati Aushadha Vigyana, Scientific Publishers (India), Jodhpur, PP. 60.

Brahmavarchas (2003), Ayurved Ka Pran Vanoshadhi Vigyan, Shanti Kunj, Haridwar, PP. 306.

Chunekar, K.C. (2004), Bhava Prakash Nighantu, Chaukhambha Bharti Academy, Varanasi, PP. 100.

Khare, C.P. (2007), Indian Medicinal Plants, Springer (India) P.L. New Delhi, PP. 428.

Kirtikar, K.R. & Basu, B.D. (1998), Indian Medicinal Plants, L.M Basu, Allahabad, Vol. 3, PP. 2350.

Misra, B.L. (2005), Dravya Guna Hastamalaka, Publication scheme, Jaipur, PP. 452.

Namjoshi, A.N. (2001), The Ayurvedic Pharmacopoeia of India, Government of India, Department of Indian Systems of Medicine & Homoeopathy, New Delhi, Part-1, Volume- 3, PP. 90.

Pareek, G.N. (2005), Sudhanidhi, Vanoshadhi Ratnakar, Dhanvantari Karyalaya, Aligarh, Vol. 2, PP. 171.

Sharma, P.C., Yelne, MB. & Denis, T.J. (2000), Database on medicinal plants used in ayurveda, Central Council for research in Ayurveda and siddha, Vol. 8, PP. 207.

Sharma, P.V. (1981), Dravya gun vigyana, Chaukhambha Bharti Academy, Varanasi, Vol. 1, PP. 575.

Singh, R.S. (2002), Vanoshadhi Nirdeshika, Uttar Pradesh Hindi Sansthan, Lucknow, PP. 93.

320. *Myristica fragrans* Houtt.

Family: Myristicaceae.

Other similar plant: *M.malabarica, M.beddomei.*

Name: English: Nutmeg, Mace, **Sanskrit:** *Jaatikosha, Maalatiphala, Jaatiphala,* **Hindi:** *Jaayaphala* (Seed kernel), *Jaavitri* (Mace) **Local:** *Jaayaphala, Jaayapatri.*

Botanical characteristics: Habit: An aromatic, evergreen, usually dioecious, moderate sized tree, height 12-18 m. **Stem:** Branches slender and with grayish black bark having lenticular spots on the outside and red juice on the inner side. **Leaf:** 7.5-8.8 cm long, coriaceous, elliptic-oblong or elliptic-lanceolate, acuminate, base acute, pale yellow brown, shiny above, dull paler with red brown nerves beneath, nerves about 8 pairs, slender, petioles 6-13 mm long. **Flower:** Creamy yellow, fragrant in umbellate cymes, flowers bracteolate, 6 mm long. Staminal column of male flowers stalked. **Fruit:** Yellow, ovoid, subglobose or pyriform, 3.8-5 cm long, pericarp fleshy, splitting into two halves at maturity. **Seed:** Oblong, obtuse, testa shiny, aril yellowish red, irregularly lobed, extending to the apex of the seed.

Flowering and fruiting period: September-October and October-November.

Habitat: Cultivated in the hotter parts of India, up to 750 m elevation with 150-300 cm rainfall per annum, mostly in Nilgiris, Kerala, Karnataka Tamilnadu and West Bengal.

Parts used: Seed kernel (nut meg), mace (Aril), oil.

Dosage: Seed kernel, mace 0.5-1g, oil 1-3 drops.

Collection period: October-November.

Ayurvedic properties: ***Ras:*** *tikta, kashaaya, katu, madhur,* ***Gun:*** *laghu, rukhsa, guru, snigdha,* ***Veerya:*** *ushna, sheeta* ***Vipaka:*** *katu, madhur* ***Tridosha*** **Effect:** alleviates ***Kapha: ++, Vaata: +.***

Chemical constituents: The **arils** contain volatile oil, dehydrodiisoeugenol, licarin B, lignans and isolignans. Aryltetrahydrofuran, aryl propanoids, macelignan, 5-methoxydehydrodiisoeugenol, thero-2-1-propane-1-ol-mrthyl ether and guaiacin. The volatile **oil** and **nut** contain d and beta-pinene, alpha-terpinene, d-camphene, dipentene, p-cymene, d-linalool, terpine-4-ol, geraniol, dl-alpha-terpeniol, safrole, eugenol, isoeugenol, methyl eugenol, myristicin, myristic acid and it's ester, elemicin and trymyristin. The **nutmeg butter** contains fatty acids as lauric, myristic, palmitic, stearic, hexadecenoic, oleic and linoleic acids.

Action and disease indications: The **nutmeg** and **mace** are aromatic, thermogenic, aphrodisiac, anti-inflammatory, anodyne, anthelmintic, deodorant, digestive, stomachic, carminative, expectorant, diuretic, emmenogogue, anti-spasmodic, febrifuge, narcotic, stimulant, ophthalmic, anti-convulsant, anti-septic, constipating and tonic, prescribed for inflammations, anorexia, distaste of mouth, dyspepsia, headache, helminthiasis, halitosis, flatulence, colic, cough, asthma, diarrhea, vomiting, strangury, dysmenorrhea, amenorrhea, ulcers, liver and spleen diseases, ophthalmopathy, impotency, penile dysfunction, premature ejaculation, skin diseases, insomnia, hyperdipsia, cardiac disorders, fever and general debility.

Clinical uses: Diarrhea, colic, Amebic dysentery of children: Fried fruit of described plant 125 mg, with water, three times a day. **Osteo arthritis, inflammation of joints:** Local massage by oil, obtained from fruits of described plant, and oil of *Brassica campestris* or *Olea europaea*, in ratio of 1:20, is beneficial. **Insomnia:** Boil the seed kernel 125 mg and mace 125 mg, of described plant, in milk and use at night. **Black spot on face:** Local application of paste of seed kernel of the plant or mace of described plant and fruit rind of Orange is beneficial. **Acne vulgaris:** Local application of paste of seed kernel of described plant, *Piper nigrum, Pterocarpus santalinus,* is very beneficial. **Rheumatism:** Mix powder of mace of described plant and *Zingerber officinalis,* 1 g, with warm water, two times a day. **General debility:** Mix powder of seed kennel 125 mg, and mace 125 mg, of described plant and *Withania somnifera* 2 g, with milk, two times a day, is very beneficial. **Diabetes mellitus:** Mix powder of seed kernel of described plant 12 g, *Zingerber officinalis* 12 g, *Piper nigrum* 12 g, *Piper longum* 12 g, gum of *Bambusa orundinacea* 12 g, seed of *Syzygium cumini* 60 g, leaves of *Gymnema sylvestre* 125 g, dose 5 g, with water, three times a day, is very useful. **Sprue:** Seed kernel of described plant 250 mg, seeds of *Holarrhena antidysenterica* 500 mg, *Cyperus rotundus* 1 g, unripe fruit pulp of *Agele marmelos* 2 g, with whey, two times a day, is beneficial. **Piles:** Seed kernel of described plant 500 mg, *Zingiber officinalis* 1 g, fruit rind of *Punica grantum* 3 g, with curd, two times a day. **Indigestion due to much milk:** Boil seed kernel of described plant 1 g, with milk, then after use the milk. **Abdominal pain, dysmenorrhea:** Fried seed kernel of described plant 1 g, with warm water, as required. **Premature ejaculation:** Seed kernel of described plant 1 part, *Pistacia lentiscus, Syzygium aromaticum, Elattaria cardamomum* each 2-2 parts, make pills of 1 g, dose 1-2 g, with milk, two times a day. Use only rice and milk in diet. **Dysmenorrhea:** Mix powder of seed kernel of described plant, *Mesua ferrea*, Borax powder, 3 g, with hot water, two times a day, 5 days before and after menstrual period, for three months, is useful.

Formulations: *Jaatiphalaadi churna, Jaatiphaladi churna, Kastooribhairava rasa, Karpoor rasa, Jirkaadhyarista, Manmathaabhra rasa, Ahiphenaasava, Kumaryaasava, Ratnagiri rasa, Swalpa kastooribhairava rasa, Mahaa gandhaka vati, Garbhachintamani rasa, Yaakriti.*

Recommended readings:

Bhutya, R.K. (2007), Vanaspati Aushadha Vigyana, Scientific Publishers (India), Jodhpur, PP. 107.

Brahmavarchas (2003), Ayurved Ka Pran Vanoshadhi Vigyan, Shanti Kunj, Haridwar, PP. 307.

Chunekar, K.C. (2004), Bhava Prakash Nighantu, Chaukhambha Bharti Academy, Varanasi, PP. 216.

Dhiman, A.K. (2006), Ayurvedic Drug Plants, Daya Publishing House, Delhi, PP. 169.

Khare, C.P. (2007), Indian Medicinal Plants, Springer (India) P.L. New Delhi, PP. 428.

Kirtikar, K.R. & Basu, B.D. (1998), Indian Medicinal Plants, L.M Basu, Allahabad, Vol. 3, PP. 2141.

Misra, B.L. (2005), Dravya Guna Hastamalaka, Publication scheme, Jaipur, PP. 451.

Nair, R.Vasudevan, (2007), Indian Medicinal Plants, Orient Longman P.L. Chennai, Vol. 4, PP. 90.

Namjoshi, A.N. (2001), The Ayurvedic Pharmacopoeia of India, Government of India, Department of Indian Systems of Medicine & Homoeopathy, New Delhi, Part-1, Volume- 2, PP. 53.

Pareek, G.N. (2005), Sudhanidhi, Vanoshadhi Ratnakar, Dhanvantari Karyalaya, Aligarh, Vol. 4, PP. 55.

Prajapati, N.D., Purohit, S.S., Sharma, A.K. & Tarun Kumar (2003), A Hand Book of Medicinal Plants, Agrobios India, Jodhpur, PP. 356.

Sharma, P.C., Yelne, MB. & Denis, T.J. (2000), Database on medicinal plants used in ayurveda, Central Council for research in Ayurveda and siddha, Vol. 4, PP. 213.

Sharma, P.V. (1981), Dravya gun vigyana, Chaukhambha Bharti Academy, Varanasi, Vol. 1, PP. 458.

Singh, R.S. (2002), Vanoshadhi Nirdeshika, Uttar Pradesh Hindi Sansthan, Lucknow, PP. 164.

Swami, K.N. (1985), Gavon Main Aushadh Ratna, Kalera Krishana Gopal, Kalera (Raj.), Vol. 1, PP. 201.

321. *Nardostachys jatamansi* DC.

Family: Valerianaceae.

Synonym: *N.grandiflora.*

Ayurvedic Groups: Charak: *Sangyasthaapan, Kandooghna,* **Sushruta:** *Vamanopaga, Tiktaskandha.*

Name: English: Spikenard, Musk-root, **Sanskrit:** *Jataamaansi, Bhutajataa, Jatilaa, Tapaswani, Maansi, Sulomashaa, Naladaa,* **Hindi:** *Jataamansi,* **Local:** *Jaatamansi.*

Botanical characteristics: Habit: An erect perennial aromatic herb, 10-70 cm in height. **Rootstock:** With woody, long, stout, tail like, covered with reddish brown fibers of petioles of radical leaves. **Stem:** More or less pubescent upwards, often glabrate below, subscapose. **Leaf:** Radical 15-20 by 2.5 cm, longitudinally nerved, elongated, spathulate, sessile, oblong or subovate, glabrous or slightly pubescent, narrowed into the petiole; cauline 1 or 2 pairs, 2.5-7.5 cm long, sessile, oblong or subovate. **Flower:** Rosy, pale pink or blue, in dense terminal corymbose cymes, flower-heads usually 1,3, or 5; bracts 6 mm, oblong, usually pubescent. **Fruit:** 4 mm long, covered with ascending white hairs, crowned by ovate, acute, often dentate calyx-teeth. The commercially available drug consists of a short portion of rhizome crowned with reddish brown fibres matted together forming a kind of network and appearing like a tail. It is highly aromatic.

Flowering and fruiting period: June-July and September-October.

Habitat: Alpine Himalayas, Kumaon to Sikkim, Bhutan, also in Himachal Pradesh, from 3300-6000 altitude.

Parts used: Root. **Dosage:** 2-4 g.

Collection period: September-October.

Ayurvedic properties: ***Ras:*** *tikta, kashaaya,* ***Gun:*** *laghu, snigdha,* ***Veerya:*** *sheeta* ***Vipaka:*** *katu,* ***Tridosha*** **Effect:** alleviates ***Vaata:*** +++, ***Kapha:*** +++,***Pitta:*** +++.

Chemical constituents: The **roots** and **rhizomes** are rich in sesquiterpenoids, contain an oil 2.5%, contains *d*-nardostachone, valeranone, and jatamansone as the major ketonic sesquiterpenes. Also jatamols A and B, jatamansic acid, nardol, nardostachonol, patochouli alcohol, isovaleric acid, alpha and beta-patchoulenes, pinoresinol, norseychelanone, seychallane, spirojatamol, valeranal, virolin, angelicin, jatamansin, jatamanasinol, oroselol and beta-sitosterol. The **oil** poentiated phenobarbital nacrosis, reduced brain cerotonin content and decreased the conditioned avoidance performance.

Action and disease indications: The **rhizome** is refrigerant, aromatic, emollient, anti-septic anodyne, digestive, carminative, laxative, stomachic, liver stimulant, deobstruent, diuretic, emmenogogue, vermifuge, expectorant, nervine tonic, intellect promoting, somniferous, aphrodisiac, trichogenous, tranquilizer, sedative, hypotensive, sodorofic, anti-pyretic and tonic, used for epilepsy, hysteria, convulsive affections, palpitation of heart, intestinal colic, hypertension, dysmenorrhea, baldness of hairs and greying of hairs, obstinate skin diseases, eryseplas, disturbed mental state, insomnia, burning sensation, cough, asthma, bronchitis, inflammations, headache, colic, dyspepsia, flatulence, heptopathy, nephropathy, strangury, amenorrhea, lumbago, pharyngitis, foul ulcers, neurosis, cardiopalmus, intermittent fever and general debility.

Clinical uses: Feeling of palpitation, tachycardia, hypertension, insomnia: (1) Cold infusion of described plant, 5 g, with honey. (2) Root powder of described plant, 2 g, root of *Withania somnifera,* 2 g, *Rauvolfia serpentina* 1 g, with juice of *Phylanthus emblica* 20 ml, two times a day, is very beneficial. (3) Mix powder of root powder of described plant, *Hyoscyamus niger, Rauvolfia serpentina,* sugar, 2 g, with fresh milk, two times a day, is beneficial. **Epilepsy, mania:** Root powder of described plant, 2 g, *Bacopa monnieri* 2g, *Acorus calamus* 250 mg, with honey 10g, three times a day, is useful. **Flatulence, abdominal pain, convulsion:** Mix powder of root powder of described plant 4 parts, *Cinamomum verum* 1 part, *Foeniculum vulgare* 2 parts, Zingiber officinale 1 part, *Piper cubeba* 1 part, sugar 8 parts. Dose 3-6 g, with lukewarm water, two or three times a day, is useful. **Amenorrhea, dysmenorrhea, chorea, hysteria:** (1) Cold infusion of 5 g root powder of described plant, two times a day, or distillate of root powder of described plant, 20 ml, two times a day, is beneficial. (2) Root powder of described plant, 2 g, *Acorus calamus* 500 mg, with honey 10 g, two times a day, is beneficial. **Canities, alopecia:** Local massage by medicated oil of *Sesamum orientale,* made by paste of root powder of described plant, is very beneficial. **Ozostoma:** Gargles by cold infusion of described plant, three times a day, is useful. **Hyperhydrosis:** Dusting of root powder of described plant, is beneficial. **Hepatitis, jaundice:** Root powder of described plant, and root powder of *Boerhavia diffusa* 5g, two times a day, is beneficial. **Migrain:** Root powder of described plant, 4 g, *Acorus calamus* 250 mg, with juice of *Bacopa monnieri* 20 ml, two times a day, is beneficial. **Depression:** Root powder of described plant 4 parts, fried gum of *Ferula narthex* 2 parts, *'Lauha bhasma'* 1 part, make pills of 250 mg. Dose 1-2 pills, with cold infusion of 5 g, of described plant, or distil water of described plant, 20 ml, is beneficial. **For fairness of skin:** Oil of root of described plant, 2-5 drops, with milk, two times a day, is beneficial. **Skin diseases:** Decoction of root powder of described plant, 5 g, *Rubia cordifolia* 10 g, two times a day, is beneficial. **Epilepsy, hysteria, headache, amnesia, fatigue:** Alcoholic solution of root powder of described plant, in ratio of 10:1, dose 10-20 ml, two times a day, is beneficial. **Hypertension:** Cold infusion of root of described plant 5 g, fruits of *Vitis vinifera* 10 g, seed powder of *Elaecarpus sphaericus* 2 g, is beneficial. **Insomnia:** (1) Root powder of described plant, 4 g, *Hyoscyamus niger* 250 mg, *Eclipta alba* 4 g, with milk of buffalo, at night, is beneficial. (2) Mix powder of root powder of described plant, *Bacopa monnieri, Convolvulus pluricaulis* 6 g, with milk, two times a day, is beneficial. **Piles:** Mix powder of root powder of described plant, *Nymphaea novchali, Pavonia odorata, Pterocarpus santalinus, Mesua ferrea,* sugar, 6 g, with water, two times a day, is beneficial. **Convulsions:** decoction of root powder of described plant, 2 g, seed powder of *Sida cordifolia* 3 g, beneficial. **Pyrexia, dipsia, burning sensation:** Decoction of described plant, *Cyperus scarissus, Foeniculum vulgare, Santalum album, Fumaria indica, Vetiveria zizaniodes,* 10 g, with honey 10 g, two times a day, is beneficial. **Bronchitis, asthma:** Mix powder of described plant, *Syzygium aromaticum,* seeds of *Amomum* *subulatum, Piper longum*, sugar, 4 g, with honey 10 g, three times a day, is useful. **Impotency:** Mix powder of described plant, *Anacyclus pyrenthrum,* sugar candy, 4 g, with milk, two times a day, is beneficial. **Cerebral arterial thrombosis, hysteria, convulsions:** Decoction of described plant, 10 g, *Withania somnifera* 3 g, *Hyoscyamus niger* 1 g, is beneficial. **Depression, insomnia:** Cold infusion of described plant, *Vitis vinifera, Elaeocarpus sphaericus,* 10 g, two times a day, is beneficial. **Menopausal syndrome, amenorrhea, dysmenorrhea:** Root powder of described plant, 2 g, *Carum bulbocastanum* 1 g, *Piper nigrum* 500 mg, two times a day, with water, or urine of cow, 20 ml, or cold infusion of described plant, 4 g, for 10 or 15 days, is beneficial.

Formulations: *Maansyaadi kwaatha, Raaakhsoghna ghrita, Laakhsaadi taila, Kumaaryasava, Agurvaadi taila, Lavangaadi churna, Aswagandhaadi churna, Arimedaadi taila, Mahaa naraayan taila, Chaangeri ghrita, Dashaanga lepa, Braahmi vati, Arvindaasava, Pippalyaasava, Pugakhanda, Mritasanjivani suraa, Guduchyaadi taila, Mahaa paisachika ghrita.*

Recommended readings:

Bhutya, R.K. (2007), Vanaspati Aushadha Vigyana, Scientific Publishers (India), Jodhpur, PP. 101.

Brahmavarchas (2003), Ayurved Ka Pran Vanoshadhi Vigyan, Shanti Kunj, Haridwar, PP. 309.

Chunekar, K.C. (2004), Bhava Prakash Nighantu, Chaukhambha Bharti Academy, Varanasi, PP. 240.

Dhiman, A.K. (2006), Ayurvedic Drug Plants, Daya Publishing House, Delhi, PP. 166.

Khare, C.P. (2007), Indian Medicinal Plants, Springer (India) P.L. New Delhi, PP. 433.

Kirtikar, K.R. & Basu, B.D. (1998), Indian Medicinal Plants, L.M Basu, Allahabad, Vol. 2, PP. 1307.

Misra, B.L. (2005), Dravya Guna Hastamalaka, Publication scheme, Jaipur, PP. 448.

Nair, R.Vasudevan, (2007), Indian Medicinal Plants, Orient Longman P.L. Chennai, Vol. 4, PP. 104.

Namjoshi, A.N. (2001), The Ayurvedic Pharmacopoeia of India, Government of India, Department of Indian Systems of Medicine & Homoeopathy, New Delhi, Part-1, Volume- 2, PP. 51.

Pareek, G.N. (2005), Sudhanidhi, Vanoshadhi Ratnakar, Dhanvantari Karyalaya, Aligarh, Vol. 4, PP. 33.

Prajapati, N.D., Purohit, S.S., Sharma, A.K. & Tarun Kumar (2003), A Hand Book of Medicinal Plants, Agrobios India, Jodhpur, PP. 358.

Sharma, P.C., Yelne, MB. & Denis, T.J. (2000), Database on medicinal plants used in ayurveda, Central Council for research in Ayurveda and siddha, Vol. 7, PP. 135.

Sharma, P.V. (1981), Dravya gun vigyana, Chaukhambha Bharti Academy, Varanasi, Vol. 1, PP. 31.

Singh, R.S. (2002), Vanoshadhi Nirdeshika, Uttar Pradesh Hindi Sansthan, Lucknow, PP. 156.

Swami, K.N. (1985), Gavon Main Aushadh Ratna, Kalera Krishana Gopal, Kalera (Raj.), Vol. 2, PP. 292.

322. *Nelumbo nucifera* Gaertn.

Family: Nymphaeaceae.

Synonym: *Nelumbium speciosum.*

Ayurvedic Groups: Charak: *Mutravarjaniya,* **Sushruta:** *Utpalaadi gana.*

Name: English: East Indian Lotus, Sacred Lotus, **Sanskrit:** *Kamal, Padma, Nalina, Arvinda, Mahotpala, Sahastrapatra, Shatadala, Jalaja, Raajiva,* **Hindi:** *Kamal,* **Local:** *Kamal.*

Botanical characteristics: Habit: A large aquatic handsome herb. **Stem:** Creeping, slender, elongated, branched, sending out roots at the nodes. **Leaf:** Membranous, 30-90 cm or more in diam., orbicular, concave or cupped, erect, exactly peltate, entire, radiately nerved, glaucous, glabrous, petiole very long, smooth or with small prickles, much raised out of water. **Flower:** Solitary, 2-10-25 cm in diam., fragrant, white or rosy, with a centrally located yellow obconical spongy torus 18 mm high, in which carples are sunken; the top flat, 2.5 cm broad, becoming enlarged in fruit to a breadth of 5-10 cm. **Fruit:** Achenes, nut like, ovoid, glabrous, ripe carples 12 mm long, **Seed:** 8-30, black.

Flowering and fruiting period: April-May and August-September.

Habitat: Throughout warmer parts of India, up to 1800 m, in marshes and ponds.

Parts used: Flower, seed, root.

Dosage: Seed 3-6 g, root powder 5-10 g, juice 10-20 ml, flower powder 2-5 g, juice 10-20 ml.

Collection period: November-December.

Ayurvedic properties: ***Ras:,*** *madhur, kashaaya,* ***Gun:*** *laghu, snigdha,* ***Veerya:*** *sheeta* ***Vipaka:*** *madhur* ***Tridosha*** **Effect:** alleviates ***Pitta:*** +++, ***Kapha:*** ++.

Chemical constituents: The **flower** contains quercetin, luteolin and their glycosides and kaempferol glycosides. The **roots** contain catecholgallocatechol, neochlorogenic acid, leucocyanidin and leucodelphinidin. The **seeds** contain nuciferin, n-nornuciferin, oxoushinsunine, n-norarmepavine, myristic, palmitic, oleic, linoleic and linolenic acids.

Action and disease indications: The **flowers** are refrigerant, cardio-tonic, used for diarrhea, cholera, fever, hapatopathy, hyperdipsia, internal injuries, bronchitis, cough, skin eruptions. The **fruits** and **seeds** are refrigerant, diuretic, tonic depurative, and aphrodisiac, used for skin diseases, hyperdipsia, halitosis, burning sensation, menorrhagia, leucorrhea, vomiting, fever and pruritis. The **roots** are cooling, emollient and diuretic, used for pharyngopathy, pectoralgia, leucorrhea, spermatorrhea, diarrhea, dysentery, cough and dipsia.

Clinical uses: Abortion, miscarriage: Cold infusion of flowers of described plant, 5 g, with honey 10 g, as required or seed powder of described plant, 5 g, with milk, three times a day, is useful. **Bleeding piles, blood in diarrhea:** Root powder of described plant, 5 g, sugar 5 g, with butter, three times a day, is useful. **Prolepse of rectum:** Powder of small leaves of described plant, 6 g, sugar 10 g, with water, two times a day, is beneficial. **Dysuria, excess and turbid micturition:** Root powder of described plant, 6 g, *Cuminum cyminum* 1 g, sugar candy 5 g, with water, two times a day, is beneficial. **General debility:** Seed powder of described plant, 5 g, sugar 10 g, with milk, two times a day, is beneficial. **Semen insufficiency:** Mix powder of seed powder of described plant 15 parts, *Asparagus racemosus, Asparagus adscendens, Orchis latifolia, Withania somnifera, Myristica fragrans* 4-4 parts, *Piper cubeba,* seeds of *Elettaria cardamomum,* gum of *Bambusa arundinacea, Zingiber officinale, Cinamomum tamala, Pistacia lentiscus* 2-2 parts,, *Crosus sativus* 1 part. Dose 5 g, with milk, two times a day, is very beneficial.

Formulations: *Arvindaasava, Draakhsaavaleha, Bhallaataka paaka, Chandanaadi arka, Kaaminividravan rasa, Shataavaryaadi ghrita, Aswagandhaa taila, Raktapittakulkandan rasa, Laakhsaadi taila, Hiberaadya taila, Mopharvaa.*

Recommended readings:

Bhutya, R.K. (2007), Vanaspati Aushadha Vigyana, Scientific Publishers (India), Jodhpur, PP. 50.

Brahmavarchas (2003), Ayurved Ka Pran Vanoshadhi Vigyan, Shanti Kunj, Haridwar, PP. 311.

Chunekar, K.C. (2004), Bhava Prakash Nighantu, Chaukhambha Bharti Academy, Varanasi, PP. 480.

Khare, C.P. (2007), Indian Medicinal Plants, Springer (India) P.L. New Delhi, PP. 435.

Kirtikar, K.R. & Basu, B.D. (1998), Indian Medicinal Plants, L.M Basu, Allahabad, Vol. 1, PP. 116.

Misra, B.L. (2005), Dravya Guna Hastamalaka, Publication scheme, Jaipur, PP. 376.

Nair, R.Vasudevan, (2007), Indian Medicinal Plants, Orient Longman P.L. Chennai, Vol. 4, PP. 110.

Namjoshi, A.N. (2001), The Ayurvedic Pharmacopoeia of India, Government of India, Department of Indian Systems of Medicine & Homoeopathy, New Delhi, Part-1, Volume- 1, PP. 69 and 3-81.

Pareek, G.N. (2005), Sudhanidhi, Vanoshadhi Ratnakar, Dhanvantari Karyalaya, Aligarh, Vol. 9, PP. 180.

Prajapati, N.D., Purohit, S.S., Sharma, A.K. & Tarun Kumar (2003), A Hand Book of Medicinal Plants, Agrobios India, Jodhpur, PP. 360.

Sharma, P.C., Yelne, MB. & Denis, T.J. (2000), Database on medicinal plants used in ayurveda, Central Council for research in Ayurveda and siddha, Vol. 4, PP. 251.

Sharma, P.V. (1981), Dravya gun vigyana, Chaukhambha Bharti Academy, Varanasi, Vol. 1, PP. 582.

Singh, R.S. (2002), Vanoshadhi Nirdeshika, Uttar Pradesh Hindi Sansthan, Lucknow, PP. 77.

Swami, K.N. (1985), Gavon Main Aushadh Ratna, Kalera Krishana Gopal, Kalera (Raj.), Vol. 1, PP. 115.

323. *Nerium indicum* Mill.

Family: Apocynaceae.

Synonym: *N.odorum.*

Name: English: Indian oleander, White oleander, **Sanskrit:** *Karveera, Ashwamaraka, Hayamara, Shatakumbha, Chandanta, Saguda, Viraka, Gauripushpa,* **Hindi:** *Kaner,* **Local:** *Kaner.*

Ayurvedic groups: Charaka: *tiktaskandha, kushthaghna,* **Sushruta:** *lakhsaadi, shirovirechana.*

Botanical characteristics: Habit: A large glabrous evergreen shrub, height 5m, with milky latex. **Stem:** Herbaceous, aerial, erect, cylindrical, solid, rough, with straight branches, nodes swollen, hyaline latex present. **Leaf:** Shortly stalked, dark green, shiny above, three leaves in a whorls, 10-15 cm long, 2.5 cm wide, thickly coriaceous, linear-lanceolate, acuminate, midrib stout; nerve numerous, spiny, glabrous, latex present. **Flower:** Red, rosy or white, fragrant, 3.75 cm diam, in terminal cyme. **Fruit:** Follicle, cylindrical, long straight, hard, flat, length 12.5-23 cm long, **Seed:** Numerous, about 1.3 cm long, tipped with coma of light brown hairs.

Flowering and fruiting period: All most throughout year and April-June.

Habitat: Throughout India, In the Himalaya up to 1950 m, cultivated in gardens as ornamental plant.

Parts used: Root bark leaves.

Dosage: Root bark 25-125 mg.

Collection period: May-June.

Ayurvedic properties: ***Ras:*** *katu, tikta,* ***Gun:*** *laghu, rukhsa* ***Veerya:*** *ushna,* ***Vipaka:*** *katu,* ***Tridosha*** **Effect:** alleviates ***Kapha:*** ++,***Vaata:*** +.

Chemical constituents: Leaves and root contains glycosides, terpenoids and steroids. **Leaves** contain oleandrin, gentiobiosyl, oleandrin, odoroside. **Stem** contains alanim, arginine, aspartic acid, cysteine, glutamic acid, glycine, histidin, leucine, isoleucine, lysine, phelylalanine, proline, serine, threonine, tryptophan, tyrosine andvaline. A polysaccharide (2.3%) containing galacturonic acid, rhamnose, arbinosone and galactose has been isolated from **leaves.**

Action and disease indications: Roots are bitter, acrid, astringent, anthelmintic, thermogenic, aphrodisiac, stomachic, febrifuge and diuretic. Useful to cure strangury, cardiac asthma, renal and vesicle calculi, chronic stomachalgia, arthralgia, leprosy and pruritis. **Root bark** is very specific for ringworm. **Leaves** are powerful repentant and useful to cure scabies and hemorrhoids. Juice of **tender leaves** is good for opthalmia with copious lacrimation.

Contra indication: All parts of the plants are poisonous, so beware to overdose. **Symptoms-** Dysphonia, dysphagia, abdominal pain, foamy hyper salivation, vomiting, purgation, weak pulse, pupil dilation, cramps, drowsiness, coma and death. **Fatal dose-** Root 12-15g, seed- 3 in number. **Fatal time-** Indefinite. **Treatment-** Make vomiting or stomach wash, with Potassium per magnate solution. Give Tannic acid as antidote. **Clinical uses:** As *Thevetia neriifolia.*

Formulations: *Karveeraadhya taila, Karveer yoga, Gunjaadhya taila, Kaasisadi taila.*

Recommended readings:

Bhutya, R.K. (2007), Vanaspati Aushadha Vigyana, Scientific Publishers (India), Jodhpur, PP. 47.

Brahmavarchas (2003), Ayurved Ka Pran Vanoshadhi Vigyan, Shanti Kunj, Haridwar, PP. 313.

Chunekar, K.C. (2004), Bhava Prakash Nighantu, Chaukhambha Bharti Academy, Varanasi, PP. 314.

Dhiman, A.K. (2006), Ayurvedic Drug Plants, Daya Publishing House, Delhi, PP. 197.

Khare, C.P. (2007), Indian Medicinal Plants, Springer (India) P.L. New Delhi, PP. 437.

Kirtikar, K.R. & Basu, B.D. (1998), Indian Medicinal Plants, L.M Basu, Allahabad, Vol. 2, PP. 1584.

Misra, B.L. (2005), Dravya Guna Hastamalaka, Publication scheme, Jaipur, PP. 303.

Nair, R. Vasudevan, (2007), Indian Medicinal Plants, Orient Longman P.L. Chennai, Vol. 4, PP. 126.

Namjoshi, A.N. (2001), The Ayurvedic Pharmacopoeia of India, Government of India, Department of Indian Systems of Medicine & Homoeopathy, New Delhi, Part-1, Volume- 2, PP. 64 and 3-84.

Prajapati, N.D., Purohit, S.S., Sharma, A.K. & Tarun Kumar (2003), A Hand Book of Medicinal Plants, Agrobios India, Jodhpur, PP. 511.

Sharma, P.V. (1981), Dravya gun vigyana, Chaukhambha Bharti Academy, Varanasi, Vol. 1, PP. 211.

Singh, R.S. (2002), Vanoshadhi Nirdeshika, Uttar Pradesh Hindi Sansthan, Lucknow, PP. 69.

Swami, K.N. (1985), Gavon Main Aushadh Ratna, Kalera Krishana Gopal, Kalera (Raj.), Vol. 2, PP. 148.

324. *Nicotiana tabacum* Linn.

Family: Solanaceae.

Other similar plant: *N.rustica.*

Name: English: Tobacco, **Sanskrit:** *Taamrapatra, Khsaarpatraa, Taamrakuttica, Dhumrapatraa,* **Hindi:** *Tambaaku,* **Local:** *Tamaakhu.*

Botanical characteristics: Habit: An erect viscidly glandular pubescent herb, height 0.6-0.8 m. **Stem:** Terete, cylindrical, with few branches. **Leaf:** Simple, large, up to 1 m in length, ovate, oblong-lanceolate or elliptic, acuminate, sessile, the lower ones semi-amplexicaul and decurent. **Flower:** Rosy, light red or white, 4-5 cm long, pedicelled bracteate, in many flowered panicled racemes. **Fruit:** Capsule, 1.5-1.8 cm, narrowly elliptic, ovoid. **Seed:** Many, brown, with fluted ridges.

Flowering and fruiting period: February-March and March-April.

Habitat: Cultivated in the hotter parts of India, mostly in Andhra Pradesh, Maharastra, Karnataka, Uttar Pradesh and West Bengal.

Parts used: Leaves, extract.

Dosage: Extract 50-100 mg, mostly for external use.

Collection period: March-April.

Ayurvedic properties: ***Ras:*** *tikta,* ***Gun:*** *laghu, tikhsna,* ***Veerya:*** *ushna,* ***Vipaka:*** *katu,* ***Tridosha*** **Effect:** alleviates ***Kapha:*** **+++,** ***Vaata:*** **++,** aggrevates ***Pitta:*** +++.

Chemical constituents: The **leaves** contain nicotine as the major alkaloid, other are nornicotine, anabasine, l-nicotine, nicotyrine, nicotimine, l-noricotine, d-nornicotine, piperidine, pyrrolidine, n-methylpyrroline, 2,3-dipyridyl, l-anabasine, n-methyl-l-anabasine, l-anatabine, n-methyl-l-anatabine, nicotoine, necotelline and myosmine.

Action and disease indications: The **leaves** are thermogenic, sedative, anodyne, narcotic, anti-inflammatory, anthelmintic, carminative, laxative, emetic, styptic, abortifacient and mental stimulant, used for dental carries, dentalgia, inflammations, dyspepsia, helminthiasis, flatulence, haemorrhage, cough, asthma, bronchitis, scabies, skin diseases, ulcers, painful tumours, strangulated hernia, purulent discharge from nose, whooping cough, and tubercular glands of the neck.

Clinical uses: Whooping cough: Black ash of stem and of described plant, 250 mg, rock salt 125 mg, with honey 10 g or cold infusion of piper *Betel betel,* 1 nos., *Elettaria cardamomum* 500 mg, three times a day, is useful. **Asthma, pyrexia, diarrhea:** Black ash of stem branches of described plant, 250 mg, with cold infusion of *Trachy spermum-ammi* 3 g, two times a day, is beneficial. **Orchitis:** Local application of paste of leaves powder of described plant, seed powder of *Caesalpinia bonduc* and Castor oil, is beneficial. **Alopecia:** Local application of medicated oil, made by paste of leaves of described plant, is beneficial. **Dental carries:** Fill the carries by leaves powder of described plant. **Piles:** Fumigation of leaves powder of described plant and *Canabis sativa,* is useful. **Spleen enlargement:** Local application of paste of leaves of described plant, with Lemon juice, is beneficial. **Leucoderma, gonorrhea, Rheumatism:** Local massage of seed oil of described plant, is beneficial. **Arthralgia:** Local application of medicated oil, made by leaves of described plant, latex of *Calotropis procera,* and juice of *Datura inoxia,* is beneficial. **Convulsions:** Fomentation by decoction of leaves of described plant is beneficial.

Formulations: *Swaasaantaka avaleha, Swaasagajankusha rasa, Baalghorkaasaghna churna.*

Recommended readings:

Bhutya, R.K. (2007), Vanaspati Aushadha Vigyana, Scientific Publishers (India), Jodhpur, PP. 113.

Chunekar, K.C. (2004), Bhava Prakash Nighantu, Chaukhambha Bharti Academy, Varanasi, PP. 825.

Khare, C.P. (2007), Indian Medicinal Plants, Springer (India) P.L. New Delhi, PP. 438.

Kirtikar, K.R. & Basu, B.D. (1998), Indian Medicinal Plants, L.M Basu, Allahabad, Vol. 3, PP. 1798.

Misra, B.L. (2005), Dravya Guna Hastamalaka, Publication scheme, Jaipur, PP. 490.

Nair, R.Vasudevan, (2007), Indian Medicinal Plants, Orient Longman P.L. Chennai, Vol. 4, PP. 134.

Pareek, G.N. (2005), Sudhanidhi, Vanoshadhi Ratnakar, Dhanvantari Karyalaya, Aligarh, Vol. 10, PP. 237.

Prajapati, N.D., Purohit, S.S., Sharma, A.K. & Tarun Kumar (2003), A Hand Book of Medicinal Plants, Agrobios India, Jodhpur, PP. 362.

Sharma, P.V. (1981), Dravya gun vigyana, Chaukhambha Bharti Academy, Varanasi, Vol. 1, PP. 386.

Swami, K.N. (1985), Gavon Main Aushadh Ratna, Kalera Krishana Gopal, Kalera (Raj.), Vol. 2, PP. 351.

325. *Nigella sativa* Linn.

Family: Ranunculaceae.

Name: English: Small fennel, Black cumin. **Sanskrit**: *Kaalaajaji, Upkunchikaa, Kaarvi, Prithvikaa, Prithvi, Kunchi, Kalicaa, Sushavi, Upkalikaa, Ajaaji,* **Hindi**: *Kalonji, Kalaa jeera,* **Local**: *Kalonji, Mangarelaa.*

Botanical characteristics: **Habit**: It is pretty herb, 30-60 cm height. Plant like the plant of *Foinicum vulgare.* **Stem:** Herbaceous, aerial, erect. **Leaf:** 2.5 to 5 cm long, compound , 2-3 pinnatisect, cut in to linear or linear-lanciolate, segments, cauline and ramal, alternate, exstipulate, sessile, leaf base sheathing, ultimate, entire, acute.

Flower: Pale-blue, 2.5 cm in diam, born on solitary long penduncles, ebrectiate, pedicillate, complete, actinomorphic, hermaphrodite, pentamerous, hypogynous and spirocyclic. **Fruits:** Capsules, 1.25 cm long round shaped. **Seed:** Trigonous, angular, black, inner matter white, rugulose-tubercular, fragrant, many, seeds 2.5 mm to 3.5 mm long and 2 mm wide.

Flowering and fruiting period: December to January and February to March.

Habitat: In Punjab, Bihar, often cultivated.

Parts used: Seeds, seed oil. **Dosage**: 1-3 g.

Collection period: March to April.

Ayurvedic properties: ***Ras:*** *katu, tikta,* ***Gun:*** *Laghu, rukhsa, tikhsana,* ***Veerya:*** *usna,* ***Vipak:*** *katu,* ***Tridosa*** **effect**: alleviates ***Kapha:***+++, ***Vaata:***++.

Chemical constituents: The fatty acids of **oil** are as follows - palmitic, myristic, stearic, oleic and linoleic and linolenic. Glyserides of oil are the following - trilinolein, oleodilinolein, dioleolinolein, palmito-oles-linolein and stearo-oleolinolein, glycerides of some volatile acids are also present in the oil in small quantities. Essential oil from **seeds** contains nigllone and 2-methyl-4-isopropyl-p quinone. The **oil** contains carvone (45-60%), d-limonone and cymene-beta-sitosterol is also present in the seeds.

Action and diseases indication: The **seeds** are bitter, acrid, thermogenic, carminative, deodorant, aromatic, diuretic, emmenagogue, anodyne, anti-inflammatory, anti-bacterial, appetizer, digestive, anthelmintic, constipating, febrifuge, sudorific, stimulant, galactogogue, expectorant, uterus-stimulant, tonic, aphrodisiac and beneficial to eyes. The **oil** exhibited CNS depressant and potent analgesic effects, possibly due to presence of an opioid principle in the oil. The seeds are useful in fever, opthalmia, anorexia, indigestion, skin diseases, piles, cephalgia, jaundice, inflammations, paralysis, halitosis, dyspepsia, flatulence, diarrhea, dysentery, cough, amenorrhea, helmenthiasis, especially tape worm, strangury, agalactia and vitiated condition of **Vata** and **Kapha**.

Contra indication: Beware to over dose to pregnant women. Due to uterus constrictions, it may be cause of abortion.

Clinical uses: **Hiccough:** Seed powder of *Nigella sativa* 2 g, 2-4 times a day, with whey, is useful.

Amenorrhea and dysmenorrhea: Seed powder of *N.sativa* 3 g, 2 times a day, with warm water. It should be given for 3 days before menstrual period, till it ends. **Alopecia:** Local application of seed powder of *N. sativa* with water or prepared medicated oil by seeds of *N. sativa,* in seed oil of *Sesamum orientale.* **Eczema**: Apply *'Upkunchika malhar'*- method: seed powder of *N. sativa* 60 g, seed powder of *Psorlia corylifolia* 60 g, gum of *Commifora mukul* 60 g, root powder of *Berberis aristata* 60 g, Sulphur 30 g, Coconut oil 1 kg. Prepare medicated oil and add melted wax 250 g, Apply on effected area locally. **Acne vulgaris, chloasma:** Local application of seed powder of *N. sativa* with vinegar. **Anorexia, indigestion:** Fried seed powder of *N. sativa* in clarified butter, roasted seed powder of *Cuminum cyminum*, fine powder of *Piper nigrum*, ripe fruit pulp of *Tamarindus indica*, rock salt powder, honey or raw sugar in equal quantity, juice of *Punica grantum*, in sufficient quantity and prepare fine paste. Dose 5-10 g in empty stomach, 2 times a day. **Common cold:** Seed powder of *N.sativa* 10 g, Seed powder of *Carum copticum* 10 g, Camphor 1g, Inhale it through a piece cloth to get quick relief. **Inflammation**: Local application of seed powder of *N. sativa* with few drops of Castor oil and make poultice with water. Apply on effected area. **Headache:** Topical use of paste of seed powder of plant and *Carum bulbocastanum* is very beneficial. **Nervous pains, flatulence, indigestion, ribs pain, lumbago:** Mixed seed powder of *Nigella sativa, Trigonella foenum-gracum, Lepideum sativum and Trachyspermum ammi,* called *'Chaturbeej churna'* 3-5 g, 2-3 times a day, with slight warm water, is very beneficial.

Formulations: *Chaturbeeja churna, Laahi churna, Dhananjaya vati, Musti yoga, Vrihat yograaj guggulu, Kaankaayan gutika, Naaraayan churna, Vrihat agnimukha churna.*

Recommended readings:

Bhutya, R.K. (2007), Vanaspati Aushadha Vigyana, Scientific Publishers (India), Jodhpur, PP. 62.

Brahmavarchas (2003), Ayurved Ka Pran Vanoshadhi Vigyan, Shanti Kunj, Haridwar, PP. 315.

Chunekar, K.C. (2004), Bhava Prakash Nighantu, Chaukhambha Bharti Academy, Varanasi, PP. 33.

Dhiman, A.K. (2006), Ayurvedic Drug Plants, Daya Publishing House, Delhi, PP. 183.

Khare, C.P. (2007), Indian Medicinal Plants, Springer (India) P.L. New Delhi, PP. 439.

Kirtikar, K.R. & Basu, B.D. (1998), Indian Medicinal Plants, L.M. Basu, Allahabad, Vol. 1, PP. 11.

Misra, B.L. (2005), Dravya Guna Hastamalaka, Publication scheme, Jaipur, PP. 258.

Nair, R. Vasudevan (2007), Indian Medicinal Plants, Orient Longman P.L. Chennai, Vol. 4, PP. 139.

Namjoshi, A.N. (2001), The Ayurvedic Pharmacopoeia of India, Government of India, Department of Indian Systems of Medicine & Homoeopathy, New Delhi, Part-1, Volume- 2, PP. 119.

Pareek, G.N. (2005), Sudhanidhi, Vanoshadhi Ratnakar, Dhanvantari Karyalaya, Aligarh, Vol. 4, PP. 107.

Prajapati, N.D., Purohit, S.S., Sharma, A.K. & Tarun Kumar (2003), A Hand Book of Medicinal Plants, Agrobios India, Jodhpur, PP. 362.

Sharma, P.C., Yelne, MB. & Denis, T.J. (2000), Database on medicinal plants used in ayurveda, Central Council for research in Ayurveda and siddha, Vol. 6, PP. 420.

Sharma, P.V. (1981), Dravya gun vigyana, Chaukhambha Bharti Academy, Varanasi, Vol. 1, PP. 596.

Singh, R.S. (2002), Vanoshadhi Nirdeshika, Uttar Pradesh Hindi Sansthan, Lucknow, PP. 291.

Swami, K.N. (1985), Gavon Main Aushadh Ratna, Kalera Krishana Gopal, Kalera (Raj.), Vol. 1, PP. 158.

326. *Nyctanthes arbor-tristis* Linn.

Family: Oleaceae; Nyctanthaceae.

Name: English: Tree of Sorrow, Night Jasmine, Coral Jasmine, **Sanskrit:** *Shephaalika, Paarijaata, Naal kunkumaka, Kharpatraka, Raagapushpi,* **Hindi:** *Haarsingaar,* **Local:** *Haarsingaar.*

Botanical characteristics: Habit: A hardy large shrub or small tree, height up to 10 m. **Stem:** With grey or greenish-white rough bark, branchlets sharply quandrangular, strigose.

Leaf: Ovate, cordate or oblong, 5-12.5 by 2.5-6.3 cm, simple, opposite, acute or acuminate, entire or with a few large distant teeth, rough and scabrous above with short bulbous hairs, densely pubescent beneath with appressed hairs, main nerves few, conspicuous beneath, petioles 0.5-1.25 cm long. **Flower:** Small, delightlly fragrant, sessile in penduculate bracteate fascicles of 3-5, 4-8 lobed, white with bright orange corolla tube, 3-7 in each head, penducles 4-angled, slender, hairy, axillary and solitary and in terminal short trichotomous cymes, bracts broadly ovate or suborbicular, 6-10 mm long, apiculate, hairy on both sides. Flowers blossom in night and get down in morning. **Fruit:** Capsules, 2 cm long and broad, sub-orbicular, compressed, chartaceous, separating in to two flat 1-seeded segments. **Seed:** Flattened, 2, ovate or orbicular, small.

Flowering and fruiting period: August-November and December-february.

Habitat: Throughout India, wild in sub-Himalayan region, from Chenab to Nepal, up to 1500 m, Rajasthan, Chota Nagpur, Madhya Pradesh and Southwards to Godavari, also cultivated in gardens.

Parts used: Leaves, bark, flowers, seeds.

Dosage: 1-3 g, juice 10-20 ml.

Collection period: All most throughout year.

Ayurvedic properties: ***Ras:*** *tikta, katu,* ***Gun:*** *laghu, rukhsa,* ***Veerya:*** *ushna,* ***Vipaka:*** *katu,* ***Tridosha*** **Effect:** alleviates ***Kapha:*** **++**, ***Vaata:*** +, ***Pitta:*** +.

Chemical constituents: The **leaves** and **seeds** contain iridoid glycosides; other are mannitol, beta-amyrin, beta-sitosterol, hentriacontane, benzoic acid, astragalin, nicotiflorin, oleanolic acid, nyctanthic acid, friedelin and lupeol. The **seeds** contain a polysaccharide glucomannan.

Action and disease indications: The **leaves** are thermogenic, anodyne, anti-inflammatory, anti-allergic, anti-bacterial, digestive, anthelmintic, cholagogue, depurative, sudorofic, febrifuge, laxative, expectorant, diuretic, trichogenous and tonic, used for obstinate sciatica, inflammations, dyspepsia, helminthiasis, pruritus, skin diseases, chronic fever, cough, asthma, bronchitis, strangury, constipation, heptomegaly, piles, greyness of hairs and baldness. The **flowers** are ophthalmic, stomachic, carminative, and trichogenous, used for inflammations, ophthalmopathy, flatulence, colic, dyspepsia, spleenomegaly, greyness of hairs and baldness.

Clinical uses: Sciatica: Decoction of leaves powder of described plant 5 g, leaves of *Vitex negundo* 5 g, with raw sugar 15 g and clarified butter 10 g, three times a day, is very useful. **Chronic fever:** Juice of leaves of described plant 15 ml, juice of fresh *Zingiber officinale* 5 ml, with honey 10 g, two times a day, is beneficial. **Asthma, bronchitis:** Stem bark of described plant, 3 g, with juice of Piper betel 5 ml and honey 10 g, three times a day, is useful. **Alopecia:** Local application of paste of seeds of described plant, with water, is beneficial. **Intestinal worms:** Leaves juice 10 ml, with sugar 10 g, at night.

Formulations: *Jaimangal rasa, Ekaangaveer rasa, Shankhapushpi taila, Nastapushpaantaka rasa.*

Recommended readings:

Bhutya, R.K. (2007), Vanaspati Aushadha Vigyana, Scientific Publishers (India), Jodhpur, PP. 150.

Brahmavarchas (2003), Ayurved Ka Pran Vanoshadhi Vigyan, Shanti Kunj, Haridwar, PP. 316.

Chunekar, K.C. (2004), Bhava Prakash Nighantu, Chaukhambha Bharti Academy, Varanasi, PP. 335.

Dhiman, A.K. (2006), Ayurvedic Drug Plants, Daya Publishing House, Delhi, PP. 156.

Khare, C.P. (2007), Indian Medicinal Plants, Springer (India) P.L. New Delhi, PP. 440.

Kirtikar, K.R. & Basu, B.D. (1998), Indian Medicinal Plants, L.M Basu, Allahabad, Vol. 2, PP. 1526.

Misra, B.L. (2005), Dravya Guna Hastamalaka, Publication scheme, Jaipur, PP. 427.

Nair, R.Vasudevan, (2007), Indian Medicinal Plants, Orient Longman P.L. Chennai, Vol. 4, PP. 149.

Prajapati, N.D., Purohit, S.S., Sharma, A.K. & Tarun Kumar (2003), A Hand Book of Medicinal Plants, Agrobios India, Jodhpur, PP. 364.

Sharma, P.C., Yelne, MB. & Denis, T.J. (2000), Database on medicinal plants used in ayurveda, Central Council for research in Ayurveda and siddha, Vol. 4, PP. 470.

Sharma, P.V. (1981), Dravya gun vigyana, Chaukhambha Bharti Academy, Varanasi, Vol. 1, PP. 550.

Singh, R.S. (2002), Vanoshadhi Nirdeshika, Uttar Pradesh Hindi Sansthan, Lucknow, PP. 225.

Swami, K.N. (1985), Gavon Main Aushadh Ratna, Kalera Krishana Gopal, Kalera (Raj.), Vol. 3, PP. 406.

327. *Nymphaea Stellata* Willd.

Family: Nymphaeaceae.

Synonym: *Castalia stellata.*

Other similar plants: *N. rubra (N. nouchali)*- Red Var., *N. alba* - White var.

Ayurvedic Groups: Charak: *Daahaprashamana, Mutravirajaniya,* **Sushruta:** *Utpalaadi gana.*

Name: English: Indian Blue Water Lily, **Sanskrit:** *Kumuda, Neelotpala,* **Hindi:** *Kumud, Utpal,* **Local:** *Nilofar.*

Botanical characteristics: Habit: A large aquatic perennial herb. **Rhizome:** Short, ovoid, acute, erect, roundish, tuberous. **Leaf:** 12.5-20 cm in diam., floating, peltate, orbicular or elliptic, the younger sagitate, sharply sinute-toothed or entire, with a narrow sinus 5-7.5 cm deep, glabrous on both surfaces, often blotched with purple beneath; petioles long, slender, submerged. **Flower:** Solitary, floating, 7.5-15 cm in diam., usually pale violate, less commonly light blue or purple, sometimes faintly fragrant, open all the day, petals linear-oblong or lanceolate; penduncle long. **Fruit:** Berry, spongy, globular, many seeded. **Seed:** Reddish-grey when unripe, greyish-black when dry, roundish, longitudinally striate.

Flowering and fruiting period: August-September and October-November.

Habitat: Throughout the hotter parts of India, found in ponds, tanks and ditches.

Parts used: Root, flower, seed.

Dosage: Root powder 1-5 g, juice 10-20 ml, flower powder 3-5 g, juice 10-20 ml, seed 5-10 g.

Collection period: November-December.

Ayurvedic properties: *Ras:* *madhur, kashaaya, tikta,* ***Gun:*** *laghu, snigdha, pichhala,* ***Veerya:*** *sheeta* ***Vipaka:*** *madhur* ***Tridosha*** **Effect:** alleviates ***Pitta:*** **+++,** ***Kapha:*** ++.

Chemical constituents: The **flowers** contain flavonoids including quercetin, kaempferol, apigenin, nymphalin and tannins.

Action and disease indications: The **flowers** are astringent, febrifuge, brain tonic and cardio tonic, used for burning sensation, dipsesis, excessive thirst, cardiac diseases, epistaxis, fevers and general debility. The **rhizome** is refrigerant and tonic, used for diarrhea, dysentery, dipsia and general debility. The **seeds** are cooling, constipating, aphrodisiac, stomachic and restorative, used for dipsia, diarrhea, dysentery.

Clinical uses: Disphonia, spermatorrhea, nocturnal emission, leucorrhea, diarrhea: Leaves juice of flowers 15 ml, with honey 10 g, three times a day, is useful. **Bleeding piles, intestinal bleeding:** Styles of flowers of described plant, 1 g, with honey 5 g, sugar candy 5 g and butter 10 g, three times a day, is useful. **Dysentery:** Root powder of described plant, 3 g, with whey 25 ml, is beneficial. **Erysipelas, skin diseases, burning sensation:** Juice of flowers of described plant, 20 ml, with sugar candy 10 g, two times a day, is beneficial. Apply paste of flowers of described plant, locally. **Dipsosis:** Sucking of tablets of 500 mg, of mix powder of flower powder of described plant, *Cyperus scarissus,* powder of roasted rice, aerial roots of *Ficus bengalensis,* four times a day, is useful. **Palpitation, tachycardia:** Flower juice of described plant, 20 ml, with sugar candy powder 10 g, three times a day, is useful. **Abortion, miscarriage, vomiting, burning sensation, anguish:** Decoction of mix powder of flowers of described plant, *Cyperus scarissus, Vetiveria zizaniodes, Santalum album, Asparagus racemosus,* 10 g, with sugar candy powder 10 g, three times a day, is useful.

Formulations: *Chyavanpraasha, Chandanaadi taila, Ashokarista, Arvindaasava, Ushiraasava, Chandanaadi lauha, Manjisthaadi taila.*

Recommended readings:

Bhutya, R.K. (2007), Vanaspati Aushadha Vigyana, Scientific Publishers (India), Jodhpur, PP. 32.

Chunekar, K.C. (2004), Bhava Prakash Nighantu, Chaukhambha Bharti Academy, Varanasi, PP. 484.

Khare, C.P. (2007), Indian Medicinal Plants, Springer (India) P.L. New Delhi, PP. 441.

Kirtikar, K.R. & Basu, B.D. (1998), Indian Medicinal Plants, L.M Basu, Allahabad, Vol. 1, PP. 111.

Misra, B.L. (2005), Dravya Guna Hastamalaka, Publication scheme, Jaipur, PP. 377.

Nair, R.Vasudevan, (2007), Indian Medicinal Plants, Orient Longman P.L. Chennai, Vol. 4, PP. 153.

Namjoshi, A.N. (2001), The Ayurvedic Pharmacopoeia of India, Government of India, Department of Indian Systems of Medicine & Homoeopathy, New Delhi, Part-1, Volume- 3, PP. 221.

Pareek, G.N. (2005), Sudhanidhi, Vanoshadhi Ratnakar, Dhanvantari Karyalaya, Aligarh, Vol. 9, PP. 250.

Sharma, P.V. (1981), Dravya gun vigyana, Chaukhambha Bharti Academy, Varanasi, Vol. 1, PP. 585.

Swami, K.N. (1985), Gavon Main Aushadh Ratna, Kalera Krishana Gopal, Kalera (Raj.), Vol. 1, PP. 253.

328. *Ochrocarpus longifolius* Bentb. & Hook. f.

Family: Guttiferae; Clusiaceae.

Synonym: *Mammea longifolia.*

Ayurvedic Groups: Sushruta: *Elaadi gana.*

Name: Sanskrit: *Nameru, Surparnikaa, Surpunnaaga.* **Hindi:** *Surpunnaaga,* **Local:** *Laal Naagkeshar.*

Botanical characteristics: Habit: A large evergreen tree. **Stem:** Bark reddish-grey, young shoots terete or slightly 4-gonous. **Leaf:** 15-20 by 5-6.3 cm, oblong, obtuse or shortly and bluntly pointed, quite glabrous, with slightly repand margins and prominent mid rib, thickly coriaceous, base rounded, veins inconspicuous; petioles 6 mm long, stout. **Flower:** Numerous, white or pink, streaked with red, fragrant, in short fascicles on tubercles from the axil of fallen leaves; buds globose, apiculate, orange-red; pedicels 1.2-2 cm long, thickened upwards; bracts numerous subulate. **Fruit:** 2.5 cm long, obliquely ovoid, tipped by the hard, pointed style, 1-4 seeded. The flower buds are popularly known as *Naag keshar.*

Flowering and fruiting period: May-June and July-August.

Habitat: Western Ghats of the Konkan to Malabar and Coimbatore.

Parts used: Flower bud.

Dosage: 1-3 g, oil 2-5 drops.

Collection period: April-May.

Ayurvedic properties: ***Ras:*** *madhur, kashaya,* ***Gun:*** *laghu, rukhsa,* ***Veerya:*** *sheeta* ***Vipaka:*** *madhur* ***Tridosha*** **Effect:** alleviates ***Kapha:*** ++, ***Pitta:*** ++.

Chemical constituents: The **flowers** contain vitexin. The **leaves** contain amentoflavone, quercetin and vitexin.

Action and disease indications: The **flowers** are refrigerant, analgesic, aphrodisiac, hypotensive, anti-inflammatory and anti-spasmodic, used for hypertension, inflammations, biliousness, indigestion, dipsesis, piles, diarrhea, skin diseases, rheumatism and osteo-arthritis.

Clinical uses: Dipsosis, piles, indigestion, diarrhea: Flower bud of described plant, 3 g, with honey 10 g, two times a day, is beneficial.

Recommended readings:

Bhutya, R.K. (2007), Vanaspati Aushadha Vigyana, Scientific Publishers (India), Jodhpur, PP. 229.

Chunekar, K.C. (2004), Bhava Prakash Nighantu, Chaukhambha Bharti Academy, Varanasi, PP. 231.

Khare, C.P. (2007), Indian Medicinal Plants, Springer (India) P.L. New Delhi, PP. 443.

Kirtikar, K.R. & Basu, B.D. (1998), Indian Medicinal Plants, L.M Basu, Allahabad, Vol. 1, PP. 269.

Misra, B.L. (2005), Dravya Guna Hastamalaka, Publication scheme, Jaipur, PP. 480.

Sharma, P.V. (1981), Dravya gun vigyana, Chaukhambha Bharti Academy, Varanasi, Vol. 1, PP. 785.

329. *Ocimum basilicum* Linn.

Family: Labiatae; Lamiaceae.

Synonym: *O. cariophyllatum, O. minimum, O. pilosum.*

Name: English: Sweet Basil, Basil Herb, **Sanskrit:** *Barbari, Tungi, Kharpushpaa,* **Hindi:** *Van Tulasi,* **Local:** *Van Tulasi.*

Botanical characteristics: Habit: An erect aromatic, branching herb, height 60-90 cm, glabrous or more or less hispidly pubescent. **Stem:** Stem and branches green or sometimes purplish. **Leaf:** Simple, opposite, ovate, acute, entire or more or less toothed or lobed; base cuneate, entire, petiole 1.3-2.5 cm long, glabrous on both surfaces. **Flower:** White or pale purple in simple or much branched racemes often thyrsoid. **Fruit:** Nutlets, about 2 mm long, ellipsoid, black and pitted. **Seed:** Black, ovate, mucilaginous when wetted.

Flowering and fruiting period: November-December and January-February.

Habitat: Indigenous on the lower hills of Punjab, cultivated throughout the greater part of India.

Parts used: Root, leaves, seed.

Dosage: Root 10-15 g, leaves 1-3 g, seed 1-3 g.

Collection period: March-April.

Ayurvedic properties: ***Ras:*** *katu, tikta,* ***Gun:*** *laghu, rukhsa, tikhsna,* ***Veerya:*** *ushna,* ***Vipaka:*** *katu,* ***Tridosha*** **Effect:** alleviates ***Kapha:*** **+++**, ***Vaata:*** **++.**

Chemical constituents: The **herb** contains an essential oil; major constituents are linalool, up to 55%, methyl ether (estragole) up to 70% and eugenol; caffeic acid derivatives; flavonoids. The **leaves** contain thymol, xanthomicrol, aesculetin, *p*-coumaric acid, eriodictyol, its 7-glucosides and vicenin-2.

Action and disease indications: The **plant** is thermogenic, aromatic, anodyne, anti-inflammatory, alexipharmic, anti-spasmodic, appetizer, galactagogue, digestive, carminative, stomachic, anthelmintic, cardio-tonic, depurative, diuretic, expectorant, emmenogogue, anti-diarrhoeal, anti-emetic, insecticidal, anti-bactirial, stimulant, pectoral, anti-pyretic and sudorofic, prescribed for inflammations, rheumatoid arthritis, headache, otalgia, halitosis, arthralgia, spasmodic affections, agalactia, anorexia, dyspepsia, flatulence, colic, intestinal worms, cardiac debility, skin diseases, leucoderma, pruritis, ringworm, cough, asthma, bronchitis, strangury, dysmenorrhea, amenorrhea, diarrhea, vomiting, neuralgia, ophthalmia, giddiness, intermittent and malarial fevers. The **flowers** are stimulant, carminative, anti-spasmodic, diuretic, and demulcent, used for flatulence and dyspepsia. The **essential oil** is anti-bacterial, anti-fungal and insecticidal. The **seeds** are anti-dysenteric, thermogenic, stimulant, vulnerary, haemostatic, aphrodisiac, diuretic and tonic, used for dipsia, wounds, sores, haemorrhages, piles, penile dysfunction, seminal weakness, strangury, diarrhea, chronic dysentery and general debility.

Contraindication: Due to high estragole content of the essential oil, the herb should not be taken during pregnancy, nursing or over extended periods of time.

Clinical uses: Penile dysfunction: Seed powder of described plant, 2 g, with milk, two times a day, is beneficial. **Bronchitis:** Leaves juice of described plant 5 ml, with honey 10 g, three times a day, is useful. **Diarrhea:** Cold infusion of seeds of described plant, 2 g, two times a day, is beneficial. **Scorpion sting:** Local application of paste of leaves of described plant is beneficial. **Dandruff, ringworm:** Local application of juice of leaves of described plant, is beneficial. **Earache, dentalgia:** Warm juice of described plant, 4-4 drops, two times a day, is beneficial. **Leucorrhea:** Mix powder of seeds of described plant, gum of *Shorea robusta, Symplocos racemosa,* 1-1 part, *Areca catechu,* Gum of *Bombax ceiba,* Gum of *Daemunorops droco,* Gum of *Butea monosperma,* flowers of *Woodfordia fruticosa,* 2-2 parts. Dose 3-5 g, with water of rise, two times a day, is beneficial.

Formulations: *Kanakakhsiri taila,* In the process of *'Swarna Bhasma'.*

Recommended readings:

Bhutya, R.K. (2007), Vanaspati Aushadha Vigyana, Scientific Publishers (India), Jodhpur, PP. 201.

Brahmavarchas (2003), Ayurved Ka Pran Vanoshadhi Vigyan, Shanti Kunj, Haridwar, PP. 318.

Chunekar, K.C. (2004), Bhava Prakash Nighantu, Chaukhambha Bharti Academy, Varanasi, PP. 512.

Khare, C.P. (2007), Indian Medicinal Plants, Springer (India) P.L. New Delhi, PP. 443.

Kirtikar, K.R. & Basu, B.D. (1998), Indian Medicinal Plants, L.M Basu, Allahabad, Vol. 3, PP. 1961.

Misra, B.L. (2005), Dravya Guna Hastamalaka, Publication scheme, Jaipur, PP. 365.

Nair, R.Vasudevan, (2007), Indian Medicinal Plants, Orient Longman P.L. Chennai, Vol. 4, PP. 160.

Pareek, G.N. (2005), Sudhanidhi, Vanoshadhi Ratnakar, Dhanvantari Karyalaya, Aligarh, Vol. 4, PP. 217.

Prajapati, N.D., Purohit, S.S., Sharma, A.K. & Tarun Kumar (2003), A Hand Book of Medicinal Plants, Agrobios India, Jodhpur, PP. 366.

Sharma, P.V. (1981), Dravya gun vigyana, Chaukhambha Bharti Academy, Varanasi, Vol. 1, PP. 516.

Singh, R.S. (2002), Vanoshadhi Nirdeshika, Uttar Pradesh Hindi Sansthan, Lucknow, PP. 181.

Swami, K.N. (1985), Gavon Main Aushadh Ratna, Kalera Krishana Gopal, Kalera (Raj.), Vol. 3, PP.

330. *Ocimum canum* Sims.

Family: Labiatae; Lamiaceae.

Synonym: *O.americanum.*

Name: English: Hoary Basil, **Sanskrit:** *Shyaam Tulasi,* **Hindi:** *Shyaam Tulasi,* **Local:** *Kaali Tualsi.*

Botanical characteristics: Habit: A pubescent erect much branched herb, height 15-60 cm. **Stem:** Stem and branches sub-quandrangular, striate, the younger pubescent. **Leaf:** 2.5-3.8 by 1-1.3 cm, elliptic-lanceolate, entire or faintly toothed, acute at both ends, glabrous and gland-dotted; petioles 1.3-2.5 cm long, slender and hairy. **Flower:** White, pink or purplish in elongate racemes 7.5-20 cm long, with more or less closely set whorls, about 6 in a whorl, bracts elliptic-lanceolate, stalked, ciliate with long white hairs. **Fruit:** Nutlets, small, 1.25 mm long, ellipsoid, pitted. **Seed:** Pinkish-black, mucilaginous when wetted.

Flowering and fruiting period: November-December and January-February.

Habitat: Throughout plains and lower hills of India, in fields and waste lands.

Parts used: Leaves, seed.

Dosage: Leaves, seeds 1-3 g.

Collection period: March-April.

Ayurvedic properties: ***Ras:*** *katu tikta,* ***Gun:*** *laghu, rukhsa, tikhsna,* ***Veerya:*** *ushna,* ***Vipaka:*** *katu,* ***Tridosha*** **Effect:** alleviates ***Kapha:*** **+++,** ***Vaata:*** **++.**

Chemical constituents: The **leaves** contain beta-sitosterol, betulinic acid and ursolic acid and flanonoids, pectolinarigenin-7-methyl ether and nevadensin. The **essential oil** contains citral as a major componentalong withmethylheptenone, methyl nonyl ketone and camphor.

Action and disease indications: The **leaves** are aromatic, thermogenic, appetizer, bechic, febrifuge, digestive, carminative, depurative, expectorant, anthelmintic, cardio-tonic, alexeteric and tonic, used for cold, bronchitis, catarrh, intestinal worms, anorexia, dyspepsia, flatulence, dysentery, vomiting, haemoptysis, strangury, migraine, malaria, fever, pruritis and skin diseases, The **essential oil** is anti-fungal. The **seeds** are hypoglycaemic, used for hypertension, hyperdipsia, malaria, migraine, emaciation, leucorrhea and other diseases of urino-genital system.

Clinical uses: Ringworm: Local application of paste of leaves of described plant, seeds of *Cassia tora, Terminalia chebula,* Rock salt, with *'Kaanji'* and whey, is beneficial. **Rib pain:** Local application of warm paste of leaves of described plant, juice of fresh *Zingiber officinale* and *Inula racemosa,* is beneficial. **Bed sore:** Dusting of leaves powder of described plant, on wounds, is useful. **Scorpion sting:** Local application of paste of leaves of described plant is beneficial. **Skin stretching of pregnancy:** Local application of paste of seeds of described plant is beneficial. **Leucoderma:** Mix powder of seeds of described plant, *Terminalia chebula, Phylanthus emblica, Terminalia belliarica, 'Ras manikya', 'Aarogyavardhani vati'* 1-1 part, *Pterocarpus santalinus* 3 parts, inner bark of *Acacia catechu,* 8 parts, soak and dry this powder 11 times by juice of *Ocimum sanctum,* make tablets of 250 mg, two times a day, with honey or *'Khadiraarista'* 25 ml, is very beneficial.

Recommended readings:

Khare, C.P. (2007), Indian Medicinal Plants, Springer (India) P.L. New Delhi, PP. 444.

Kirtikar, K.R. & Basu, B.D. (1998), Indian Medicinal Plants, L.M Basu, Allahabad, Vol. 3, PP. 1960.

Nair, R.Vasudevan, (2007), Indian Medicinal Plants, Orient Longman P.L. Chennai, Vol. 4, PP. 157.

Pareek, G.N. (2005), Sudhanidhi, Vanoshadhi Ratnakar, Dhanvantari Karyalaya, Aligarh, Vol. 4, PP. 219.

Prajapati, N.D., Purohit, S.S., Sharma, A.K. & Tarun Kumar (2003), A Hand Book of Medicinal Plants, Agrobios India, Jodhpur, PP. 365.

Sharma, P.V. (1981), Dravya gun vigyana, Chaukhambha Bharti Academy, Varanasi, Vol. 1, PP. 514.

Singh, R.S. (2002), Vanoshadhi Nirdeshika, Uttar Pradesh Hindi Sansthan, Lucknow, PP. 181.

331. *Ocimum gratissimum* Linn.

Family: Labiatae; Lamiaceae.

Name: English: Shrubby Basil, Wild Basil, **Sanskrit:** *Fanijjaka, Arjaka,* **Hindi:** *Raam Tulasi,* **Local:** *Raam Tulasi.*

Botanical characteristics: Habit: A perennial shrubby herb, height 1.2-1.8 m. **Stem:** Much branched, woody below; stem and branches sub-quandrangular, the young ones pubescent. **Leaf:** Opposite, 6.3-12.5 by 3.8-5.7 cm, elliptic-lanceolate, acute, coarsely crenate-serrete, pubescent on both surfaces, gland dotted, base cuneate; petioles 2.5-6.3 cm long, selender, more or less pubescent. **Flower:** White, in simple or branched rather short racemes, in close whorls, inflorescence axillary or terminal; rachis quandrangular, softly pubescent,; bracts sessile. **Fruit:** Nutlets, 1.5 mm diam., sub-globose, rugose, brown. **Seed:** Greenish-pale, triangular, shape like Cumin.

Flowering and fruiting period: November-December and January-February.

Habitat: Throughout hotter parts of India, often cultivated.

Parts used: Leaves, seed.

Dosage: 1-3 g, leaves juice 10-20 ml.

Collection period: March-April.

Ayurvedic properties: ***Ras:*** *katu, tikta,* ***Gun:*** *laghu, rukhsa,* ***Veerya:*** *ushna,* ***Vipaka:*** *katu,* ***Tridosha*** **Effect:** alleviates ***Kapha:*** **+++,** ***Vaata:*** **++.**

Chemical constituents: The **plant** contains an essential oil (0.6-0.8%) , consisting of eugenol 45-70%, methyl eugenol 20%, carbacrol, ocimene, *p*-cymene, camphene, limonene, *a*-pinene and *b*-pinene.

Action and disease indications: The **plant** is thermogenic, alexiteric, used for skin diseases, erysipelas, inflammations, strangury, neurological and rheumatic affections, seminal weakness, aphthae of children, sun stroke, headache and influenza. The **seeds** used in cephalgia and neuralgia. The **essential oil** is anti-bacterial and anti-fungal.

Clinical uses: Eaeache: Drop lukewarm juice of leaves of described plant 4-4 drops, two times a day, is beneficial. **Spermatorrhea, gonorrhea, pyrexia, bronchitis, leucoderma, colic, excess and turbid micturition, strangury:** Cold infusion of seeds 2 g, and leaves 10 g, of described plant, with honey, two times a day, is beneficial. **Headache, hypomnesia, somasthenia, migrain, hemicrenia, liver enlargement:** Seed powder of described plant, 2 g, with water, two times a day, is beneficial. **Rheumatism, paralysis:** Oil of seeds 3-5 drops, with milk, two times a day, is beneficial, and hot fomentation by decoction of leaves of described plant, is very useful. **Leucorrhea:** Juice of leaves of described plant 10 ml, with rice water, two times a day, is beneficial. **Vomiting of children:** Seed powder of described plant, 0.5 g, honey 5 g, three times a day, is useful.

Recommended readings:

Bhutya, R.K. (2007), Vanaspati Aushadha Vigyana, Scientific Publishers (India), Jodhpur, PP. 190.

Brahmavarchas (2003), Ayurved Ka Pran Vanoshadhi Vigyan, Shanti Kunj, Haridwar, PP. 322.

Chunekar, K.C. (2004), Bhava Prakash Nighantu, Chaukhambha Bharti Academy, Varanasi, PP. 509.

Khare, C.P. (2007), Indian Medicinal Plants, Springer (India) P.L. New Delhi, PP. 445.
Kirtikar, K.R. & Basu, B.D. (1998), Indian Medicinal Plants, L.M Basu, Allahabad, Vol. 3, PP. 1964.
Pareek, G.N. (2005), Sudhanidhi, Vanoshadhi Ratnakar, Dhanvantari Karyalaya, Aligarh, Vol. 4, PP. 221.
Prajapati, N.D., Purohit, S.S., Sharma, A.K. & Tarun Kumar (2003), A Hand Book of Medicinal Plants, Agrobios India, Jodhpur, PP. 366.
Sharma, P.V. (1981), Dravya gun vigyana, Chaukhambha Bharti Academy, Varanasi, Vol. 1, PP. 709, 513.
Singh, R.S. (2002), Vanoshadhi Nirdeshika, Uttar Pradesh Hindi Sansthan, Lucknow, PP. 181.
Swami, K.N. (1985), Gavon Main Aushadh Ratna, Kalera Krishana Gopal, Kalera (Raj.), Vol. 3, PP. 322.

332. *Ocimum kilimandscharicum* Guerke.

Family: Labiatae; Lamiaceae.

Synonym: *O.camphora.*

Name: English: Camphor Basil, **Sanskrit:** *Karpoor Tulasi,* **Hindi:** *Kapoor Tulsi,* **Local:** *Kapoor tulsi.*

Botanical characteristics: Habit: An aromatic undershrub, 60-90 cm height. **Stem:** With pubescent quandrangular branchelets. **Leaf:** Simple, opposite, ovate or oblong, narrow at the base, deeply serrated, acute, pubescent on both surfaces. **Flower:** White, in 4-6 flowered whorls or racemes with a densely pubescent axis, corolla 2-3 times the length of the calyx. **Fruit:** Nutlets, ovoid-oblong, brownish-black.

Flowering and fruiting period: September-October and November-December.

Habitat: Cultivated in West Bengal, Assam, Tamilnadu, Karnataka and Deharadun.

Parts used: Leaves, seed. **Dosage:** 1-3 g.

Collection period: December-January.

Ayurvedic properties: ***Ras:*** *katu, tikta,* ***Gun:*** *laghu, rukhsa, tikhsna,* ***Veerya:*** *ushna,* ***Vipaka:*** *katu,* ***Tridosha*** **Effect:** alleviates ***Kapha:*** +++, ***Vaata:*** ++.

Chemical constituents: The **essential oil** contains camphor, pinene, limonene, terpinolene, myrcene, beta-phellandrene, linalool, camphene, *p*-cymene, borneol and alpha-selinene.

Action and disease indications: The **leaves** are thermogenic, aromatic, insecticidal, anti-bacterial, anti-viral, appetizer, deodorant and ophthalmic, used for cough, asthma, bronchitis, catarrh, foul ulcers and wounds, halitosis, bacterial and viral infections, anorexia and ophthalmopathy.

Clinical uses: Abscess: Poultice of leaves powder of described plant, with Vinegar, is useful. **Rib pain:** Local application of warm paste of leaves of described plant is beneficial. **Neuralgia:** Local massage of medicated oil, made by leaves juice of described plant, is beneficial. **Earache:** 4-4 drops of medicated oil, made by leaves juice of described plant, is beneficial.

Recommended readings:

Khare, C.P. (2007), Indian Medicinal Plants, Springer (India) P.L. New Delhi, PP. 445.
Nair, R.Vasudevan, (2007), Indian Medicinal Plants, Orient Longman P.L. Chennai, Vol. 4, PP. 164.
Pareek, G.N. (2005), Sudhanidhi, Vanoshadhi Ratnakar, Dhanvantari Karyalaya, Aligarh, Vol. 4, PP. 222.
Singh, R.S. (2002), Vanoshadhi Nirdeshika, Uttar Pradesh Hindi Sansthan, Lucknow, PP. 181.

333. *Ocimum sanctum* Linn.

Family: Labiatae; Lamiaceae.

Synonym: *O.tenuiflorum.*

Other similar plants: 1. *O.canum (americanum)- Kaali tulsi* 2. *O. basilicum- Van tulsi, barbari (syn. O. cariophyllum, O. minimum, O. pilosum),* 3. *O. gratissimum- Raam tulsi,* 4. *O. kilimandscharicum- Kapoor tulsi,* 5. *O. viride- Tapmaari tulsi-* found in Maharastra and culted in Jammu tabi, gives maximum oil yield (0.4%) and highest percentage of thymol (55.12%) in oil.

Name: English: Sacred basil, Holy basil, **Sanskrit:** *Surasa, Tulasi, Bhutaghni, Shyaamaa, Bahumanjari, Apetarakhsasi, Devdundubhi, Gauri,* **Hindi:** *Tulsi,* **Local:** *Tulsi.*

Ayurvedic groups: Charaka: *swaashahara,* **Sushruta:** *Surashaadi, shirovirechana.*

Botanical characteristics: Habit: An annual much branched herb, 30-90 cm high. **Stem:** Herbaceous, erect, sub quandrangular, branched, solid, pubescent, green or purple, clothed with soft spreading hairs. **Leaves:** Opposite, ovate, 2.5-5 cm long, 1.6-3.2 cm broad, elliptic-oblong, entire or serrate, acute or obtuse, pubescent on both sides, minutely gland-dotted, aromatic smell present. **Flower:** Small, purplish or crimson in elongated racemes in close whorls, stamens exerted, upper pair with a small bearded appendage at the base, complete, pentamerous, **Fruit:** Nutlets subglobose or broadly ellipsoid. **Seed:** 16 mm long, oblong, black, one side convex and other side flat, smooth, not mucilaginous when wetted.

Flowering and fruiting period: All most throughout year, chiefly during winter.

Habitat: Throughout India, grown in houses, gardens and temples, also cultivated and often runs wild up to 1800 m.

Parts used: Leaves and seeds.

Dosage: Leaves juice 5-10 ml, powder 1-3 g, seeds 1-2 g.

Collection period: March-April.

Ayurvedic properties: ***Ras:*** *katu, tikta,* ***Gun:*** *rukhsa,* ***Veerya:*** *ushna,* ***Vipaka:*** *katu,* ***Tridosha*** **Effect:** alleviates ***Kapha:*** +++, ***Vaata:*** ++, aggregats ***Pitta:*** +.

Chemical constituents: Major components of **oil** are eugenol, carvecrol, nerol, and eugenol-methylether. **Leaves** contain ursolic acid, apigenine, leuterolin, apigenin-7-0-glucoronide, luleoln-7-0-glucoronide,orientin and molludistin. **Seed oil** contains sitosterol, palmitic, stearic, oleic, linoleic and linolenic acids.

Action and disease indications: Plant is aromatic, stomachic, adoptogenic, anti stress, diaphoretic, demulcent, diuretic, digestive, febrifuge, expectorant, vermifuge and alexeteric. **Leaves** are carminative, stomachic, anti asthmatic, anti rheumatic, expectorant, stimulant, heptoprotective, anti periodic, antipyretic and diaphoretic. **Seeds** are used for urino-genital diseases, psychological disorders including fear psycosis and obsessions. Essential **oil** is anti bacterial, anti fungal. **Plant** is useful to cure cardiopathy, leucoderma, hemopathy, asthma, hiccough, opthalmia, gastropathy in children, genitor-urinary disorders, ringworm, verminosis and skin diseases. **Leaves and seeds** are useful to cure rhinitis and influenza. Urosolic acid isolated from leaves, exhibited significant protection of mast cell membrane by preventing granulation and decreased histamine release. The ethanolic extract (50%) of fresh Leaves, volatile **oil** from fresh leaves and fixed **oil** from seeds showed anti asthmatic activity, dyspnea and anti inflammatory activity. The ethemol extract (90%) of the Leaves showed heptoprotective effect against paracetamol induced live damage. The plant extract exhibited anti ulcerogenic property. Oral administration of alcoholic extract of leaves lowers blood sugar level in normal glucose-fed hyperglycemic and streptozotocin induced diabetic rats. Administration of the juice of the plant affected a significant reduction in the size of urinary brushite crystals. Methanolic extract and aqueous suspension of the leaves showed immuno stimulation of humoral immunologic response indicating the adoptogenic action of the plant.

Clinical uses: Dysuria: Seed powder of plant 2 g, with *'Punarnawastaka kwatha'* 20 g, 2 times a day. **Tuberculosis, bronchitis, asthma, ribs pain:** Leaves juice of plant 10 ml, with honey 10 g, 3 times a day. **Ear pain, insect stings, skin diseases:** Local application of paste of leaves of described plant. **Headache:** Use juice of leaves 4-4 drops, as nasal drops, 2 times a day. **Influenza, rhinitis, malaria:** Leaves juice of plant 10 ml, added seed powder of *Piper nigrum* 500 mg, with honey 10 g, 3 times a day.

General debility: Seed powder of the described plant 2 g, with milk 200 ml, 2 times a day.

Ring worm: Local application of leaves paste of the described plant, made with lemon juice, 3 times a day. **Ulcerative colitis:** Cold infusion of seed powder of the described plant 2 g, at morning. **Leukoderma:** Mixed powder of *Ocimum basilicum* 80 g, seed powder of *Cassia ablucifolia* 5 g, *Vernonia anthelmintica* 5 g, internal stem bark of *Acacia catechu* 40 g, *Pterocarpus santalinus* 15 g, *'Triphalaa churna'* 10 g, *'Ras maanikya'* 5 g, *'Aarogyavardhani vati'* 5 g, soak and dry it 11 times by juice of *Ocimum santum,* make pills of 125 mg. Dose 1-2 tablets, 2 times a day, with *'Khadiraarista'* 25 ml and water 25 ml. **Leukorrhea, menorrhagia:** Mixed powder of *Ocimum basilicum,* gum of *Shorea robusta, Symplocos crataegoides* 25-25 g, *Areca catuchu* 50 g, *Daemunorops droco* 50 g, gum of *Butea monosperma* 50g, *Woodfordia fruticosa* 50 g. Dose 3 g, 2 times a day, with rice water.

Formulations: *Madhuraantak vati, Tribhuvankirti rasa, Pratisyaayahar sarbata, Mahaa jwaraankusha rasa, Jwarasanhaaraka rasa, Muktaapanchamrita rasa.*

Recommended readings:

Acharya, B.K. (2008), Ayurveda Jadi-buti Rahasya, Patanjali Yogapitha, Haridwar, PP. 407.

Bhutya, R.K. (2007), Vanaspati Aushadha Vigyana, Scientific Publishers (India), Jodhpur, PP. 119.

Brahmavarchas (2003), Ayurved Ka Pran Vanoshadhi Vigyan, Shanti Kunj, Haridwar, PP. 323.

Chunekar, K.C. (2004), Bhava Prakash Nighantu, Chaukhambha Bharti Academy, Varanasi, PP. 509.

Dhiman, A.K. (2006), Ayurvedic Drug Plants, Daya Publishing House, Delhi, PP. 385.

Khare, C.P. (2007), Indian Medicinal Plants, Springer (India) P.L. New Delhi, PP. 445.

Kirtikar, K.R. & Basu, B.D. (1998), Indian Medicinal Plants, L.M Basu, Allahabad, Vol. 3, PP. 1965.

Misra, B.L. (2005), Dravya Guna Hastamalaka, Publication scheme, Jaipur, PP. 364.

Nair, R.Vasudevan, (2007), Indian Medicinal Plants, Orient Longman P.L. Chennai, Vol. 4, PP. 168.

Namjoshi, A.N. (2001), The Ayurvedic Pharmacopoeia of India, Government of India, Department of Indian Systems of Medicine & Homoeopathy, New Delhi, Part-1, Volume- 1, PP. 165.

Pareek, G.N. (2005), Sudhanidhi, Vanoshadhi Ratnakar, Dhanvantari Karyalaya, Aligarh, Vol. 4, PP. 184.

Prajapati, N.D., Purohit, S.S., Sharma, A.K. & Tarun Kumar (2003), A Hand Book of Medicinal Plants, Agrobios India, Jodhpur, PP. 367.

Sharma, P.C., Yelne, MB. & Denis, T.J. (2000), Database on medicinal plants used in ayurveda, Central Council for research in Ayurveda and siddha, Vol. 2, PP. 500.

Sharma, P.V. (1981), Dravya gun vigyana, Chaukhambha Bharti Academy, Varanasi, Vol. 1, PP. 513.

Singh, R.S. (2002), Vanoshadhi Nirdeshika, Uttar Pradesh Hindi Sansthan, Lucknow, PP. 181, 72.

334. *Olea europaea* Linn.

Family: Olaeceae.

Name: English: Olive, **Hindi:** *Jaitoon,* **Local:** *Jetoon.*

Botanical characteristics: Habit: An evergreen medium sized tree, height 10 m. **Stem:** deeply grooved grey trunk. **Leaf:** Small, leathery. **Flower:** Greenish-white, small, clustered. **Fruit:** Ovate, green when unripe, turning black when ripe. **Seed:** Small, oily, oil tasteless.

Habitat: Cultivated in Jammu and Kashmir and Himachal Pradesh.

Parts used: leaves, fruit.

Dosage: Leaves 10-20 g, oil 5-10 g.

Ayurvedic properties: ***Ras:*** *madhur,* ***Gun:*** *snigdha,* ***Veerya:*** *sheeta* ***Vipaka:*** *madhur* ***Tridosha*** **Effect:** alleviates ***Kapha:*** **++,** ***Vaata:*** **++.**

Chemical constituents: The **leaves** contain iridoid monoterpens including oleuropein and oleuroside; triterpens including oleanolic and maslinic acids; flavonoids including leutiolin and epigenine derivatives. The **olive oil** contains about 75% glycerides of oleic acid, with smaller amounts of linoleic, palmitic and stearic acid glycerides.

Action and disease indications: The **oil** is demulcent, refrigerant, laxative, anti-inflammatory, used for inflammations, chronic constipation, piles, intestinal worms, colic, anal fissure, renal and gall bladder calculus, burning sensation and general debility.

Clinical uses: Cholelithiasis: Oil of seeds of described plant, 20 ml, with lemon juice 5 ml and water 25 ml, repeat this process after 15 minutes, give this drug at night, for 3 to 7 days. **Hypertension, cystitis, diabetes mellitus:** Leaves powder of described plant 5-10 g, with water, two times a day, is beneficial. **Burn:** Local application of paste of seed oil of described plant, and limewater, in ratio of 1:5, is beneficial. **Cracked lips:** Local application of seed oil of described plant, is beneficial. **Acne vulgaris, acne rosecea, wrinkles:** Local application of oil of described plant, lemon juice and honey, is beneficial. **Hypomastia:** Local and round massage of seed oil of described plant, is beneficial. **Mastoptosis:** Local application of paste of seed oil of described plant, powder of fruit rind of *Punica grantum,* bark of *Gmelina arborea,* with water, is very beneficial. Put this paste on breasts for one hour and use tight bra at this time. After one hour, remove paste and wash well.

Recommended readings:

Bhutya, R.K. (2007), Vanaspati Aushadha Vigyana, Scientific Publishers (India), Jodhpur, PP. 111.

Chunekar, K.C. (2004), Bhava Prakash Nighantu, Chaukhambha Bharti Academy, Varanasi, PP. 824.

Khare, C.P. (2007), Indian Medicinal Plants, Springer (India) P.L. New Delhi, PP. 448.

Kirtikar, K.R. & Basu, B.D. (1998), Indian Medicinal Plants, L.M Basu, Allahabad, Vol. 2, PP. 1534.

Misra, B.L. (2005), Dravya Guna Hastamalaka, Publication scheme, Jaipur, PP. 428.

Pareek, G.N. (2005), Sudhanidhi, Vanoshadhi Ratnakar, Dhanvantari Karyalaya, Aligarh, Vol. 10, PP. 202.

Prajapati, N.D., Purohit, S.S., Sharma, A.K. & Tarun Kumar (2003), A Hand Book of Medicinal Plants, Agrobios India, Jodhpur, PP. 368.

335. *Operculina turpethum* (Linn.) Silva Manso.

Family: Convolvulaceae.

Synonym: *Ipomoea turpenthum.*

Ayurvedic Groups: Charak: *Bhedaniya,* **Sushruta:** *Shyaamaadi gana.*

Name: English: Indian Jalap, Turpeth, **Sanskrit:** *Trivrita, Tribhandi, Triputaa, Saralaa, Nishotha, Rechani,* **Hindi:** *Nishotha,* **Local:** *Pitrohari.*

Botanical characteristics: Habit: A large stout perennial twining herb, with milky juice. **Root:** Long, slender, fleshy, much branched. **Stem:** Very long, twining and much twisted together, angled and winged, pubescent, tough and brown when old. **Leaf:** Simple, large, 5-10 by 1.3-7 cm, ovate or oblong, very variable in shape, rarely slightly lobulate, subacute, mucronate, base cordate or truncate, more or less pubescent on both sides, especially when young; petioles 2.5

cm long, pubescent. **Flower:** White tubular, companulate, in few flowered cymes, pendunclesstout, 2.5 cm long; bracts large, lanceolate, pubescent, 2.5 cm long; pedicels 0.6-2.5 cm long, stout, pubescent, slightly thickened upwards, corolla 3.8-5 cm long. **Fruit:** Capsules, globose, 8-13 mm diam., enclosed in the enlarged brittle imbricate sepals, glabrous or faintly pubescent. **Seed:** 4 or less, dull black, glabrous.

Flowering and fruiting period: December-January and February-March.

Habitat: Throughout India, up to 1000 m, sometimes cultivated in gardens.

Parts used: Root bark. **Dosage:** 1-3 g.

Collection period: March-April.

Ayurvedic properties: ***Ras:*** *tikta, katu,* ***Gun:*** *laghu, rukhsa, tikhsna,* ***Veerya:*** *ushna,* ***Vipaka:*** *katu,* ***Tridosha*** **Effect:** alleviates ***Kapha:*** ++, ***Pitta:*** ++.

Chemical constituents: The **roots** contain an active principle a glycosidic resin 10%, an ether insoluble glycoside-turpethin and two other soluble glycosides as alpha and beta-turpetheins, coumarin, scopoletin, along with glucose, rhamnose, fructose, luteolin and its derivative, gentisicprotacatechuic, vanillic, *p*-coumaric, melilotic and ferulic acids, turpethinic acids A, B, C, D and E and saponins.

Action and disease indications: The **roots** are thermogenic, purgative, carminative, anthelmintic, anti-pyretic, expectorant, hepatic stimulant, prescribed for constipation, colic, dropsy, paralysis, arthralgia, myalgia, pectoralgia, bronchitis, helminthiasis, obesity, ascitis, inflammations, intermittent fever, leucoderma, piles, pruritis, tuberculosis, epistaxis, ulcers, erysipelas, tumours, jaundice and ophthalmia.

Clinical uses: Piles, inflammation: Root powder of described plant, 2 g, with decoction of *'Triphala churna'* 10 g, two times a day, is beneficial. **Tympanites:** Mix powder of root powder of described plant, 4 parts, sugar 4 parts, *Piper longum* 1 part, dose 3-6 g, with honey 10 g, before meal, two times a day, is beneficial. **Obesity:** Root powder of described plant, 2 g, with urine of cow 20 ml or honey water, two times a day, is beneficial. **Helminthiasis:** Mix powder of root powder of described plant, seeds of *Butea monosperma, Hyoscyamus niger, Trachy spermum-ammi, Embelia ribes, Mallolotus philipensis,* raw sugar, dose 5 g, with whey, at night, is beneficial. **Constipation:** (1) Root powder of described plant, 1.5 g, seed powder of *Holarrhena antidysentrica* 1 g, *Zingiber officinale* 750 mg, *Piper longum* 500 mg, make tablet with paste of *Vitis vinifera* , dose 1 tablet, at night, with honey water, is beneficial. (2) Root powder of described plant, 2 g, *Glycyrrhiza glabra* 1 g, with honey water, is beneficial.

Formulations: *Trivrittaadi churna, Trivrittaadi ghrita, Avipattikar churna, Panchasama churna, Punarnavaa mandoor, Chandraprabhaa vati, Yogaraaj guggulu, Aswagandhaarista.*

Recommended readings:

Bhutya, R.K. (2007), Vanaspati Aushadha Vigyana, Scientific Publishers (India), Jodhpur, PP. 141.

Brahmavarchas (2003), Ayurved Ka Pran Vanoshadhi Vigyan, Shanti Kunj, Haridwar, PP. 327.

Chunekar, K.C. (2004), Bhava Prakash Nighantu, Chaukhambha Bharti Academy, Varanasi, PP. 397.

Dhiman, A.K. (2006), Ayurvedic Drug Plants, Daya Publishing House, Delhi, PP. 281.

Khare, C.P. (2007), Indian Medicinal Plants, Springer (India) P.L. New Delhi, PP. 449.

Kirtikar, K.R. & Basu, B.D. (1998), Indian Medicinal Plants, L.M Basu, Allahabad, Vol. 2, PP. 1730.

Misra, B.L. (2005), Dravya Guna Hastamalaka, Publication scheme, Jaipur, PP. 328.

Nair, R.Vasudevan, (2007), Indian Medicinal Plants, Orient Longman P.L. Chennai, Vol. 4, PP. 172.

Namjoshi, A.N. (2001), The Ayurvedic Pharmacopoeia of India, Government of India, Department of Indian Systems of Medicine & Homoeopathy, New Delhi, Part-1, Volume- 3, PP. 213.

Pareek, G.N. (2005), Sudhanidhi, Vanoshadhi Ratnakar, Dhanvantari Karyalaya, Aligarh, Vol. 4, PP. 235.

Prajapati, N.D., Purohit, S.S., Sharma, A.K. & Tarun Kumar (2003), A Hand Book of Medicinal Plants, Agrobios India, Jodhpur, PP. 369.

Sharma, P.C., Yelne, MB. & Denis, T.J. (2000), Database on medicinal plants used in ayurveda, Central Council for research in Ayurveda and siddha, Vol. 1, PP. 462.

Sharma, P.V. (1981), Dravya gun vigyana, Chaukhambha Bharti Academy, Varanasi, Vol. 1, PP. 420.

Singh, R.S. (2002), Vanoshadhi Nirdeshika, Uttar Pradesh Hindi Sansthan, Lucknow, PP. 214.

336. *Opuntia dellenii* (Ker-Gawl.) Haw.

Family: Cactaceae.

Synonym: *O.stricta* Var.*dellenii, O.elator.*

Other similar plant: *O.ficus-indica, O.vulgaris.*

Name: English: Prickly Pear, Slipper Thorn. **Sanskrit:** *Kanthaari, Kanthar, Kumbhaari,* **Hindi:** *Naagaphani,* **Local:** *Thaapaathor, Dakhanithor.*

Botanical characteristics: Habit: A perennial shrub, height 1.5-3 m. **Stem:** Large spatula-shaped, covered in clusters of spines, branched from the base. **Leaf:** 3.8 mm long, pale green, conical from a broad base. Joints 30-40 by 15-20 cm, broadly obovate, undulate, not very thick, dull bluish green, areoles large, bearing 4-6 prickles, the largest very stout, subulate, firm and sharp, 2.5-3.8 cm long, usually somewhat curved and of a horny appearance; glochidia numerous about 1.3 cm long, yellowish. **Flower:** Brilliant yellow, tinged with orange, 7.5 cm across, perianth rotate, the outer segment ovate, acute, rounded, with membranous margins, the inner obovate, rounded, mucronate. **Fruit:** Berry, pyriform, truncate, depressed at the apex, often angular or warty when not unripe, bearing tufts of glochidia, deep reddish- purple when ripe.

Flowering and fruiting period: September-October and November-December.

Habitat: Naturalized in semi-tropical regions of India.

Parts used: Leaves, flower, fruit.

Dosage: Leaves and flower juice 10 drops, fruit 3-6 g.

Collection period: October-December.

Ayurvedic properties: ***Ras:*** *tikta,* ***Gun:*** *laghu, tikhsna,* ***Veerya:*** *ushna,* ***Vipaka:*** *katu,* ***Tridosha*** **Effect:** alleviates ***Kapha: ++***, ***Vaata: +***.

Chemical constituents: The **pods** contain a polysaccharide, arbinogalactan and betanin, also contains mucilage, vitamin C. The **flowers** contain the glycosides of isorhamnetin and quercetin, with small amount of the free flavonols.

Action and disease indications: The **plant** is thermogenic, laxative, carminative, stomachic, anti-pyretic, alexiteric, prescribed for biliousness, burning sensation, leucoderma, spleen enlargement, urinary complaints, tumours, ascitis, piles, unconsciousness, inflammations, renal and vesical calculi, anemia, ulcers. The **leaves** are stomachic, used for inflammations, ascitis, pains, tumours. The **flowers** are astringent and haemostatic, used for irritable bowel syndrome, mucous colitis, diarrhea, prostatitis, asthma, bronchitis. The **fruits** are anti-convulsion, used for whooping cough.

Clinical uses: Asthma, bronchitis, whooping cough: Juice 10 drops, or syrup of flowers of described plant, 10 ml, three times a day, is useful. **Chronic rheumatism, arthritis:** Decoction of root powder of described plant, 5 g, with honey, two times a day, is beneficial. Make local application of paste of leaves (after removing the spines and outer layer) of described plant, with *Curcuma longa* and rock salt, is beneficial. **Inflammation, abscess, glands:** Poultice of leaves (after removing the spines and outer layer) of described plant, is beneficial.

Formulations: *Siddhasaarkar.*

Recommended readings:

Bhutya, R.K. (2007), Vanaspati Aushadha Vigyana, Scientific Publishers (India), Jodhpur, PP. 134.

Khare, C.P. (2007), Indian Medicinal Plants, Springer (India) P.L. New Delhi, PP. 451.

Kirtikar, K.R. & Basu, B.D. (1998), Indian Medicinal Plants, L.M Basu, Allahabad, Vol. 2, PP. 1176.

Prajapati, N.D., Purohit, S.S., Sharma, A.K. & Tarun Kumar (2003), A Hand Book of Medicinal Plants, Agrobios India, Jodhpur, PP. 370.

Swami, K.N. (1985), Gavon Main Aushadh Ratna, Kalera Krishana Gopal, Kalera (Raj.), Vol. 1, PP. 238.

337. *Orchis latifolia* Linn.

Family: Orchidaceae.

Synonym: *Dactylorhiza hatagirea.*

Other similar plants: *Eulophia campaetris-Saalamgatta, E. herbacea, Orchis mascular, O.maculata, O. laxiflora, Allium macleanii-Baadshaahi Saalab* (Afghanistan), used as a substitute of Saalam Mishri.

Name: English: Orchis, Salep, **Sanskrit:** *Munjaataka,* **Hindi:** *Saalam Mishri,* **Local:** *Saalam Mishri, Saalam panjaa.*

Botanical characteristics: Habit: A tuberous terrestrial erect leafy herb. **Tuber:** Yellowish-white or grayish, palmate, rounded or ovate, translucent, odourless or nearly tasteless. **Stem:** Height 30-90 cm, usually fistular, leafy upwards. **Leaf:** Many, 5-15 cm long, erect, oblong, linear-oblong or lanceolate, tip flat or concave. **Flower:** 17 mm long, dull purple in cylindric spikes 2.5-15 cm long, dense flowered; bracts green, acuminate, sepals and petals acute or obtuse, lip oblong or rhomboid, entire or 3-lobed, spotted with dark purple, spur straight or curved, stout, pendulous. **Fruit:** 2.5 cm long, ovate.

Flowering and fruiting period: August-September to September-October.

Habitat: West temperate Himalaya, from Kashmir to Nepal, at altitudes of 2500-5000 m, in damp places.

Parts used: Tuber. **Dosage:** 3-6 g.

Collection period: September-October.

Ayurvedic properties: ***Ras:*** *madhur,* ***Gun:*** *guru, snigdha,* ***Veerya:*** *sheeta,* ***Vipaka:*** *madhur*

Tridosha **Effect:** alleviates ***Vaata:*** **+++**, ***Pitta:*** **++**.

Chemical constituents: The **tubers** contain mucilage 50%- glucans, gluco-mannans, starch 25%, proteins 5-15 %. The leaves contain a glucoside, loraglossin.

Action and disease indications: The **tubers** are refrigerant, emollient, diuretic, anti-diarrheal, anthelmintic, anodyne, aphrodisiac, rejuvenating, seminiferous, promoting body waight and tonic, used for diabetes, seminal weakness, penile dysfunction, hemiplegia, dysentery, cephalgia, burning sensation, dipsia, strangury, helminthiasis, phthisis, chronic diarrhea, neurasthenia, tonic after child birth, emaciation and general debility.

Clinical uses: Chronic diarrhea, dysentary: Tuber powder of described plant, 3 g, with water, two times a day, is beneficial. **Asthma:** Tuber powder of described plant 3 g, *Piper longum* 500 mg, with milk of she-goat, two times a day, is beneficial. **Leucorrhea, spermatorrhea:** Mix powder of tuber powder of described plant, tuber of *Eulophia dabia, Asparagus adscendens, Cucurligo orchioides,* with milk, two times a day, is very beneficial. **General debility, somasthenia, neuralgia, penile dysfunction: premature ejaculation, excess and turbid micturition, lumbago, spermacresia:** Mix powder of tuber powder of described plant, seeds of *Mucana pruriens,* seeds of *Tamarindus indica, Asparagus adscendens, Cucurligo orchioides,* seeds of *Hygrophila auriculata, Asparagus racemosus,* flower buds of *Butea monosperma,* unripe fruits and gum of *Acacia nilotica, Lepidium iberis, Centaurea behen* and sugar. Dose 10 g, with milk, two times a day, is very beneficial.

Formulations: *Saalam paka, Kaamoddipaka churna, Siddhamaasaadi yoga, Navajivan yoga, Phalaaspaavaleha.*

Recommended readings:

Bhutya, R.K. (2007), Vanaspati Aushadha Vigyana, Scientific Publishers (India), Jodhpur, PP. 227.

Chunekar, K.C. (2004), Bhava Prakash Nighantu, Chaukhambha Bharti Academy, Varanasi, PP. 835.

Khare, C.P. (2007), Indian Medicinal Plants, Springer (India) P.L. New Delhi, PP. 452.

Kirtikar, K.R. & Basu, B.D. (1998), Indian Medicinal Plants, L.M Basu, Allahabad, Vol. 4, PP. 2413.

Nair, R.Vasudevan, (2007), Indian Medicinal Plants, Orient Longman P.L. Chennai, Vol. 4, PP. 172.

Prajapati, N.D., Purohit, S.S., Sharma, A.K. & Tarun Kumar (2003), A Hand Book of Medicinal Plants, Agrobios India, Jodhpur, PP. 371.

Sharma, P.V. (1981), Dravya gun vigyana, Chaukhambha Bharti Academy, Varanasi, Vol. 1, PP. 567.

Singh, R.S. (2002), Vanoshadhi Nirdeshika, Uttar Pradesh Hindi Sansthan, Lucknow, PP. 372.

Swami, K.N. (1985), Gavon Main Aushadh Ratna, Kalera Krishana Gopal, Kalera (Raj.), Vol. 3, PP. 319.

338. *Oroxylum indicum* (Linn.) Vent.

Family: Bignoniaceae.

Ayurvedic Groups: Charak: *Shothahara, Sheetaprashamana, Anuvaasanopaga,* **Sushruta:** *Panchamoola, Rodhraadi, Veertarvaadi gana.*

Name: English: Indian Trumpet Flower, **Sanskrit:** *Syonaaka, Shoshana, Nata, Katavanga, Tuntuka, Mandookaparna, Shukanaasha, Dirghavrinta, Aralu, Prithushimba, Katambhara,* **Hindi:** *Shyonaaka,* **Local:** *Sonaaka, Sonaapathaa.*

Botanical characteristics: Habit: A small to medium sized deciduous tree, height 7.5-12 m. **Stem:** Bark soft light brown with numerous corky lenticles, with green juice. **Leaf:** Very large, 90-180 cm long, 2-3 pinnate with 5 or more pairs of primary pinnae, rachis very soft, cylindric, swollen at the junction of the branches, leaflets 2-4 pairs, 6.3-12.5 by 3.8-10 cm, ovate or elliptic, acuminate, glabrous, base rounded or sometimes cordate, petiolules of the lateral leaflets 6-15 mm long. Usually in march-April, tree becomes leafless and only with pendulous pods. **Flower:** Lurid to reddish purple outside, dull or pale pinkish yellow within, large, fleshy, shape like trumpet, mouth 5-7.5 cm, numerous, fetid, in large erect racemes 30-60 cm long or even more; penducle 60-90 cm lon, pedicels 0.6-3.2 cm long. **Fruit:** Capsule, 0.3-0.9 m by 5-9 cm, straight, sword shaped, tapering to both ends, flat, 8 mm thick, acute, valves semi-woody. **Seed:** Very numerous, 6.3 cm long, broad silvery winged all round expect at the base. The fresh **root bark** is soft and juicy and cream yellow to grey. It is sweet, later becoming bitter. On drying, the bark shrinks, adheres closely to the wood and becomes faintly fissured.

Flowering and fruiting period: July-August and December-March.

Habitat: Throughout the greater part of India, in deciduous forests, in moist areas, except in the western drier areas.

Parts used: Root bark. **Dosage:** 10-20 g.

Collection period: May-June.

Ayurvedic properties: ***Ras:*** *kashaaya, tikta, madhur,* ***Gun:*** *laghu, rukhsa,* ***Veerya:*** *ushna,* ***Vipaka:*** *katu,* ***Tridosha*** **Effect:** alleviates ***Kapha:*** *++,* ***Vaata:*** *+,* ***Pitta:*** *+.*

Chemical constituents: The **leaves** contain flavones and their glycosides including baicalein and scutellarein, anthraquinone and aloe-emodin. The **bark of roots** contain chrysin, baicalein, oroxylin A and dihydrobaicalein. The **heart wood** contain beta-sitosterol and an iso-flavone, prunetin.

Action and disease indications: The **roots** are refrigerant, anodyne, anti-inflammatory, aphrodisiac, appetizer, sudorofic, expectorant, carminative, digestive, anthelmintic, constipating, diaphoretic, diuretic, febrifuge and tonic, used for rheumatism, diarrhea, dysentery, bronchitis, anorexia, fever, inflammations, dropsy, neuralgia, hiccough, cough, asthma, dyspepsia, flatulence, colic, helminthiasis, strangury, gout, vomiting, leucoderma, wounds, rheumatoid arthritis and sprains. The leaves are stomachic, and anodyne, used for stomachalgia, cephalgia, flatulence, ulcers and spleenomegaly. The tender fruits are carminative, expectorant and stomachic, used for cough, asthma, bronchitis, dyspepsia, flatulence, colic and leucoderma.

Clinical uses: Rheumatoid arthritis, inflammation: Hot fomentation by decoction of bark of described plant 10 g, *Zingiber officinale* 2 g, is beneficial. **Diarrhea, dysentery:** Juice of inner bark of described plant 10 ml, or powder of inner bark of described plant 3 g, with whey, two times a day, is beneficial. **Otorrhea, otalgia:** 4-4 drops of medicated oil, made by bark decoction of described plant, is useful. **Epilepsy:** Inner bark of described plant 5 g, with water, two times a day, is beneficial. **Piles:** Mix powder of bark of described plant, bark of *Plumbego zeylanica,* Seeds of *Holarrhena antidysentrica, Zingiber officinale, Holoptelia integrifolia,* rock salt, dose 4 g, with whey, two times a day, is beneficial.

Formulations: *Dashamool kwaatha, Chyavanprasha, Brahmarasaayan, Dashamoolaarista, Kaalkoota rasa, Mushakaadhya taila.*

Recommended readings:

Acharya, B.K. (2008), Ayurveda Jadi-buti Rahasya, Patanjali Yogapitha, Haridwar, PP. 91.

Bhutya, R.K. (2007), Vanaspati Aushadha Vigyana, Scientific Publishers (India), Jodhpur, PP. 219.

Brahmavarchas (2003), Ayurved Ka Pran Vanoshadhi Vigyan, Shanti Kunj, Haridwar, PP. 329.

Chunekar, K.C. (2004), Bhava Prakash Nighantu, Chaukhambha Bharti Academy, Varanasi, PP. 333.

Dhiman, A.K. (2006), Ayurvedic Drug Plants, Daya Publishing House, Delhi, PP. 368.

Khare, C.P. (2007), Indian Medicinal Plants, Springer (India) P.L. New Delhi, PP. 453.

Kirtikar, K.R. & Basu, B.D. (1998), Indian Medicinal Plants, L.M Basu, Allahabad, Vol. 3, PP. 1839.

Misra, B.L. (2005), Dravya Guna Hastamalaka, Publication scheme, Jaipur, PP. 409.

Nair, R.Vasudevan, (2007), Indian Medicinal Plants, Orient Longman P.L. Chennai, Vol. 4, PP. 186.

Namjoshi, A.N. (2001), The Ayurvedic Pharmacopoeia of India, Government of India, Department of Indian Systems of Medicine & Homoeopathy, New Delhi, Part-1, Volume- 3, PP. 209.

Pareek, G.N. (2005), Sudhanidhi, Vanoshadhi Ratnakar, Dhanvantari Karyalaya, Aligarh, Vol. 9, PP. 58.

Sharma, P.C., Yelne, MB. & Denis, T.J. (2000), Database on medicinal plants used in ayurveda, Central Council for research in Ayurveda and siddha, Vol. 2, PP. 490.

Sharma, P.V. (1981), Dravya gun vigyana, Chaukhambha Bharti Academy, Varanasi, Vol. 1, PP. 466.

Singh, R.S. (2002), Vanoshadhi Nirdeshika, Uttar Pradesh Hindi Sansthan, Lucknow, PP. 392.

339. *Oryza sativa* Linn.

Family: Gramineae; Poaceae.

Synonym: *O.pleno.*

Ayurvedic Groups: Charak: *Stanyajanan, Chhardinigrahan,* **Sushruta:** *Trinapanchamoola.*

Name: English: Rice, **Sanskrit:** *Shaali, Dhaanya, Tandul,* **Hindi:** *Chaaval,* **Local:** *Garadaa, Dhan, Bhaat.*

Botanical characteristics: Habit: An annual or perennial erect herb, height 0.6-3 m. **Stem:** Clums hollow, fistular, nodes slightly thickened, glabrous. **Leaf:** 30-60 cm by 6-8 mm, simple with sheathing bases, long and narrow, linear-lanceolate, striate, scaberulous, spiny hairs on the margins, 1-nerved, glabrous below, panicles 10-20 cm long. **Flower:** Spikelets generally single, laterally compressed, cuneately oblong, pale green, awns 5-13 cm long, golden yellow, reddish-purple, brown or smoky black becoming straw-coloured on ripening, shining. **Fruit:** Caryopsis, oblong to ovoid, somewhat angular, surface rough, due to minutes trichomes, faintly longitudinal ridges and furrows, mostly six rows, somewhat compressed, flattened, small, 0.6-1 cm by 0.2-0.3 cm, red or dirty-white, free within the lemma and palea.

Flowering and fruiting period: August-September and October-November.

Habitat: Cultivated throughout India, extensively in the river valleys, deltas and low-lying coastal areas, mostly in Punjab, Uttar Pradesh, Bihar, West Bengal and coastal areas.

Parts used: Seed, root.

Dosage: Seed 25-50 g, root for decoction 25-50 g.

Collection period: October-November.

Ayurvedic properties: ***Ras:*** *madhur,* ***Gun:*** *laghu, snigdha,* ***Veerya:*** *sheeta* ***Vipaka:*** *madhur* ***Tridosha*** **Effect:** alleviates ***Vaata:*** ++, aggravates ***Kapha:*** ++,***Pitta:*** +.

Chemical constituents: The **roots** contain stachydrine, trigonellin, 1,5-resorcinol along with four other alkyl resorcinols. The **seeds** contains starch, glucose, dextrin, fructose, galactose, raffinose, maltose, isomaltose, maltotriose, maltotetrose, hemicelluloses of rice are made up of arabinose and xylose, mannose, uronic acid.

Action and disease indications: The **roots** are refrigerant, diuretic, and febrifuge, prescribed for burning sensation, dipsia, bilious fever, diabetes and strangury. The **grains** are oleaginous, demulcent, galactogogue aphrodisiac, carminative, diuretic, anti-dysenteric, good for eyes and tonic, used for diarrhea, piles, anemia, burns wounds, dysentery, pneumonosis, pulmonary consumption and colonopathy.

Clinical uses: Vomiting: Roasted seeds of described plant, 10 g, as required. **Pyrexia, burning sensation:** Rice water 50 ml, three times a day, is useful. **Oligogalactia:** Mix powder of seeds of described plant 10 g, *Asparagus racemosus* 2 g, *Cuminum cyminum* 1.5 g, with milk, two times a day, is beneficial. **Burning sensation of urine, dysurea:** Decoction of seeds of described plant, 20 g, *'Panchamool kwath'* 10 g, with honey 10 g, two times a day, is beneficial. **Menorrhagia, metrorrhagia:** Extract of *Aloe barbadensis,* root of *Amaranthus spinosa,* with water of rice 50 ml is beneficial. **Abortion, miscarriage:** Paste of *Cynodon dactylon,* with rice water, 50 ml, two or three times a day, is useful.

Formulations: *Trinapanchamool kwaatha, Brahmarasaayan, Elaadi churna, Yavanyaadi churna, Abhayaarista, Asmarihar Kashaaya.*

Recommended readings:

Bhutya, R.K. (2007), Vanaspati Aushadha Vigyana, Scientific Publishers (India), Jodhpur, PP. 214.

Chunekar, K.C. (2004), Bhava Prakash Nighantu, Chaukhambha Bharti Academy, Varanasi, PP. 639.

Khare, C.P. (2007), Indian Medicinal Plants, Springer (India) P.L. New Delhi, PP. 454.

Kirtikar, K.R. & Basu, B.D. (1998), Indian Medicinal Plants, L.M Basu, Allahabad, Vol. 4, PP. 2651.

Nair, R.Vasudevan, (2007), Indian Medicinal Plants, Orient Longman P.L. Chennai, Vol. 4, PP. 193.

Namjoshi, A.N. (2001), The Ayurvedic Pharmacopoeia of India, Government of India, Department of Indian Systems of Medicine & Homoeopathy, New Delhi, Part-1, Volume- 1, PP. 145 and 3-181.

Pareek, G.N. (2005), Sudhanidhi, Vanoshadhi Ratnakar, Dhanvantari Karyalaya, Aligarh, Vol. 10, PP. 127.

Prajapati, N.D., Purohit, S.S., Sharma, A.K. & Tarun Kumar (2003), A Hand Book of Medicinal Plants, Agrobios India, Jodhpur, PP. 374.

Sharma, P.C., Yelne, MB. & Denis, T.J. (2000), Database on medicinal plants used in ayurveda, Central Council for research in Ayurveda and siddha, Vol. 8, PP. 325.

Sharma, P.V. (1981), Dravya gun vigyana, Chaukhambha Bharti Academy, Varanasi, Vol. 2, PP. 148.

340. *Ougeinia dalbergioides* Benth.

Family: Papilionaceae; Fabaceae.

Synonym: *O.oojeinensis.*

Ayurvedic Groups: Sushruta: *Saalsaaraadi gana.*

Name: English: Chariot Tree, Punjab Kino, **Sanskrit:** *Tinisha, Syandana, Nemi, Rathadru, Vanjula,* **Hindi:** *Tinisha,* **Local:** *Saanan, Sandan, Paanan.*

Botanical characteristics: Habit: A medium sized deciduous pretty tree, height 6-12 m. **Stem:** With short crooked trunk and dark brown deeply cracked bark, branches slender, terete. **Leaf:** Pinnately 3-foliate, 30 cm long with petiole, petiole 3.8-5 cm long, stipules 6 mm long, lanceolate, acute, caduceus, leaflets large, rigidly coriaceous, the terminal broadly elliptic or roundish, sometimes trapezoidal, 7.5-15 by 5-10 cm, the lateral leaflets opposite, obliquely ovate, cordate, 7.5-10 by 3.8-7.5 cm, on petiolules 3 mm long, all glabrous above, glabrous or more or less downy beneath, distantly and shallowly crenate, bluntly pointed, main nerves 4-8 pairs, prominent; stipules subulate. **Flower:** Numerous, white or pink, somewhat fragrant, in short fascicled racemes from the nodes of old branches, pediceles 1.2-2 cm long, filiform; bracts 1.25 mm long, ovate, acuminate, broader than long, villous outside; bracteole 1 beneath the clyx, minute, villous. **Fruit:** Pods 5-7.5 cm long, linear, elongate, flat, light brown. **Seed:** 2-5 per pods.

Flowering and fruiting period: February-March and April-May.

Habitat: Outer Himalaya and sub-Himalayan tract from Jammu to Bhutan, up to an altitude of 1500 m, Northern and Central India, Deccan Peninsula and Marwar of Rajasthan.

Parts used: Bark, gum.

Dosage: Bark 10-20 g, gum 2-5 g.

Collection period: March-April.

Ayurvedic properties: ***Ras:*** *kashaaya,* ***Gun:*** *laghu, rukhsa,* ***Veerya:*** *sheeta* ***Vipaka:*** *katu,* ***Tridosha*** **Effect:** alleviates ***Kapha:*** ***++,*** ***Pitta:*** *+.*

Chemical constituents: The **leaves** and **heart wood** contain iso-flavonoids- dalbergion, hemoferritin, urgenin, flavonoids-quercetin, kaempferol and leucopelargonidin. The **stem bark** contains triterpenes, lupeol and betulin.

Action and disease indications: The **bark** is refrigerant, stimulant, anti-inflammatory, constipating, urinary astringent, anthelmintic, depurative, sudorofic, styptic, rejuvenating, febrifuge, anti-diarrheal and spasmolytic, used for inflammations, burning sensation, diarrhea, dysentery, urorrhagia, diabetes, verminosis, leucoderma, haemorrhages, fevers, ulcers, gonorrhea, anaemia and general debility.

Clinical uses: Excess and turbid micturition, skin diseases, epistaxis: Decoction of stem bark of described plant, 15 g, with honey 10 g, two times a day, is beneficial. **Diarrhea, dysentery:** Gum of described plant, 4 g, three times a day, is useful. **Inflammation, leucoderma, skin diseases:** Local application of paste of stem bark of described plant is beneficial.

Formulations: *Trikantaka taila, Varunaadi kwaatha, Chandanaadi taila.*

Recommended readings:

Bhutya, R.K. (2007), Vanaspati Aushadha Vigyana, Scientific Publishers (India), Jodhpur, PP. 116.

Chunekar, K.C. (2004), Bhava Prakash Nighantu, Chaukhambha Bharti Academy, Varanasi, PP. 548.

Khare, C.P. (2007), Indian Medicinal Plants, Springer (India) P.L. New Delhi, PP. 456.

Kirtikar, K.R. & Basu, B.D. (1998), Indian Medicinal Plants, L.M Basu, Allahabad, Vol. 1, PP. 755.

Misra, B.L. (2005), Dravya Guna Hastamalaka, Publication scheme, Jaipur, PP. 486.

Nair, R.Vasudevan, (2007), Indian Medicinal Plants, Orient Longman P.L. Chennai, Vol. 4, PP. 199.

Pareek, G.N. (2005), Sudhanidhi, Vanoshadhi Ratnakar, Dhanvantari Karyalaya, Aligarh, Vol. 10, PP. 257.

Prajapati, N.D., Purohit, S.S., Sharma, A.K. & Tarun Kumar (2003), A Hand Book of Medicinal Plants, Agrobios India, Jodhpur, PP. 374.

Sharma, P.V. (1981), Dravya gun vigyana, Chaukhambha Bharti Academy, Varanasi, Vol. 1, PP. 676.

341. *Oxalis corniculata* Linn.

Family: Oxalidaceae.

Other similar plant: *O.actesella-* leaves sessile, larger, flowers white-pink, fruit 8 mm long, 2-3 seeds in each septum.

Name: English: Indian Sorrel, **Sanskrit:** *Chaangeri, Chukrikaa, Dantashathaa, Ambasthaa, Amlapatraka, Amlalonikaa, Asmantaka, Shafari, Kushali,* **Hindi:** *Chaangeri,* **Local:** *Khatti Buti, Tinpatiyaa, Ambilonaa,*

Botanical characteristics: Habit: An annual or perennial, procumbent or more or less erect, creeping, Acidic, hairy herb, 6-25 cm in height. **Stem:** Diffuse and rooting at nodes, much branched. **Leaf:** Palmately 3-foliate; petioles 3.8-9 cm long, very slender, pubescent, leaflets obcordate, 1.2-2.5 cm long, entire, cuneate at the base, glabrous or with a few appressed hairs and with ciliate margins, sessile or sub-sessile. **Flower:** Yellow, in small, long stalked umbellate cymes, 2-5 at each petiole. **Fruit:** Capsules, tomentose, oblong or linear-oblong, 1.2-2.5 cm long, 5-angled, shortly beaked. **Seed:** Numerous, broadly ovoid, acute, transversely striate, dark brown. All parts are acidic.

Flowering and fruiting period: Almost throughout year, mostly in November-December.

Habitat: Throughout the warmer parts of India, up to an altitude of 3000 m in North-West Himalayas. In damp and moist places at banks of river and streams.

Parts used: Whole parts.

Dosage: Juice 5-10 ml, powder 1-3 g.

Collection period: November-December.

Ayurvedic properties: ***Ras:*** *Amla, kashaaya,* ***Gun:*** *laghu, rukhsa,* ***Veerya:*** *ushna,* ***Vipaka:*** *amla,* ***Tridosha*** **Effect:** alleviates ***Kapha:*** ***++,*** ***Vaata:*** ***++,*** aggrevates ***Pitta:*** *+.*

Chemical constituents: The **leaves** contain flavonoids, vitexin, isovitexin and vitexin-2"-O-beta-D-glucopyranoside, also contain 1.47% of lipid, a rich source of essential fatty acids and alpha and beta-tocopherol (1.58 and 6.18mg/g dry basis), good source of vitamin C (125 mg/100g), carotene (3.6 mg/100g) and calcium (5.6% of dry material), but high content of oxalates (12% of dry basis). The **leaves** and **stem** content tartaric and citric acid; stem also malic acid.

Action and disease indications: The **Plant** and **leaves** are thermogenic, anodyne, appetizer, digestive, anti-inflammatory, carminative, liver tonic, diuretic, constipating, febrifuge, vermifuge, anti-bacterial, emmenogogue, styptic and antiseptic, prescribed for anorexia, dyspepsia, piles, prolepse of rectum and uterus, anaemia, fevers, tympanites, diarrhea, dysentery, scurvy, corns, warts, excrescences of skin, ulcers, cephalgia, ophthalmopathy, toxicity of *Datura innoxia* and *Papaver sommniferum*, haemorrhage, cardiopathy, dysmenorrhea, amenorrhea, strangury, burning sensation and heptomegaly.

Clinical uses: Anal prolepse, basillary dysentery, menorrhagia, metrorrhagia: Medicated Clarified butter, made by juice of described plant and *Marsilea minuta,* dose 10 g, with milk, two times a day, is beneficial. **Intoxication of** *Datura inoxia,* **piles, sprue, bleeding diasthesis:** Juice of described plant, 10 ml three times a day, is useful. **Inflammation:** Poultice of leaves of described plant, is beneficial. **Gingivitis, menorrhagia, metrorrhagia:** Juice of described plant, 10 ml three times a day, is useful. **Sprue:** Medicated clarified butter, made by juice of described plant, *Piper longum* and curd, 10 g, two times a day, is beneficial. **Malaria:** Fried jelly of described plant, 20 g, two times a day, is beneficial. **Burning sensation:** Juice of leaves of described plant, 10 ml, with sugar candy powder 10 g, two times a day, is beneficial. **Gingivitis:** Gargles of juice of described plant, is beneficial. **Intestinal pain:** Decoction of described plant, 20 ml, fried gum of *Ferula narthex* 125 mg, rock salt 250 mg, two times a day, is beneficial. **Nocturnal emission:** Alkali of described plant, 250 mg, powder of *Curcuma longa* 1 g, *'Triphalaa churna'* 2 g, with water, two times a day, is beneficial. **Bleeding piles:** Extract of described plant, 1 g, gum of *Acacia nilotica* 2 g, *Santalum album* 2 g, with water, two times a day, is beneficial.

Formulations: *Changeri ghrita, Vaantihrida rasa, Agurvaadi taila, Hriberaadi ghrita, Naagaraadi ghrita.*

Recommended readings:

Acharya, B.K. (2008), Ayurveda Jadi-buti Rahasya, Patanjali Yogapitha, Haridwar, PP. 158.

Bhutya, R.K. (2007), Vanaspati Aushadha Vigyana, Scientific Publishers (India), Jodhpur, PP. 95.

Brahmavarchas (2003), Ayurved Ka Pran Vanoshadhi Vigyan, Shanti Kunj, Haridwar, PP. 331.

Chunekar, K.C. (2004), Bhava Prakash Nighantu, Chaukhambha Bharti Academy, Varanasi, PP. 671.

Khare, C.P. (2007), Indian Medicinal Plants, Springer (India) P.L. New Delhi, PP. 457.

Kirtikar, K.R. & Basu, B.D. (1998), Indian Medicinal Plants, L.M Basu, Allahabad, Vol. 1, PP. 437.

Misra, B.L. (2005), Dravya Guna Hastamalaka, Publication scheme, Jaipur, PP. 470.

Nair, R.Vasudevan, (2007), Indian Medicinal Plants, Orient Longman P.L. Chennai, Vol. 4, PP. 202.

Namjoshi, A.N. (2001), The Ayurvedic Pharmacopoeia of India, Government of India, Department of Indian Systems of Medicine & Homoeopathy, New Delhi, Part-1, Volume- 3, PP. 36.

Pareek, G.N. (2005), Sudhanidhi, Vanoshadhi Ratnakar, Dhanvantari Karyalaya, Aligarh, Vol. 10, PP. 119.

Prajapati, N.D., Purohit, S.S., Sharma, A.K. & Tarun Kumar (2003), A Hand Book of Medicinal Plants, Agrobios India, Jodhpur, PP. 375.

Sharma, P.C., Yelne, MB. & Denis, T.J. (2000), Database on medicinal plants used in ayurveda, Central Council for research in Ayurveda and siddha, Vol. 4, PP. 82.

Sharma, P.V. (1981), Dravya gun vigyana, Chaukhambha Bharti Academy, Varanasi, Vol. 1, PP. 347.

Singh, R.S. (2002), Vanoshadhi Nirdeshika, Uttar Pradesh Hindi Sansthan, Lucknow, PP. 148.

Swami, K.N. (1985), Gavon Main Aushadh Ratna, Kalera Krishana Gopal, Kalera (Raj.), Vol. 1, PP. 37.

342. *Paederia scandens* (Lour.) Merr.

Family: Rubiaceae.

Synonym: *P.foetida.*

Name: Sanskrit: *Prasaarini, Rajbalaa, Bhadraparni, Prataanini, Sarani, Saarini, Bhadra, Balaa, Katambharaa,* **Hindi:** *Gandhaprasaarini,* **Local:** *Pasaran.*

Botanical characteristics: Habit: A slender twining, foetid shrub, glabrous or puberulous. **Leaf:** Opposite, ovate or lanceolate, entire, acute or cuspidate, base broad or narrowed, rather thin, nerves 4-5 pairs, fine, 5-7.5 by 2.5-3.8 cm, petioles 1.3-3.8 cm long, stipules ovate-lanceolate, bifid. **Flower:** Purple or violate, tubular or funnel shaped, nearly sessile, in axillary or terminal, often scorpiod cymose panicles 15 cm long. **Fruit:** Pyrene, ellipsoid or orbicular, compressed, red or black, wings pale, 1.1 cm across. **Seed:** Much dorsally compressed.

Flowering and fruiting period: August-October and December-January.

Habitat: Central and Eastern Himalaya, extending to Assam, West Bengal, Bihar and Orissa, up to an altitude of 1500 m,

Parts used: Root, stem, leaves.

Dosage: Powder 2-4 g, juice 10-20 ml.

Collection period: January-February.

Ayurvedic properties: ***Ras:*** *tikta,* ***Gun:*** *guru,* ***Veerya:*** *ushna,* ***Vipaka:*** *katu,* ***Tridosha*** **Effect:** alleviates ***Vaata: ++, Kapha: +.***

Chemical constituents: The **aerial parts** contain *epi*-friedelanol, embelin and beta-sitosterol. The leaves and stem contain iridoid glycoside, sitosterol, stigmasterol, campesterol, ursolic acid, hetriacontanol, ceryl alcohol, palmitic acid and methyl mercaptan. The foetid smell is due to methyl mercaptan.

Action and disease indications: The **Plant** is indigestible, aphrodisiac, anodyne, carminative, nervine tonic, diuretic, emmenogogue, styptic, laxative and tonic, used for inflammations, piles, fever, night blindness, epistaxis, gout, rheumatism, lumbago and leucoderma.

Clinical uses: Rheumatism, gout, arthritis: Decoction of root powder of described plant, 4 g, root of *Plumbego zeylanica* 250 mg, *'Trikatu churna'* 1 g, with honey 10 g, two times a day, is beneficial. **Colic, flatulence, constipation:** Warm jelly of leaves of described plant, 10 g, with lukewarm water, two times a day, is beneficial. **Dysuria, renal and vesical calculus:** Decoction of leaves of described plant, 10 g, two times a day, is beneficial. **Neuralgia:** Massage of medicated oil, made by whole plant of described plant, is beneficial.

Formulations: *Prasaarani taila, Kubjaprasaarani taila, Dashamoolaarista, Mashabalaadi taila, Mahaamasha taila, Naraayan taila.*

Recommended readings:

Bhutya, R.K. (2007), Vanaspati Aushadha Vigyana, Scientific Publishers (India), Jodhpur, PP. 83.

Chunekar, K.C. (2004), Bhava Prakash Nighantu, Chaukhambha Bharti Academy, Varanasi, PP. 424.

Dhiman, A.K. (2006), Ayurvedic Drug Plants, Daya Publishing House, Delhi, PP. 302.

Khare, C.P. (2007), Indian Medicinal Plants, Springer (India) P.L. New Delhi, PP. 459.

Kirtikar, K.R. & Basu, B.D. (1998), Indian Medicinal Plants, L.M Basu, Allahabad, Vol. 2, PP. 1297.

Misra, B.L. (2005), Dravya Guna Hastamalaka, Publication scheme, Jaipur, PP. 262.

Namjoshi, A.N. (2001), The Ayurvedic Pharmacopoeia of India, Government of India, Department of Indian Systems of Medicine & Homoeopathy, New Delhi, Part-1, Volume- 1, PP. 137.

Pareek, G.N. (2005), Sudhanidhi, Vanoshadhi Ratnakar, Dhanvantari Karyalaya, Aligarh, Vol. 10, PP. 25.

Prajapati, N.D., Purohit, S.S., Sharma, A.K. & Tarun Kumar (2003), A Hand Book of Medicinal Plants, Agrobios India, Jodhpur, PP. 375.

Sharma, P.C., Yelne, MB. & Denis, T.J. (2000), Database on medicinal plants used in ayurveda, Central Council for research in Ayurveda and siddha, Vol. 3, PP. 500.

Sharma, P.V. (1981), Dravya gun vigyana, Chaukhambha Bharti Academy, Varanasi, Vol. 1, PP. 62.

Singh, R.S. (2002), Vanoshadhi Nirdeshika, Uttar Pradesh Hindi Sansthan, Lucknow, PP. 253.

Swami, K.N. (1985), Gavon Main Aushadh Ratna, Kalera Krishana Gopal, Kalera (Raj.), Vol. 3, PP. 426.

343. *Paeonia emodi* Wall ex Royle.

Family: Paeoniaceae, Ranunculaceae.

Other similar plants: *P.officinalis.*

Name: English: Himalayan Paeony, **Hindi:** *Udsaleeba,* **Local:** *Udsaleeba.*

Botanical characteristics: Habit: An erect, stout, perennial glabrous leafy herb. **Stem:** 0.3-0.6 m high. **Leaf:** Alternate, compound, 15-30 cm long, leaflets 3, usually 3-parted, segments lanceolate, pointed entire. **Flower:** Few, showy, 7.5-10 cm across, usually solitary in the axils of the upper leaves, buds globose, sepals 5, orbicular, concave, green, persistent, the outer ones ending in a leaf-like point, petals 5-10, broadly ovate, concave, red or white, stamens many, ovaries 1-3, densely hairy, many-ovuled, seated on a fleshy disk; style short, broad, recurved, stalk long, purple slightly curved. **Fruit:** Follicles, ovoid, 2.5-5 cm long, 1.25 cm thick, grayish, linear. **Seed:** Few, large. **Root:** Fleshy, in bunches.

Flowering and fruiting period: May-June and July-August.

Habitat: North-western Himalaya, from Kashmir to Kumaon, at 2000-3000 m.

Parts used: Root. **Dosage:** 1-3 g.

Collection period: May-June.

Ayurvedic properties: ***Ras:*** *tikta, katu,* ***Gun:*** *laghu, rukhsa, tikhsna,* ***Veerya:*** *ushna,* ***Vipaka:*** *katu,* ***Tridosha*** **Effect:** alleviates ***Kapha:*** ***++,*** ***Vaata:*** ***+.***

Chemical constituents: The **root** contains an essential oil, with salicylaldehyde as the chief component, a fixed oil, benzoic acid and sucrose. The plant contains gallo tannin and glucogallin.

Action and disease indications: The **leaves** are carminative, anti-inflammatory, astringent, spasmolytic, anti-diarrhoeal, diuretic, anti-lithitic. The **roots** are anti-inflammatory, used for epilepsy, headache, skin diseases, colic, ascitis, jaundice, renal colic, bladder calculus, rheumatic affections, piles, inflammations of the liver, spleen and chest.

Clinical uses: Epilepsy: Fresh juice of roots of described plant, 10 ml, with honey 10 g, two times a day, is beneficial. **Diarrhea:** Cold infusion of dry flowers of described plant, 10 ml, two times a day, is beneficial. **Measels:** Seed powder of described plant, 1 g, honey 10 g, two times a day, is beneficial. **Inflammation, convulsions, chorea, hysteria:** Root powder of described plant, 2 g, with water, two times a day, is beneficial.

Recommended readings:

Bhutya, R.K. (2007), Vanaspati Aushadha Vigyana, Scientific Publishers (India), Jodhpur, PP. 35.

Khare, C.P. (2007), Indian Medicinal Plants, Springer (India) P.L. New Delhi, PP. 457.

Kirtikar, K.R. & Basu, B.D. (1998), Indian Medicinal Plants, L.M Basu, Allahabad, Vol. 1, PP. 25.

Pareek, G.N. (2005), Sudhanidhi, Vanoshadhi Ratnakar, Dhanvantari Karyalaya, Aligarh, Vol. 9, PP. 124.

Sharma, P.V. (1981), Dravya gun vigyana, Chaukhambha Bharti Academy, Varanasi, Vol. 1, PP. 86.

Swami, K.N. (1985), Gavon Main Aushadh Ratna, Kalera Krishana Gopal, Kalera (Raj.), Vol. 2, PP. 127.

344. *Panax pseudoginseng* Wall.

Family: Araliaceae.

Other similar plants: *P.quinquefolium, P.schinseng.*

Name: English: Indian Ginseng, Indian Pseudo-ginseng, **Sanskrit:** *Laxamanaa,* **Hindi:** *Laxamana,* **Local:** *Laxamana.*

Botanical characteristics: Habit: A perennial herb. **Root:** Tuberous, short and fleshy. **Stem:** Erect, 30-50 cm high, usually withered in the dry season. **Leaf:** Palmate, long petioled in whorls; leaflets 5-7, margins dentate, hairy on both sides. **Flower:** Small, yellowish-green, inflorescence in terminal simple umbel. **Fruit:** Berry, globose, slightly compressed, red when ripe. **Seed:** 2 in a fruit.

Flowering and fruiting period: August-September and September-October.

Habitat: Found in western Himalayas, Pithoragarh district of Uttarakhand.

Parts used: Tuberous root. **Dosage:** 1-3 g.

Collection period: October-November.

Ayurvedic properties: ***Ras:*** *madhur, tikta,* ***Gun:*** *guru, snigdha,* ***Veerya:*** *sheeta* ***Vipaka:*** *madhur* ***Tridosha*** **Effect:** alleviates ***Vaata:*** **+++,** ***Pitta:*** ++.

Chemical constituents: The **roots** contain triterpenoid saponins A,B,C,D, oleanolic acid, amino acid, leucine, valine, praline, oxyproline, histidine, lysine, cysteine, iron and calcium.

Action and disease indications: The **roots** are adaptogen, digestive, relaxant, old age tevitalizer, anti-arrhythmic, haemostatic, tonic, hormonal and circulation promoter, and sustains nerves and immune system in physical exhaustion and during convalescence, used for haematemesis, metrorrheagia, menorrhagia, bloody stool, epistaxis, rheumatism, post-partum haematometra, ocular congestion, anaemia and general debilitye specially in parturients and sterility.

Clinical uses: Sexual debility, spermacresia: Root powder of described plant, 2 g, with milk, two times a day, is beneficial.

Recommended readings:

Khare, C.P. (2007), Indian Medicinal Plants, Springer (India) P.L. New Delhi, PP. 460.

Prajapati, N.D., Purohit, S.S., Sharma, A.K. & Tarun Kumar (2003), A Hand Book of Medicinal Plants, Agrobios India, Jodhpur, PP. 378.

345. *Pandanus fascicularis* Lam.

Family: Pandanaceae.

Synonym: *P.tectorius, P.odoratissimus.*

Name: English: Screw Pine, **Sanskrit:** *Ketaka, Suchikaapushpa, Jambooka, Krakachachhada,* **Hindi:** *Kewara,* **Local:** *Kewara.*

Botanical characteristics: Habit: A tortuous scandent shrub or small tree, up to 6 m high, rarely erect. **Stem:** Supported by stilt aerial roots, densely branched. **Leaf:** Glaucous-green, 90-150 cm long, coriaceous, ensiform or linear, caudate-acuminate, the marginal spines pointing forward and those of the midrib forward and backward. **Flower:** Male flowers: in numerous sub-sessile cylindric spikes 5-10 by 2.5-3.8 cm, enclosed in long white fragrant caudate-acuminate spathes. Female flowers: in solitary spadix, 5 cm in diam. **Fruit:** Syncarpium, oblong or globose, 15-25 cm long and broad, yellow or red, drupes numerous, each consisting of 5-12 carples; 5-7.5 cm long, turbinate, angular, the crown smooth, convex, more or less depressed round the reniform stigmas.

Flowering and fruiting period: July-August and October-November.

Habitat: Throughout the hotter moister parts of India, especially in coastal areas of Indian peninsula on both sides an Andaman Islands.

Parts used: Flower, leaves, root.

Dosage: Distillate of flowers 40-60 ml, syrup 20-40 ml, root 10-20 g, leaves for external use.

Collection period: July-August.

Ayurvedic properties: ***Ras:*** *katu, madhur, tikta,* ***Gun:*** *laghu, snigdha,* ***Veerya:*** *ushna,* ***Vipaka:*** *katu,* ***Tridosha*** **Effect:** alleviates ***Kapha:*** ++,***Pitta:*** ++. ***Vaata:*** +.

Chemical constituents: The **oil** contain methyl ether of beta-phenyllethyl alcohol, diterpene, *d*-linalool, phenyl ethyl acetate, citral, phenyl ethyl alcohol, ester of phthalic acid, fatty acids and stearoptene. The leaves contain the piperidine alkaloids.

Action and disease indications: The **roots** are thermogenic, emollient, depurative, anti-septic, procreant, cephalic, aphrodisiac, anodyne, suppurative, carminative, stomachic, deodorant, urinary astringent, vulnerary, ophthalmic, cardio-tonic, brain tonic, epilepsy, disuria, febrifuge, sudorofic and tonic, prescribed for skin diseases, coxalgia, otalgia, cephalgia, wounds, ulcers, fevers, diabetes, dyspepsia, flatulence, colic, sterility, spontaneous abortion and general debility. The **flowers** are anodyne, aphrodisiac, and demulcent, used for otalgia, cephalgia, pruritus, leucoderma and skin eruptions. The **oil** obtained from the bracts is stimulant and anti-spasmodic used for cephalgia, coxalgia and rheumatoid arthritis.

Clinical uses: Skin diseases: Local application of paste of leaves of described plant is beneficial. **Dysuria, chronic gonorrhea:** Distillate of described plant, 20 ml, two times a day, is beneficial. **Colic, flatulence:** Alkali of roots of described plant 1 g, Soda bi carb 500 mg, *Sausurea costus* 500 mg, with oil of *Sesamum orientale* 40 ml or *Ricinus communis* 20 ml or 10 g clarified butter, with warm water, two times a day, is beneficial. **Menorrhagia, metrorrhagia, habitual abortion:** Root powder of described plant, 5-10 g, sugar candy powder 10 g, with water, two times a day, is beneficial.

Formulations: *Ark Kevaraa, Sharbat Kevaraa.*

Recommended readings:

Bhutya, R.K. (2007), Vanaspati Aushadha Vigyana, Scientific Publishers (India), Jodhpur, PP. 74.

Brahmavarchas (2003), Ayurved Ka Pran Vanoshadhi Vigyan, Shanti Kunj, Haridwar, PP. 332.

Chunekar, K.C. (2004), Bhava Prakash Nighantu, Chaukhambha Bharti Academy, Varanasi, PP. 498.

Dhiman, A.K. (2006), Ayurvedic Drug Plants, Daya Publishing House, Delhi, PP. 209.

Khare, C.P. (2007), Indian Medicinal Plants, Springer (India) P.L. New Delhi, PP. 461.

Kirtikar, K.R. & Basu, B.D. (1998), Indian Medicinal Plants, L.M Basu, Allahabad, Vol. 4, PP. 2592.

Misra, B.L. (2005), Dravya Guna Hastamalaka, Publication scheme, Jaipur, PP. 473.

Nair, R.Vasudevan, (2007), Indian Medicinal Plants, Orient Longman P.L. Chennai, Vol. 4, PP. 206.

Namjoshi, A.N. (2001), The Ayurvedic Pharmacopoeia of India, Government of India, Department of Indian Systems of Medicine & Homoeopathy, New Delhi, Part-1, Volume- 2, PP. 69.

Pareek, G.N. (2005), Sudhanidhi, Vanoshadhi Ratnakar, Dhanvantari Karyalaya, Aligarh, Vol. 9, PP. 276.

Prajapati, N.D., Purohit, S.S., Sharma, A.K. & Tarun Kumar (2003), A Hand Book of Medicinal Plants, Agrobios India, Jodhpur, PP. 379.

Sharma, P.C., Yelne, MB. & Denis, T.J. (2000), Database on medicinal plants used in ayurveda, Central Council for research in Ayurveda and siddha, Vol. 3, PP. 378.

Sharma, P.V. (1981), Dravya gun vigyana, Chaukhambha Bharti Academy, Varanasi, Vol. 1, PP. 141.

Singh, R.S. (2002), Vanoshadhi Nirdeshika, Uttar Pradesh Hindi Sansthan, Lucknow, PP. 103.

Swami, K.N. (1985), Gavon Main Aushadh Ratna, Kalera Krishana Gopal, Kalera (Raj.), Vol. 2, PP. 214.

346. *Papaver sommniferum* Linn.

Family: Papaveraceae.

Similar plants: *Papaver sommniferum* var.*glabrum, Papaver sommniferum* var.*nigrum.*

Name: English: Opium Poppy, **Sanskrit:** *Aafooka, Tilbheda, Khasatil, Khaakhasa, Ahifenaka,* **Hindi:** *Afima,* **Local:** *Aafu, Amala, Postaa.*

Botanical characteristics: Habit: An erect annual robust, usually glaucous green herb, height 60-120 cm. **Stem:** Scarcely branched. **Leaf:** Simple, sessile, alternate, 15-25 by 8-15 cm, ovate-oblong, shallowly pinnatifid, lobed, clasping the stem by their cordate base, irregularly toothed margin, acute, amplexicaule. **Flower:** Large, 5-6 cm across, attractive, bisexual, scarlet, white or sometimes purple or variegated with a dark stain at the base. **Fruit:** Capsule, globose or ovoid, glabrous, up to 4 cm in diam., stalked. **Seed:** White or grayish-brown to black, reniform. **Opium** is the latex obtained by incising unripe capsule

Flowering and fruiting period: January-February and February-March.

Habitat: Cultivated in Uttar Pradesh, Madhya Pradesh, Punjab and Rajasthan.

Parts used: Fruit gum, seed,

Dosage: Fruit gum 30-125 mg, seeds 1-3 g, tincture 5-30 drops.

Collection period: February-March.

Ayurvedic properties: ***Ras:*** *tikta, kashaaya,* ***Gun:*** *laghu, rukhsa, sukhsma, vyvai, vikaasi,* ***Veerya:*** *ushna,* ***Vipaka:*** *katu,* ***Tridosha*** **Effect:** alleviates ***Kapha:*** ***++,*** aggrevates ***Vaata: ++, Pitta: +.***

Chemical constituents: The **fruit latex** contains isoquinoline alkaloids; the major one is morphine with narcotine, codeine, papaverine and thebaine. Others are organic acids: meconic, lactic, malic, tartaric, citric, acetic, succinic; in addition proteins, dextrose and pectin. The **seeds** contain thiamine 420, riboflavin 49, folic acid 30, pantothenic acid 2667, niacin 1877 mcg/100g. The **seed oil** contains gamma-tocopherol 220, alpha-tocopherol 40, beta-tocopherol 20 mcg/100g. Some low-molecular proteins (15% of total protein) have been isolated, along with cystein, glutamic acid and arginine. The **seeds** contain a fatty oil (45%) containing palmitic, stearic, oleic, linoleic and linolenic acids.

Action and disease indications: The **latex of fruit** is constipating bitter, astringent, anaphrodisiac, sedative, narcotic, anodyne, anti-spasmodic, sudorofic, hyptonic, analgesic, and nervine tonic, prescribed for cough, bronchitis, anxiety, depression, sciatica, neuritis, arthralgia, lumbago, dysmenorrhea, colic, bilious pain, calculus, ptyalism, leucorrhea, diabetes mellitus, otitis, proctalgia, coxalgia, due to diarrhea and dysentery, internal haemorrhage. The **seeds** are constipating, aphrodisiac, nutritive, demulcent, emollient, spasmolytic, and tonic used for diarrhea, dysentery and general debility.

Contraindication: Opium is highly toxic drug, beware of over dose.

Fatal dose: Fruit gum- 0.9 to 1.3 g, Tincture- 60-120 drops. **Fatal time:** 8-12 hours.

Symptoms: Symptoms begin in about half to one hour when drug taken by mouth. There are following three stages. (1) Stage of euphoria: Increased sense of well-being, talkativeness, restlessness, dryness of mouth and throat, flushed face, tachycardia, delirium, paranoia, children may display convulsions. (2) Stage of stupor: Headache, giddness, fatigue, drowsiness and an uncontrollable desire to sleep, itching of skin, cyanosis of the face and lips, pupils contracted, No effect on respiration and pulse, anuria. (3) Stage of narcosis: The patient becomes comatose and cannot be aroused, muscular flaccidity with areflexia, face dull, cyanosis of lips, dropped jaw, reflexes absent, pupils contracted to pin points, all secretions absent, cold perspiration, slow respiration, about 2-4 per minute, and laboured; blood pressure falls and the pulse becomes slow and weak,. If not treated properly, then pulse becomes irregular and very weak, dyspnea, respiration slow and irregular (cheyne-strokes breathing), apnea and death occurs from asphyxia and respiratory failure.

Diagnosis: The characteristics of opium poisoning are coma, markedly slow respiration and pinpoint or small pupils.

Deferential diagnosis: (1) Apoplexy (2) Compression of the brain (3) Renal failure (4) Intoxication of carbolic acid (5) Alcoholism(6) diabetic or post epilepsy coma (7) Barbiturate poisoning.

Treatment: (1) The stomach must be washed out as the drug is also excreted into the stomach. Dilute potassium permagnate solution (1:10000) is used and lavage continued till the returning fluid is of the same colour. (2) Naloxone 0.8-2 mg IV, repeated at intervals of 2-3 minutes to a maximum of 10 mg, should improve respiration; if not, question the diagnosis. (3) Body warmth should be maintained by hot water bottles and hot drinks as tea or coffee. (4) Nikathamide 5-15 ml, intramuscularly or intravenously should given as a respiratory stimulant. (5) Nalorphine hydrobromide (N-allylmorphine) 5-10 mg, which has a partial antagonistic action, should given intramuscularly as required at intervals of 10 to 15 minutes. It is an effective antidote. (6) These cardiac stimulants can be used as *'Siddha makardhwaj'* or *'Vrihat kasturibhairava rasa'* or *'Rasa sindoora rasa'* 125 mg, with *'Khamira marvarid khas'* or *'Khamira gavajavan ambari'* 5 g, as required. (7) Oxygen inhalation if necessary.

Clinical uses: Acute rheumatic arthritis: Fruit gum of described plant 50 mg, root powder of *Calotropis procera* 250 mg, Soda bi carb 1 g, with water, two times a day, is beneficial. **Pain of piles, bleeding piles:** Local application of paste of fruit gum of described plant 12 g, *Quercus infectoria* 50 g, washed clarified butter or Vaseline 200 g, is beneficial. **Diarrhea with flatulence:** Mix powder of fruit gum of described plant 25 mg, *Cinamomum camphora* 50 mg, *Zingiber officinale* 500 mg, with water or whey, three times a day, is useful. **Abortion, miscarriage:** Enema of tincture of fruit gum of described plant, 25 drops, with water 100 ml, is useful. **Nocturnal emission, spermatorrhea, premature ejaculation:** Mix powder of fruit gum of described plant 2 parts, *Cinamomum camphora, Piper cubeba* 6 parts, *Curcuma longa* 12 parts, sugar candy powder 25 parts, dose 2 g, with water, at night, is beneficial.

Formulations: *Ahifenaasava, Karpoor rasa, Dugdha vati, Aakaarkarbhaadi vati, Jaatiphalaadi vati, Nidrodaya vati, Nidrodaya rasa, Swalpa grahanikapaat rasa.*

Recommended readings

Acharya, B.K. (2008), Ayurveda Jadi-buti Rahasya, Patanjali Yogapitha, Haridwar, PP. 22.

Bhutya, R.K. (2007), Vanaspati Aushadha Vigyana, Scientific Publishers (India), Jodhpur, PP. 12.

Brahmavarchas (2003), Ayurved Ka Pran Vanoshadhi Vigyan, Shanti Kunj, Haridwar, PP. 334.

Chunekar, K.C. (2004), Bhava Prakash Nighantu, Chaukhambha Bharti Academy, Varanasi, PP. 145.

Khare, C.P. (2007), Indian Medicinal Plants, Springer (India) P.L. New Delhi, PP. 462.

Kirtikar, K.R. & Basu, B.D. (1998), Indian Medicinal Plants, L.M Basu, Allahabad, Vol. 1, PP. 126.

Misra, B.L. (2005), Dravya Guna Hastamalaka, Publication scheme, Jaipur, PP. 428.

Nair, R.Vasudevan, (2007), Indian Medicinal Plants, Orient Longman P.L. Chennai, Vol. 4, PP. 214.

Pareek, G.N. (2005), Sudhanidhi, Vanoshadhi Ratnakar, Dhanvantari Karyalaya, Aligarh, Vol. 1, PP. 255.

Prajapati, N.D., Purohit, S.S., Sharma, A.K. & Tarun Kumar (2003), A Hand Book of Medicinal Plants, Agrobios India, Jodhpur, PP. 381.

Sharma, P.C., Yelne, MB. & Denis, T.J. (2000), Database on medicinal plants used in ayurveda, Central Council for research in Ayurveda and siddha, Vol. 8, PP. 1.

Sharma, P.V. (1981), Dravya gun vigyana, Chaukhambha Bharti Academy, Varanasi, Vol. 1, PP. 19.

Singh, R.S. (2002), Vanoshadhi Nirdeshika, Uttar Pradesh Hindi Sansthan, Lucknow, PP. 20.

Swami, K.N. (1985), Gavon Main Aushadh Ratna, Kalera Krishana Gopal, Kalera (Raj.), Vol. 1, PP. 21, 162.

347. *Parmelia perlata* (Huds) Ach.

Family: Parmeliaceae.

Other similar plants: *P.perforata, P.kamtschadalis.*

Name: English: Stone Flowers, **Sanskrit:** *Sheleya, Shilaapushpa, Vriddha, Kaalaanusaaryaka,* **Hindi:** *Chharilaa,* **Local:** *Chharilla.*

Botanical characteristics: Habit: The vegetative body of lichen (thallus) is flat, growing in rosettes or irregularly spreading over the substratum giving the appearance of a flower-hence the name 'stone flower'. It is mainly composed of fungal mycelia which form a network enclosing algal cells or gonidia. Reproduction is by means of spores or soredia, which are dispersed by wind, water or insects. When deposited on suitable sustrata they develop in to new lichen thalli. When dry, upper surface becomes black and lower surface silvery white.

Habitat: On the rock hills and sometimes on tree trunks, in Himalaya, Punjab and Kashmir.

Parts used: Thallus. **Dosage:** 2-4 g.

Collection period: May-June.

Ayurvedic properties: ***Ras:*** *tikta, kashaaya,* ***Gun:*** *laghu, snigdha,* ***Veerya:*** *sheeta* ***Vipaka:*** *katu,* ***Tridosha*** **Effect:** alleviates ***Kapha:*** ++, ***Pitta:*** ++.

Chemical constituents: The **plant** contains lecanoric acid and atranorin.

Action and disease indications: The **Plant** is refrigerant, fragrant, anti-inflammatory, emollient, vulnerary, diuretic, lithontriptic, alterant, anodyne, anti-pruritic, digestive, carminative, constipating, cardio-tonic, febrifuge, aphrodisiac and detergent, used for inflammations, strangury, renal and vesical calculi, pruritus, cephalgia, skin diseases, wounds, ulcers, dyspepsia, vomiting, heptodynia, uteralgia, diarrhea, dysentery, cough, asthma, bronchitis, cardiac debility, fever, seminal weakness and amenorrhea.

Clinical uses: Anuria, dysuria, renal and vesical calculus, strangury: Decoction of described plant, 10 g, with *Cuminum cyminum* 1 g and sugar candy powder 10 g, two times a day, is beneficial. **Headache:** Fumigation of smoke of described plant, and local application of paste of described plant, is beneficial. **Orchitis, itching:** Local application of paste of described plant, is beneficial. **Pyrexia, burning sensation, liver pain:** Cold infusion of described plant, 10 g, two times a day, is beneficial.

Formulations: *Agaraadi dhupa, Naaraayan taila, Dhulep.*

Recommended readings:

Bhutya, R.K. (2007), Vanaspati Aushadha Vigyana, Scientific Publishers (India), Jodhpur, PP. 100.

Chunekar, K.C. (2004), Bhava Prakash Nighantu, Chaukhambha Bharti Academy, Varanasi, PP. 242.

Khare, C.P. (2007), Indian Medicinal Plants, Springer (India) P.L. New Delhi, PP. 464.

Kirtikar, K.R. & Basu, B.D. (1998), Indian Medicinal Plants, L.M Basu, Allahabad, Vol. 4, PP. 2760.

Misra, B.L. (2005), Dravya Guna Hastamalaka, Publication scheme, Jaipur, PP. 496.

Nair, R.Vasudevan, (2007), Indian Medicinal Plants, Orient Longman P.L. Chennai, Vol. 4, PP. 223.

Namjoshi, A.N. (2001), The Ayurvedic Pharmacopoeia of India, Government of India, Department of Indian Systems of Medicine & Homoeopathy, New Delhi, Part-1, Volume- 3, PP. 172.

Sharma, P.V. (1981), Dravya gun vigyana, Chaukhambha Bharti Academy, Varanasi, Vol. 1, PP. 725.

Singh, R.S. (2002), Vanoshadhi Nirdeshika, Uttar Pradesh Hindi Sansthan, Lucknow, PP. 155.

Swami, K.N. (1985), Gavon Main Aushadh Ratna, Kalera Krishana Gopal, Kalera (Raj.), Vol. 2, PP. 288.

348. *Pavonia odorata* Willd.

Family: Malvaceae.

Name: English: Fragrant Sticky Mallow, **Sanskrit:** *Baal, Hriber, Barhistha, Udichya,* **Hindi:** *Netrabaala, Sugandhabaala,* **Local:** *Sugandhabaala.*

Botanical characteristics: Habit: An erect branching annual herb, height 45-90 cm. **Root:** 15-20 cm long, 0.8 cm thick, glabrous, brown, tortuous, aromatic. **Stem:** Covered with soft viscous pubescence and a few longer hairs. **Leaf:** Roundish, ovate, cordate, 2.5-7.5 cm long, 3-5 lobed, dentate or the lower ones entire, stellate-hairy on both surfaces, often felted and whitish beneath; lower petioles longer than the blades. **Flower:** Pale pink or white, peduncles as long as the leaves, 1-flowered, clustered at the ends of the branches. Bracteoles 10-12, sepals lanceolate, corolla pale pink or white, twice the length of calyx. Carples gibbous on their backs, wingless unarmed, dehiscent. **Fruit:** Ovate, small, size like Gram. **Seed:** Brown, oily, fibrous, without smell.

Flowering and fruiting period: October-November and December-January.

Habitat: North-West India, Bundelkhand, Bengal, Konkan and West Rajasthan.

Parts used: Root. **Dosage:** 3-6 g.

Collection period: February-March.

Ayurvedic properties: ***Ras:*** *tikta, kashaaya,* ***Gun:*** *laghu, rukhsa,* ***Veerya:*** *sheeta* ***Vipaka:*** *katu,* ***Tridosha*** **Effect:** alleviates ***Pitta:*** +++, ***Vaata:*** ++.

Chemical constituents: The **roots** contain an essential oil containing isovaleric acid, isovaleraldehyde, armomadendrene, pavonene, alpha-terpinene, azulene and pavonenol.

Action and disease indications: The **roots** are stomachic, appetizer, strengthener, refrigerant, astringent, demulcent and tonic, used for dysentery, intestinal haemorrhages, ptyalism, vomiting, thirst, skin eruptions, fever, asthma, ulcers and bleeding disorders.

Clinical uses: Pyrexia, epistaxis, burning sensation, dispesis, nausea, vomiting, diarrhea, erysipelas: Decoction of mix powder of described plant, *Cyperus scarissus, Fumaria indica, Vetiveria zizaniodes, Santalum album, Zingiber officinale,* 10 g, three times a day, is useful. **Sprue:** Root powder of described plant 5 g, unripe fruit pulp of *Aegle marmelos* 3 g, two times a day, is beneficial. **Epistaxis:** Root powder of described plant 3 g, *Santalum album* 1 g, sugar candy powder 10 g, with rice water 20 ml, two times a day, is beneficial. **Erysipelas:** Local application of paste of root of described plant, two times a day, is beneficial.

Formulations: *Shadanga paaniya, Chandana-asava, Dashamoolaarista, Vrihat kastooribhairava rasa, Kiraataadi taila.*

Recommended readings:

Bhutya, R.K. (2007), Vanaspati Aushadha Vigyana, Scientific Publishers (India), Jodhpur, PP. 142.

Chunekar, K.C. (2004), Bhava Prakash Nighantu, Chaukhambha Bharti Academy, Varanasi, PP. 237.

Khare, C.P. (2007), Indian Medicinal Plants, Springer (India) P.L. New Delhi, PP. 468.

Kirtikar, K.R. & Basu, B.D. (1998), Indian Medicinal Plants, L.M Basu, Allahabad, Vol. 1, PP. 323.

Misra, B.L. (2005), Dravya Guna Hastamalaka, Publication scheme, Jaipur, PP. 309.

Sharma, P.V. (1981), Dravya gun vigyana, Chaukhambha Bharti Academy, Varanasi, Vol. 1, PP. 64.

349. *Pedalium murex* Linn.

Family: Pedaliaceae.

Ayurvedic Groups: Charak: *Mutravirechaniya, Shothahar, Krimighna, Anuvaasanopaga,* **Sushruta:** *Vidaarigandhaadi, Veertarvaadi, Laghupanchamoola, Kantaka panchamoola, Vaataasmari bhedan.*

Name: English: Caltrops (Bigger var.), **Sanskrit:** *Gokhsuraka, Trikantaka, Swadukantaka, Gokantaka, Swadanstraa, Palankashaa, Vanshrangaata, Ikhsugandhikaa,* **Hindi:** *Gokharu Baraa,* **Local:** *Baara Gokharu, Dakhani Gokharu.*

Botanical characteristics: Habit: A much branched, glabrous, annual, foetid smelling succulent herb, height 15-38 cm. **Stem:** Stem and branches often slightly rough with scaly glands. **Leaf:** Opposite, simple, pale glacous-green, somewhat fleshy, 2.5-5 by 2-3.8 cm, broadly ovate-oblong, truncate or obtuse, coarsely crenate-serrate or sub-lobate, glabrous above, the lower side usually covered with minute scales, base acute; petioles 6-20 mm long. **Flower:** Bright yellow, axillary or solitary, pedicels 4 mm long, 2 cm across the mouth. **Fruit:** 1.3-2 cm long, narrowed at the base, pyramidal-ovoid above the spines, bluntly 4-angled with stout, sharp, conical horizontal spines from the angles, 2-chambered. **Seed:** 2-2 in each chamber, oblong and pendulous.

Flowering and fruiting period: July-August and September-October.

Habitat: Throughout the plains of India, especially in the coastal areas of South India.

Parts used: Root, Fruit, whole parts.

Dosage: Root, Fruit 2-5 g, whole parts 5-10 g.

Collection period: October-November.

Ayurvedic properties: ***Ras:*** *madhur,* ***Gun:*** *guru, snigdha,* ***Veerya:,*** *sheeta,* ***Vipaka:*** *madhur* ***Tridosha*** **Effect:** alleviates ***Vaata:*** **+++,** ***Pitta:*** ++.

Chemical constituents: The **stem** and **fruits** contain flavonoids pedalitin, and its glucoside (pedaliin), diometin, dinatin and its derivatives. The **Fruits** contain nonacosane, tritriacontane, triacontanoic acid, sitosterol, beta-D-glucoside, rubusic acid, luteolin. The **leaves** and **fruits** contain phenolic acid, which include caffeic, protocatechuic, *p*-coumaric and ferulic acids. The **flowers** gave dinatin, quercetin and quercetin-7-glucoside. The solubility of uric acid in aqueous extract is reported to be 45% more than water alone.

Action and disease indications: The **plant** is refrigerant, mucilaginous, diuretic, lithontriptic, anti-spasmodic, aphrodisiac, emmenogogue, anti-inflammatory, carminative,, digestive, rejuvenating and tonic, prescribed for renal and vesical calculi, strangury, aphthae, spermato-rrhea, spasmodic, affections, dysmenorrhea, amenorrhea, inflammations, dyspepsia, flatulence, spleenomegaly, fevers, ulcers and general debility.

Clinical uses: Nocturnal emission, sexual debility, lack of control of urination: Cold infusion of roots and flowers of described plant, 10 g, with honey 10 g, is useful. **Enlargement of liver and spleen:** Decoction of described plant, 10 g, or juice of described plant, 10-20 ml, two times a day, is beneficial. **Gonorrhea:** Cold infusion of fresh plant, 15 g, or decoction of fruits of described plant 10g, *Cyperus scarissus* 2 g, *Glycyrrhiza glabra* 1 g, two times a day, is beneficial. **For rejuvenating, spermacresia:** Fruit powder of described plant, 3 g, *Tinospora cordifolia* 2g, *Phylanthus emblica* 3 g, with milk, two times a day, is beneficial. **Leucorrhea:** Fruit powder of described plant, 6 g, with clarified butter of cow 10 g, and milk, two times a day, is beneficial.

Formulations: *Chyavanpraasha, Dashamoola kwaatha, Gokhsuraadi kwaatha, Gokhsuraadi guggulu, Dashamoolaarista.*

Recommended readings:

Bhutya, R.K. (2007), Vanaspati Aushadha Vigyana, Scientific Publishers (India), Jodhpur, PP. 88.

Brahmavarchas (2003), Ayurved Ka Pran Vanoshadhi Viyan, Shanti Kunj, Haridwar, PP. 336.

Chunekar, K.C. (2004), Bhava Prakash Nighantu, Chaukhambha Bharti Academy, Varanasi, PP. 293.

Dhiman, A.K. (2006), Ayurvedic Drug Plants, Daya Publishing House, Delhi, PP. 72.

Khare, C.P. (2007), Indian Medicinal Plants, Springer (India) P.L. New Delhi, PP. 468.

Kirtikar, K.R. & Basu, B.D. (1998), Indian Medicinal Plants, L.M Basu, Allahabad, Vol. 3, PP. 1856.

Misra, B.L. (2005), Dravya Guna Hastamalaka, Publication scheme, Jaipur, PP. 499.

Nair, R.Vasudevan, (2007), Indian Medicinal Plants, Orient Longman P.L. Chennai, Vol. 4, PP. 230.

Prajapati, N.D., Purohit, S.S., Sharma, A.K. & Tarun Kumar (2003), A Hand Book of Medicinal Plants, Agrobios India, Jodhpur, PP. 385.

Sharma, P.V. (1981), Dravya gun vigyana, Chaukhambha Bharti Academy, Varanasi, Vol. 1, PP. 632.

Singh, R.S. (2002), Vanoshadhi Nirdeshika, Uttar Pradesh Hindi Sansthan, Lucknow, PP. 139.

Swami, K.N. (1985), Gavon Main Aushadh Ratna, Kalera Krishana Gopal, Kalera (Raj.), Vol. 2, PP. 256.

350. *Peganum harmala* Linn.

Family: Zygophylaceae.

Name: English: Wild Rue; Foreign Henna, Syrian Rue, **Hindi:** *Harmal,* **Local:** *Isabanda Lahori.*

Botanical characteristics: Habit: A perennial branching herb, height 30-90 cm. **Stem:** Dicotomously and corymbosely branched. **Leaf:** Alternate, 5-7.5 cm long, multifid, the segments narrow, linear, acute. **Flower:** White, 2-2.5 cm across, solitary, sessile or pedicelled, sepal narrow, linear, acute, usually extending the petals, petals white, elliptic-oblong. **Fruit:** Capsule, globose, 4.5-8 mm diam., deeply lobed, veined, glabrous, trilobed. **Seed:** 1 seed in each lobe, 3-angled, grey.

Flowering and fruiting period: September-October and November-December.

Habitat: Throughout Northern and Northwestern India, and in drier regions of Deccan. Mostly in Punjab, Kashmir, Kaccha, Delhi, Bihar, Uttar Pradesh and Konkan.

Parts used: Seed. **Dosage:** 2-4 g.

Collection period: November-December.

Ayurvedic properties: ***Ras:*** *tikta, katu,* ***Gun:*** *laghu, rukhsa,* ***Veerya:*** *ushna,* ***Vipaka:*** *katu,* ***Tridosha*** **Effect:** alleviates ***Kapha:*** **++,** ***Vaata:*** **++,** aggravates ***Pitta:*** **+++.**

Chemical constituents: The **seeds** and **aerial parts** contain alkaloids- harmine, haemaline and harmalol. Other are vasicinone, deoxyvasicinone and 8-hydroxy glucosylhsrmine. The **plant** contain flavonoids-kaempferol, quercetin and acacetin.

Action and disease indications: The **seeds** are thermogenic, narcotic, hypnotic, coronary dilators, embolic, anti-tumour, hypertensive, anti-fungal, anti-bacterial, anti-fungal, anti-spasmodic, anodyne, aphrodisiac, galactagogue, carminative, anthelmintic, abortifacient and emetic, used for asthma, hiccough, colic, neuralgia, hysteria and dysmenorrhea.

Clinical uses: Neuralgia, sciatica: Local application of paste of seeds of described plant is beneficial. **Wounds:** Seed powder of described plant, with oil of *Sesamum orientale* is beneficial. **Renal and vesical calculus, anuria:** Seed powder of described plant 2 g, with water, two times a day, is beneficial.

Recommended readings:

Bhutya, R.K. (2007), Vanaspati Aushadha Vigyana, Scientific Publishers (India), Jodhpur, PP. 236.

Chunekar, K.C. (2004), Bhava Prakash Nighantu, Chaukhambha Bharti Academy, Varanasi, PP. 842.

Khare, C.P. (2007), Indian Medicinal Plants, Springer (India) P.L. New Delhi, PP. 470.

Kirtikar, K.R. & Basu, B.D. (1998), Indian Medicinal Plants, L.M Basu, Allahabad, Vol. 1, PP. 456.

Misra, B.L. (2005), Dravya Guna Hastamalaka, Publication scheme, Jaipur, PP. 361.

Prajapati, N.D., Purohit, S.S., Sharma, A.K. & Tarun Kumar (2003), A Hand Book of Medicinal Plants, Agrobios India, Jodhpur, PP. 385.

Sharma, P.V. (1981), Dravya gun vigyana, Chaukhambha Bharti Academy, Varanasi, Vol. 1, PP. 607.

Singh, R.S. (2002), Vanoshadhi Nirdeshika, Uttar Pradesh Hindi Sansthan, Lucknow, PP. 401.

Swami, K.N. (1985), Gavon Main Aushadh Ratna, Kalera Krishana Gopal, Kalera (Raj.), Vol. 3, PP. 395.

351. *Pentapetus phoenicea* Linn.

Family: Sterculiaceae.

Name: English: Noon-Plant, **Sanskrit:** *Bandhooka, Bandhujiva, Rakta,* **Hindi:** *Dupahariaa,* **Local:** *Dupahariaa, Gojuniaa.*

Botanical characteristics: Habit: A pretty branched annual herb or shrub, height 0.6-1.5 m, growing in marshy and wet places. **Stem:** Glabrous or with a few scattered stellate hairs. **Leaf:** 7.5-13 cm long, lanceolate, sharply toothed or crenate-serrate, with only a primary nerve. **Flower:** Red or scarlet, large, pendulous, solitary or in pairs on short penducles, blooming at noon and closing at the following dawn. Sepals stellate and bristly. **Fruit:** Capsule, 5-chambered, sub-globose, bristly, axis wooly. **Seed:** 8-12 in each chamber, sub-globose, dotted.

Flowering and fruiting period: September-October and November-December.

Habitat: Throughout North-West India, in ponds and with Rice plants, also cultivated as an ornamental throughout the hotter parts of India.

Parts used: Root, flower, fruit.

Dosage: Root, flower, fruit 3-6 g.

Collection period: September-December.

Ayurvedic properties: ***Ras:*** *tikta, kashaaya,* ***Gun:*** *laghu, snigdha,* ***Veerya:*** *sheeta,* ***Vipaka:*** *katu,* ***Tridosha*** **Effect:** alleviates, ***Vaata: ++, Pitta: ++***, aggrevates ***Kapha:*** +.

Action and disease indications: The **fruits** are refrigerant, mucilaginous, emollient, used for bowels diseases and fevers. The **roots** are astringent, anti-bilious, emollient, digestive, diuretic, expectorant, anti-phlegmonous, febrifuge, and constipating, used for fever, burning sensation, diarrhea, leucoderma, skin diseases, cough, asthma, bronchitis, otalgia, vomiting, heptomegaly and psychopathy.

Clinical uses: Skin diseases: Local application of paste of described plant is beneficial. **Otalgia:** Warm juice of described plant, 4-4 drops, in the ear, two times a day, is beneficial. **Asthma, bronchitis:** Root powder of described plant, 3 g, with honey 10 g, three times a day, is useful.

Recommended readings:

Bhutya, R.K. (2007), Vanaspati Aushadha Vigyana, Scientific Publishers (India), Jodhpur, PP. 126.

Chunekar, K.C. (2004), Bhava Prakash Nighantu, Chaukhambha Bharti Academy, Varanasi, PP. 506.

Khare, C.P. (2007), Indian Medicinal Plants, Springer (India) P.L. New Delhi, PP. 471.

Kirtikar, K.R. & Basu, B.D. (1998), Indian Medicinal Plants, L.M Basu, Allahabad, Vol. 1, PP. 376.

Nair, R.Vasudevan, (2007), Indian Medicinal Plants, Orient Longman P.L. Chennai, Vol. 4, PP. 233.

Prajapati, N.D., Purohit, S.S., Sharma, A.K. & Tarun Kumar (2003), A Hand Book of Medicinal Plants, Agrobios India, Jodhpur, PP. 385.

352. *Pergularia daemia* (Forsk.) Chiov.

Family: Asclepiadaceae; Pariplocaceae.

Synonym: *P. extensa.*

Name: English: Hairknot Plant, Whitlow Plant, **Sanskrit:** *Uttamaarani, Indivari, Vrischikaali,* **Hindi:** *Utaran,* **Local:** *Utaran.*

Botanical characteristics: Habit: A perennial slender foul smelling milky twining herb. **Stem:** Clothed with spreading hairs. **Leaf:** simple, opposite, thin, 5-10 by 3.8-9 cm, broadly ovate or sub-orbicular cordate, acuminate, glabrous or more or less shortly pubescent above, velvety pubescent beneath, margins ciliate, petioles 2-6.3 cm long. **Flower:** Greenish-yellow or dull white, tinged with purple, in axillary long peduncled umbellate or corymbose clusters. Peduncle pubescent, 7.5-15 cm long, pedicels capillary, 2-3.2 cm long, pubescent, bracts minute, lanceolate, acute. **Fruit:** Follicles, reflexed, 5-7.5 by 1.3 cm, lanceolate, with long beak and soft spines. **Seed:** Numerous, ovate, truncate at the apex, densely velvety-pubescent on both sides, narrowly margined, crenate at the rounded base; coma 2.5-3.2 cm long.

Flowering and fruiting period: February-March and April-May.

Habitat: Throughout hotter parts of India.

Parts used: Whole plant. **Dosage:** 10-20 g.

Collection period: April-May.

Ayurvedic properties: ***Ras:*** *tikta, kashaaya,* ***Gun:*** *laghu, rukhsa,* ***Veerya:*** *ushna,* ***Vipaka:*** *katu,* ***Tridosha*** **Effect:** alleviates ***Vaata:*** **++,** ***Kapha:*** +.

Chemical constituents: The **plant** contain betaine, a polypeptide, hentriacontane, lupeol, alpha and beta-amyrin, beta-sitosterol. The seeds and stem contain cardenolides-calactin, calotropin, calotrppagenin, uzarigenin and coroglaucigenin. The plant extract exhibits stimulating action on uterine and other involuntary muscles, useful inuterine and menstrual disorders and in facilitating parturition. The extracts cause rise in arterial blood pressure, increase in movement and tone of urinary bladder and stimulation of gastric secretions. An aqueous extract of leaves shows anti-bacterial activity against *E.coli* and *Micrococcus pyogenes* var. *aureus.*

Action and disease indications: The **Plant** is thermogenic, uterine stimulant, tones up urinary bladder, stimulates gastric secretion, expectorant, emetic, emmenogogue, anthelmintic, anti-pyretic and laxative, used for dysmenorrhea, amenorrhea, urethrorrhoea, strangury, metropathy, inflammations, cough, asthma, bronchitis, intermittent fevers and leucoderma. The **leaves** are thermogenic, anthelmintic and depurative, used for helminthiasis, piles, leprosy and carbuncles. The **fruits** are thermogenic and digestive, used for dyspepsia.

Clinical uses: Boils, abscess: Poultice of leaves of described plant, is useful. **Rheumatism:** Root bark powder of described plant, 3 g, with milk, two times a day, is beneficial.

Recommended readings:

Bhutya, R.K. (2007), Vanaspati Aushadha Vigyana, Scientific Publishers (India), Jodhpur, PP. 31.

Chunekar, K.C. (2004), Bhava Prakash Nighantu, Chaukhambha Bharti Academy, Varanasi, PP. 813.

Khare, C.P. (2007), Indian Medicinal Plants, Springer (India) P.L. New Delhi, PP. 472.

Kirtikar, K.R. & Basu, B.D. (1998), Indian Medicinal Plants, L.M Basu, Allahabad, Vol. 2, PP. 1616.

Nair, R.Vasudevan, (2007), Indian Medicinal Plants, Orient Longman P.L. Chennai, Vol. 4, PP. 236.

Prajapati, N.D., Purohit, S.S., Sharma, A.K. & Tarun Kumar (2003), A Hand Book of Medicinal Plants, Agrobios India, Jodhpur, PP. 386.

353. *Peristrophe bicalyculata* (Retz.) Nees.

Family: Acanthaceae.

Similar plant: 1. *Vitex penducularis* Wall. (Verbanaceae) *Chiraigoda, Mijurgorba,* found in Assam, Bihar, Madhya Pradesh and Bengal,- a tree height up to 7.5m, flower white 3 foliate. 2. *Leea hirta* Roxb. (Vitaceae), found in Sikkim, Assam, Bengal, Andamans, a shrub, height up to 1.2-3 m, flower white.

Name: Sanskrit: *Nadikantaa, Kaktiktaa, Sulomashaa, Kaakaa, Paaraavatpadi, Praachi, Balaa,* **Hindi:** *Kaakjangha,* **Local:** *Kaakjangha, Masi, Kaala, Andhijhaaraa.*

Botanical characteristics: Habit: An annual erect herb, height 90-180 cm. **Stem:** Herbaceous, erect, usually 6 angular, solid, branched, rough, green, more or less hairy, nodes swollen. **Leaf:** Ovate, acuminate, densely lineolate, more or less hairy above, base usually rounded, 5-7.5 cm long and 2.5-3.8 cm wide, petiole 6-15 mm long. **Flower:** Small, rosy or purple, nearly 1.5 cm long, complete, pentamerous. **Fruit:** Capsule, 4 seeded, purple beaked, size 2.5 by 3 mm, narrowed into a cylindrical stalk 2.5 cm long, pointed, pubescent. **Seed:** 2.5-3 mm diam., orbicular or round, papillose, slightly rugose, pale-brown or white, like seeds of *Capsicum annum.*

Flowering and fruiting period: November-December and January-February.

Habitat: Distributed Throughout India.

Parts used: Whole plant, root.

Dosage: Plant 5-10 g, root 1-5 g.

Collection period: January-February.

Ayurvedic properties: ***Ras:*** *tikta, kashaaya,* ***Gun:*** *laghu, rukhsa, sara, picchila,* ***Veerya:*** *sheet,* ***Vipaka:*** *katu,* ***Tridosha*** **Effect:** alleviates ***Kapha:*** ++, ***Pitta:*** +.

Chemical constituents: **Flowers** contain petunidin-3-rhamnoglucoside; **Aerial parts** contain 14-methyl-tritriacont-14-en-15-ol, 35-hydroxynonatricontanol.

Action and disease indications: **Plant** is febrifuge, anti toxic, used for tuberculosis, leucorrhoea, otorrhea, fevers, hemoptysis, ulcers, pruritis, intestinal worms. **Root** used for insomnia, fear psychosis in children and snake bite.

Clinical uses: Leucorrhea: Plant juice 25 ml, with stem bark powder of *Symplocos racemosa* 3 g, with honey 10 g, 3 times a day. Or powder of plant 3 g, with rice water 100 ml, 2 times a day.

Tinnitus, lack of audibility: 4-4 drops of juice of plant, as ear drops, 2 times a day. **Ulcers, otopyorrhea:** Local application of medicated oil made with juice and paste of described plant.

Formulations: *Mahaa vishagarbha taila, Aaragvadhaadi kwaatha churna, Paniyakasara, Sphatikaadi churna.*

Recommended readings:

Bhutya, R.K. (2007), Vanaspati Aushadha Vigyana, Scientific Publishers (India), Jodhpur, PP. 57.

Chunekar, K.C. (2004), Bhava Prakash Nighantu, Chaukhambha Bharti Academy, Varanasi, PP. 441.

Khare, C.P. (2007), Indian Medicinal Plants, Springer (India) P.L. New Delhi, PP. 473.

Kirtikar, K.R. & Basu, B.D. (1998), Indian Medicinal Plants, L.M Basu, Allahabad, Vol. 3, PP. 1910.

Pareek, G.N. (2005), Sudhanidhi, Vanoshadhi Ratnakar, Dhanvantari Karyalaya, Aligarh, Vol. 9, PP. 200.

Sharma, P.C., Yelne, MB. & Denis, T.J. (2000), Database on medicinal plants used in ayurveda, Central Council for research in Ayurveda and siddha, Vol. 6, PP. 74.

Swami, K.N. (1985), Gavon Main Aushadh Ratna, Kalera Krishana Gopal, Kalera (Raj.), Vol. 2, PP. 173.

354. *Phaseolus mungo* Linn. non-Roxb. & Auct.

Family: Papilionaceae; Fabaceae.

Synonym: *Vigna mungo.*

Other similar plant: *P. rediatus.*

Name: English: Kidney Bean, Black Gram, **Sanskrit:** *Maasha,* **Hindi:** *Urada,* **Local:** *Urada.*

Botanical characteristics: Habit: An erect or sub-erect hairy annual herb, 30-90 cm high, diffusely spreading hairy, whole plant much more hairy with reddish brown pubescence which gives the foliage a lighter tint. **Stem:** With long twining branches, longer and more trailing than those of the *P.rediatus.* **Leaf:** Alternate, trifoliate, leaflets elliptic-ovate or oblong-lanceolate, apex acute or acuminate, entire, 5-10 cm long. **Flower:** Yellow, small, bisexual, terminal, usually 8-12 on 10-15 cm long peduncle. **Fruit:** Pods, 3-5 cm long, cylindrical, very hairy, terete with a short, hooked beak. **Seed:** 10-15 per pod, oblong with square ends, about 3 mm long, larger and longer than those of the *P.rediatus*, black or greenish-black with a white hilum.

Flowering and fruiting period: September-October and November-December

Habitat: Cultivated vastly throughout India, as a major pulse crop.

Parts used: seed. **Dosage:** 10-20 g.

Collection period: November-December.

Ayurvedic properties: ***Ras:*** *madhur,* ***Gun:*** *guru, snigdha,* ***Veerya:*** *ushna,* ***Vipaka:*** *madhur* ***Tridosha*** **Effect:** alleviates ***Vaata:*** +++, aggrevates ***Kapha:*** ++, ***Pitta:*** ++.

Chemical constituents: The **seeds** contain genistein, kievitone, dalbergioidin, cyclokievitone, isoferreirin, eurenol, glycinol, demethylvestitol, kievitone hydrate, cyclokievitone hydrate, hemicellulose A, hemicellulose pectin, starch and hexosans. It contains protein about 24, fat 1.2, fibres 0.8-4.1, carbohtdrate 56.7-59.9%. Also calcium 154, Phosphorus 385, iron 9.1, magnesium 185, sodium 39.8, potassium 800, copper 0.72, sulpher 174 mg/100g and 2.2% fixed oil.

Action and disease indications: The **seeds** are thermogenic, emollient, diuretic, aphrodisiac, tonic, nutritious, galactagogue, demulcent, appetizer, laxative and nervine tonic, used for dyspepsia, anorexia, seminal weakness, bell's palsy, strangury, constipation, piles, heptomegaly, abdominal pain, asthma, neuropathy and agalactia. The **roots** are narcotic, used for ostalgia, abscess and inflammations.

Clinical uses: Arthralgia, bell's palsy: Root powder of described plant, 5 g, with *'Dashamoola kwatha'* 20 g, two times a day, is beneficial. **Bell's palsy, paralysis, neuralgia:** Decoction of mix powder of seeds of described plant, *Abutilon indicum, Mucana pruriens,* roots of *Cymbopogon martinii, Pluchea lanceolata, Withania somnifera,* bark of *Ricinus communis,* 25 g, with Rock salt 1 g and fried gum of *Ferula* *narthex* 125 mg, two times a day, is beneficial. Local application of warm paste of mix powder of seeds of described plant, leaves of *Pluchea lanceolata,* root of *Zizyphus nummularia,* seeds of *Macrotyloma uniflorum,* heart wood of *Cedrus deodara,* seeds of *Linum usitatissimum,* seeds of *Sesamum orientale,* seeds of *Ricinus communis,* roots of *Saussurea costus,* roots of *Acorus calamus,* seeds of *Hordeum vulgare,* with *'Kanji'* is also beneficial. **Sermacresia, somasthenia, general debility:** (1) Mix powder of seeds of described plant 80 parts, *Prunus amyadalus,* 20 parts, seeds of *Mucana pruriens* 10 parts, roots of *Asparagus racemosus* 10 parts, *Crosus sativus* 1 part, with milk, two times a day, is very beneficial. (2) Mix powder of seeds of described plant 20 parts, seeds of *Mucana pruriens* 20 parts, roots of *Withania somnifera* 1 part, roots of *Asparagus racemosus* 1 part, *Pueraria tuberosa* 1 part, dose 10 g, add *Piper longum* 500 mg and gum of *Bambusa arundinacea* 1 g, with milk, two times a day, is very beneficial. (3) Seeds powder of described plant, 20 g, seeds powder *Oryza sativa* 20 g, fry it in clarified butter, then add sugar powder 10 g, with milk, two times a day, is beneficial.

Formulations: *Maashabalaadi kwaatha, Maashabalaadi taila, Mahaamaasha taila, Siddhamaashaadi yoga, Balaadi taila, Shataavaryaadi ghrita, Maashaadi modaka, Ashok ghrita, Vrihachhaagalaadhya ghrita.*

Recommended readings:

Bhutya, R.K. (2007), Vanaspati Aushadha Vigyana, Scientific Publishers (India), Jodhpur, PP. 179.

Chunekar, K.C. (2004), Bhava Prakash Nighantu, Chaukhambha Bharti Academy, Varanasi, PP. 644.

Dhiman, A.K. (2006), Ayurvedic Drug Plants, Daya Publishing House, Delhi, PP. 256.

Khare, C.P. (2007), Indian Medicinal Plants, Springer (India) P.L. New Delhi, PP. 476.

Kirtikar, K.R. & Basu, B.D. (1998), Indian Medicinal Plants, L.M Basu, Allahabad, Vol. 1, PP. 797.

Nair, R.Vasudevan, (2007), Indian Medicinal Plants, Orient Longman P.L. Chennai, Vol. 5, PP. 367.

Pareek, G.N. (2005), Sudhanidhi, Vanoshadhi Ratnakar, Dhanvantari Karyalaya, Aligarh, Vol. 9, PP. 108.

Prajapati, N.D., Purohit, S.S., Sharma, A.K. & Tarun Kumar (2003), A Hand Book of Medicinal Plants, Agrobios India, Jodhpur, PP. 538.

Sharma, P.C., Yelne, MB. & Denis, T.J. (2000), Database on medicinal plants used in ayurveda, Central Council for research in Ayurveda and siddha, Vol. 8, PP. 241.

Sharma, P.V. (1981), Dravya gun vigyana, Chaukhambha Bharti Academy, Varanasi, Vol. 1, PP. 393.

Swami, K.N. (1985), Gavon Main Aushadh Ratna, Kalera Krishana Gopal, Kalera (Raj.), Vol. 2, PP. 171.

355. *Phaseolus radiatus* Linn. non-Roxb.& Auct

Family: Papilionaceae; Fabaceae.

Synonym: *P. aureus, Vigna radiata.*

Other similar plants: *P. mungo.*

Name: English: Green Gram, Golden Gram, **Sanskrit:** *Mudga,* **Hindi:** *Moonga,* **Local:** *Moonga.*

Botanical characteristics: Habit: An sub-erect herbaceous annual herb, height 40-120 cm. **Stem:** With twining upper branches and clothed with brownish silky hairs. **Leaf:** Trifoliate, leaflets dark green, entire or rarely trilobed, membranous. **Flower:** Yellow, in clusters of 10-25 on long pedicels. **Fruit:** Thin, sub-cylindrical pods, 3.8-6.3 cm long, hairy, curved. **Seed:** 10-15 green, more or less globular.

Flowering and fruiting period: September-October and November-December.

Habitat: Extensively cultivated all over India.

Parts used: Seed. **Dosage:** 10-20 g.

Collection period: November-December.

Ayurvedic properties: ***Ras:*** *madhur,* ***Gun:*** *laghu, rukhsa,* ***Veerya:*** *sheeta* ***Vipaka:*** *katu,* ***Tridosha*** **Effect:** alleviates ***Kapha:*** +++, ***Pitta:*** ++, *aggrevates* ***Vaata:*** ++.

Chemical constituents: The **seeds** contain protein 22, carbohydrate 54-56, fats 1.3-2.7, fibers 4.1-5.8 and ash 3.6-4.4%.

Action and disease indications: The **seeds** are refrigerant, aphrodisiac, diuretic, galactagogue, styptic, constipating, digestive and tonic, strangury, agalactia, piles, epistaxis, skin diseases, scabies, leucoderma, gonorrhea, asthma, vertigo, paralysis, cephalgia, dropsy, neuropathy, ophthalmia, fevers and general debility.

Clinical uses: Pyrexia, abdominal pain: *'Yusha'* of seeds of described plant 50 g, extract of *Acacia catechu* 1 g, two times a day, is beneficial. **Erysipelas:** Decoction of seeds of described plant 20 g, *Trichosanthus dioica* 5 g, *Phylanthus emblica* 5 g, with clarified butter 10 g, two times a day, is beneficial. **Vomiting, dispesis:** Cold infusion of seeds of described plant 20 g, *Piper longum* 1 g, as required. **Bronchitis:** *'Yusha'* of Seeds of described plant, 20 g, with juice of *Solunum surattense* 20 ml, is beneficial. **Excess and turbid micturition, skin diseases:** Seed powder of described plant 10 g, *Phylanthus emblica* 4 g, with water, two times a day, is beneficial. **Epistaxis:** Roasted seeds of *Oryza sativa* 10 g, with *'Yusha'* Of seeds of described plant 20 g, in cold infusion of *Vetiveria zizaniodes* 10 g, two times a day, is beneficial.

Formulations: *Saptamustika yusha, Siddha-parpataka, Pratisaarana, Siddha krisharaa.*

Recommended readings:

Bhutya, R.K. (2007), Vanaspati Aushadha Vigyana, Scientific Publishers (India), Jodhpur, PP. 181.

Chunekar, K.C. (2004), Bhava Prakash Nighantu, Chaukhambha Bharti Academy, Varanasi, PP. 643.

Khare, C.P. (2007), Indian Medicinal Plants, Springer (India) P.L. New Delhi, PP. 477.

Kirtikar, K.R. & Basu, B.D. (1998), Indian Medicinal Plants, L.M Basu, Allahabad, Vol. 1, PP. 795.

Misra, B.L. (2005), Dravya Guna Hastamalaka, Publication scheme, Jaipur, PP. 270.

Nair, R.Vasudevan, (2007), Indian Medicinal Plants, Orient Longman P.L. Chennai, Vol. 5, PP. 374.

Namjoshi, A.N. (2001), The Ayurvedic Pharmacopoeia of India, Government of India, Department of Indian Systems of Medicine & Homoeopathy, New Delhi, Part-1, Volume- 3, PP. 123.

Sharma, P.V. (1981), Dravya gun vigyana, Chaukhambha Bharti Academy, Varanasi, Vol. 2, PP. 169.

356. *Phaseolus trilobus* Sensu Ait. & Auct.

Family: Papilionaceae; Fabaceae.

Synonym: *Vigna trilolobata.*

Other similar plant: *P. trilobus.*

Name: English: Wild Gram, **Sanskrit:** *Mudgaparni, Kaakaparni, Suryaparni, Alpikaa, Sahaa, Kaakamudgaa, Maarjaargandhikaa,* **Hindi:** *Mudgaparni,* **Local:** *Vanmunga, Jangali Munga, Mungavan.*

Botanical characteristics: Habit: An annual or perennial diffuse prostrate or trailing herb. **Stem:** Numerous, from a woody rootstock, 0.6-0.9 m long, with strong wiry branches and slender extensively spreading hairy stem. **Leaf:** 3-foliate, alternate, petioles 3.8-7.5 cm long, grooved, glabrous, or with a few scattered hairs, stipules variable in length, 4-16 mm long, ovate-oblong, sub-acute, ciliate, leaflets large, 1.5-4.5 by 0.8-5.3 cm, membranous, shallowly lobed, middle lobe largest, spathulate, lateral leaflets spathulate with sub-acute or obtuse apex, hairy on both sides, all pale green, glabrous, base sub-acute, petiolules 1.5-2.5 mm long, stiples small, lanceolate, acute. **Flower:** Yellow, in sub-capitate few flowered racemes; peduncle 10-23 cm long, glabrous or sparsely hairy; pedicels 2.5 mm long; bracts ovate, acute deciduous. **Fruit:** Pods, 2.5-5 cm long and 3 mm diam., straight, glabrous or sparingly hairy, sub-cylindrical, slightly curved, pendulous. **Seed:** 6-12 per pods, brownish-black, reniform, shining.

Flowering and fruiting period: September-October and November-December.

Habitat: Throughout India, from West Himalaya to Sikkim, up to an altitude of 2100 m, in open rich soil or wastelands.

Parts used: Whole plant. **Dosage:** 3-5 g.

Collection period: November-December.

Ayurvedic properties: ***Ras:*** *tikta, madhur,* ***Gun:*** *laghu, rukhsa,* ***Veerya:*** *sheeta,* ***Vipaka:*** *madhur* ***Tridosha*** **Effect:** alleviates ***Vaata: +++, Pitta: +++, Kapha: ++.***

Chemical constituents: The **plant** contains friedelin, epifriedelin, stigmasterol and tannins. The **seeds** contain methionine tryptophan, tyrosine, strepogenin, uridine, diphosphate-galacturonic acid. The **seed protein** contained lysine, valine, leucine and phenyl-alanine.

Action and disease indications: The **roots** are aphrodisiac, germicidal, refrigerant, used for cough, fever, diarrhea, piles, ophthalmic disorders, burning sensation, dyspepsia. The **leaves** are sedative, cooling, febrifuge and tonic, used for biliousness, ophthalmia, gout, piles, fevers. The **seeds** are refrigerant, aphrodisiac, ophthalmic, used for fevers, inflammations, consumption, burning sensation, dipsia. The **plant** is anti-pyretic, seminiferous, used for fevers, inflammations, wounds, seminal weakness and tuberculosis.

Clinical uses: General debility: Decoction of described plant, 10 g, with honey 10 g, two times a day, is beneficial. **Rat bite fever:** Decoction of half grinded mix powder described plant, *Vitex negundo, Tinospora cordifolia,* 10 g, with honey 10 g, is beneficial. **Spermacresia:** Decoction of mix powder of described plant, *Teramnus labialis, Desmodium gangaticum,* 15 g, with honey 10 g, two times a day, is beneficial. **Pruritis, scabies:** Local application of paste of seeds of described plant, with urine of cow is beneficial. **Gonorrhea, skin diseases:** Local application of seed oil of described plant is beneficial.

Formulations: *Chyavanpraasha, Balaa ghrita, Vrihat aswagandhaa ghrita, Shataavaryaadi ghrita, Balaa taila, Brahmarasaayan.*

Recommended readings:

Bhutya, R.K. (2007), Vanaspati Aushadha Vigyana, Scientific Publishers (India), Jodhpur, PP. 181.

Brahmavarchas (2003), Ayurved Ka Pran Vanoshadhi Vigyan, Shanti Kunj, Haridwar, PP. 339.

Chunekar, K.C. (2004), Bhava Prakash Nighantu, Chaukhambha Bharti Academy, Varanasi, PP. 297.

Khare, C.P. (2007), Indian Medicinal Plants, Springer (India) P.L. New Delhi, PP. 477.

Kirtikar, K.R. & Basu, B.D. (1998), Indian Medicinal Plants, L.M Basu, Allahabad, Vol. 1, PP. 794.

Misra, B.L. (2005), Dravya Guna Hastamalaka, Publication scheme, Jaipur, PP. 270.

Prajapati, N.D., Purohit, S.S., Sharma, A.K. & Tarun Kumar (2003), A Hand Book of Medicinal Plants, Agrobios India, Jodhpur, PP. 539.

Sharma, P.C., Yelne, MB. & Denis, T.J. (2000), Database on medicinal plants used in ayurveda, Central Council for research in Ayurveda and siddha, Vol. 6, PP. 237.

Sharma, P.V. (1981), Dravya gun vigyana, Chaukhambha Bharti Academy, Varanasi, Vol. 1, PP. 745.

357. *Phoenix dactylifera* Linn.

Family: Palmae; Aracaceae.

Ayurvedic Groups: Charak: *Shramahara, Virechanopaga, Madhurskandha, Kashaayaskandha.*

Other similar plants: *P.sylvestris.*

Name: English: Date Palm, **Sanskrit:** *Pindakharjurikaa,* **Hindi:** *Pinda Kharjoora,* **Local:** *Pinda Khajoora.*

Botanical characteristics: Habit: A tall tree, height 30-36 m and with a thick hemispherical crown. **Stem:** The trunk solitary and covered over by persistent bases of petioles, the base often surrounded by a dense mass of root suckers which is never the case in *P.sylvestris.* **Leaf:** Grey, longer than those of *P.sylvestris,* pinnate, up to 5 m long, pinnae 20-40 by 1.7-2.5 cm, regularly distichous, forming a very acute angle with the petiole, lower pinnae modified into spines, petiole grey, laterally compressed, almost flat. **Flower:** In long spadices, unisexual, male panicles white, compact, 12-23 cm long, on a short peduncle, flowers 6-8 mm long, sweet scented, sheaths outside with rusty down. peduncle of female inflorescence 8-13 mm broad, spikes 30-60 cm long. **Fruit:** Berry, oblong,2.5-7.5 cm long, reddish or yellowish brown when ripe, pulp fleshy, sweet. **Seed:** Cylindric, 1.8 cm long, hard with a longitudinal furrow in front, and a small cylindric, embryo in the middle of the rounded back.

Flowering and fruiting period: May-June and September-October.

Habitat: Cultivated in Punjab and Rajasthan.

Parts used: Fruit.

Dosage: Fresh 10-50 g, Dry 10-15 g.

Collection period: November-December.

Ayurvedic properties: ***Ras:*** *madhur,* ***Gun:*** *guru, snigdha,* ***Veerya:*** *sheeta* ***Vipaka:*** *madhur* ***Tridosha*** **Effect:** alleviates ***Vaata:*** **+++**, ***Pitta:*** ++.

Chemical constituents: The **fruits** contain ascorbic acid (vitamin C), carotene (vitamin A), nicotinic acid, riboflavin, thiamine, sugars (60-80%), besides sucrose and inverted sugars, rhamnose, xylose, arabinose, ribose, galactose and galacturonic acid. The dry date contains protein 2.5-3, fat 0.5, carbohydrates 75.8-82.9% and calcium 35.9, phosphorus 129.3 and iron 3.4 mg/100g. Presence of sterols of ergesterol group, and esterone has been reported from dried date seeds.

Action and disease indications: The **fruits** are refrigerant, anti-tussive, expectorant, demulcent, laxative, diuretic, restorative, fattening, aphrodisiac, alexiteric, used for thirst, asthma, seminal weakness, penile dysfunction, bronchitis, fatigue, tuberculosis, fever, vomiting, neuropathy, epistaxis, strangury, burning sensation and anorexia. The **toddy** is aphrodisiac, digestive, appetizing, intoxicating and tonic, used for penile dysfunction and indigestion.

Clinical uses: Dysuria: Juice of stem of the plant 20 ml, 3 times a day. **Dentalgia:** Gargles of decoction of root powder of the described plant 4 g, with water, 2 times a day. **General debility, Somasthenia, hypotension:** Fruit powder 10 g, with milk, 2 times a day. or Soak fruits of plant in water for 3 hours, make longitudinal cut and draw out seed, fill with seeds of *Hygrophila auriculata*, tie with a thread, make coating with knead flour of wheat, deep fry in clarified butter and drop in honey or treacle, keep slight warm the pot for 3 hours. Dose 1-2 Nos., with milk, at night. Avoid summer season. It is very effective medicine. **Diarrhea:** Fruit powder of plant 10 g, with water, 2 times a day. **Hair loss of eyebrow and eyelid:** Local application of ash of seeds of the described plant with water. **Intestinal worms:** Decoction of leaves powder of the described plant 20 g, with honey 10 g, for seven days. **Bleeding piles:** Black ash of leaves of the described plant 2 g, 3-4 times a day. **Burning sensation, pain and burning sensation of glens penis due to retention of semen fluid, piles, pain of calculi, spermacresia, penile dysfunction:** Mix powder of fruit of described plant, seed of *Phylanthus emblica, Piper longum,* Bitumen, *Elettaria cardamomum, Santalum album, Glycyrrhiza glabra, Bergenia ciliata,* seeds of *Cucumis sativus, Cuminum cyminum, Corian-*

drum sativum, 1-1 part and sugar 10 parts. Dose 5-10 g, with rice water or milk, 2 times a day. **Flatulence, loss of appetite, sprue, vomiting, colic:** Use *'Surochan Kharvella'*- Soak fruits of plant 1 kg, in Lemon juice 2 liter and Rock salt 500 g, after 3 days, make longitudinal cut and draw out seeds and fill this material in the fruits. Powder of *Piper nigrum, Piper longum, Anacyclus pyrenthrum, Amomum subulatum,* each 35 g, roasted seeds of *Carum bulbocastanum* and *Cuminum cyminum* each 95 g, *Cinamomum tamala* 18 g, seed kernel and mace of *Myristica fragrans* each 12 g, *Zingiber officinale* 125 g, Rock salt 185 g, fruit powder of described plant 375 g, soak in Lemon juice 1 kg. Now put them in glass pot, keeping cuts of fruits upward and fill the remaining Lemon juice in the pot. Use after 15 days. Dose 1-1 Nos. This drug gives very quick relief.

Formulations: *Kharjuraasava, Antravriddhihar churna, Vaatebhakesari rasa, Swadvifalaavaleha, Swadista chuhaare.*

Recommended readings:

Bhutya, R.K. (2007), Vanaspati Aushadha Vigyana, Scientific Publishers (India), Jodhpur, PP. 77.

Chunekar, K.C. (2004), Bhava Prakash Nighantu, Chaukhambha Bharti Academy, Varanasi, PP. 587.

Dhiman, A.K. (2006), Ayurvedic Drug Plants, Daya Publishing House, Delhi, PP. 212.

Khare, C.P. (2007), Indian Medicinal Plants, Springer (India) P.L. New Delhi, PP. 478.

Kirtikar, K.R. & Basu, B.D. (1998), Indian Medicinal Plants, L.M Basu, Allahabad, Vol. 4, PP. 2561.

Misra, B.L. (2005), Dravya Guna Hastamalaka, Publication scheme, Jaipur, PP. 370.

Nair, R.Vasudevan, (2007), Indian Medicinal Plants, Orient Longman P.L. Chennai, Vol. 4, PP. 240.

Prajapati, N.D., Purohit, S.S., Sharma, A.K. & Tarun Kumar (2003), A Hand Book of Medicinal Plants, Agrobios India, Jodhpur, PP. .

Sharma, P.V. (1981), Dravya gun vigyana, Chaukhambha Bharti Academy, Varanasi, Vol. 1, PP. 810.

358. *Phoenix sylvestris* (Linn.) Roxb.

Family: Palmae; Aracaceae.

Variety: 1. *P.dactylifira- Pind khajoor, Chhuhara is a half ripe and dried fruit.* 2. *P.aculis.*

English name: Wild date palm. **Sanskrit name:** *Swadvi, Durarohaa, Mriduchhadaa, Skandaphalaa, Bhumikharjurikaa, Kharajura, Kharjuraka.* **Hindi name:** *Khajur.* **Local name:** *Khajur.*

Ayurvedic groups: Charaka: *shramhara, virechanopaga, madhur skandha, kashaaya skandha.*

Botanical characteristics: Habit: A very graceful tall tree, height upto 35 m, with a thick hemispherical crown. **Stem:** Woody, erect, cylindrical, covered with the persistent bases of petioles, unbranched, solid, rough and brown. Base surrounded by a dense mass of root suckers. **Leaf:** Forming a dense terminal crown, pinnate, 3-5 m long, grayish-green, quite glabrous, leaflets 15-45 cm long and 2.5 cm wide, modified into spines. **Flower:** 60-95 cm long, fragrant, unisexual. **Fruit:** Berry, oblong-ellipsoid, reddish or yellowish-brown when ripe, 2.5-3.5 cm long, pulp fleshy, sweet, fruiting penducles are about 15 cm long, fruiting spadix is 90 cm long, flat, 3-5 cm wide and fibrous. **Seed:** 2 cm long, round at both ends, cylindrical, hard with a longitudinal furrow in front.

Flowering and fruiting period: May-June and June-July.

Habitat: All over India, mostly in Andhra Pradesh, Karnataka, Madhya Pradesh and Rajasthan.

Parts used: Fruits, juice.

Dosage: Fruits 50-100 g, juice 10-20 ml.

Collection period: November-December.

Ayurvedic properties: ***Ras:*** *madhur,* ***Gun:*** *guru, snigdha,* ***Veerya:*** *sheet,* ***Vipaka:*** *madhur,* ***Tridosha*** **Effect:** alleviates ***Vaata:*** *++,* ***Pitta:*** ++.

Chemical constituents: *P.sylvestris* - fresh unfermented **sap** (*Niraa*) is a good sourse of ascorbic acid, nichotinic and isonitotinic acids, riboflavin, thiamine, sugars, crystine, leucine, isoleucine, lysine, phenylanine, threonine, tyrosine. **Fruits** contain protein1.2, fat 0.4, Calcium 0.022 and phosphorus 0.38%. *P.dactylifera* – **fruits** contains ascorbic acid, carotene (as vit.A), nicotinic acid, riboflavin, thiamine, sugars, (60-80%) besides sucrose and invert sugars, rhamnose, xylose, arabinose, ribose, glactose and galacturonic acid. **Half ripe fruits** (*Chuhara*) contain protein 2.5-3, fat 0.5, carbohydrates 75.8-82.9% and calcium35.9, phosphorus 129.3 and iron3.4mg/100g. Presence of sterols of ergosterol group and ester-1has been reported from dried date palm.

Action and disease indications: Fruits are restorative, anti-tussive, expectorant, demulcent, laxative, diuretic, used for general debility, sexual debility, urinary disorders, fatigue, bronchitis, cough, cold, loss of appetite, cardiac disorders, hemoptosis, bleeding diathesis, pyrexia, diarrhea, excessive thirst, asthma, cyncope, also beneficial to physical strength and gaining body weight. **Sap** cooling laxative, gastric stimulant, digestive, appetizer, used for burning sensation, lose of appetite and weakness. **Root** used for nervous debility. **Gum** used for diarrhea, and genitor urinary disorders.

Clinical uses: Dysuria: Juice of stem of the plant 20 ml, 3 times a day. **Dentalgia:** Gargles of decoction of root powder of the described plant 4 g, with water, 2 times a day. **General debility, somasthenia, hypotension:** Fruit powder 10 g, with milk, 2 times a day. or Soak fruits of plant in water for 3 hours, make longitudinal cut and draw out seed, fill with seeds of *Hygrophila auriculata*, tie with a thread, make coating with knead flour of wheat, deep fry in clarified butter and drop in honey or treacle, keep slight warm the pot for 3 hours. Dose 1-2 Nos, with milk, at night. Avoid summer season. It is very effective medicine. **Diarrhea:** Fruit powder of plant 10g, with water, 2 times a day. **Hair loss of eyebrow and eyelid:** Local application of ash of seeds of the described plant with water. **Intestinal worms:** Decoction of leaves powder of the described plant 20 g, with honey 10 g, for seven days. **Bleeding piles:** Black ash of leaves of the described plant 2g, 3-4 times a day. **Burning sensation, pain and burning sensation of glens penis due to retention of semen fluid, piles, pain of calculi, somasthenia, spermacresia, penile dysfunction:** Mix powder of fruit of described plant, seed of *Phylanthus emblica, Piper longum*, Bitumen, *Elettaria cardamomum, Santalum album, Glycyrrhiza glabra, Bergenia ciliata*, seeds of *Cucumis sativus, Cuminum cyminum, Coriandrum sativum*, 1-1 part and sugar 10 parts. Dose 5-10 g, with rice water or milk, 2 times a day. **Flatulence, loss of appetite, sprue, Vomiting, colic:** Use *'Surochan Kharvella'*- Soak fruits of plant 1 kg, in Lemon juice 2 kg and Rock salt 500 g, after 3 days, make longitudinal cut and draw out seeds and fill this material in the fruits. Powder of *Piper nigrum, Piper longum, Anacyclus pyrenthrum, Amomum subulatum*, each 35 g, roasted seeds of *Carum bulbocastanum* and *Cuminum cyminum* each 95 g, *Cinamomum tamala* 18 g, seed kernel and mace of *Myristica fragrans* each 12 g, *Zingiber officinale* 125 g, Rock salt 185 g, fruit powder of described plant 375 g, soak in Lemon juice 1liter. Now put them in glass pot, keeping cuts of fruits upward and fill the remaining Lemon juice in the pot. Use after 15 days. Dose 1-1 Nos. This drug gives very quick relief.

Formulations: *Kharjuraasava, Antravriddhihar churna, Vatebhakesari rasa, Swdviphalavaleha, Surochan karvella.*

Recommended readings:

Bhutya, R.K. (2007), Vanaspati Aushadha Vigyana, Scientific Publishers (India), Jodhpur, PP. 77.

Chunekar, K.C. (2004), Bhava Prakash Nighantu, Chaukhambha Bharti Academy, Varanasi, PP. 587.

Dhiman, A.K. (2006), Ayurvedic Drug Plants, Daya Publishing House, Delhi, PP. 212.

Khare, C.P. (2007), Indian Medicinal Plants, Springer (India) P.L. New Delhi, PP. 479.

Kirtikar, K.R. & Basu, B.D. (1998), Indian Medicinal Plants, L.M Basu, Allahabad, Vol. 4, PP. 2563.

Misra, B.L. (2005), Dravya Guna Hastamalaka, Publication scheme, Jaipur, PP. 370.

Nair, R.Vasudevan, (2007), Indian Medicinal Plants, Orient Longman P.L. Chennai, Vol. 4, PP. 240.

Pareek, G.N. (2005), Sudhanidhi, Vanoshadhi Ratnakar, Dhanvantari Karyalaya, Aligarh, Vol. 3, PP. 153.

Sharma, P.V. (1981), Dravya gun vigyana, Chaukhambha Bharti Academy, Varanasi, Vol. 1, PP. 810.

Singh, R.S. (2002), Vanoshadhi Nirdeshika, Uttar Pradesh Hindi Sansthan, Lucknow, PP. 175.

359. *Phyla nodiflora* (L.) E. Greene.

Family: Verbenaceae.

Synonym: *Lippia Nodiflora.*

Name: English: Purpul Lippia, **Sanskrit:** *Jalapippali, Shaaradi, Shakulaadani, Matsyagandha, Laangali,* **Hindi:** *Jalpippali,* **Local:** *Jalpipal, Devakaandar, Mokana, Maionkara.*

Botanical characteristics: Habit: A creeping much branched perennial herb. **Stem:** Rooting at the nodes and sub-quandrangular stem and branches. **Leaf:** Simple, opposite, sub-sessile, 2-3.2 by 1-2 cm, cuneate-spathulate, or obovoid, sharply serrate towards the apex, appressedly hairy on both sides with medifixed white hairs. **Flower:** White or pale pink, sessile, densely packed in axillary spikes, globose at first, afterwards elongating, 2.5-7.5 cm long, usually single, bracts 2.5 mm long, broadly elliptic or obovate with a somewhat cuneate base, mucronate, glabrous. **Fruit:** 1.5 mm long, globose-oblong, dry, splitting into one-seeded, plano-convex glabrous pyrenes.

Flowering and fruiting period: September-October and November-December.

Habitat: Throughout India, up to 900 m, in wet places along bunds of irrigation channels, canals and river banks.

Parts used: Fruit, plant.

Dosage: 2-5 g, plant juice 10-20 ml.

Collection period: November-December.

Ayurvedic properties: ***Ras:*** *katu kashaya,* ***Gun:*** *laghu, rukhsa,* ***Veerya:*** *sheeta* ***Vipaka:*** *katu,* ***Tridosha*** **Effect:** alleviates ***Pitta:*** ++, ***Vaata:*** +.

Chemical constituents: The **plant** contains flavone glycosides-nodiflorins-A and B, lipiflorins A and B, as well as free flavones including 6-hydroxyluteolin, nepetin and nodifloretin along with beta-sitosterol and stigmasterol glucosides.

Action and disease indications: The **plant** is refrigerant, stomachic, appetizer, constipating, anthelmintic, digestive, vulnerary, aphrodisiac, seminiferous, ophthalmic, diuretic, febrifuge and alexeteric, prescribed for anorexia, flatulence, burning sensation, colic, dyspepsia, helminthiasis, diarrhea, ulcers, strangury, cough, asthma, bronchitis, knee joint pain, gonorrhea, piles, cardiopathy, lymphadenitis, erysipelas and fever.

Clinical uses: Inflammation, Burning sensation: Warm poultice of leaves of described plant, is beneficial. **Indigestion, diarrhea of children:** Cold infusion of leaves of described plant, 2 g, two times a day, is beneficial. **Bleeding piles:** Juice of described plant, 10 ml, three times a day, for three days, is very useful. **Headache, arthralgia:** Local application of paste of leaves of described plant, is beneficial. **Arthritis, joints pain:** Juice of described plant, 10 ml, three times a day, is useful. **Constipation of inflants:** Leaves juice of described plant, 10-20 drops, with honey 5 g, two times a day, is beneficial.

Recommended readings:

Bhutya, R.K. (2007), Vanaspati Aushadha Vigyana, Scientific Publishers (India), Jodhpur, PP. 104.

Chunekar, K.C. (2004), Bhava Prakash Nighantu, Chaukhambha Bharti Academy, Varanasi, PP. 470.

Khare, C.P. (2007), Indian Medicinal Plants, Springer (India) P.L. New Delhi, PP. 480.

Kirtikar, K.R. & Basu, B.D. (1998), Indian Medicinal Plants, L.M Basu, Allahabad, Vol. 3, PP. 1916.

Nair, R.Vasudevan, (2007), Indian Medicinal Plants, Orient Longman P.L. Chennai, Vol. 4, PP. 248.

Swami, K.N. (1985), Gavon Main Aushadh Ratna, Kalera Krishana Gopal, Kalera (Raj.), Vol. 2, PP. 304.

360. *Phylanthus distichus* Muell-Arg.

Family: Euphorbiaceae.

Synonym: *P.acidus, Cicca acida.*

Name: English: Country Gooseberry, Star Gooseberry, **Sanskrit:** *Lavali, Sugandhamoola, Paandu, Komalvalkalaa.* **Hindi:** *Harphaarevari,* **Local:** *Harphaarevari.*

Botanical characteristics: Habit: A pretty tree, height 4.5-6 m. **Stem:** With erect branches at top; branchlets slender. **Leaf:** Alternate, shape like leaves of *Cassia occidentalis,* distichous thin, obliquely ovate, acute, base rounded, tip acute, 5 by 2.5 cm, light green, petioles 2.5 mm long, upper larger cordate, acute, lower small globose. **Flower:** Very small, slender racemes 5 cm long, from the thick branches, sepals orbicular, pink at base. Disk of male of large glands; of females annular crenate. **Fruit:** Yellow-green, 2.5 cm long, globose, fleshy, acidic, obscurely 6-lobed, depressed at both ends, with 8-10 furrows, shape like fruit of *Phylanthus embelica.*

Flowering and fruiting period: May-June and June-July.

Habitat: Cultivated throughout India, in gardens.

Parts used: Fruit, seed. **Dosage:** 1-2 g.

Collection period: June-July.

Ayurvedic properties: ***Ras:*** *madhur, amla,* ***Gun:*** *rukhsa, guru, vishada,* ***Veerya:*** *sheeta* ***Vipaka:*** *madhur,* ***Tridosha*** **Effect:** alleviates ***Kapha:*** ++,***Pitta:*** +.

Chemical constituents: The **fruit** contains acetic acid 1.7%. The **root bark** contains tannin 18%, saponin, gallic acid and a crystalline substance. The **bark** contains beta-amyrin and phyllanthol.

Action and disease indications: The **fruits** are liver tonic, appetizer, used for biliousness, constipation, vomiting, bronchitis and piles.

Clinical uses: Anorexia, renal and vesical calculus, piles: Fruit powder of described plant, 2 g, with water, three times a day, is useful. **Snake bite:** Root and leaves powder of described plant, 2-2 g, three times a day, is useful.

Recommended readings:

Bhutya, R.K. (2007), Vanaspati Aushadha Vigyana, Scientific Publishers (India), Jodhpur, PP. 235.

Chunekar, K.C. (2004), Bhava Prakash Nighantu, Chaukhambha Bharti Academy, Varanasi, PP. 574.

Khare, C.P. (2007), Indian Medicinal Plants, Springer (India) P.L. New Delhi, PP. 481.

Kirtikar, K.R. & Basu, B.D. (1998), Indian Medicinal Plants, L.M Basu, Allahabad, Vol. 3, PP. 2227.

Sharma, P.V. (1981), Dravya gun vigyana, Chaukhambha Bharti Academy, Varanasi, Vol. 2, PP. 258.

361. *Phylanthus emblica* Linn.

Family: Euphorbiaceae.

Synonym: *Emblica officinalis.*

Ayurvedic Groups: Charak: *Virechanopaga, Vayahsthaapana,* **Sushruta:** *Triphalaa, Parushakaadi gana.*

Name: English: Emblic, Indian Gooseberry, **Sanskrit:** *Aamalaki, Vayasyaa, Vrishyaa, Jaatiphalrasaa, Shivaa, Dhaatriphaala, Shreephala, Amritaphala,* **Hindi:** *Aamala,* **Local:** *Aavala.*

Botanical characteristics: Habit: A small to medium sized deciduous tree, height 8-18 m. **Stem:** With crooked trunk and spreading branches and thin light grey bark exfoliating in small thin irregular flakes; branchlets glabrous or finely pubescent, 10-20 cm long, often deciduous. Stem bark 0.65 cm thick, heart wood red-brown. **Leaf:** Simple, numerous, shape like leaves of *Tamarindus indica,* sub-sessile, 10-13 by 2.5-3 mm, closely set along the branchlets, distichous, light green, glabrous, narrowly linear, obtuse, imbricate when young, having the appearance of pinnate leaves; stipules ovate, finely acute. **Flower:** Greenish-yellow, in axillary fascicles on the leaf-bearing branchlets, often on the naked portion below the leaves, with fimbriate bracts at the base, appears at the time of falling of leaves, fragrant. Male flowers numerous on short slender pedicels, female flowers few, sub-sessile, ovary 3-celled. **Fruit:** 1.3-1.6 cm diam., appears closely set on branches, fleshy, globose, with 6 obscure vertical furrows, green when unripe and pale yellow, somewhat reddish, shiny, of three 2-seeded crustaceous cocci. The **Seed:** 6, 3-gonous, oily. Wild trees are larger in height but fruits are smaller in size but more sour, fibrous and in quality, 15-25 g in weight. Cultivated trees are smaller and fruits are larger and 30-50 g in weight.

Flowering and fruiting period: February-May and October-April.

Habitat: Throughout India, in deciduous forests and on hill slopes, up to 1400 m, also cultivated in plains.

Parts used: Fruit, seed, leaves.

Dosage: Fruit dry 3-5 g, fresh 10-20 g, juice 5-10 ml, seed 2-5 g, leaves 1-3 g.

Collection period: January-March.

Ayurvedic properties: ***Ras:*** *Amla, madhur, kashaaya, tikta, katu,* ***Gun:*** *laghu, rukhsa,* ***Veerya:*** *sheeta,* ***Vipaka:*** *madhur,* ***Tridosha Effect:*** alleviates ***Pitta:*** ++++, ***Vaata:*** ++, ***Kapha:*** ++.

Chemical constituents: The **fruits** contain large quantity of vitamin C, carotene, nicotinic acid, riboflavin, minerals, amino acids, zeatin, zeatin riboside, zeatin nucleotide, phylembin, D-glucose, D-fructose, myoinositoland a pectin with D-galacturonic acid, D-arbinosyl, D-xylosyl, L-rhmnosyl, D-glucosyl, D-mannosyl, and D-galactosyl residues, embicol, mucic, indole acetic and four other auxins, two growth inhibitors-R-1 and R-2; phyllembic acid and phyllembin. The fruits also contain considerably higher concentration of most minerals, amino acids, protein and vitamin C. The fruit suspension culture gave phyllembin exhibits CNS depressant and spasmolytic activity, potentiates action of adrenaline and hyptonic action of Nembutol. The fruit contains superoxide dismutase 482.14 units/g fresh weight and exhibits anti-senescent (anti-ageing) activity. Fruit Juice, its sediment and residue areanti-oxidant due to galic acid. EtOH (50%) extract is anti-viral. Preliminary evidence suggests that the fruit and its juice may lower serum cholesterol, LDL, triglycerides and phospholipids without affecting HDL level and may have positive effect on atherosclerosis. An aqueous extract of the fruit has been reported to provide protection against radiation-induced chromosomal damage in both pre and post irradiation treatment. The fruit is reported to enhance natural killer cell activity and antibody dependent cellular cytotoxicity. The extract of the fruit and ascorbic acid prevented heptotoxic and nephrotoxic effects induced by lead and aluminium. The fruits are to activate trypsin (proteolytic enzyme) activity. The fruits can be consumed safely all round the year.

Action and disease indications: The **fruits** are refrigerant, anabolic, anti-emetic, bechic, antioxydant, anodyne, ophthalmic, digestive, carminative, laxative, stomachic, rejuvenating, alterant, brain tonic, alexeteric, diuretic, aphrodisiac, anti-pyretic, trichogenous and tonic, used for diabetes, cough, asthma, bronchitis, vomiting, epistaxis, hiccough, anaemia, cephalgia, ophthalmopathy, dyspepsia, colic, flatulence, hyperacidity, peptic ulcer, erysipelas, skin diseases, leprosy, haematemesis, bacillary dysentery, inflammations, emaciation, heptome-galy, jaundice, strangury, diarrhea, dysentery, haemorrhage, leucorrhea, menorrhagia, cardiac disorders, intermittent fevers and greyness of hair. The **leaves** are used for conjunctivitis, inflammations, dyspepsia, diarrhea and dysentery.

Clinical uses: Anuria, dysuria: Local application of paste of fruit of described plant and Salt petre, in ratio of 10:1, is beneficial. **Stomatitis:** Gargles of leaves decoction of described plant, is useful. **Indigestion:** Leaves powder of described plant 3 g, with whey, two or three times a day, is useful. **For Rejuvenating, penile dysfunction, gloominess, somasthenia, spermacresia, abulia:** Soak and dry the fruit powder of described plant, 21 times, by juice of fruits of described plant, dose 3 g, with sweet milk, two times a day, is very beneficial. Or use above powder with clarified butter of cow 5 g, honey 10 g, two times a day, is beneficial. Use this medicine, by three months. **Excess and turbid micturition, leucorrhea, cystitis:** Decoction of fruit powder of described plant, *Curcuma longa, Berberis aristata, Tinospora cordifolia, Glycyrrhiza glabra,* 10 g, with honey 10 g, two times a day, is beneficial. **Chronic Dysentery:** Cold infusion of leaves powder of described plant 5 g, powder of seeds of *Trigonella foenum-graecum* 3 g, with honey 10 g, two times a day, is beneficial. **Vomiting:** Cold infusion of fruit powder of described plant, 5 g, heart wood powder of *Santalum album* 5 g, with sugar candy powder 10 g and honey 10 g, three times a day, is useful. **Burning sensation of urine, strangury, loss of power of control of urine flow in female:** Fresh juice of fruits of described plant, fresh juice of Sugar cane 50 ml, with honey 10 g, two times a day, is useful. **Hyperacidity:** Fruit powder of described plant, 5 g, with juice of stem of *Musa paradisiaca* 25 ml, or Coconut water 50 ml; two times a day, or cold infusion of described plant, 5 g, *Zingiber officinale* 1 g, *Cuminum cyminum* 1 g, two times a day, is beneficial. **Headache, epistaxis:** Fruit powder of described plant, 5 g, sugar candy powder 10 g, with honey 10 g, two times a day, is beneficial. **Allergic bronchitis:** Fruit powder of described plant, 5 g, with milk, two times a day, is beneficial. **Anemia, Jaundice, disphonia, hyperhidrosis:** Juice of described plant 20 ml, with honey 10 g, two times a day, is beneficial. **Chronic Dysentery, Acne vulgaris:** Cold infusion of fruit powder of described plant 5 g, with honey 10 g, two times a day, is beneficial. **Canitis:** (1) Mix powder of fruit powder of described plant, black seeds of *Sesamum orientale, Eclipta alba,* sugar candy powder, 6 g, with water or milk, for 6 months, is very beneficial. (2) Washing the hairs with cold infusion of mix powder of fruit powder of described plant, fruit powder of *Sapindus emarginatus, Acacia sinuta,* leaves powder of *Zizyphus jujuba,* is very beneficial. **Alopecia:** Local application of paste of mix powder of fruit of described plant, seeds of *Mangifera indica,* fruit powder of *Spondias pinnata,* is beneficial. **Hypertension:** Mix powder of fruit powder of described plant, *Rauvolfia serpentina, Tinospora cordifolia,* 2 g, with water, two times a day, is beneficial. **Hiccough:** Juice of fruits of described plant, 20 ml, with *Limonia acidissima* 5 g, *Piper longum* 1 g, sugar candy powder 10 g, two or three times a day, is useful. **Ringworm, pruritis, scabies:** (1) Local application of paste of fruit of described plant, seeds of *Casia tora,* extract of *Acacia catechu,* with curd, is beneficial. (2) Local application of paste of black ash of fruit powder of described plant, with Coconut oil, is beneficial. **Diabetes inspidus:** Cold infusion of seeds of described plant, 12 g, with honey 10 g and sugar candy powder 10 g, two times a day, for 3 weeks, is beneficial. **Leucorrhea:** (1) Mix powder of fruit powder of described plant, seeds of *Mangifera indica, Glycyrrhiza glabra,* fresh *Cynodon dactylon,* sugar candy powder, 10 g, with water, two times a day, is beneficial. (2) Mix powder of fruit of described plant, *Areca catechu, Quercus infectoria, Trapa natans,* sugar candy powder, 5-10 g, with rice water, is beneficial. (3) Seeds powder of described plant, 5 g, *Mesua ferrea* 3 g, sugar 10 g, with honey water 10 g, two times a day, is beneficial.. **Epistaxis:** (1) Cold infusion of mix powder of fruits of described plant, *Vitis vinifera, Fumaria indica, Coriandrum sativum,* leaves of *Justisia adhatoda,* 10 g, two times a day, is beneficial. (2) Juice of fruits of described plant, 20 ml, juice of *Punica grantum* 50 ml, two times a day, is beneficial. **Bronchitis:** Fruit powder of described plant 2 g, *Curcuma longa* 2 g, *Zingiber officinale* 1 g, with juice of *Piper betel* 5 ml and honey 10 g, three times a day, is useful. **Jaundice:** Juice of fresh fruits of described plant 20 ml, juice of *Raphanus sativus* 10 ml, juice of roots of *Boerhavia diffusa* 10 ml, powder of *Piper longum* 1 g, with honey 10 g, two times a day, for 5 days, is very beneficial. **Oligospermia, spermacresia:** Mix powder of fruit powder of described plant, *Asparagus racemosus, Asparagus adscendens, Withania somnifera,* 6 g, with milk, two times a day, is beneficial.

Formulations: *Chyavanpraasha, Brahmarasaayana, Aamalaki rasayaana, Dhaatri lauha, Vrihachhaagaladhya ghrita, Dhaatryarista, Phalaarista, Aamalakyavaleha, Triphalaa churna.*

Recommended readings:

Acharya, B.K. (2008), Ayurveda Jadi-buti Rahasya, Patanjali Yogapitha, Haridwar, PP. 53.

Bhutya, R.K. (2007), Vanaspati Aushadha Vigyana, Scientific Publishers (India), Jodhpur, PP. 25.

Brahmavarchas (2003), Ayurved Ka Pran Vanoshadhi Vigyan, Shanti Kunj, Haridwar, PP. 207.

Chunekar, K.C. (2004), Bhava Prakash Nighantu, Chaukhambha Bharti Academy, Varanasi, PP. 10.

Dhiman, A.K. (2006), Ayurvedic Drug Plants, Daya Publishing House, Delhi, PP. 28.

Khare, C.P. (2007), Indian Medicinal Plants, Springer (India) P.L. New Delhi, PP. 238.

Kirtikar, K.R. & Basu, B.D. (1998), Indian Medicinal Plants, L.M Basu, Allahabad, Vol. 3, PP. 2220.

Nair, R.Vasudevan, (2007), Indian Medicinal Plants, Orient Longman P.L. Chennai, Vol. 4, PP. 256.

Namjoshi, A.N. (2001), The Ayurvedic Pharmacopoeia of India, Government of India, Department of Indian Systems of Medicine & Homoeopathy, New Delhi, Part-1, Volume- 2, PP. 4.

Pareek, G.N. (2005), Sudhanidhi, Vanoshadhi Ratnakar, Dhanvantari Karyalaya, Aligarh, Vol. 1, PP. 286.

Prajapati, N.D., Purohit, S.S., Sharma, A.K. & Tarun Kumar (2003), A Hand Book of Medicinal Plants, Agrobios India, Jodhpur, PP. 391.

Sharma, P.C., Yelne, MB. & Denis, T.J. (2000), Database on medicinal plants used in ayurveda, Central Council for research in Ayurveda and siddha, Vol. 3, PP. 11.

Sharma, P.V. (1981), Dravya gun vigyana, Chaukhambha Bharti Academy, Varanasi, Vol. 1, PP. 758.

Singh, R.S. (2002), Vanoshadhi Nirdeshika, Uttar Pradesh Hindi Sansthan, Lucknow, PP. 32.

Swami, K.N. (1985), Gavon Main Aushadh Ratna, Kalera Krishana Gopal, Kalera (Raj.), Vol. 1, PP. 67.

362. *Phylanthus fraternus* Webster & Amaru.

Family: Euphorbiaceae.

Synonym: *P.neruri.*

Variety: 1. *P.uranaria- Tamravalli-* red flower, large in size, 2. *P.simplex* (syn. *P.vergalus*)- *Mothi-Bhuiaamvalli-* found in Maharastra, 3. *P.madraspatensis.*

Name: Sanskrit: *Shivaa, Taamalaki, Bahupatraa, Bahuphalaa, Bahuveeryaa, Ajaataa, Bhudha-atri,* **Hindi:** *Bumyaamalaki,* **Local:** *Bhuiaama-laa, Ghoraa daal, Jarmalaa, Jangali aamala.*

Ayurvedic groups: Charaka: *Kaasahar, swaasahar.*

Botanical characteristics: Habit: Erect annual glabrous herb, height 15-60 cm. **Stem:** Herbaceous, erect, cylindrical, branched, solid, smooth and green. **Leaf:** Distichous, elliptic-oblong or linear-oblong, alternate, elliptical, entire, obtuse, glabrous, size 0.5-2 by 0.2-0.6 cm. **Flower:** Yellowish, greenish or whitish, male flowers 1-3, female flowers solitary, **Fruit:** Capsule, depressed globose, smooth, scarcely lobed, 2-3 mm across, underneath the branches. **Seed:** Pale brown, 1.5 mm long, 3-gonous, 6-7 straight longitudinal ribes on the back.

Flowering and fruiting period: May-June and August-September.

Habitat: Throughout the hotter parts of India, as a weed in cultivated and waste lands, up to 1000 m.

Parts used: All parts.

Dosage: Fresh juice 10-20 ml, powder 1-3 g.

Collection period: November-December.

Ayurvedic properties: ***Ras:*** *tikta, kashaaya,* ***Gun:*** *laghu, rukhsa,* ***Veerya:*** *sheet,* ***Vipaka:*** *madhur,* ***Tridosha*** **Effect:** alleviates ***Kapha:*** *+++,* ***Pitta:*** ++.

Chemical constituents: Leaves contain liganans - lintetralin, niranthin, nirtetralin, phyllathin, hypophyllanthin, phyltetralin, vitamin C, The **whole plant** gave a number of flavonoids, including quercetin, quercitrin, astragalin, rutin, laempferol, isolation of ahydrolysable tannins, amarulene.

Action and disease indications: The **plant** is cooling, anti bacterial, anti fungal, diuretic, deobstruant, stomachic, febrifuge, anti septic, astringent, anti inflammatory, analgesic, styptic, hypotensive, hypoglycemic, heptoprotective, useful to cure jaundice, dyspepsia, hypertension, excess cholesterol, indigestion, chronic dysentery, urinary track diseases, diabetes, skin eruption, gastropathy, dropsy, diarrhea, intermittent fever, opthalmopathy, ulcers wounds, dipsesis, bronchitis and asthma. This drug used as a single drug in jaundice and shows anti viral activity against hepatitis-B virus and related hepadina virus, effectively repair CC14-induced lever damage.

Clinical uses: Dysentery: Cold infusion of plant of 10 g, 3 times a day, for 3 days. **Jaundice:** Root powder of the described plant 10 g, 2 times a day, with milk. **Menorrhagia**: Seed powder of the described plant 2 g, or whole plant 10 g, with cold milk, 2 times a day. **Mastitis**: Local application of paste of plant is beneficial. **Pyrexia, malaria, enlargement of liver and spleen**: Decoction of plant 10 g, 2 times a day, is useful. **Boils and ulcers**: Local application of poultice of plant, with rice, 2 times a day. **Skin diseases:** Local application of paste of plant with common salt, in ratio of 10:1, is beneficial.

Hiccough: 4-4 drops of juice of plant, as nasal drops and oral use of root juice 10 ml, with Sugar cube powder 10 g, 3 times a day. **Bronchitis, asthma:** Decoction of plant with honey 10 g, 3 times a day, is useful. **Diabetes mellitus**: Powder of plant 10 g, with *Piper nigrum* 1 g, 3 times a day, with water, for 7 days. **Metrorrhagia**: Seed powder of the described plant 3 g, with water of rice 50 ml, 2 times a day.

Formulations: *Chyavanpraasha, Nirocil, Jivantyadi ghrita, Chitraka haritaki, Shatavari guda, Laghu vishagarbha taila, Madhuyastyaadi taila, Swaasahar kashaaya.*

Recommended readings:

Bhutya, R.K. (2007), Vanaspati Aushadha Vigyana, Scientific Publishers (India), Jodhpur, PP. 168.

Chunekar, K.C. (2004), Bhava Prakash Nighantu, Chaukhambha Bharti Academy, Varanasi, PP. 460.

Dhiman, A.K. (2006), Ayurvedic Drug Plants, Daya Publishing House, Delhi, PP. 83.

Khare, C.P. (2007), Indian Medicinal Plants, Springer (India) P.L. New Delhi, PP. 481.

Kirtikar, K.R. & Basu, B.D. (1998), Indian Medicinal Plants, L.M Basu, Allahabad, Vol. 3, PP. 2225.

Misra, B.L. (2005), Dravya Guna Hastamalaka, Publication scheme, Jaipur, PP. 347.

Nair, R.Vasudevan, (2007), Indian Medicinal Plants, Orient Longman P.L. Chennai, Vol. , PP. .

Prajapati, N.D., Purohit, S.S., Sharma, A.K. & Tarun Kumar (2003), A Hand Book of Medicinal Plants, Agrobios India, Jodhpur, PP. 392.

Sharma, P.C., Yelne, MB. & Denis, T.J. (2000), Database on medicinal plants used in ayurveda, Central Council for research in Ayurveda and siddha, Vol. 3, PP. 512.

Sharma, P.V. (1981), Dravya gun vigyana, Chaukhambha Bharti Academy, Varanasi, Vol. 1, PP. 640.

Singh, R.S. (2002), Vanoshadhi Nirdeshika, Uttar Pradesh Hindi Sansthan, Lucknow, PP. 290.

Swami, K.N. (1985), Gavon Main Aushadh Ratna, Kalera Krishana Gopal, Kalera (Raj.), Vol. 3, PP. 159.

363. *Physalis minima* Linn.

Family: Solanaceae.

Other similar plant: *P.indica.*

Name: English: Sun-berry, Country goose berry, **Sanskrit:** *Tankaari, Laxmipriyaa, Chirpotaa,* **Hindi:** *Chirpotali,* **Local:** *Chirpotali.*

Botanical characteristics: Habit: A hebaceous annual, height 15-30 cm. **Stem:** Erect, striate, more or less pubescent. **Leaf:** Simple, alternate, 2.5-6.3 by 1.3-3.8 cm, ovate, acute, shallowly toothed or lobed, more or less pubescent, thin, base cuneate,; petioles 1.3-3.2 cm long, slender, more or less pubescent. **Flower:** Yellow, solitary, pedicels filiform, nodding, 3.8 mm long. **Fruit:** Berry, 8 mm diam., green, 1.3-2.5 cm long, many seeded, round, membranous, 5- or sometimes 10- ribbed, reticulately veined, entirely enveloped in the enlarged calyx, which is ovoid or sub-globose. **Seed:** Many, discoid or sub-reniform, 2 mm diam., finely muriculate, orange yellow.

Flowering and fruiting period: September-October and November-December.

Habitat: More or less throughout India, up to 2300 m, as a weed on cultivated land.

Parts used: Fruit, root, leaves.

Dosage: Fruit, root, leaves 3-6 g.

Collection period: November-December.

Ayurvedic properties: ***Ras:*** *tikta,* ***Gun:*** *laghu,* ***Veerya:*** *ushna,* ***Vipaka:*** *katu,* ***Tridosha*** **Effect:** alleviates ***Vaata: +, Kapha: +.***

Chemical constituents: The **plant** contains withasteroids, physalindicanols, withaminimin and withaphysalin, 3-O-glucosides of kaempferol and quercetin, in addition to beta-sitosterol and its glucoside. Quercetin 3-O-glucosides, isolated from the crude extract of bthe leaves, is reported to exhibit anti-inflammatory activity comparable to phenylbutazone. The diuretic action of leaves is attributed to the high content of potassium nitrate (8-10%).

Action and disease indications: The **plant** is diuretic, aperient, alterative, laxative, expectorant, appetizer and tonic, prescribed for gout, burning sensation, strangury, ascitis, spleenomegaly, gastropathy, cough, asthma, bronchitis, colic, ulcers, pruritus and erysipelas.

Clinical uses: Gonorrhea, constipation: Fruit powder of described plant, 5 g, with water, two times a day, is beneficial. **Mastoptosis:** Local application of paste of described plant, with rice water, is beneficial. **Bronchial asthma:** Root powder of described plant, Borax 250 mg, with fried rice 5 g and honey 10 g, two times a day, is useful.

Recommended readings:

Bhutya, R.K. (2007), Vanaspati Aushadha Vigyana, Scientific Publishers (India), Jodhpur, PP. 97.

Brahmavarchas (2003), Ayurved Ka Pran Vanoshadhi Vigyan, Shanti Kunj, Haridwar, PP. 342.

Chunekar, K.C. (2004), Bhava Prakash Nighantu, Chaukhambha Bharti Academy, Varanasi, PP. 360.

Khare, C.P. (2007), Indian Medicinal Plants, Springer (India) P.L. New Delhi, PP. 483.

Kirtikar, K.R. & Basu, B.D. (1998), Indian Medicinal Plants, L.M Basu, Allahabad, Vol. 3, PP. 1766.

Nair, R.Vasudevan, (2007), Indian Medicinal Plants, Orient Longman P.L. Chennai, Vol. 4, PP. 266.

Prajapati, N.D., Purohit, S.S., Sharma, A.K. & Tarun Kumar (2003), A Hand Book of Medicinal Plants, Agrobios India, Jodhpur, PP. 394.

364. *Picrorhiza kurroa* Royle ex Benth.

Family: Scrophulariaceae.

Ayurvedic Groups: Charak: *Bhedaniya, lekhaniya, Stanyashodhan,* **Sushruta:** *Patolaadi, Pippalyaadi, Mustaadi gana.*

Name: English: Picrorhiza. **Sanskrit:** *Katukaa, Tiktaa, Katurohini, Kaandaruhaa, Katvi, Katambharaa, Ashokaa, Rohini, Katurohini,* **Hindi:** *Kutaki,* **Local:** *Kutaki.*

Botanical characteristics: Habit: A small trailing nearly hairy, perennial herb, height 15-25 cm. **Rootstock:** Woody, thick, clothed with withered leaf-bases. **Rhizome**: Elongate creeping, zig-zag, 2-8 cm long, grayish-brown, rooting at nodes, bitter. **Leaf:** Sub-radical, Simple, alternate, spathulate, dentate-serrate, 5-10 cm long, coriaceous, tip rounded, base narrowed into a winged sheathing petiole. **Flower:** White or bluish or blue-purple, dimorphic, flowering stem or scapes ascending, stout, longer than the leaves, naked or with a few bracts below the inflorescence. Spikes 5-10 cm long, sub-cylindric, obtuse, many flowered, sub-hirsute; bracts oblong or lanceolate, as long As calyx. **Fruit:** Capsule, 1.3 cm long, ovoid and conical, turgid, acute. **Seed:** Of an oblong curved nucleus, enclosed in the large bladdery loose hyaline reticulated testa.

Flowering and fruiting period: June-July and August-September.

Habitat: Alpine Himalaya, from Kashmir to Sikkim, at an elevation of 2700-4500 m.

Parts used: Root. **Dosage:** 1-3 g.

Collection period: September-October.

Ayurvedic properties: ***Ras:*** *tikta,* ***Gun:*** *laghu, rukhsa,* ***Veerya:*** *sheeta* ***Vipaka:*** *katu,* ***Tridosha*** **Effect:** alleviates ***Kapha:*** *+++,* ***Pitta:*** *++.*

Chemical constituents: The **roots** contain a glycosidal bitter principle, kutkin, found to be a mixture of two iridoid glycosides, picroside 1 and kutkoside, also D-mannitol, kutkiol, kutkisterol and a ketone-apcynin. Kutkin exhibits haptoprotective activity.

Action and disease indications: The **roots** are refrigerant, laxative, carminative, digestive, stomachic, anthelmintic, anti-inflammatory, expectorant, depurative, cardio tonic, galacto-purifier, anti-periodic, anti-pyretic, anti-diarrhoeal, cholagogue, heptoprotective, and purgative in large doses, prescribed for hepatitis, chronic dysentery, amoebiasis, burning sensation, constipation, flatulence, colic, inflammations, verminosis, anorexia, leucoderma, skin diseases, hypotension, cough, asthma, bronchitis, hiccough, fever, bilious fever, intermittent fever, diabetes, Jaundice, piles, impurity of breast milk and general debility.

Clinical uses: Jaundice, dental carries: Leaves juice of described plant 20 ml, two times a day, is beneficial. **Jaundice:** (1) Decoction of root powder of described plant, '*Trifala, Tinospora cordifolia, Hemidesmus indicus,* 15 g, with honey 10 g, two times a day, is useful. (2) Root powder of described plant 2 g, with juice of root of *Raphanus sativus* 20 ml, or sugar cane juice 50 ml, two times a day, is beneficial. (3) Mix powder of roots of described plant, *Coriandrum sativum,* raw sugar, 15 g, with water, two times a day, is beneficial. **Malaria:** Mix powder of bark and seeds of described plant, roots of *Picrorhiza kurroa,* leaves of *Trichosanthus dioica,* 5-10 g, two times a day, is beneficial. **Bleeding piles:** (1) Decoction of bark of described plant, 10 g, with *Aconitum heterophyllum* 500 mg, two times a day, is useful. (2) Seed powder of described plant 5 g, *Zingiber officinale* 1 g, with water, two times a day, is beneficial. **Colic:** Seed powder of described plant 5 g, fried gum of *Ferula narthex* 125 mg, with lukewarm water, is beneficial. **Leucorrhea, laxity of vagina:** Make black charcoal of Alum 1 part and sugar 10 parts, by warming, add bark of described plant 2 parts and make vaginal tablet of 2 g. Use I tablet at night. Daily for 3 days, alternate for 7 days, twice in week for two weeks, and weekly as required. **Chronic amebic dysentery, bleeding in diarrhea:** Mix powder of seeds of described plant, *Plantago ovata, Aconitum heterophyllum, Acorus calamus,* gum of *Bombax ceiba,* 5 g, two times a day, is beneficial. **Rheumatism, Osteo arthritis:** Local application of paste of bark of described plant is beneficial. **Dentalgia, pyorrhea:** Bark of described plant, 6 g, with water, three times a day, and gargles of decoction of bark of described plant, or use of bark of described plant as tooth powder, is beneficial. **Renal and vesical calculus:** Seed powder of described plant, 5 g, roots of *Operculina turpenthum* 1 g, with cold milk or rice water, is beneficial. **Vomiting:**

Roasted seeds of described plant 5 g, or decoction or cold infusion of seeds of described plant, 5 g, with honey 10 g, as required, is beneficial. **Leucoderma:** Local application of paste of bark and seeds of described plant, is beneficial. **Sun stroke, strangury:** Fresh bark of described plant, 10-20 g, with water, two times a day, is useful. **Inflammation:** Local application of paste of root of described plant, root bark of *Moringa oleifera,* leaves of *Solunum nigrum,* is beneficial. **Ascitis:** Root powder of described plant 2 g, root of *Boerhavia diffusa* 3 g, with distillate of *solunum nigrum* 20 ml, two times a day, is beneficial. **Cirrhosis of liver:** Root powder of described plant 4 g, *Trachy spermum-ammi* 4 g, leaves of *Cassia senna* 2 g, with warm water, at 12 o'clock and 9 PM, is beneficial. **Leucoderma:** (1) Mix powder of roots of described plant, seeds of *Cassia tora, Sapindus emarginatus, Vernonia anthelmintica,* pure Sulphur, Red iron oxide 8-8 parts, *Curcuma zedoria,* 4 parts, *Psoralea corylifolia* 16 parts, *'Ras manikya'* 1 part, mix all matter and make tablets of 500 mg each. Dose 2-3 tablets, with water, three times a day, is very useful. Local application of these tablets, with urine of cow, is also useful. 3 or 4 months are sufficient for complete treatment. (2) Local application of paste of roots of described plant, leaves of *Ocimum sanctum,* Green Vitriol, at morning, and paste of Red iron oxide, with water, at night, is very beneficial. **Spleen enlargement:** Decoction of roots of described plant 4 g, roots of *Boerhavia diffusa* 4 g, *Tinospora cordifolia* 4 g, *Berberis aristata* 12 g, with honey 10 g, two times a day, is very useful.

Formulations: *Aarogyavardhani, Katukaadhya lauha, Tiktaadhya ghrita, Phala ghrita, Jaatyadi ghrita, Mahaatikta ghrita, Kumaaryaasava, Rodhraasava, Saarivadhyaasava, Patolaadi kwaatha, Kiraataadi kwaatha, Nimbaadi churna.*

Recommended readings:

Bhutya, R.K. (2007), Vanaspati Aushadha Vigyana, Scientific Publishers (India), Jodhpur, PP. 67.

Brahmavarchas (2003), Ayurved Ka Pran Vanoshadhi Vigyan, Shanti Kunj, Haridwar, PP. 344.

Chunekar, K.C. (2004), Bhava Prakash Nighantu, Chaukhambha Bharti Academy, Varanasi, PP. 70.

Dhiman, A.K. (2006), Ayurvedic Drug Plants, Daya Publishing House, Delhi, PP. 230.

Khare, C.P. (2007), Indian Medicinal Plants, Springer (India) P.L. New Delhi, PP. 485.

Kirtikar, K.R. & Basu, B.D. (1998), Indian Medicinal Plants, L.M Basu, Allahabad, Vol. 2, PP. 1825.

Misra, B.L. (2005), Dravya Guna Hastamalaka, Publication scheme, Jaipur, PP. 383.

Nair, R.Vasudevan, (2007), Indian Medicinal Plants, Orient Longman P.L. Chennai, Vol. 4, PP. 269.

Namjoshi, A.N. (2001), The Ayurvedic Pharmacopoeia of India, Government of India, Department of Indian Systems of Medicine & Homoeopathy, New Delhi, Part-1, Volume- 1, PP. 85.

Pareek, G.N. (2005), Sudhanidhi, Vanoshadhi Ratnakar, Dhanvantari Karyalaya, Aligarh, Vol. 2, PP. 185.

Prajapati, N.D., Purohit, S.S., Sharma, A.K. & Tarun Kumar (2003), A Hand Book of Medicinal Plants, Agrobios India, Jodhpur, PP. 396.

Sharma, P.C., Yelne, MB. & Denis, T.J. (2000), Database on medicinal plants used in ayurveda, Central Council for research in Ayurveda and siddha, Vol. 7, PP. 179.

Sharma, P.V. (1981), Dravya gun vigyana, Chaukhambha Bharti Academy, Varanasi, Vol. 1, PP. 441.

Swami, K.N. (1985), Gavon Main Aushadh Ratna, Kalera Krishana Gopal, Kalera (Raj.), Vol. 2, PP. 190.

365. *Pinus gerardiana* Wall.

Family: Pinaceae.

Name: English: Neosia Pine, Edible Pine, Chilgoza Pine, **Sanskrit:** *Nikochaka,* **Hindi:** *Chilgojaa,* **Local:** *Chilgojaa.*

Botanical characteristics: Habit: A medium sized tree, 6-8 m high. **Stem:** Bark grey, thin, smooth, peeling off on large thin flakes, roughish on old trees near the base, branches not or obscurely whorled. **Leaf:** In bundles of 3, 5-10 cm long, stiffish, dark green, serrulate, sheath of bud-scales deciduous. **Flower:** Male catkins 7.5-13 mm long. Female cones near the middle of the shoots. **Fruit:** Ripe cones 15-23 by 10-12.5 cm, scales very thick and woody with a stout recurved beak. **Seed:** 2.5 cm long, cylindric with a short caduceus wing, cotyledons 3-8.

Flowering and fruiting period: July-August and September-October.

Habitat: North-West Himalaya, from Garwal eastwards at altitudes of 1800-3000 m.

Parts used: Fruit. **Dosage:** 10-20 g.

Collection period: October-November.

Ayurvedic properties: ***Ras:*** *madhur,* ***Gun:*** *guru, snigdha,* ***Veerya:*** *ushna,* ***Vipaka:*** *madhur,* ***Tridosha*** **Effect:** alleviates ***Vaata:* +++,** aggrevates ***Pitta:* +.**

Chemical constituents: The **seed kernels** contain protein 15.9, fat 49.9, carbohydrate 21.6, and mineral matter 2.9%. The Minerals are calcium 90.8, phosphorus 92.4 and iron 2.4 mg/100g. The seed protein on hydrolysis gave amino acids-leucine, isoleucine, valine, lysine, phenylalanine, tryptophan and methionine. The oil gave glycerides. The essential oil from oleoresin contains alpha and beta-pinene as major constituents; other are sesquiterpenes.

Action and disease indications: The **kernels** are stimulant, thermogenic, appetizer, carminative, expectorant, tonic, aphrodisiac, used for weakness, biliousness, paralysis, deafness, pain in the joints, ophthalmia, liver disorders, chronic bronchitis and fatigue.

Clinical uses: Somasthenia, sexual debility, spermacresia, general debility: Fruits of described plant, 20 g, two times a day, is beneficial.

Recommended readings:

Chunekar, K.C. (2004), Bhava Prakash Nighantu, Chaukhambha Bharti Academy, Varanasi, PP. 823.

Khare, C.P. (2007), Indian Medicinal Plants, Springer (India) P.L. New Delhi, PP. 488.

Kirtikar, K.R. & Basu, B.D. (1998), Indian Medicinal Plants, L.M Basu, Allahabad, Vol. 3, PP. 2388.

366. *Pinus roxburghii* Sarg.

Family: Pinaceae.

Synonym: *P. longifolia.*

Ayurvedic Groups: Charak: *Purishavirjaniya, Elaadi gana.*

Other similar plants: *P.Khasya, P.excelsa.*

Name: English: Long-leaved Pine, Three-leaved Pine, Chir Pine, **Sanskrit:** *Peetavrikhsa, Surabhidaaru, Dhoopavrikhsa,* Oleo-resin-*Shreevestaka.* **Hindi:** *Saral* Oleo-resin-*Gandhaa-birojaa.* **Local:** *Chir, Dhupasarala.*

Botanical characteristics: Habit: A large coniferous tree, 30-38 m high, it is evergreen but becomes completely or partially deciduous in dry season, grow in group. **Stem:** With spreading crown, branches whorled, bark dark grey or reddish, 2.5-5 cm thick, deeply fissured and rough, exfoliating bark. **Leaf:** 20-30 cm long, in bundles of 3, triquetrous, acicular, bright green, pendulous, each bundle surrounded at the base by a persistent sheath of bud-scales 1.3-2.5 cm long. Leaves remain about 30 months on the tree. **Flower:** Male flowers about 15 mm long, arranged in form of cones, female cones solitary or often 2-5 together, 10-20 cm long, 7.5-12.5 cm diam., on short stiff stalk, scales very thick and woody with a pyramidal pointed or recurved beak. Dry cones remain on the tree for a very long time. **Seed:** Winged, 7.5 mm long with a long thin membranous wings, cotyledons 10-14. The **sapwood** is white to creamy white and heartwood light red, turning reddish-brown on exposure.

Flowering and fruiting period: April-June and October-January (second year after flowering). This process takes duration of about 26 months.

Habitat: Throughout the Himalayas, from Kashmir to Bhutan, Siwalik hills, Ooty, Kodaikanal, at altitude of 450-2400 m.

Parts used: Heartwood, oleoresin, oil.

Dosage: Heartwood 1-3 g, oleoresin 1-2 g, oil 1-3 drops.

Collection period: April-June.

Ayurvedic properties: ***Ras:*** *madhur, tikta, katu,* ***Gun:*** *laghu, snigdha,* ***Veerya:*** *ushna,* ***Vipaka:*** *katu,* ***Tridosha*** **Effect:** alleviates ***Kapha:*** ***++,*** ***Vaata:*** ***++.***

Chemical constituents: The **oil** obtained from the stem, commonly known as turpentine oil, contains alpha-longipinene, beta-pinene, careen-3. The **heartwood** contains stilbene, flavonoids-pinosylvin, pinocembrin, pinobanksin. The **essential oil** from oleoresin contains chiefly alpha and beta-pinene; careen and longifolin.

Action and disease indications: The **terpentine oil** is aromatic, anti-spasmodic, anodyne, anti-septic, expectorant, rubefacient, carminative and stomachic, useful in neuralgia, chronic bronchitis, gangrene of lungs, inflammations, obstinate constipation,, dyspepsia, flatulence and colic. The **wood** is thermogenic, emollient, aromatic, anti-septic, deodorant, haemostatic, stimulant, anthelmintic, digestive, diaphoretic, rubefacient, diuretic and liver tonic, used for halitosis, foul ulcers, haemorrhage, haemoptysis, helminthiasis, dyspepsia, flatulence, skin diseases, pruritis, giddiness, heptopathy, strangury, bronchitis, diseases of eyes, ear and throat and inflammations. The **oleoresin** is thermogenic, expectorant, anodyne, anti-inflammatory, purgative and demulcent, prescribed for cough, asthma, bronchitis, otalgia, odontalgia, inflammations, gonorrhea, scabies, epilepsy, liver and spleen diseases, lumbago, piles and tuberculous glands.

Clinical uses: Inflammation, insect stings, skin diseases, neuragia: Local application of paste of heartwood of described plant is beneficial. **Arthritis, pneumonia, rib pain:** Local massage of heartwood oil (Turpentine oil), is beneficial. **Flatulence:** Local fomentation on abdomen by mixture of Turpentine oil and water, in ratio of 1: 10, is beneficial. **Intestinal strangulation, flatulence:** Enema of mixture of Turpentine oil 10 ml and lukewarm water 100 ml is beneficial. **Gonorrhea:** Oleoresin of described plant 2 g, seeds of *Elettaria cardamomum* 1 g, sugar candy powder 5 g, with cold milk or cold water, two times a day, is beneficial. **Inflammation:** Local application of paste of heartwood of described plant, with cow urine, is beneficial.

Formulations: *Panchaguna taila, Pramehaantaka vati, Agurvaadi taila, Usnavaataghna churna, Rudra taila, Shataavari taila, Dashamool-aadhya ghrita, Chandanaadhya taila, Saralaadi pradeha, Shrivaasaadi dhoopa.*

Recommended readings:

Bhutya, R.K. (2007), Vanaspati Aushadha Vigyana, Scientific Publishers (India), Jodhpur, PP. 224.

Brahmavarchas (2003), Ayurved Ka Pran Vanoshadhi Vigyan, Shanti Kunj, Haridwar, PP. 346.

Chunekar, K.C. (2004), Bhava Prakash Nighantu, Chaukhambha Bharti Academy, Varanasi, PP. 197.

Dhiman, A.K. (2006), Ayurvedic Drug Plants, Daya Publishing House, Delhi, PP. 337.

Khare, C.P. (2007), Indian Medicinal Plants, Springer (India) P.L. New Delhi, PP. 488.

Kirtikar, K.R. & Basu, B.D. (1998), Indian Medicinal Plants, L.M Basu, Allahabad, Vol. 3, PP. 2387.

Misra, B.L. (2005), Dravya Guna Hastamalaka, Publication scheme, Jaipur, PP. 425.

Nair, R.Vasudevan, (2007), Indian Medicinal Plants, Orient Longman P.L. Chennai, Vol. 4, PP. 273.

Namjoshi, A.N. (2001), The Ayurvedic Pharmacopoeia of India, Government of India, Department of Indian Systems of Medicine & Homoeopathy, New Delhi, Part-1, Volume- 3, PP. 191.

Pareek, G.N. (2005), Sudhanidhi, Vanoshadhi Ratnakar, Dhanvantari Karyalaya, Aligarh, Vol. 10, PP. 141.

Prajapati, N.D., Purohit, S.S., Sharma, A.K. & Tarun Kumar (2003), A Hand Book of Medicinal Plants, Agrobios India, Jodhpur, PP. 400.

Sharma, P.C., Yelne, MB. & Denis, T.J. (2000), Database on medicinal plants used in ayurveda, Central Council for research in Ayurveda and siddha, Vol. 6, PP. 337.

Sharma, P.V. (1981), Dravya gun vigyana, Chaukhambha Bharti Academy, Varanasi, Vol. 1, PP. 308.

Singh, R.S. (2002), Vanoshadhi Nirdeshika, Uttar Pradesh Hindi Sansthan, Lucknow, PP. 123.

367. *Piper betel* Linn.

Family: Piperaceae.

Other similar plants: *P.thomson- Giri taamboola-* found in Kedaar valley.

Name: English: Betel pepper, **Sanskrit:** *Taamboo-lavalli, Naagavallari, Taambooli, Naagini, Naagvallari,* **Hindi:** *Naagarbel, Tamboola,* **Local:** *Paan, Naagarbel kaa paan.*

Botanical characteristics: Habit: A perennial dioecious root climber, 4.5-6 m long. **Stem:** Semi-woody, much thickened at nodes, young parts glabrous. **Leaf:** Large, coriaccous, 10-20 by 5-12.5 cm, broadly ovate, slightly cordate, acuminate or acute, entire, glabrous, margin often rather undulate, usually 7-nerved, thick, bright green, shining on both sides, petiole 2-2.5 cm long, stout. **Flower:** Male spikes dense, cylindrical, female spikes pendulous, 2.5-5 cm long, bracts triangular-rotundate, rachis pilose. **Fruit:** Rarely produced, often sunk in the fleshy spike, forming nodule-like structure, about 5 cm long and pendulous.

Flowering and fruiting period: February-March and May-June.

Habitat: Cultivated in warmer and damper parts of India, mostly in Assam, West Bengal, Bihar, Uttar Prdesh, Karnataka and Kerala.

Parts used: leaves. **Dosage:** Juice 5-10 ml.

Collection period: September-October.

Ayurvedic properties: ***Ras:*** *katu, tikta,* ***Gun:*** *laghu, rukhsa, tikhsna, vishada,* ***Veerya:*** *ushna,* ***Vipaka:*** *katu,* ***Tridosha*** **Effect:** alleviates ***Kapha: +++, Vaata: +.***

Chemical constituents: The **leaves** contain beta and gama-sitosterol, hentriacontane, pentatriacontane, *n*-triacontane, stearic acid and chavicol, Vitamin A and C, thiamin, riboflavin, nicotinic acid, glucose, fructose, maltose, sucrose, malic acid, oxalic acid and several amino acids. The essential oil from leaves contained carvacrol, eugenol, chavicol, allyl catecgol, cineole, estragol, caryophyllene, cardinene, *p*-cymene and eugenol methyl ether.

Action and disease indications: The **leaves** are thermogenic, astringent, carminative, stomachic, sialogogue, anthelmintic, aromatic, desiccative, exhilarant, aphrodisiac, expectorant, laxative, febrifuge and tonic, used for cough, asthma, bronchitis, catarrh, dipsia, penile dysfunction, leprosy, alcoholism, syncope, rheumatism, dyspepsia, otalgia, fever, halitosis, impotency, colic, diarrhea, dysentery, laryngitis and pharygopathy.

Clinical uses: Poisoning of mercury: Decoction of leaves of described plant, 5 g, *Eclipta alba* 10 g, *Ocimum sanctum* 2 g, milk of she goat 50 g, two times a day, is beneficial. Local application of this decoction is also beneficial. **Disphonia:** Sucking of root of described plant, 5 g, is useful. **Whooping cough:** Juice of leaves of described plant 5 ml, with honey 10 g, three times a day, is useful. **Ozostomia:** Gargles of decoction of leaves of described plant, 10 g, powder of *Piper cubeba* 1 g, *Myristica fragrans* 125 mg, seeds of *Elettaria cardamomum* 250 mg, *Cinamomum camphora* 25 mg, is beneficial. **Phlegmatic bronchitis:** Juice of leaves of described plant 5 ml, *Piper nigrum* 1 g, with honey 10 g, three times a day, is useful. **Disphonia:** Sucking of root powder or peice of described plant, 2 g, is beneficial. **Hiccough:** Decoction of root powder of described plant, 3 g, with clarified butter 5 g, as required, is beneficial.

Formulations: *Taamboolasava, Laxmi vilaasa rasa naaradiya, Laghu sootashekhara rasa, Naaga gutikaa, Ardhaangavaataari rasa, Swaaskaasa chintaamani rasa, Kaalkoota rasa, Puspadhanvaa rasa.*

Recommended readings:

Acharya, B.K. (2008), Ayurveda Jadi-buti Rahasya, Patanjali Yogapitha, Haridwar, PP. 332.

Bhutya, R.K. (2007), Vanaspati Aushadha Vigyana, Scientific Publishers (India), Jodhpur, PP. 135.

Brahmavarchas (2003), Ayurved Ka Pran Vanoshadhi Vigyan, Shanti Kunj, Haridwar, PP. 347.

Chunekar, K.C. (2004), Bhava Prakash Nighantu, Chaukhambha Bharti Academy, Varanasi, PP. 272.

Dhiman, A.K. (2006), Ayurvedic Drug Plants, Daya Publishing House, Delhi, PP. 375.

Khare, C.P. (2007), Indian Medicinal Plants, Springer (India) P.L. New Delhi, PP. 489.

Kirtikar, K.R. & Basu, B.D. (1998), Indian Medicinal Plants, L.M Basu, Allahabad, Vol. 3, PP. 2131.

Misra, B.L. (2005), Dravya Guna Hastamalaka, Publication scheme, Jaipur, PP. 402.

Nair, R.Vasudevan, (2007), Indian Medicinal Plants, Orient Longman P.L. Chennai, Vol. 4, PP. 279.

Namjoshi, A.N. (2001), The Ayurvedic Pharmacopoeia of India, Government of India, Department of Indian Systems of Medicine & Homoeopathy, New Delhi, Part-1, Volume- 3, PP. 131.

Pareek, G.N. (2005), Sudhanidhi, Vanoshadhi Ratnakar, Dhanvantari Karyalaya, Aligarh, Vol. 4, PP. 139.

Prajapati, N.D., Purohit, S.S., Sharma, A.K. & Tarun Kumar (2003), A Hand Book of Medicinal Plants, Agrobios India, Jodhpur, PP. 401.

Sharma, P.C., Yelne, MB. & Denis, T.J. (2000), Database on medicinal plants used in ayurveda, Central Council for research in Ayurveda and siddha, Vol. 3, PP. 425.

Sharma, P.V. (1981), Dravya gun vigyana, Chaukhambha Bharti Academy, Varanasi, Vol. 1, PP. 208.

Swami, K.N. (1985), Gavon Main Aushadh Ratna, Kalera Krishana Gopal, Kalera (Raj.), Vol. 1, PP. 239.

368. *Piper chaba* Hunter non Blume.

Family: Piperaceae.

Synonym: *P. retrofractum, P. officinarum.*

Ayurvedic Groups: Charak: *Triptighana, Arshoghana, Deepaniya, Shoolaprashamana,* **Sushruta:** *Panchakola, Pippalyaadi gana.*

Name: English: Java Long Pepper. **Sanskrit:** *Chavikaa, Ushana, chavya.* **Hindi:** *Chavya,* **Local:** *Chaam, Chava.*

Botanical characteristics: Habit: A climbing glabrous herb, rather fleshy. **Stem:** Climbing by roots, with many minute furrows, usually 20 lines. **Leaf:** oblong, ovate or lanceolate, acuminate, base round unequal, cordate, nerves at base 3, with 2 pairs from midrib, 12.5-18 by 6.3-7 cm, petioles 6-13 mm long. **Flower:** Penducles 13-25 mm long. **Fruit:** Drupes very small, globose sunk, spikes cylindro-conic, widest at base, bright red, 2.5-7.5 cm long, 6 mm through.

Flowering and fruiting period: July-August and September-October.

Habitat: Cultivated in various parts of India, mostly in Bengal and Assam.

Parts used: Root, fruit. **Dosage:** 1-2 g.

Collection period: September-October.

Ayurvedic properties: ***Ras:*** *katu,* ***Gun:*** *laghu, rukhsa,* ***Veerya:*** *ushna,* ***Vipaka:*** *katu,* ***Tridosha*** **Effect:** alleviates ***Kapha:*** **+++,** ***Vaata:*** **++,** aggrevates ***Pitta:*** ++.

Chemical constituents: The **long pepper** is similar in composition to black pepper; it contains less piperine 4.5% and volatile oil 1.5%. The **stem** contains alkaloids piperine and piplartine. Beta-sitosterol, glycosides, glucose and fructose and mucilage. Active principle show muscle relaxant property.

Action and disease indications: The **fruits** are stimulant, thermogenic, anthelmintic, expectorant, appetizer, carminative, used for spleenomegaly, liver stimulant, renal diseases, chlorosis, abdomen diseases, intestinal worms, cough, asthma, bronchitis, fever, piles.

Clinical uses: Rhinitis, asthma, bronchitis, hiccough, disphonia: Root powder of described plant, 2 g, with honey 10 g, and tea, three times a day, is useful. **Epilepsy:** Snuff of Fruit powder of described plant, 500 mg, two times a day, is beneficial. **Sciatica, lumbago:** Local massage of medicated oil, made from paste of root of described plant, *Zingiber officinale,* is beneficial. **Anorexia:** (1) Mix powder of root of described plant, rock salt, roasted gum of *Ferula narthex,* 1.5 g, with water, two times a day, is beneficial.

(2) Mix powder of root of described plant, *Plumbego zeylanica,* roasted seeds of *Trachy spermum-ammi,* roasted roots of *Zingiber officinale,* roasted seeds of *Cuminum cyminum,* seeds of *Amomum subulatum,* seeds of *Punica grantum,* Rock salt, Black salt, 4 g, two times a day, is very beneficial.

Formulations: *Panchakol phaanta, Praandaa gutikaa, Chavyaadi ghrita.*

Recommended readings:

Bhutya, R.K. (2007), Vanaspati Aushadha Vigyana, Scientific Publishers (India), Jodhpur, PP. 94.

Chunekar, K.C. (2004), Bhava Prakash Nighantu, Chaukhambha Bharti Academy, Varanasi, PP. 20.

Khare, C.P. (2007), Indian Medicinal Plants, Springer (India) P.L. New Delhi, PP. 490.

Kirtikar, K.R. & Basu, B.D. (1998), Indian Medicinal Plants, L.M Basu, Allahabad, Vol. 3, PP. 2130.

Misra, B.L. (2005), Dravya Guna Hastamalaka, Publication scheme, Jaipur, PP. 402.

Nair, R.Vasudevan, (2007), Indian Medicinal Plants, Orient Longman P.L. Chennai, Vol. 4, PP. 284.

Namjoshi, A.N. (2001), The Ayurvedic Pharmacopoeia of India, Government of India, Department of Indian Systems of Medicine & Homoeopathy, New Delhi, Part-1, Volume- 1, PP. 29.

Pareek, G.N. (2005), Sudhanidhi, Vanoshadhi Ratnakar, Dhanvantari Karyalaya, Aligarh, Vol. 3, PP. 345.

Prajapati, N.D., Purohit, S.S., Sharma, A.K. & Tarun Kumar (2003), A Hand Book of Medicinal Plants, Agrobios India, Jodhpur, PP. 401.

Sharma, P.V. (1981), Dravya gun vigyana, Chaukhambha Bharti Academy, Varanasi, Vol. 1, PP. 335.

Singh, R.S. (2002), Vanoshadhi Nirdeshika, Uttar Pradesh Hindi Sansthan, Lucknow, PP. 126.

Swami, K.N. (1985), Gavon Main Aushadh Ratna, Kalera Krishana Gopal, Kalera (Raj.), Vol. 1, PP. 188.

369. *Piper cubeba* Linn. f.

Family: Piperaceae.

Other similar plants: *P.ribesiodes, P.sumatrana.*

Name: English: Cubeb, Tailed Piper, **Sanskrit:** *Kankola, Kolaka, Koshaphala,* **Hindi:** *Kankol, Kabaabchini,* **Local:** *Sheetal mircha, Sheetal chini, Kubaab chini.*

Botanical characteristics: Habit: A perennial woody climber. **Stem:** Tender, smooth, glandular, ash grey, rooted at the joints. **Leaf:** Simple, glabrous, coriaceous, ovate-oblong, base cordate or rounded, tip pointed, entire, petioled, lower surface densely provided with minute sunken glands. **Flower:** Small, unisexual, male and female flowers are borne on separate plant, in smooth scaly spikes, female spikes often curved. **Fruit:** Drupes, globose or sub-globose, stalked, somewhat apiculate, resembling with that of Black pepper and are 6-8 meridian.

Flowering and fruiting period: February-March and March-April.

Habitat: Cultivated in Assam and Karnataka.

Parts used: Unripe fruit, oil.

Dosage: 1-2 g, oil 1-5 drops.

Collection period: March-April.

Ayurvedic properties: ***Ras:*** *tikta, katu,* ***Gun:*** *laghu, rukhsa, tikhsna,* ***Veerya:*** *ushna,* ***Vipaka:*** *katu,* ***Tridosha*** **Effect:** alleviates ***Kapha: ++, Vaata: +.***

Chemical constituents: The **Unripe fruits** contain volatile 10-20%, consisting of sesquiterpene hydrocarbons; lignans, mainly cubebine 2%, with (-)-cubebine and kinokinin; cubebic acid. The oxygenated cyclohexanes, piperenol A and B, together with (+)-crotepoxide and (+)-zeylenol, have been isolated from the fruit. Polyhydroxy cyclohexanes possess anti-tumour, anti-leukaemic and anti-biotic activity.

Action and disease indications: The **fruits** are thermogenic, carminative, diuretic, aromatic, stimulant, anodyne, dentifrice, anti-inflammatory, anthelmintic, deobstruent, vulnerary, expectorant, appetizer, digestive, stomachic, cardio-tonic, rejuvenating, emmenogogue, sedative and anti-septic, used for cough, asthma, bronchitis, urinary tract infection, amoebic dysentery, halitosis, inflammations, stomatalgia, odontalgia, cephalgia, helminthiasis, wounds, ulcers, catarrh, anorexia, dyspepsia, flatulence, piles, cardiac debility, dysmenorrhea, amenorrhea, strangury, gonorrhea, cystitis, gleet and rheumatism.

Clinical uses: Disphonia: Mix the fruit powder of described plant, *Acorus calamus, Alpina galanga-uniflorum,* make tablets of 500 mg each, sucking of 1-2 tablets is very beneficial. **Nocturnal emission:** Mix powder of fruit of described plant, *Piper longum, seeds of Elettaria cardamomum,* gum of *Bambusa arundinacea,* sugar candy powder, 5 g, with water, two times a day, is beneficial. **Cystitis, oligouria:** Fruit powder of described plant 3 g, Alum 125 mg, with milk, two times a day, is beneficial.

Formulations: *Jirakaadhyarista, Khadiraadi vati, Balaa taila.*

Recommended readings:

Bhutya, R.K. (2007), Vanaspati Aushadha Vigyana, Scientific Publishers (India), Jodhpur, PP. 41.

Chunekar, K.C. (2004), Bhava Prakash Nighantu, Chaukhambha Bharti Academy, Varanasi, PP. 259.

Dhiman, A.K. (2006), Ayurvedic Drug Plants, Daya Publishing House, Delhi, PP. 178.

Khare, C.P. (2007), Indian Medicinal Plants, Springer (India) P.L. New Delhi, PP. 490.

Kirtikar, K.R. & Basu, B.D. (1998), Indian Medicinal Plants, L.M Basu, Allahabad, Vol. 3, PP. 2130.

Misra, B.L. (2005), Dravya Guna Hastamalaka, Publication scheme, Jaipur, PP. 403.

Nair, R. Vasudevan, (2007), Indian Medicinal Plants, Orient Longman P.L. Chennai, Vol. 4, PP. 287.

Namjoshi, A.N. (2001), The Ayurvedic Pharmacopoeia of India, Government of India, Department of Indian Systems of Medicine & Homoeopathy, New Delhi, Part-1, Volume- 2, PP. 58.

Prajapati, N.D., Purohit, S.S., Sharma, A.K. & Tarun Kumar (2003), A Hand Book of Medicinal Plants, Agrobios India, Jodhpur, PP. 402.

Sharma, P.V. (1981), Dravya gun vigyana, Chaukhambha Bharti Academy, Varanasi, Vol. 1, PP. 642.

Singh, R.S. (2002), Vanoshadhi Nirdeshika, Uttar Pradesh Hindi Sansthan, Lucknow, PP. 75.

Swami, K.N. (1985), Gavon Main Aushadh Ratna, Kalera Krishana Gopal, Kalera (Raj.), Vol. 2, PP. 156.

370. *Piper longum* Linn.

Family: Piperaceae.

Other similar plant: *P. sylvaticum.*

Ayurvedic Groups: Charak: *Kaasahar, Hikkaanigrahana, Shirovirechana, Vamanopag, Triptighna, Deepaniya, Shoolaprashamana,* **Sushruta:** *Pippalyaadi, Urdhvabhaagahara, Shirovirechana.*

Name: English: Indian Long Pepper, Joborandi, **Sanskrit:** *Pippali, Maagadhi, Krishnaa, Vaidehi, Chapalaa, Kanaa, Ushana, Kolaa,* **Hindi:** *Pippali,* **Local:** *Pipal, Choti Pipal.*

Botanical characteristics: Habit: A slender aromatic climbing herb. **Stem:** Numerous, 60-90 cm long, ascending or prostate, much branched, stout, cylindrical, thickened at nodes, finely pubescent, branches erect, sub-scandent. **Leaf:** Numerous, 5-9 by 3-5 cm, alternate, lower ones broadly ovate, cordate, upper ones oblong, oval, all entire, smooth, thin with reticulate venation, veins raised beneath; petioles of lower leaves 5-7.5 cm, stout, of upper leaves very short or none; stipules about 1.3 cm membranous, lanceolate, obtuse, soon falling. **Flower:** Spikes solitary, pedunculate, male slender, bracts narrow, female 1.3-2.5 cm, bracts circular, flat, paltate. **Fruit:** Berries, very small, ovoid, red when ripe and blackish-grey when ripe, complete sunk in solid fleshy spike which is 2.5-3.8 cm, ovoid-oblong, erect, blunt, blackish-green, shining. The mature spikes collected dried form the commercial form of *Pippali.* Roots are known as *Pippalimool.*

Flowering and fruiting period: July-August and October-November.

Habitat: Throughout the warmer parts of India, from central Himalayas to Assam, lower hills of West Bengal, Utter Pradesh, Andhra Pradesh, and Western Ghats, in evergreen forests, often cultivated.

Parts used: Fruit, root. **Dosage:** 0.5-1 g.

Collection period: October-November.

Ayurvedic properties: ***Ras:*** *katu,* ***Gun:*** *laghu, snigdha,* ***Veerya:*** *ushna,* ***Vipaka:*** *Madhur,* ***Tridosha*** **Effect:** alleviates ***Kapha:*** ***+++,*** ***Vaata:*** ***++.***

Chemical constituents: The **fruits** contain several aristolactams and dioxoaporphines, also contains the long chain isobutylamide, longamide, besides guineensine and the lignans, pluviatilol, methyl pulviatilol, sesamin and asarinine. Piperine is the major alkaloid of peppers. Piperine is anti-pyretic, hypotensive, CNS stimulant, exert significant protection against hepatotoxicity, and enhanced bioavailability of hexobarbitol, phenytoin, propranolol and theophylline. N-isobutyl-deca-trans-2-4-dienamide, isolated from fruit, exhibited anti-tubercular property. Milk extract of fruit effectively reduced passive cutaneous anaphylaxis. The **root** powder exhibites anti-fertility activity.

Action and disease indications: The **fruits** are thermogenic, aphrodisiac, stomachic, expectorant, carminative, febrifuge, laxative, digestive, emollient, anti-septic and tonic, prescribed for anorexia, dyspepsia, flatulence, colic, epilepsy, fever, cough, asthma, bronchitis, hiccough, gastropathy, piles, gonorrhea, gout and lumbago. The **roots** are thermogenic, tonic, diuretic, purgative, expectorant, anthelmintic, stomachic, digestive and emmenogogue, used for gout, lumbago, dyspepsia, apoplexy, stomachalgia and spleenomegaly.

Clinical uses: Rhinitis, asthma, bronchitis, hiccough, disphonia: Fruit powder of described plant, 500 mg, with honey 10 g, and tea, three times a day, is useful. **Paraplegia, chronic bronchitis, asthma, tuberculosis, enlargement of spleen, piles, chronic fever:** Apply *'Kalpa prayoga'* : Give Cold infusion of fruits of described plant, or medicated milk of fruit powder, 3 in number on first day at morning only, second day give 4 in number, increase 1-1 daily till 21 in number, then decrease 1-1 daily, till 3 in number. Give in three or four divided doses. This application is very useful. **Chronic sprue:** Use *'Kalpa prayoga'* of fruit powder of described plant, 3 to 21 fruits, by above method, in three or four divided doses, with whey or curd 500 g, or juice of *Punica grantum* 100-100 ml, or Mango juice 200 ml, is very beneficial. These medications should be used in supervision of well-qualified Ayurvedic doctor. **For rejuvenating:** Use *'Kalpa prayoga'* of fruit powder of described plant, of 3-21 fruits, in two divided doses, with milk **Sciatica, lumbago, hemiplegia:** Local massage of medicated oil, made from fruit powder of described plant, *Zingiber officinale,* is beneficial. **Sciatica, irritable bowel's syndrome:** Fruit powder of described plant, 1 g, with urine of cow 20 ml, or Castor oil 10 ml, at morning, take warm water 1-1 draught, by 5 minutes, three times. **Chronic fever:** (1) Cold infusion of fruits of described plant 500 mg, *Zingiber officinale* 1 g, *Trachy spermum-ammi* 4 g, *Tinospora cordifolia* 12 g, with rock salt 2 g, at morning, is useful. (2) Soak and dry the fruit powder of described plant, by urine of cow, by 3 times, then dry it well. 1 g of this powder, roasted seeds of *Cuminum cyminum,* sugar candy powder 10 g, with honey 10 g, three times a day, is useful. Give hot water 1-1 draught, by 5-5 minutes, 5 times. **Amnesia, demensia:** Fruit powder of described plant 1 g, *Convolvulus pluricaulis* 2 g, *Bacopa monnieri* 2 g, with milk, two times a day, is beneficial. **Insomnia:** Fruit powder of described plant 500 mg, *Withania somnifera* 1.5 g, with milk of buffalo, two times a day, is beneficial. **Low blood pressure:** Mix powder of fruit powder of described plant 4 parts, *'Lauha bhasma'* 2 parts, *'Ras sindoora'* 1 part, dose 250 mg, with *'Drakhsavaleha'* 10 g, two times a day, is very beneficial. **Hiccough:** Snuff of fruit powder of described plant, 250 mg, fine powder of sugar 1 g, is beneficial. **Headache, Migraine:** Soak and dry the fruit powder of described plant, by urine of cow, by 11 times, and then dry it well. 1 g of this powder and root powder of described plant 1 g, with hot water, by 2 hours, three times a day, is useful. **Ascitis:** Soak and dry the fruit powder of described plant, by latex of *Euphorbia ligularia,* 3 times, make pills of 250 mg, dose 1-2 pills, with milk of she camel or cow, Avoid salt in meal. If purgation is being more, reduce the dose. It is very beneficial treatment.

Formulations: *Pippalyaasava, Gur pippali, Pippali paaka, Pugakhanda, Vyaghriharitaki avaleha, Astaangaavaleha, Pippalikhanda, Vrihat aswagandhaavaleha, Kalyaanvaleha.*

Recommended readings:

Acharya, B.K. (2008), Ayurveda Jadi-buti Rahasya, Patanjali Yogapitha, Haridwar, PP. 345.

Bhutya, R.K. (2007), Vanaspati Aushadha Vigyana, Scientific Publishers (India), Jodhpur, PP. 151.

Brahmavarchas (2003), Ayurved Ka Pran Vanoshadhi Vigyan, Shanti Kunj, Haridwar, PP. 349.

Chunekar, K.C. (2004), Bhava Prakash Nighantu, Chaukhambha Bharti Academy, Varanasi, PP. 16.

Dhiman, A.K. (2006), Ayurvedic Drug Plants, Daya Publishing House, Delhi, PP. 300.

Khare, C.P. (2007), Indian Medicinal Plants, Springer (India) P.L. New Delhi, PP. 491.

Kirtikar, K.R. & Basu, B.D. (1998), Indian Medicinal Plants, L.M Basu, Allahabad, Vol. 3, PP. 2128.

Misra, B.L. (2005), Dravya Guna Hastamalaka, Publication scheme, Jaipur, PP. 399.

Nair, R.Vasudevan, (2007), Indian Medicinal Plants, Orient Longman P.L. Chennai, Vol. 4, PP. 290.

Namjoshi, A.N. (2001), The Ayurvedic Pharmacopoeia of India, Government of India, Department of Indian Systems of Medicine & Homoeopathy, New Delhi, Part-1, Volume- 1, PP. 133.

Pareek, G.N. (2005), Sudhanidhi, Vanoshadhi Ratnakar, Dhanvantari Karyalaya, Aligarh, Vol. 6, PP. 28.

Prajapati, N.D., Purohit, S.S., Sharma, A.K. & Tarun Kumar (2003), A Hand Book of Medicinal Plants, Agrobios India, Jodhpur, PP. 403.

Sharma, P.C., Yelne, MB. & Denis, T.J. (2000), Database on medicinal plants used in ayurveda, Central Council for research in Ayurveda and siddha, Vol. 3, PP. 472.

Sharma, P.V. (1981), Dravya gun vigyana, Chaukhambha Bharti Academy, Varanasi, Vol. 1, PP. 275.

Singh, R.S. (2002), Vanoshadhi Nirdeshika, Uttar Pradesh Hindi Sansthan, Lucknow, PP. 243.

Swami, K.N. (1985), Gavon Main Aushadh Ratna, Kalera Krishana Gopal, Kalera (Raj.), Vol. 1, PP. 285.

371. *Piper nigrum* Linn.

Family: Piperaceae.

Ayurvedic Groups: Charak: *Deepaniya, Shoolaprashamana, Krimighna, Shirovirechana,* ***Sushruta***: *Tryushana, Pippalyaadi gana.*

Name: English: Black Pepper, **Sanskrit:** *Maricha, Vellaja, Krishana, Ushana, Dharmapattana, Suvritta,* **Hindi:** *Kali Mirch,* **Local:** *Kalimirch.*

Botanical characteristics: Habit: A stout glabrous perennial woody climber. **Stem:** Much branched, terete, rooting at nodes. **Leaf:** Simple, alternate, cordate, coriaceous, 10-19-8 by 5-12.5 cm, very variable in breadth, broadly ovate,

288. *Macrotyloma uniflorum*-Kulathi

289. *Madhuca indica*-Mahua

290. *Majorana hortensis*-Marua

291. *Malaxis acuminata*-Jivaka

292. *Malaxis muscifera*-Rishabhaka

293. *Mallotus philipensis*-Kampillaka

294. *Malus pumila*-Seb

295. *Malva sylvestris*-Khubbaji

296. *Mangifera indica*-Aam

297. *Manilkara hexandra*-Khirani

298. *Marsdenia tenacissima*-Murva

299. *Marsilia minuta*-Chopatiya

300. *Martynia annua*-Kaakanasa

301. *Matricaria chamomilla*-Baabuna

302. *Melaleuca leucadendra*-Kayaputi

303. *Melia azedarach*-Mahanimba

304. *Mentha pipertia*-Piparment

305. *Mentha spicata*-Pudina

306. *Merremia gangetica*-Musakarni

307. *Mesua ferrea*-Nagkesar

308. *Michelia champaka*-Champa

309. *Mimosa pudica*-Lajvanti

310. *Mimusops elengi*-Maulashree

311. *Mitragyna parviflora*-Kalam

312. *Momardica charantia*-Karela

313. *Momordica dioica*-Kakoda

315. *Morus alba*-Shahtoot

314. *Moringa oleifera*-Shobhanjan

316. *Mucana pruriens*-Kavancha

317. *Murraya koenigii*-Mitha Neem

318. *Musa paradisiaca*-Kela

319. *Myrica nagi*-Kayaphala

320. *Myristica fragrans*-Jayaphala

321. *Nadostachys jatamansi*-Jatamaansi

322. *Nelumbo nucifera*-Kamal

323. *Nerium indicum*-Kaner

324. *Nicotiana tabacum*-Tambaku

325. *Nigella sativa*-Kaalaajaaji

326. *Nyctanthes arbor-tristis*-Harsingar

327. *Nymphaea stellata*-Nilophar

328. *Ochrocarpus longifolia*-Surpunnaga

329. *Ocimum basilicum*-Van Tulasi

330. *Ocimum canum*-Shyam Tulasi

331. *Ocimum gratissimum* -Raam Tulasi

332. *Ocimum kilimandscharicum* -Karpoor Tulasi

333. *Ocimum sanctum*-Tulasi

334. *Olea europaea*-Jetoon

335. *Operculina turpenthum*-Nisotha

336. *Opuntia dellenii*-Nagaphani

337. *Orchis latifolia-Saalam* Mishree

338. *Orxylum indicum*-Shyonak

339. *Oryza sativa*-Chaval

340. *Ougeinia oojeinensis*-Tinisha

341. *Oxalis corniculata*-Changeri

342. *Paederia scandens*-Gandhaprasarini

343. *Paeonia emodi*-Udasaliba

344. *Panax pseudoginseng*-Laxamanaa

345. *Pandanus fascicularis*-Kevara

346. *Papaver sommniferum*-Afima

347. *Parmelia perlata*-Chharila

348. *Pavonia odorata*-Netrabala

349. *Pedilium murex*-Gokharu Bara

350. *Peganum harmala*-Harmal

351. *Pentapetus phoenicea*-Dupahariya

352. *Pergularia daemia*-Utaran

353. *Peristrophe bicalyculata* -Kaakajangha

354. *Phaseolus mungo*-Urada

355. *Phaseolus radiatus*-Munga

356. *Phaseolus trilobus*-Mudgaparni

357. *Phoenix dactylifera*-Pindakharjoora

358. *Phoenix sylvestris*-Kharjoora

359. *Phyla nodiflora*-Jalpippali

360. *Phylanthus distichus*-Harpharevadi

361. *Phylanthus emblica*-Aawala

362. *Phylanthus fratrnus*-Bhumyamalaki

363. *Physalis minima*-Chirpotali

365. *Pinus gerardiana*-Chilgoja

364. *Picrorhiza kurroa*-Kutaki

366. *Pinus roxburghii*-Saral

367. *Piper betel*-Nagarbel

368. *Piper chaba*-Chavya

369. *Piper cubeba*-Kabaabachini

370. *Piper longum*-Pippali

371. *Piper nigrum*-Kali Mircha

373. *Pistacia integerrima*-Kaakaraasingi

374. *Pistacia lentiscus*-Roomi mastangi

375. *Pistia stratiotes*-Jalkumbhi

376. *Pisum sativum*-Matar

377. *Plantago ovata*-Isabagol

378. *Pluchea lanceolata*-Rasna

379. *Plumbago zeylanica* - Chitraka

acuminate, glabrous, 5-9-nerved, more or less oblique, petioles 1.3-2.5 cm long. **Flower:** minute in spikes, usually dioecious. **Fruit:** Fruiting spikes very variable in length, fruit ovoid or globose, 6 mm diam., one-seeded berries, bright red when ripe. **Seed:** Globose, testa thin, perisperm hard and white.

Flowering and fruiting period: June-July and December-January.

Habitat: Cultivated in Western Ghats, Karnataka, Maharastra, Assam and Kerala.

Parts used: Fruit. **Dosage:** 1-2 g.

Collection period: December-January.

Ayurvedic properties: ***Ras:*** *katu,* ***Gun:*** *laghu, rukhsa, tikhsna,* ***Veerya:*** *ushna,* ***Vipaka:*** *katu,* ***Tridosha*** **Effect:** alleviates ***Kapha:*** +++, ***Vaata:*** ++.

Chemical constituents: The **seeds** contain piperine, piperatine, and piperidine; amides, piperyline, piperoleins A and B, and N-*iso*-butylcicosa-*trans*-2-*trans*-4-dienamide.

Action and disease indications: The **fruits** are thermogenic, carminative, alterant, anthelmintic, aphrodisiac, anti-cholerin, sialagogue, bechic, alexeteric, anti-periodic, deobstruent, diuretic, digestive, emmenogogue, rubifacient, stimulant and stomachic, used for cough, asthma, bronchitis, arthritis, intestinal worms, pharyngodynia, fever, catarrh, dysentery, dyspepsia, flatulence, hiccough, piles, skin diseases.

Clinical uses: Dysentery, cholera: Fruit powder of described plant, 500 mg, roasted gum of *Ferula narthex 125 mg,* gum of *Papaver somniferum* 25 mg, with water, two times a day, is beneficial. **Piles, rectum prolepse:** Fruit powder of described plant 500 mg, with honey 10 g, two times a day, is useful. **Asthma, bronchitis:** (1) Mix powder of fruit powder of described plant, *Piper longum, Zingiber officinale,* 2 g, with clarified butter 5 g and honey 10 g, three times a day, is useful. (2) Sucking tablets of 1 g, of mix powder of seeds of described plant, *Piper longum*, fruit rind of *Punica grantum,* Nitrate of potas 1-1 part, raw sugar 8 parts, 4 times a day, is beneficial. **Pruritis, skin diseases, rheumatism, paralysis:** Local application of paste of fruit of described plant, and oil of *Brassica campestris,* or local massage of medicated oil, made by fruit powder of described plant, and cow urine, is beneficial. **Ringworm of scalp:** Local application of paste of fruit of described plant, common salt and *Allium cepa* is beneficial. **Leucoderma:** Local application of paste of seed powder of described plant, with vinegar, is beneficial. **Scorpion stings:** Local application of paste of seeds of described plant, Orpimint, with water, is beneficial. **Rhinitis:** Decoction of seed powder of described plant 1 g, *Zingiber officinale* 2 g, *Mentha spicata* 2 g, *Cinamomum verum* 1 g, *Glycyrrhiza glabra* 2 g, sugar candy powder 10 g, two times a day, is beneficial. **Hiccough:** Seed powder of described plant, 1 g, Nitrate of potash 500 mg, with warm water, two or three times a day, is useful. **Urticaria:** (1) Seed powder of described plant, 1 g, with clarified butter 10 g, two times a day, is beneficial. (2) Seed powder of described plant 1g, Amonium chloride 125 mg, Red iron oxide 500 mg, with water, three times a day, is useful. **Hemicrania:** Seed powder of described plant 1g, *Coriandrum sativum* 3 g, *Prunella vulgaris* 3 g, with honey water 10 g, two times a day, is beneficial. **Prolepse of anus:** Seed powder of described plant, 1 g, *Apium graveolens* 2 g, with honey 10 g, two times a day, is useful. **Penile dysfunction:** Seed powder of described plant 1 g, fruits of *Myristica fragrans* 500 mg, *Syzygium aromaticum* 500 mg, *Cinamomum camphora* 125 mg, *Crosus sativus* 10 mg, with creame, two times a day, is beneficial. **Sciatica, convulsion:** Seed powder of described plant 500 mg, Opium 25 mg, pure seeds of *Strychnos nux-vomica* 75 mg, *'Samir gaj kesari rasa'* 125 mg, with honey 10 g, two times a day, is very beneficial. It should be used under qualified Ayurvedic doctors supervision.

Formulations: *Marichyadi taila, Marichyadi vati, Marichyadi ghrita, Karpoorasava, Jwaraankusha rasa, Guduchyaadi lauha, Trikatu churna, Mrityunjaya rasa, Elaadi ghrita, Ayastriti.*

Recommended readings:

Acharya, B.K. (2008), Ayurveda Jadi-buti Rahasya, Patanjali Yogapitha, Haridwar, PP. 280.

Bhutya, R.K. (2007), Vanaspati Aushadha Vigyana, Scientific Publishers (India), Jodhpur, PP. 174.

Brahmavarchas (2003), Ayurved Ka Pran Vanoshadhi Vigyan, Shanti Kunj, Haridwar, PP. 351.

Chunekar, K.C. (2004), Bhava Prakash Nighantu, Chaukhambha Bharti Academy, Varanasi, PP. 17.

Dhiman, A.K. (2006), Ayurvedic Drug Plants, Daya Publishing House, Delhi, PP. 184.

Khare, C.P. (2007), Indian Medicinal Plants, Springer (India) P.L. New Delhi, PP. 492.

Kirtikar, K.R. & Basu, B.D. (1998), Indian Medicinal Plants, L.M Basu, Allahabad, Vol. 3, PP. 2133.

Misra, B.L. (2005), Dravya Guna Hastamalaka, Publication scheme, Jaipur, PP. 401.

Nair, R.Vasudevan, (2007), Indian Medicinal Plants, Orient Longman P.L. Chennai, Vol. 4, PP. 297.

Namjoshi, A.N. (2001), The Ayurvedic Pharmacopoeia of India, Government of India, Department of Indian Systems of Medicine & Homoeopathy, New Delhi, Part-1, Volume- 3, PP. 115.

Pareek, G.N. (2005), Sudhanidhi, Vanoshadhi Ratnakar, Dhanvantari Karyalaya, Aligarh, Vol. 7, PP. 68.

Prajapati, N.D., Purohit, S.S., Sharma, A.K. & Tarun Kumar (2003), A Hand Book of Medicinal Plants, Agrobios India, Jodhpur, PP. 404.

Sharma, P.C., Yelne, MB. & Denis, T.J. (2000), Database on medicinal plants used in ayurveda, Central Council for research in Ayurveda and siddha, Vol. 5, PP. 187.

Sharma, P.V. (1981), Dravya gun vigyana, Chaukhambha Bharti Academy, Varanasi, Vol. 1, PP. 362.

Singh, R.S. (2002), Vanoshadhi Nirdeshika, Uttar Pradesh Hindi Sansthan, Lucknow, PP. 295.

Swami, K.N. (1985), Gavon Main Aushadh Ratna, Kalera Krishana Gopal, Kalera (Raj.), Vol. 1, PP. 127.

372. *Piper wallichii* Hand.-Mazz.

Family: Piperaceae.

Synonym: *P.aurantiacum.*

Name: Sanskrit: *Renukaa, Raajputri, Nandini, Kapilaa, Dvijaa, Harenukaa,* **Hindi:** *Renukaa,* **Local:** *Renukaa-Beeja.*

Botanical characteristics: Habit: A rather stout climber, of a yellowish colour when dry. **Stem:** Climbing and rooting, glabrous; branches not hard or woody, glabrous. **Leaf:** 7.5-10 cm long, with petioles 2-2.5 cm, coriaceous, ovate elliptic or orbicular-ovate, caudate-acuminate, 5-nerved, hairy or glabrate beneath, almost shining above, base rounded or acute; nerves very slender above, strong beneath. **Flower:** Spikes 3.8-7.5 cm, grooping, peduncle of both sexesabout as long as the petioles; flowers densely crowded; bracts peltate, quite glabrous. **Fruit:** Fruiting spikes variable in length, fruit pyramidal when young and dry, when ripe about 4 mm diam., globose.

Flowering and fruiting period: June-July and October-November.

Habitat: Nepal, Lakhimpur and Khasi hills in Assam.

Parts used: Seed. **Dosage:** 1-3 g.

Collection period: October-November.

Ayurvedic properties: ***Ras:*** *tikta, katu,* ***Gun:*** *laghu, rukhsa,* ***Veerya:*** *ushna,* ***Vipaka:*** *katu,* ***Tridosha*** **Effect:** alleviates ***Kapha:*** *++,* ***Vaata:*** *+,* aggrevates ***Pitta:*** *+.*

Chemical constituents: The **fruits** contain piperine, piperettine and sylvatine, besides beta-sitosterol. The **seeds** contain aurantiamide, its acetate and auranamide. The fraction, containing alkaloids, showed oxytocic activity. The lignin constituents inhibited platelet aggregation caused by platelet-activating factor.

Action and disease indications: The **fruits** are appetizer, digestive, brain tonic, used for dipsia, pruritis, burning sensation, penile dysfunction and flatulence.

Clinical uses: Chronic dry bronchitis: Seed powder of described plant, 2 g, *Piper longum* 1 g, with curd, 25 g, two times a day, is beneficial. **Hiccough:** Decoction of seeds of described plant 2 g, *Piper longum* 1 g, with roasted gum of *Ferula narthex* 125 mg, by 1 hour, is beneficial. **Paralysis:** Decoction of seeds of described plant 2 g, is beneficial. **Asthonopia:** Seed powder of described plant 2 g, flower powder of *Mangifera indica and Syzygium cumini* 10 ml, two times a day, is beneficial.

Formulations: *Madhvaarista, Laakhsaadi taila, Vrihat yogaraaja guggulu, Amarsundari vati.*

Recommended readings:

Bhutya, R.K. (2007), Vanaspati Aushadha Vigyana, Scientific Publishers (India), Jodhpur, PP. 193.

Chunekar, K.C. (2004), Bhava Prakash Nighantu, Chaukhambha Bharti Academy, Varanasi, PP. 251.

Khare, C.P. (2007), Indian Medicinal Plants, Springer (India) P.L. New Delhi, PP. 493.

Kirtikar, K.R. & Basu, B.D. (1998), Indian Medicinal Plants, L.M Basu, Allahabad, Vol. 3, PP. 2136.

Sharma, P.V. (1981), Dravya gun vigyana, Chaukhambha Bharti Academy, Varanasi, Vol. 1, PP. 68.

Swami, K.N. (1985), Gavon Main Aushadh Ratna, Kalera Krishana Gopal, Kalera (Raj.), Vol. 3, PP. 248.

373. *Pistacia intergerrima* Stewart ex Brandis

Family: Anacardiaceae.

Synonym: *P.chinensis.*

Ayurvedic Groups: Charak: *Kaasahar, Hikkaanigrahana,* **Sushruta:** *Kaakolyaadi gana.*

Name: Sanskrit: *Shringi, Kulirvishaanikaa, Ajashringi, Chakraa, Karkataakhyaa.* **Hindi:** *Kakarasingi,* **Local:** *Kaakarasingi, Kaakkar.*

Botanical characteristics: Habit: A moderate sized deciduous tree, height up to 18 m, nearly glabrous. **Stem:** Bark dark grey or blackish. **Leaf:** Alternate, pinnately compound, 15-23 cm long, leaflets opposite, 4-5 pairs, with short petioles, lanceolate from oblique base, entire, long-acuminate, with 10-18 arcuate lateral nerves, jointed by reticulate veins. **Flower:**

Small, reddish in lateral panicles. Male panicles short, compact, pubescent, female on short pedicles, in long lax panicles. **Fruit:** Drupes, dry, globose, glabrous, wrinkled, rugose, grey when ripe. **Seed:** With a membranous testa. The **Galls** produces on the leaves and branches, and are pale greenish brown or pinkish, elongate, horn-shaped, hollow, twisted, curved or straight. When young they are coriaceous, but later become hard. They persist for long periods on branches after the escape of the aphids. The galls caused by the insect *Dasia aedifactor* (Homoptera).

Flowering and fruiting period: March-May and June-October.

Habitat: The outer ranges of North-west Himalaya, from Indus to Kumaon, Bengal and Assam, at 500-2500 m.

Parts used: Gall. **Dosage:** 1-3 g.

Collection period: May-June.

Ayurvedic properties: ***Ras:*** *kashaaya, tikta,* ***Gun:*** *laghu, rukhsa,* ***Veerya:*** *ushna,* ***Vipaka:*** *katu,* ***Tridosha* Effect:** alleviates ***Kapha:*** **++**, ***Vaata:*** **+**.

Chemical constituents: The **galls** contain Resin, two isomeric triterpenic acids- pistacienoic acids A and B, tannins, a triterpene alcohol-tirucallol, beta-sitosterol, tetracyclic triterpenes, pistacigerrimones A,B,C. The **essential oil** from galls contain alpha-pinene 21.8, beta-pinene 16.2, alpha-phellandrene 15.5 and delta-carene 11%.

Action and disease indications: The **galls** are thermogenic, depurative, digestive, anti-inflammatory, constipating, febrifuge, aromatic, tonic, expectorant, used for fever, cough, asthma, bronchitis, diarrhea, dysentery, hiccough, ulcers, consumption, stomach irritability, psoriasis, skin diseases, dyspepsia, inflammations, dipsia, anorexia, pharyngitis, leucorrhea and general debility. The oil obtained from galls is CNS depressant, anti-spasmodic, carminative, anti-bacterial, anti-protozoal, anti-amoebic, anthelmintic, used for intestinal worms, flatulence, colic and indigestion.

Clinical uses: Sprue: Fried powder (in clarified butter) of described plant 2 g, with honey 10 g, two times a day, is useful. **Allergic bronchitis, asthma, rhinitis:** Mix powder of described plant, *Clerodendron serratum, Zingiber officinale, Piper longum, Curcuma zedoria, Vitis vinifera,* 2 g, with decoction of *Solunum surattense* 10 g, and honey 10 g, three times a day, is useful. **Nausea, vomiting:** Powder of described plant 1 g, *Cyperus scarissus* 5 g, with honey 10 g, two times a day, is useful. **Psoriasis:** Local application of paste of described plant is beneficial. **Gingivitis, pyorrhea:** Gargles of Decoction of described plant, 5 g, three times a day, is useful. **Diarrhea:** powder of described plant 2 g, unripe fruit pulp of *Aegle marmelos* 4 g, two times a day, is beneficial. **Whooping cough:** Mix powder of described plant, *Glycyrrhiza glabra,* Borax, leaves powder of *Achyranthus aspera, Hyoscyamus niger,* 250 mg, with honey 10 g, three times a day, is useful. **Asthma:** Mix powder of described plant, *Inula racemosa, Piper longum, Terminalia belliarica,* Amonium chloride, Red iron oxide, 500 mg to 1.5 g, with honey 10 g, two or three times a day, is useful.

Formulations: *Chyavanpraasha, Dashamoola-arista, Shringyaadi churna, Baalchaaturbhadra churna, Sudarsan churna, Devadaarvyadi kwaatha, Satavaryaadi ghrita, Dashamoolar-ista, Kantakaaryaavaleha, Shivaa gutika, Khadiraadi gutika.*

Recommended readings:

Bhutya, R.K. (2007), Vanaspati Aushadha Vigyana, Scientific Publishers (India), Jodhpur, PP. 53.

Chunekar, K.C. (2004), Bhava Prakash Nighantu, Chaukhambha Bharti Academy, Varanasi, PP. 98.

Dhiman, A.K. (2006), Ayurvedic Drug Plants, Daya Publishing House, Delhi, PP. 199.

Khare, C.P. (2007), Indian Medicinal Plants, Springer (India) P.L. New Delhi, PP. 494.

Kirtikar, K.R. & Basu, B.D. (1998), Indian Medicinal Plants, L.M Basu, Allahabad, Vol. 1, PP. 650.

Misra, B.L. (2005), Dravya Guna Hastamalaka, Publication scheme, Jaipur, PP. 405.

Nair, R.Vasudevan, (2007), Indian Medicinal Plants, Orient Longman P.L. Chennai, Vol. 4, PP. 304.

Namjoshi, A.N. (2001), The Ayurvedic Pharmacopoeia of India, Government of India, Department of Indian Systems of Medicine & Homoeopathy, New Delhi, Part-1, Volume- 2, PP. 66.

Pareek, G.N. (2005), Sudhanidhi, Vanoshadhi Ratnakar, Dhanvantari Karyalaya, Aligarh, Vol. 2, PP. 323.

Prajapati, N.D., Purohit, S.S., Sharma, A.K. & Tarun Kumar (2003), A Hand Book of Medicinal Plants, Agrobios India, Jodhpur, PP. 405.

Sharma, P.C., Yelne, MB. & Denis, T.J. (2000), Database on medicinal plants used in ayurveda, Central Council for research in Ayurveda and siddha, Vol. 7, PP. 169.

Sharma, P.V. (1981), Dravya gun vigyana, Chaukhambha Bharti Academy, Varanasi, Vol. 1, PP. 284.

Singh, R.S. (2002), Vanoshadhi Nirdeshika, Uttar Pradesh Hindi Sansthan, Lucknow, PP. 91.

374. *Pistacia lentiscus* Linn.

Family: Anacardiaceae.

Other similar plants: *P.khinjuk, P.terebinthus.*

Name: English: Mastic Tree, **Hindi:** *Mastagi, Roomimastagi,* **Local:** *Roomimastagi.*

Botanical characteristics: Habit: A shrub or small tree. The gum resin obtained from stem and branches. The gum is yellowish-white. It is aromatic, sweetish in taste and sticky.

Habitat: Mediterranean countries. The resin imported into India.

Parts used: Gum-resin. **Dosage:** 1-3 g.

Collection period: June-August.

Ayurvedic properties: ***Ras:*** *madhur, kashaaya,* ***Gun:*** *laghu, rukhsa,* ***Veerya:*** *ushna,* ***Vipaka:*** *madhur* ***Tridosha*** **Effect:** alleviates ***Vaata:*** *++,* ***Pitta:*** *+*.

Chemical constituents: The **gum-resin** contains triterpenes are mastic acid, isomastic acid, oleanolic acid and tirucallol. The **mastic gum** contains 2% essential oil, contains 90% monoterpene hydrocarbons, the major constituents of which are alpha-pinene 79%, and mycrene 3%.

Action and disease indications: The **gum-resin** is astringent, carminative, diuretic, hypotensive, stimulant, anti-inflammatory, good for complexion, used for bronchitis, indigestion, inflammations, haemorrhages and ozostomia.

Clinical uses: Rib pain: Local application of paste of gum of described plant is beneficial. **Amenorrhea, dysmenorrhea:** Gum of described plant, 3 g, with lukewarm water, three times a day, is useful. **Sexual debility:** Gum of described plant, 3 g, with milk, two times a day, is beneficial.

Formulations: *Saalam paaka, Mahaa drakhsaasava, Pramehaantaka vati, Jangi churna, Aamaatisaarahara yoga.*

Recommended readings:

Bhutya, R.K. (2007), Vanaspati Aushadha Vigyana, Scientific Publishers (India), Jodhpur, PP. 193.

Chunekar, K.C. (2004), Bhava Prakash Nighantu, Chaukhambha Bharti Academy, Varanasi, PP. 837.

Khare, C.P. (2007), Indian Medicinal Plants, Springer (India) P.L. New Delhi, PP. 494.

Kirtikar, K.R. & Basu, B.D. (1998), Indian Medicinal Plants, L.M Basu, Allahabad, Vol. , PP.

Misra, B.L. (2005), Dravya Guna Hastamalaka, Publication scheme, Jaipur, PP. 407.

Prajapati, N.D., Purohit, S.S., Sharma, A.K. & Tarun Kumar (2003), A Hand Book of Medicinal Plants, Agrobios India, Jodhpur, PP. 406.

Sharma, P.V. (1981), Dravya gun vigyana, Chaukhambha Bharti Academy, Varanasi, Vol. 1, PP. 258.

Singh, R.S. (2002), Vanoshadhi Nirdeshika, Uttar Pradesh Hindi Sansthan, Lucknow, PP. 297.

375. *Pistia stratiotes* Linn.

Family: Araceae.

Other similar plants: *Eichhornia crassipes* (Pontaderiaceae)-pitcher like plant, flowers bluish purple.

Name: English: Water Lettuce, Tropical Duckweed, **Sanskrit:** *Vaariparni, Vaarimooli, Kumbhikaa, Khamoolikaa,* **Hindi:** *Jalakumbhi,* **Local:** *Jalkumbhi.*

Botanical characteristics: Habit: A floating stemless stoloniferous herb, with a peculiar muriatic odour; roots of tufted simple white fibers clothed with fibrillae. **Leaf:** 3.2-10 cm long, variable in breadth, obovate-cuneate, rounded or retuse at the apex, densely and closely pubescent on both surfaces; nerves few or many, flabellately arranged, converging within the margin. **Flower:** Spathe about 13 mm long, obliquely campanulate, white, gibbousand closed below, contracted about the middle, dileted and nearly orbicular above.

Flowering and fruiting period: May-June and August-September.

Habitat: Throughout India, in ponds.

Parts used: Whole plant. **Dosage:** Juice 10-20 ml.

Collection period: April-May.

Ayurvedic properties: ***Ras:*** *tikta, katu,* ***Gun:*** *laghu, rukhsa,* ***Veerya:*** *sheeta,* ***Vipaka:*** *katu,* ***Tridosha*** **Effect:** alleviates ***Pitta:*** ***++,*** ***Vaata:*** ***+,*** ***Kapha:*** ***+.***

Chemical constituents: The **plant** contains 2-*di*-C-glycosylflavones of vicenin and lucenin type, anthocyanin-cyanidin-3-glucoside, luteolin-7-glycoside and mono-C-glyco-sylflavons-vitexin and orientin.

Action and disease indications: The **plant** is refrigerant, laxative, anti-tussive, demulcent, anti-dysenteric, diuretic, used for dysuria, piles, skin diseases, tapeworm infestation, fever and tuberculous glands.

Clinical uses: Intestinal worms: Alkali of described plant 500 mg, with clarified butter 10 g, two times a day, is beneficial. **Dysentery:** Juice of described plant 20 ml, Coconut water 50 ml, and boiled rice 100 g, two times a day, is beneficial. **Dry cough:** Juice of described plant 20 ml, Distillate of *Rosa Centifolia* 10 ml, sugar 10 g, three times a day, is useful. **Dysuria:** Juice or decoction of described plant 20 ml, with sugar 10 g, two times a day, is beneficial. **Otopyorrhea, otorrhea, otalgia:** Medicated oil, made by juice of described plant, 4-4 drops, two times a day, is beneficial.

Formulations: *Chandanaadi taila.*

Recommended readings:

Bhutya, R.K. (2007), Vanaspati Aushadha Vigyana, Scientific Publishers (India), Jodhpur, PP. 104.

Chunekar, K.C. (2004), Bhava Prakash Nighantu, Chaukhambha Bharti Academy, Varanasi, PP. 485.

Khare, C.P. (2007), Indian Medicinal Plants, Springer (India) P.L. New Delhi, PP. 495.

Kirtikar, K.R. & Basu, B.D. (1998), Indian Medicinal Plants, L.M Basu, Allahabad, Vol. 4, PP. 2600.

Misra, B.L. (2005), Dravya Guna Hastamalaka, Publication scheme, Jaipur, PP. 498.

Pareek, G.N. (2005), Sudhanidhi, Vanoshadhi Ratnakar, Dhanvantari Karyalaya, Aligarh, Vol. 10, PP. 173.

Sharma, P.V. (1981), Dravya gun vigyana, Chaukhambha Bharti Academy, Varanasi, Vol. 1, PP. 796.

Singh, R.S. (2002), Vanoshadhi Nirdeshika, Uttar Pradesh Hindi Sansthan, Lucknow, PP. 161.

Swami, K.N. (1985), Gavon Main Aushadh Ratna, Kalera Krishana Gopal, Kalera (Raj.), Vol. 2, PP. 302.

376. *Pisum sativum* Linn.

Family: Leuminosae, Fabaceae.

Name: English: Garden Pee, **Sanskrit:** *Kalaaya, Vartula, Satin, Harenuk,* **Hindi:** *Matar,* **Local:** *Batalaa, Matar.*

Botanical characteristics: Habit: An annual herbaceous tendril climber, 1 m high. **Stem:** Hollow. **Leaf:** Pinnately compound, leaflets entire, 3-4 by 2-3 cm; stipules auricled. **Flower:** White, red or pink. **Fruit:** Pods, straight or curved, 5-10 cm long. **Seed:** Globular, smooth, 6-8 mm diam., green, yellowish green, bluish green, white, grey or brown, 6-9 per pod.

Flowering and fruiting period: September-October and October-November.

Habitat: Cultivated throughout India, at higher altitudes.

Parts used: Seed. **Dosage:** 25-50 g.

Collection period: October-November.

Ayurvedic properties: ***Ras:*** *madhur,* ***Gun:*** *laghu, rukhsa,* ***Veerya:*** *sheeta,* ***Vipaka:*** *madhur,* ***Tridosha*** **Effect:** alleviates ***Kapha:*** **+++,** aggrevates ***Vaata:*** **++++,** ***Pitta:*** +.

Chemical constituents: The **seeds** contain protein 23, carbohydrate 54, fat 1, fibers 5 and ash 2%, also trigonellin alkaloid. The **oil** has anti-sex-hormone, which produce impotency.

Action and disease indications: The **seeds** are cooling, laxative, depurative, emollient, and resolvent, used for burning sensation, cough, bronchitis, skin diseases, leprosy, measles, cuts and wounds.

Clinical uses: Satyriasis: Seed oil of described plant, 3-6 drops, with milk two times a day, is beneficial. This medication is not for prolonged use.

Recommended readings:

Bhutya, R.K. (2007), Vanaspati Aushadha Vigyana, Scientific Publishers (India), Jodhpur, PP. 55.

Chunekar, K.C. (2004), Bhava Prakash Nighantu, Chaukhambha Bharti Academy, Varanasi, PP. 649.

Kirtikar, K.R. & Basu, B.D. (1998), Indian Medicinal Plants, L.M Basu, Allahabad, Vol. 1, PP. 772.

Nair, R.Vasudevan, (2007), Indian Medicinal Plants, Orient Longman P.L. Chennai, Vol. 4, PP. 308.

Sharma, P.V. (1981), Dravya gun vigyana, Chaukhambha Bharti Academy, Varanasi, Vol. 2, PP. 177.

377. *Plantago ovata* Forsk.

Family: Plantaginaceae.

Synonym: *P. ispaghula.*

Other similar plants: *P. major, P. lanceolata, P. menoria.*

Name: English: Ispaghula, Spogel seeds, Blond Psyllium, **Sanskrit:** *Aswagol, Isadagol, Aswakarnabeeja, Sheetabeeja, Snigdhajiraka,* **Hindi:** *Isabgol,* **Local:** *Isabgol.*

Botanical characteristics: Habit: An annual, erect, scapigerous, stemless or very short stemmed, softly hairy or woolly herb, height 60-90 cm. **Stem:** none or very short. **Leaf:** Simple, 7.5-23 cm by 6 mm, narrowly linear or filiform, finely acuminate, entire or distantly toothed, attenuated at the base, usually 3-nerved, scapes longer or shorter than the leaves, glabrous or pubescent. **Flower:** Small, in ovoid or cylindric spikes 1.3-3.8 cm long; bracts 4 by 4 mm, ovate or sub-orbicular, concave, membranous, glabrous. **Fruit:** Capsule, ellipsoid obtuse, 8 mm long, membranous, glabrous, the upper half coming off as a blunt conical lid. **Seed:** 3 mm long, smooth, yellowish brown, ovoid-oblong, boat-shaped.

Flowering and fruiting period: December-January and February-March.

Habitat: Cultivated in Punjab, Hariyana, Rajasthan and Gujarat.

Parts used: Seed, Seed coat. **Dosage:** 3-5 g.

Collection period: March-April.

Ayurvedic properties: ***Ras:*** *madhur,* ***Gun:*** *guru, snigdha, pichhala,* ***Veerya:*** *sheeta,* ***Vipaka:*** *madhur,* ***Tridosha*** **Effect:** alleviates ***Vaata:*** ++, ***Pitta:*** +.

Chemical constituents: The **seeds** contain amino acids including valine, alanine, glutamic acid, glycine, cystine, lysine, leucine and tyrosine; and a mucilage consisting of a mixture of polysaccharides composed mainly of xylose, arabinose and galacturonic acid; rhmnose and galactose, are also present. Also gave aucubin, the anti-bacterial principle. Other are ascorbic acid, linoleic, linolenic, lignoceric, oleic, palmitic and stearic acids, hydrocarbons, sitosterol and tannin.

Action and disease indications: The **seeds** are refrigerant, emollient, mucilaginous, diuretic, laxative, anti-inflammatory, anti-dysenteric, expectorant, aphrodisiac, roborant and tonic, prescribed for habitual constipation, irritable bowel syndrome, burning sensation, strangury, gastritis, chronic diarrhea, dysentery, colonalgia, dry cough, erysipelas, gonorrhea, bilious fever, gout, duodenal ulcers, piles, nephropathy, emaciation and general debility.

Contraindication: Do not make powder of seeds and husk.

Clinical uses: Diarrhea, dysentery: (1) Fried seed and husk, 5 g, seeds of *Holarrhena antidysentrica* 1 g, with whey, two times a day, is beneficial. (2) Mix powder of husk of described plant, unripe fruit pulp of *Aegle marmelos,* Gum of *Cochlospermum religiasum, Cordia dichotoma,* gum of *Pistacia lentiscus, Zingiber officinale,* 5 g, with milk of she goat at morning and evening and with water at noon, is useful. **Nocturnal emission:** Husk of described plant, 5 g, sugar 10 g, with milk, two times a day, is beneficial. **Poisoning of Arsenic:** Seed powder of described plant 5 g, seeds of *Cydonia oblonga* 3 g, with curd or whey, two times a day, is beneficial. **Dry bronchitis:** Mucilage of husk of described plant, 10 g, with sugar candy powder 10 g, two times a day, is beneficial. **Gonorrhea:** Mucilage of husk of described plant, 10 g, *Piper cubeba,* 1 g, with water, two times a day, is beneficial. **Chronic dysentery, amaebic dysentery:** Mix powder of husk of described plant 8 parts, seeds of *Aegle marmelos* 4 parts, seeds of *Holarrhena antidysentrica* 2 parts, *Aconitum heterophylum* 1 part, *Zingiber officinalis* 2 parts, bark of *Holorrhena antidysentrica* 4 parts, Flowers of *Woodfordia fruticosa* 2 parts, *Coriandrum sativum* 1 part, sugar, 2 parts, dose 10-15 g, with water, two or three times a day, is beneficial. **General debility:** Mix powder of husk of described plant, *Withania somnifera,* unripe fruits of *Terminalia chebula,* 2-2 parts, *Symplocos racemosa* 1 part, sugar candy powder 7 parts, dose 10 g, with fresh milk, two times a day, is beneficial.

Formulations: *Pravaahikaantaka churna, Snigdhajiraka paaka.*

Recommended readings:

Acharya, B.K. (2008), Ayurveda Jadi-buti Rahasya, Patanjali Yogapitha, Haridwar, PP. 191.

Bhutya, R.K. (2007), Vanaspati Aushadha Vigyana, Scientific Publishers (India), Jodhpur, PP. 31.

Chunekar, K.C. (2004), Bhava Prakash Nighantu, Chaukhambha Bharti Academy, Varanasi, PP. 812.

Dhiman, A.K. (2006), Ayurvedic Drug Plants, Daya Publishing House, Delhi, PP. 53.

Khare, C.P. (2007), Indian Medicinal Plants, Springer (India) P.L. New Delhi, PP. 498.

Kirtikar, K.R. & Basu, B.D. (1998), Indian Medicinal Plants, L.M Basu, Allahabad, Vol. 3, PP. 2039.

Misra, B.L. (2005), Dravya Guna Hastamalaka, Publication scheme, Jaipur, PP. 458.

Nair, R.Vasudevan, (2007), Indian Medicinal Plants, Orient Longman P.L. Chennai, Vol. 4, PP. 312.

Pareek, G.N. (2005), Sudhanidhi, Vanoshadhi Ratnakar, Dhanvantari Karyalaya, Aligarh, Vol. 1, PP. 352.

Prajapati, N.D., Purohit, S.S., Sharma, A.K. & Tarun Kumar (2003), A Hand Book of Medicinal Plants, Agrobios India, Jodhpur, PP. 408.

Sharma, P.C., Yelne, MB. & Denis, T.J. (2000), Database on medicinal plants used in ayurveda, Central Council for research in Ayurveda and siddha, Vol. 7, PP. 17.

Sharma, P.V. (1981), Dravya gun vigyana, Chaukhambha Bharti Academy, Varanasi, Vol. 1, PP. 414.

Singh, R.S. (2002), Vanoshadhi Nirdeshika, Uttar Pradesh Hindi Sansthan, Lucknow, PP. 45.

Swami, K.N. (1985), Gavon Main Aushadh Ratna, Kalera Krishana Gopal, Kalera (Raj.), Vol. 2, PP. 116.

378. *Pluchea lanceolata* C.B. Clarke.

Family: Compositae; Asteraceae.

Ayurvedic Groups: Charak: *Anuvaasanopaga, Vayahsthaapana,* **Sushruta:** *Arkaadi gana, Slesmasansamana varga.*

Different opinion: Many different plants are being use in the different parts of India. By the name of `Raasnaa' These are: 1. *Pluchea lanceolata- Raisan* - in Uttar Pradesh, Punjab, Gujarat, Bihar. 2. *Vanda roxburghii- Baandaa-* in Bengal. 3. *Alpinia galangal- Kulinjan-* in South

India. 4. *Inula racemosa- Pushkarmoola.* 5. *Saccolabium Papilosum-Baandaa.* 6. *Tylophora asthmatica- Arkapatri-* in Mumbai.

Name: Sanskrit: *Raasnaa, Yuktarasaa, Rasyaa, Suvahaa, Rasanaa, Rasaa, Elaaparni, Surasaa, Sugandhaa, Sreyasi,* **Hindi:** *Raasna,* **Local:** *Raasna, Vaayusurai, Raayasan.*

Botanical characteristics: Habit: An erect, stiff herb or undershrub, height up to 1.5 m. **Root:** Very long. **Stem:** Stem and branches terete, slender, softly ashy-pubescent. **Leaf:** Sessile, very coriaceous, 2.5-5.7 by 0.6-1.3 cm, oblong or oblanceolate, obtuse, apiculate, narrowed at the base, finely ashy-pubescent on both sides, entire; main nerves prominent. Shape like the leaves of *Cassia senna,* but large. **Flower:** Heads in compound corymbs, pink or with purple tinge, invulucre contracted at the mouth; outer bracts 2-3-serrete, oblong, very obtuse, pubescent; the inner most bracts linear, sub-acute, few. **Fruit:** Achenes, minute, oblong, pappus connate at base.

Flowering and fruiting period: March-December.

Habitat: Punjab, Upper Gangetic plains, Gujarat and Rajasthan.

Parts used: Leaves, whole plant. **Dosage:** 3-6 g.

Collection period: April-May.

Ayurvedic properties: ***Ras:*** *tikta,* ***Gun:*** *guru,* ***Veerya:*** *ushna,* ***Vipaka:*** *katu,* ***Tridosha* Effect:** alleviates ***Kapha: +++, Vaata: +++.***

Chemical constituents: The **leaves** contain quercetin, quercitrin, isorhamnetin, pluchioside, pleuchiol, 23-methyldotriacontan-3-one, 22-methylhentriacontane-3 and 19-dione.

Action and disease indications: The **leaves** are thermogenic, digestive, analgesic, febrifuge, alexiteric, laxative, nervine tonic, anti-inflammatory, inflammations, asthma, gout, neuralgia, gastropathy, bronchitis, fever, ptyrasis versicolor, pains and rheumatism.

Clinical uses: Jaundice: Root powder of described plant, 2 g, with milk, two times a day, is beneficial. **Constipation:** Root powder of described plant 5 g, with water, at night, is beneficial. **Hypothermia, inflammation, pains:** Local application of paste of roots of described plant, *Aquilaria malaccensis,* or medicated oil, made by root powder of described plant, is beneficial. **Asthma, bronchitis, anorexia:** Sauce of root powder of described plant, *Zingiber officinale, Piper longum,* 4 g, with warm water, two times a day, is beneficial. **Piles:** Hot fomentation by root powder of described plant, is beneficial. **Sciatica:** Root powder of described plant 2 g, gum of *Commiphora mukul* 2 g, with warm water, two times a day, is beneficial. **Gout:** Local application of paste of mix powder of root powder of described plant, *Tinospora cordifolia, Glycyrrhiza glabra, Sida cordifolia,* is beneficial. **Rheumatism:** Decoction of root powder of described plant, *Tinospora cordifolia.* roots of *Ricinus communis, Cedrus deodara, Zingiber officinale,* 10 g, with Castor oil 10 ml mg, at morning, is beneficial.

Formulations: *Raasnaadi kwaatha, Raasnaadi taila, Raasnaadi ghrita, Laakhsaadi taila.*

Recommended readings:

Bhutya, R.K. (2007), Vanaspati Aushadha Vigyana, Scientific Publishers (India), Jodhpur, PP. 191.

Brahmavarchas (2003), Ayurved Ka Pran Vanoshadhi Vigyan, Shanti Kunj, Haridwar, PP. 358.

Chunekar, K.C. (2004), Bhava Prakash Nighantu, Chaukhambha Bharti Academy, Varanasi, PP. 79.

Khare, C.P. (2007), Indian Medicinal Plants, Springer (India) P.L. New Delhi, PP. 500.

Kirtikar, K.R. & Basu, B.D. (1998), Indian Medicinal Plants, L.M Basu, Allahabad, Vol. 2, PP. 1345.

Misra, B.L. (2005), Dravya Guna Hastamalaka, Publication scheme, Jaipur, PP. 297.

Namjoshi, A.N. (2001), The Ayurvedic Pharmacopoeia of India, Government of India, Department of Indian Systems of Medicine & Homoeopathy, New Delhi, Part-1, Volume- 3, PP. 162.

Pareek, G.N. (2005), Sudhanidhi, Vanoshadhi Ratnakar, Dhanvantari Karyalaya, Aligarh, Vol. 7, PP. 209.

Prajapati, N.D., Purohit, S.S., Sharma, A.K. & Tarun Kumar (2003), A Hand Book of Medicinal Plants, Agrobios India, Jodhpur, PP. 409.

Sharma, P.C., Yelne, M.B. & Denis, T.J. (2000), Database on medicinal plants used in ayurveda, Central Council for research in Ayurveda and siddha, Vol. 7, PP. 375.

Sharma, P.V. (1981), Dravya gun vigyana, Chaukhambha Bharti Academy, Varanasi, Vol. 1, PP. 39.

Singh, R.S. (2002), Vanoshadhi Nirdeshika, Uttar Pradesh Hindi Sansthan, Lucknow, PP. 327.

379. *Plumbago zeylanica* Linn.

Family: Plumbaginaceae.

Ayurvedic Groups: Charak: *Triptighna, Bhedaniya, Deepaniya, Shoolaprashamana, Arshoghna, Lekhaniya, Katuskandha,* **Sushruta:** *Pippalyaadi, Mustaadi, Aamalakyaadi, Mushkakaadi, Varunaadi, Aaragvadhaadi Gana.*

Other similar plants: *P. indica* - rose var., *P. auriculata* - blue var.

Name: English: Ceylon Leadwort, leadwort, **Sanskrit:** *Agni, chitraka, Paathi, Vyaala,*

Usana, **Hindi:** *Chitraka,* **Local:** *Chitraka, Chitaa, Chataawal.*

Botanical characteristics: Habit: An erect or straggling, perennial, pretty undershrub, height 60-150 cm. **Root:** 30 cm long, 6 mm in diam., cylindrical, irregularly bent, light yellowish brown with smooth surface. **Stem:** Semi-woody, straight, spreading, terete, glabrous and flexible branches. **Leaf:** Simple, alternate, 3.8-10 by 1.5-6 cm, ovate, acute, glabrous, somewhat glaucous beneath, reticulately veined entire, thin, narrowed into the petiole, stalk short. **Flower:** White, borne in terminal and axillary racemes, spikes often branched, glandular and elongated 10-30 cm long, rhachis glandular, striate; bracteoles ovate, acuminate, shorter than the calyx, glandular or not. **Fruit:** Capsule, oblong, pointed, longitudinally furrowed, which are enclosed by persistent and viscid calyx; pericarp thin below, thick and hardened above. **Seed:** Small, oblong.

Flowering and fruiting period: October-November and December-January.

Habitat: Found wild in peninsular India and West Bengal, also grown in gardens throughout India.

Parts used: Root, alkaloid.

Dosage: Root 1-2 g, Alkali 500 mg.

Collection period: March-April.

Ayurvedic properties: ***Ras:*** *katu,* ***Gun:*** *laghu, rukhsa, Tikhsna,* ***Veerya:*** *ushna,* ***Vipaka:*** *katu,* ***Tridosha*** **Effect:** alleviates ***Kapha:*** *+++,* ***Vaata:*** *+.*

Chemical constituents: The **roots** contain naphthoquinone derivatives-mostly plumbagin, 3-chloroplumbagin, 3,3'-biplumbagin, elliptinone, chitranone, zeylinone, isozeylinone, droserone, plumbagic acid, plumbazeylanone, naphthelenone and isoshinanolone.

Action and disease indications: The **roots** are thermogenic, anthelmintic, expectorant, anti-inflammatory, abortifacient, constipating, alterant, anti-periodic, digestive, carminative, sudorofic, narcotic, gastric and nervous stimulant and rejuvenating, prescribed for inflammations, dyspepsia, colic, cough, asthma, bronchitis, helminthiasis, rheumatism, aneamia, piles, elephantiasis, chronic intermittent fever, leucoderma, ringworm, scabies, hepato-spleenomagaly, amenorrhea and odontalgia.

Contraindication: Do not give in pregnancy period.

Clinical uses: Anorexia, indigestion, Diarrhea: Mix powder of root powder of described plant 1 g, *Embelia ribes,* 1 g, *Cyperus scarissus* 5 g, with water, two times a day, is beneficial. **Piles:** (1) Root powder of described plant, 1 g, with curd, two times a day, is beneficial. (2) Root powder of described plant, fruit powder of *Juniperus communis,* fried gum of *Ferula narthex,* 1.5 g, with whey, two times a day, is beneficial. **Liver and spleen enlargement:** Alkali of described plant, 500 mg, with whey, two times a day, is beneficial. **Rheumatism, arthritis:** Massage by medicated oil, made by root powder of described plant, is beneficial. **Leucoderma:** (1) Local application of paste of root of described plant, and root bark of *Nerium indicum,* with water is beneficial. Use it for 3 weeks. (2) Local application of paste of root of described plant, and seeds of *Psoralea corylifolia,* with urine of cow, is beneficial. (3) Local application of paste of root of described plant, *Saussurea costus,* seeds of *Abrus precatorius, Acorus calamus,* with leaves juice of *Azadirachta indica,* is beneficial. **Renal and vesical calculus:** Decoction of root powder of described plant, 2 g, with honey 10 g, two times a day, is useful.

Formulations: *Chitrakaadi vati, Chitraka ghrita, Chitrakaharitaki avaleha, Dashamoolaarista, Drakhsaasava, Lauhaasava, Aswagandhaarista, Yakritaplihaari lauha, Chitrakaadi taila.*

Recommended readings:

Acharya, B.K. (2008), Ayurveda Jadi-buti Rahasya, Patanjali Yogapitha, Haridwar, PP. 160.

Bhutya, R.K. (2007), Vanaspati Aushadha Vigyana, Scientific Publishers (India), Jodhpur, PP. 98.

Brahmavarchas (2003), Ayurved Ka Pran Vanoshadhi Vigyan, Shanti Kunj, Haridwar, PP. 355.

Chunekar, K.C. (2004), Bhava Prakash Nighantu, Chaukhambha Bharti Academy, Varanasi, PP. 22.

Dhiman, A.K. (2006), Ayurvedic Drug Plants, Daya Publishing House, Delhi, PP. 105.

Khare, C.P. (2007), Indian Medicinal Plants, Springer (India) P.L. New Delhi, PP. 501.

Kirtikar, K.R. & Basu, B.D. (1998), Indian Medicinal Plants, L.M Basu, Allahabad, Vol. 2, PP. 1466.

Misra, B.L. (2005), Dravya Guna Hastamalaka, Publication scheme, Jaipur, PP. 461.

Nair, R.Vasudevan, (2007), Indian Medicinal Plants, Orient Longman P.L. Chennai, Vol. 4, PP. 321.

Namjoshi, A.N. (2001), The Ayurvedic Pharmacopoeia of India, Government of India, Department of Indian Systems of Medicine & Homoeopathy, New Delhi, Part-1, Volume- 2, PP. 29.

Pareek, G.N. (2005), Sudhanidhi, Vanoshadhi Ratnakar, Dhanvantari Karyalaya, Aligarh, Vol. 3, PP. 355.

Prajapati, N.D., Purohit, S.S., Sharma, A.K. & Tarun Kumar (2003), A Hand Book of Medicinal Plants, Agrobios India, Jodhpur, PP. 410.

Sharma, P.C., Yelne, MB. & Denis, T.J. (2000), Database on medicinal plants used in ayurveda, Central Council for research in Ayurveda and siddha, Vol. 1, PP. 102.

Sharma, P.V. (1981), Dravya gun vigyana, Chaukhambha Bharti Academy, Varanasi, Vol. 1, PP. 359.

Singh, R.S. (2002), Vanoshadhi Nirdeshika, Uttar Pradesh Hindi Sansthan, Lucknow, PP. 148.

380. *Polyalthia longifolia* Thw.

Family: Annonaceae.

Name: English: Mast Tree, Fake Asoka Tree, False Devadaru, Cemetry Tree, **Sanskrit:** *Kaastha-daru, Devadaari,* **Hindi:** *Aashaapaalaa,* **Local:** *Aashaapaalaa.*

Botanical characteristics: Habit: A tall handsome evergreen tree, height 12-20 m. **Stem:** With a straight trunk and strictly drooping, slender, glabrous branches, bark smooth, grayish brown, thick. **Leaf:** Simple, green, membranous, 7.5-23 by 1.8-3.8 cm, narrowly lanceolate, tapering to a fine point, shining with undulate margins, both surfaces glabrous; petioles about 6 mm long. **Flower:** 2.5-3.8 cm across, yellowish-green or white, in fascicles or shortly peduncled umbels; pedicels slender, 2.5-3.8 cm long, with a small, pubescent deciduous bract about or above the middle. **Fruit:** Carpels, small, ovoid, one-seeded, purple, 18 cm long, numerous, stalked, obtuse on both ends, glabrous, born in clusters, stalk 12 mm long, stout, glabrous. **Seed:** Smooth, shining.

Flowering and fruiting period: April-May and July-August.

Habitat: Grown in gardens throughout the hotter parts of India.

Parts used: Bark. **Dosage:** 5-10 g.

Collection period: April-May.

Ayurvedic properties: ***Ras:*** *tikta, katu,* ***Gun:*** *laghu, snigdha,* ***Veerya:*** *ushna,* ***Vipaka:*** *katu,* ***Tridosha*** **Effect:** alleviates ***Kapha:*** **+++,** ***Pitta:*** ++.

Chemical constituents: The **stem bark** contains clerodane diterpenes, polyalthialdoic acid, and kolavenic acid and cytotoxic aporphine alkaloid, liriodenin, *nor*-oli-veroline and oliveroline-beta-N-oxide and azufluorene alkaloid.

Action and disease indications: The **bark** is cooling, digestive, febrifuge, and anthelmintic, used for diabetes, fever, hypertension, skin diseases, helminthiasis and indigestion.

Clinical uses: Diarrhea with bleeding: Cold infusion of bark of described plant 5 g, with honey 10 g, two times a day, is beneficial. **Stomatitis:** Gargles by bark of described plant, and *Bauhinia racemosa,* 10 g, two times a day, is beneficial. **Hypertension:** Bark powder of described plant, 5 g, with milk, two times a day, is beneficial. **Skin diseases:** Local application of paste of bark of described plant, and *Acacia catechu,* with water, is beneficial.

Recommended readings:

Bhutya, R.K. (2007), Vanaspati Aushadha Vigyana, Scientific Publishers (India), Jodhpur, PP. 28.

Chunekar, K.C. (2004), Bhava Prakash Nighantu, Chaukhambha Bharti Academy, Varanasi, PP. 501.

Dhiman, A.K. (2006), Ayurvedic Drug Plants, Daya Publishing House, Delhi, PP. 50.

Khare, C.P. (2007), Indian Medicinal Plants, Springer (India) P.L. New Delhi, PP. 505.

Kirtikar, K.R. & Basu, B.D. (1998), Indian Medicinal Plants, L.M Basu, Allahabad, Vol. 1, PP. 72.

Misra, B.L. (2005), Dravya Guna Hastamalaka, Publication scheme, Jaipur, PP. 478.

Nair, R.Vasudevan, (2007), Indian Medicinal Plants, Orient Longman P.L. Chennai, Vol. 4, PP. 330.

Prajapati, N.D., Purohit, S.S., Sharma, A.K. & Tarun Kumar (2003), A Hand Book of Medicinal Plants, Agrobios India, Jodhpur, PP. 412.

Sharma, P.V. (1981), Dravya gun vigyana, Chaukhambha Bharti Academy, Varanasi, Vol. 1, PP. 701.

381. *Polygonatum cirrhifolium* (Wall.) Rolye.

Family: Liliaceae.

Name: Sanskrit: *Mahaamedaa, Vasuchchidra, Tridanti, Devataamani, Devagandhaa, Somaa, Suramedaa, Divyaa, Jivani, Devamani,* **Hindi:** *Mahaameda,* **Local:** *Mahaameda, Devarigaanal.*

Other similar plant: *P.multiflorum-* Solomon's Seal.

Ayurvedic Groups: Charak: *Jivaniya gana.*

Substitute: *Asparagus racemosus-Shataavari.*

Botanical characteristics: Habit: A herb, height 30-130 cm. **Stem:** cylindrical, upper part of stem creeping, leafy and grooved, with thick rootstock. **Leaf:** In whorls of 4, sessile, linear, acute, 5-8 by 3-5 cm, glabrous. **Flower:** Purplish, tinged with white or green, 2-3 together, diam. 5 mm. **Fruit:** Berry, blue-black, spherical, red when ripe. **Rhizome:** Like fresh Ginger, white or light white, sweetish.

Flowering and fruiting period: July-August and August-September.

Habitat: In the Northern Himalaya, 1200-4200 m, in Uttarakhand and Himachal Pradesh.

Parts used: Root. **Dosage:** 3-6 g.

Collection period: September-October.

Ayurvedic properties: ***Ras:*** *madhur,* ***Gun:*** *guru, snigdha,* ***Veerya:*** *sheeta* ***Vipaka:*** *madhur,* ***Tridosha*** **Effect:** alleviates ***Pitta:*** **++**, ***Vaata:*** **++**.

Chemical constituents: The **rootstock** containsn-eoprazerigenin A-3-O-beta-lycotetraoside and its methyl proto-type congener and steroidal saponins, sibiricoside A and sibiricoside B.

Action and disease indications: The **rootstocks** are cooling, emollient, aphrodisiac, galactagogue, depurative, vulnerary, expectorant, rejuvenating, febrifuge, tonic for nervous system and general tonic, used for agalactia, burning sensation, wounds, ulcers, skin diseases, tuberculosis, cough, asthma, bronchitis, fever and general debility.

Clinical uses: Oligogalactia, seminal weakness, penile dysfunction, general debility: Root powder of described plant, 3 g, *Asparagus racemosus* 3 g, with milk, two times a day, is beneficial.

Recommended readings:

Acharya, B.K. & Sharma, B.D. (2005), Jivani Shaktivardhak Astavarga Padapa, Divya Yoga Mandir, Haridwar, PP. 43.

Bhutya, R.K. (2007), Vanaspati Aushadha Vigyana, Scientific Publishers (India), Jodhpur, PP. 176.

Chunekar, K.C. (2004), Bhava Prakash Nighantu, Chaukhambha Bharti Academy, Varanasi, PP. 62.

Khare, C.P. (2007), Indian Medicinal Plants, Springer (India) P.L. New Delhi, PP. 507.

Kirtikar, K.R. & Basu, B.D. (1998), Indian Medicinal Plants, L.M Basu, Allahabad, Vol. 4, PP. 2506.

Nair, R.Vasudevan, (2007), Indian Medicinal Plants, Orient Longman P.L. Chennai, Vol. 4, PP. 333.

Prajapati, N.D., Purohit, S.S., Sharma, A.K. & Tarun Kumar (2003), A Hand Book of Medicinal Plants, Agrobios India, Jodhpur, PP. 414.

382. *Polygonatum verticillatum* All.

Family: Liliaceae.

Ayurvedic Groups: Charak: *Jivaniya gana.*

Substitute: *Asparagus racemosus-Shataavari.*

Name: Sanskrit: *Medaa, Shalyaparni, Manichchidra, Medobhavaa, Adhvaraa,* **Hindi:** *Medaa,* **Local:** *Medaa.*

Botanical characteristics: Habit: An erect glabrous herb, height 30-120 cm. **Rhizome:** like fresh Ginger, white, inner portion white, sweet in taste. **Stem:** With thick rootstock, upper part of stem leafy, zig-zag and grooved. **Leaf:** Whorled, 4-8, sessile, lanceolate or linear, 10-20 by 5-12 cm, acute. **Flower:** 2-3 together, white, pinkish-white, or pale green, 5 mm across, in whorled racemes. **Fruit:** Berry, 6-7 mm in diam., green when unripe and red or orange when ripe.

Flowering and fruiting period: July-August and August-September.

Habitat: temperate Himalaya and Manipur, at a height of 1800-3900 m.

Parts used: Root. **Dosage:** 3-6 g.

Collection period: September-October.

Ayurvedic properties: ***Ras:*** *madhur,* ***Gun:*** *guru, snigdha,* ***Veerya:*** *sheeta,* ***Vipaka:*** *madhur* ***Tridosha*** **Effect:** alleviates ***Pitta:*** **++**, ***Vaata:*** **++**.

Chemical constituents: The **rootstock** contain 6.2-9% diosgenin, amino acid revealed presence of 28% aspartic acid and asparagines and gave digitalis glucoside.

Action and disease indications: The **rootstocks** are sweet, cooling, emollient, galactagogue, appetizer, diuretic, expectorant, febrifuge, rejuvenating, aphrodisiac and tonic, used for emaciation, senility, pulmonary affections, burning sensation, fever, skin diseases, bronchitis, ulcers, strangury, seminal weakness, anorexia and general debility.

Clinical uses: Oligogalactia, seminal weakness, penile dysfunction, general debility: Root powder of described plant, 3 g, *Asparagus racemosus* 3 g, with milk, two times a day, is beneficial.

Formulations: *Chyavanpraasha.*

Recommended readings:

Acharya, B.K. & Sharma, B.D. (2005), Jivani Shaktivardhak Astavarga Padapa, Divya Yoga Mandir, Haridwar, PP. 42.

Bhutya, R.K. (2007), Vanaspati Aushadha Vigyana, Scientific Publishers (India), Jodhpur, PP. 186.

Chunekar, K.C. (2004), Bhava Prakash Nighantu, Chaukhambha Bharti Academy, Varanasi, PP. 62.

Khare, C.P. (2007), Indian Medicinal Plants, Springer (India) P.L. New Delhi, PP. 508.

Nair, R.Vasudevan, (2007), Indian Medicinal Plants, Orient Longman P.L. Chennai, Vol. 4, PP. 336.

Prajapati, N.D., Purohit, S.S., Sharma, A.K. & Tarun Kumar (2003), A Hand Book of Medicinal Plants, Agrobios India, Jodhpur, PP. 413.

383. *Polygonum aviculare* Linn.

Family: Polygonaceae.

Name: English: Knotgrass, Knotweed, Maxican Sanguinaria, **Sanskrit:** *Granthitrina, Granthika, Kaakapuchha, Guchhaka, Neelapushpa, Sugandha, Tailaparnaka,* **Hindi:** *Granthiparni,* **Local:** *Mochoti, Kesri.*

Botanical characteristics: Habit: A small herb, height 30-60 cm. **Stem:** And branches prostrate, smooth, leafy, finely grooved. **Leaf:** 1.3-2.5 cm long, alternate, narrowly lanceolate, nearly sessile, sometimes glandular dotted; stipules tubular, long, nerves several, strong, straight, the tips more or less projecting. **Flower:** Small, hermaphrodite, green, tipped with white or red, axillary clusters, perianth 4-or 5-parted, stamens 4 or 5, styles 3, free, minute. **Fruit:** Nut, 3-angled, minutely wrinkled. **Seed:** Albuminous.

Flowering and fruiting period: July-August and August-September.

Habitat: In Himalaya, from Kashmir to Kumaon, up to an altitude of 2400-4800 m.

Parts used: Root, leaves, seed. **Dosage:** 3-6 g.

Collection period: September-October.

Ayurvedic properties: ***Ras:*** *tikta, katu,* ***Gun:*** *laghu, tikhsna,* ***Veerya:*** *ushna,* ***Vipaka:*** *katu,* ***Tridosha*** **Effect:** alleviates ***Kapha:*** ***++*** ***Vaata:*** +.

Chemical constituents: The **plant** contain flavonoids including quercetin, avicularin, quercitrin and derivatives of kaempferol, esculetin and scopoletin, also gave gallic, caffeic, oxalic, silisic, chlorogenic and *p*-coumaric acids, tannins including catechin.

Action and disease indications: The **roots** are astringent, styptic, deodorant, antipyretic, appetizer, used for asthma, scabies, fever, menorrhagia, bleeding piles, mucous colitis and calculus. The **seeds** are diuretic, laxative, used for burning sensation, stomachalgia, bladder pain and erysipelas.

Clinical uses: Renal and vesical calculus, dysuria: Decoction of described plant, 5 g, or juice of roots of described plant 10 ml, with honey 10 g, two times a day, is useful. **Chronic diarrhea, malaria:** Juice of roots of described plant, 10 ml, two times a day, is beneficial. **Pneumonitis, whooping cough:** Decoction of described plant, 10 g, with honey 10 g, two times a day, is useful. **Pain, erysipelas, urinary bladder pain:** Local application of paste of leaves of described plant is beneficial.

Recommended readings:

Bhutya, R.K. (2007), Vanaspati Aushadha Vigyana, Scientific Publishers (India), Jodhpur, PP. 91.

Chunekar, K.C. (2004), Bhava Prakash Nighantu, Chaukhambha Bharti Academy, Varanasi, PP. 253.

Khare, C.P. (2007), Indian Medicinal Plants, Springer (India) P.L. New Delhi, PP. 508.

Kirtikar, K.R. & Basu, B.D. (1998), Indian Medicinal Plants, L.M Basu, Allahabad, Vol. 3, PP. 2096.

Namjoshi, A.N. (2001), The Ayurvedic Pharmacopoeia of India, Government of India, Department of Indian Systems of Medicine & Homoeopathy, New Delhi, Part-1, Volume- 3, PP. 58.

384. *Pongamia pinnata* Pierre.

Family: Papilionaceae; Fabaceae.

Synonym: *P.glabra, Derris indica.*

Ayurvedic Groups: Charak: *Kandooghna, Virechana, Katuskandha, Tiktaskandha,* **Sushruta:** *Aaragvadhaadi, Varunaadi, Arkaadi, Shyaamaadi, Shirovirechana, Kaphashamana.*

Name: English: Pongam Oil Tree, Indian Beech, **Sanskrit:** *Guchhapushpaka, Prakirya, Ghratapoora, Snigdhapatra, Pootika, Somavalka, Pootikaranja,* **Hindi:** *Karanja,* **Local:** *Dithori.*

Botanical characteristics: Habit: A medium sized, semi-evergreen glabrous tree, height 15-18 m or sometimes even more. **Stem:** with short bole and spreading crown, bark grayish-green or brown, very often mottled with dark brown dots, specks, lines or streaks. **Leaf:** Alternate, imperipinnate, leaflets opposite, 5-7, ovate or elliptic or acuminate, glabrous, shining; stipules small. **Flower:** Lilac or pinkish white, fragrant, in axillary racemes. **Fruit:** Pods, 4-7.5 by1.7-3.5 cm, thick, woody, smooth, compressed, indehiscent, with a short curved beak. **Seed:** 1-2, white, 1.7-2 by 1.2-1.8 cm, reniform or elliptical, oily, rather thick; hilum small, wrinkled or smooth, testa reddish brown, leathery.

Flowering and fruiting period: May-June and December-January.

Habitat: Throughout India, Western Ghats, in tidal and beach forests; up to 1200 m, also cultivated as avenue trees.

Parts used: Seed, seed oil, flower, root bark.

Dosage: Seed 1-2 g, seed oil 2-5 drops, flower juice 5-10 ml, root bark 1-3 g.

Collection period: December-January.

Ayurvedic properties: ***Ras:*** *katu,* ***Gun:*** *laghu, tikhsna,* ***Veerya:*** *ushna,* ***Vipaka:*** *katu,* ***Tridosha*** **Effect:** alleviates ***Kapha:*** **++,** ***Vaata:*** **++,** aggrevates ***Pitta:*** **+.**

Chemical constituents: The **plant** contain flavonoids and related compounds. These are simple flavones furanoflavonoids, chromeno-flavones, coumarones, flavone glucosides, sterols, triterpenes and a modified phenyl-alanine dipeptide. The **seed** and **seed oil** gave karanjin, pongamol, pongapin and kanjone and fatty acids as palmitic, stearic, arachidic, cerotic, lignoceric, oleic, linoleic, eicosenoic, myristic, dihydroxy stearic, cerotic acids. The aqueous extract of stem bark shows significant sedative, anti-spasmodic and anti-pyretic. The aqueous extract of seeds shows significant anti-viral activity against herpes simplex viruses HSV-1 and 2 cell lines experimentally.

Action and disease indications: The **seeds** are anthelmintic, carminative, haematinic, used for lumbago, inflammations, otalgia, chronic fever, malaria, intestinal worms, pectoral diseases, hydrocele, piles and anaemia. The **oil** is anthelmintic, stypic and depurative, recommended for ophthalnia, scabies, piles, ulcers, herpes and lumbago. The **roots** are good for ulcers, cleaning teeth, strengthening gums and gonorrhca. The **bark** is mucilaginous anthelmintic, alexeteric, used for piles, beriberi, ophthalmopathy, skin diseases, veginopathy and ulcers.

Clinical uses: Wounds, ulcers: Local application of oil of fruit of described plant is beneficial. **Ringworm, pruritis, scabies, eczema, herpes, arthritis:** Local application of oil of described plant, with Lemon juice, is beneficial. **Bronchitis, whooping cough:** Seed powder of described plant, 1 g, with honey 10 g, two times a day, is useful. **Diabetes mellitus:** Cold infusion of flowers of described plant, 10 g, two times a day, is beneficial. **Alopecia:** Local application of paste of flowers of described plant is beneficial. **Bleeding piles:** Root powder of described plant 2 g, with urine of cow, 10 ml, two times a day, is beneficial. **Boil, abscess:** Poultice of leaves of described plant and *Vitex negundo,* is beneficial. **Leucoderma:** Local application of paste of seeds of described plant, root powder of *Nerium indicum,* with water is beneficial. **Acne vulgaris:** Local application of paste of seeds of described plant, with milk, two times a day, is beneficial. **Diabetes inspidus:** Flower powder of described plant, 5 g, with water, two times a day, is beneficial. **Gingivitis:** Seed powder of described plant 3 g, sugar candy powder 10 g, with water, two times a day, is beneficial.

Formulations: *Kauncha paaka, Karanjaadi taila, Rudra taila, Mahaa rudra taila, Somaraali taila.*

Recommended readings:

Bhutya, R.K. (2007), Vanaspati Aushadha Vigyana, Scientific Publishers (India), Jodhpur, PP. 51.

Brahmavarchas (2003), Ayurved Ka Pran Vanoshadhi Vigyan, Shanti Kunj, Haridwar, PP. 359.

Chunekar, K.C. (2004), Bhava Prakash Nighantu, Chaukhambha Bharti Academy, Varanasi, PP. 350.

Dhiman, A.K. (2006), Ayurvedic Drug Plants, Daya Publishing House, Delhi, PP. 195.

Khare, C.P. (2007), Indian Medicinal Plants, Springer (India) P.L. New Delhi, PP. 511.

Kirtikar, K.R. & Basu, B.D. (1998), Indian Medicinal Plants, L.M Basu, Allahabad, Vol. , PP. .

Misra, B.L. (2005), Dravya Guna Hastamalaka, Publication scheme, Jaipur, PP. 267.

Nair, R.Vasudevan, (2007), Indian Medicinal Plants, Orient Longman P.L. Chennai, Vol. 4, PP. 339.

Namjoshi, A.N. (2001), The Ayurvedic Pharmacopoeia of India, Government of India, Department of Indian Systems of Medicine & Homoeopathy, New Delhi, Part-1, Volume- 2, PP. 63 and 1-75.

Pareek, G.N. (2005), Sudhanidhi, Vanoshadhi Ratnakar, Dhanvantari Karyalaya, Aligarh, Vol. 2, PP. 291.

Prajapati, N.D., Purohit, S.S., Sharma, A.K. & Tarun Kumar (2003), A Hand Book of Medicinal Plants, Agrobios India, Jodhpur, PP. 418.

Sharma, P.C., Yelne, MB. & Denis, T.J. (2000), Database on medicinal plants used in ayurveda, Central Council for research in Ayurveda and siddha, Vol. 2, PP. 292.

Sharma, P.V. (1981), Dravya gun vigyana, Chaukhambha Bharti Academy, Varanasi, Vol. 1, PP. 144.

Singh, R.S. (2002), Vanoshadhi Nirdeshika, Uttar Pradesh Hindi Sansthan, Lucknow, PP. 81.

Swami, K.N. (1985), Gavon Main Aushadh Ratna, Kalera Krishana Gopal, Kalera (Raj.), Vol. 2, PP. 150.

385. *Portulaca oleracea* Linn.

Family: Portulacaceae.

Other similar plant: *P. quandrifolia*- small var.

Name: English: Common Purslane, **Sanskrit:** *Lonaa, Loni, Ghotikaa, Vrihalloni,* **Hindi:** *Lonaa,* **Local:** *Lonaa, Lunakhyaa.*

Botanical characteristics: Habit: A succulent prostrate or erect annual herb, 15-50 cm long. **Stem:** Green, purple or reddish, swollen at the nodes, quite glabrous. **Leaf:** Simple, fleshy, variable, oblong-ovate, sub-sessile, 6-25 mm long, alternate or sub-opposite, cuneiform, rounded and truncate at the apex, margins reddish. **Flower:** Bright yellow, few together, in sessile terminal or axillary clusters. **Fruit:** Capsule, ovoid or obovoid, circumsciss. **Seed:** Numerous, black, reniformconcetrically striate and granulate.

Flowering and fruiting period: September-October and November-December.

Habitat: All over India, as a weed up to 1500 m, also cultivated as a vegetable.

Parts used: Whole plant.

Dosage: Powder 2-4 g, juice 5-10 ml.

Collection period: November-December.

Ayurvedic properties: ***Ras:*** *Lavan, amla,* ***Gun:*** *laghu, rukhsa,* ***Veerya:*** *ushna,* ***Vipaka:*** *amla, madhur,* ***Tridosha*** **Effect:** alleviates ***Vaata:*** ++, ***Kapha:*** +.

Chemical constituents: The **stem** and **leaves** contain *l-nor*-adrenaline, dopamine and l-dopa, also catechol, oleracins 1 and 2, acylated beta-cyanins, pyrocatechol, alanine, vitamin B and C, beta-carptene and oxalic acid.

Action and disease indications: The **stem** and **leaves** are salty, thermogenic, alexteric, anti-bacterial, stomachic, anti-scorbutic, sudorofic, aperient, alterant, diuretic, vulnerary and tonic, used for gastropathy, inflammations, tumours, renal diseases, cystalgia, cystitis, spleenomegaly, Jaundice, piles, diabetes, scalds and burns, dipsia, cephalgia, otalgia, odontalgia, scurvy, burning sensation, cough, asthma, bronchitis, dysentery, skin diseases, vomiting, dysuria, haematuria, gonorrhea and ulcerative stomatitis.

Clinical uses: Erysipelas: Local application of paste of described plant is beneficial. **Dysuria:** Cold infusion of described plant, 10 g, with honey 10 g, two times a day, is useful. **Helminthiasis:** Seed powder of described plant, 3 g, with water, two times a day, is beneficial.

Recommended readings:

Bhutya, R.K. (2007), Vanaspati Aushadha Vigyana, Scientific Publishers (India), Jodhpur, PP. 198.

Brahmavarchas (2003), Ayurved Ka Pran Vanoshadhi Vigyan, Shanti Kunj, Haridwar, PP. 361.

Chunekar, K.C. (2004), Bhava Prakash Nighantu, Chaukhambha Bharti Academy, Varanasi, PP. 670.

Khare, C.P. (2007), Indian Medicinal Plants, Springer (India) P.L. New Delhi, PP. 513.

Kirtikar, K.R. & Basu, B.D. (1998), Indian Medicinal Plants, L.M Basu, Allahabad, Vol. 1, PP. 242.

Misra, B.L. (2005), Dravya Guna Hastamalaka, Publication scheme, Jaipur, PP. 474.

Nair, R.Vasudevan, (2007), Indian Medicinal Plants, Orient Longman P.L. Chennai, Vol. 4, PP. 345.

Namjoshi, A.N. (2001), The Ayurvedic Pharmacopoeia of India, Government of India, Department of Indian Systems of Medicine & Homoeopathy, New Delhi, Part-1, Volume- 1, PP. 95.

Prajapati, N.D., Purohit, S.S., Sharma, A.K. & Tarun Kumar (2003), A Hand Book of Medicinal Plants, Agrobios India, Jodhpur, PP. 420.

Sharma, P.C., Yelne, MB. & Denis, T.J. (2000), Database on medicinal plants used in ayurveda, Central Council for research in Ayurveda and siddha, Vol. 3, PP. 387.

Swami, K.N. (1985), Gavon Main Aushadh Ratna, Kalera Krishana Gopal, Kalera (Raj.), Vol. 2, PP. 197.

386. *Premna integrifolia* Linn.

Family: Verbenaceae.

Synonym: *P. obtusifolia, P. corimbosa.*

Other similar plants: *P. latifolia, P. tomentosa.*

Ayurvedic Groups: Charak: *Shothahara, Sheetaprashamana, Anuvaasanopaga,* **Sushruta:** *Vrihat Panchamoola, Vaatasanshamana, Veeratarvaadi, Varunaadi gana.*

Name: English: Headache Tree, **Sanskrit:** *Agnimantha, Jayaa, Shreeparni, Ganikaarikaa, Jayanti, Tarkaari, Naadei, Vaijayantikaa,* **Hindi:** *Agnimantha,* **Local:** *Arani, Oran, Girani, Irani, Ganiyari, Agetha.*

Botanical characteristics: Habit: A large shrub or small tree, height up to 9 m. **Root:** Yellowish brown woody, aromatic. **Stem:** Yellowish, lenticellate, spinous large branches. young parts glabrous or slightly pubescent. **Leaf:** 5-9 by 3.2-6.3 cm, simple, opposite, sometimes whorled, membranous when young, coriaceous when mature, elliptic-ovate, obtuse, very shortly acuminate, glabrous, entire or the upper part dentate, base rounded or sub-acute; main nerves 4-5 pairs; petioles 1-1.6 cm long. **Flower:** Small, greenish-yellow or greenish-white, with a strong disagreeable odour in corimbiform cymose panicles; bracts minute, lanceolate. **Fruit:** 4 mm long, globose drupes, pear-shaped, black when ripe with the persistent saucer-shaped calyx surrounding its base; endocarp ridged, bony, 4-celled. **Seed:** 4 seeds in fruit, oblong.

Flowering and fruiting period: May-June and July-August.

Habitat: Throughout the drier parts of India, at sea coasts.

Parts used: Root bark, leaves. **Dosage:** 1-3 g.

Collection period: December-January.

Ayurvedic properties: ***Ras:*** *tikta, kashaaya, katu, madhur,* ***Gun:*** *laghu, rukhsa,* ***Veerya:*** *ushna,* ***Vipaka:*** *katu,* ***Tridosha*** **Effect:** alleviates ***Kapha:*** +++, ***Vaata:*** ++.

Chemical constituents: The **roots** contain chiefly three alkaloids - premnine, ganiarine and ganikarine. The **leaves** contain an isoxazole alkaloid premnazole, which was found to reduce granuloma formation, its activity was comparable to phynylbutazone. It also reduce GPT and GOT in serum and liver, by controlling the activity of the adreno-corticotropic hormone.

Action and disease indications: The **leaves** are carminative, galactagogue, and stomachic, used for flatulence, colic, dyspepsia, agalactia, cough, fever, rheumatism, neuralgia, piles and tumours. The **roots** are thermogenic, anodyne, anti-inflammatory, expectorant, alterant, alexeteric, cardio-tonic, depurative, digestive, stomachic, laxative, febrifuge, anti-bacterial, carminative, galactagogue and tonic used for neuralgia, rheumatism, gout, dysmenorrhea, amenorrhea, inflammations, cough, asthma, bronchitis, cardiac disorders, hepatopathy, skin diseases, dyspepsia, flatulence, colic, anorexia, constipation, diabetes, fever, piles and general debility.

Clinical uses: Rhinitis: Decoction of root powder of described plant 5 g, with honey 10 g, two times a day, or juice of leaves 5 ml, with *Piper longum* 1 g, two times a day, is beneficial. **Vomiting:** Flower juice of described plant 10 ml, *'Praval pisti'* 250 mg, three times a day, is useful. **Spermatorrhea, lipuria, dysmenorrhea:** Decoction of root powder of described plant 5 g, with honey 10 g, two times a day, is useful. Give it for 1-2 months. **Urticaria:** Root powder of described plant, 3 g, fried seeds of *Cuminum cyminum* 1g, with clarified butter 5 g and honey 10 g, two times a day, is beneficial. **Hypogalactia:** Vegatable of leaves of described plant, 50 g, is beneficial. **Paralysis, arthritis:** Local massage of medicated oil, made from root and leaves of described plant, is beneficial. **Orchitis:** Local application of warm paste of leaves of described plant is beneficial. **Obesity:** Leaves juice of described plant 5 ml, with Bitumen 1 g, two times a day, is beneficial. **Amenorrhea, dysmenorrhea:** Decoction of mix powder of leaves powder of described plant, leaves of *Solunum surattense,* 7-7 parts, *Nigella sativa, Embelia ribes,* seeds of *Raphanus sativus,* 1-1 part, dose 10 g, with raw sugar 10 g, two times a day, from 3 days before from menstrual period to it's end, for three months, is beneficial. **Cloasma:** Local application of paste root bark of described plant, with milk of she goat, two times a day, is beneficial. **Sprain, calcaneodynia:** Local application of warm paste of leaves of described plant is beneficial.

Formulations: *Dashamoolaarista, Dashamoola kwaatha, Brahmarasaayana, Chyavanpraasha.*

Recommended readings:

Acharya, B.K. (2008), Ayurveda Jadi-buti Rahasya, Patanjali Yogapitha, Haridwar, PP. 95.

Bhutya, R.K. (2007), Vanaspati Aushadha Vigyana, Scientific Publishers (India), Jodhpur, PP. 5.

Chunekar, K.C. (2004), Bhava Prakash Nighantu, Chaukhambha Bharti Academy, Varanasi, PP. 282.

Dhiman, A.K. (2006), Ayurvedic Drug Plants, Daya Publishing House, Delhi, PP. 16.

Khare, C.P. (2007), Indian Medicinal Plants, Springer (India) P.L. New Delhi, PP. 516.

Kirtikar, K.R. & Basu, B.D. (1998), Indian Medicinal Plants, L.M Basu, Allahabad, Vol. 3, PP. 1929.

Nair, R.Vasudevan, (2007), Indian Medicinal Plants, Orient Longman P.L. Chennai, Vol. 4, PP. 348.

Pareek, G.N. (2005), Sudhanidhi, Vanoshadhi Ratnakar, Dhanvantari Karyalaya, Aligarh, Vol. 1, PP. 79.

Prajapati, N.D., Purohit, S.S., Sharma, A.K. & Tarun Kumar (2003), A Hand Book of Medicinal Plants, Agrobios India, Jodhpur, PP. 421.

Sharma, P.C., Yelne, MB. & Denis, T.J. (2000), Database on medicinal plants used in ayurveda, Central Council for research in Ayurveda and siddha, Vol. 2, PP. 1.

Sharma, P.V. (1981), Dravya gun vigyana, Chaukhambha Bharti Academy, Varanasi, Vol. 1, PP. 221.

Singh, R.S. (2002), Vanoshadhi Nirdeshika, Uttar Pradesh Hindi Sansthan, Lucknow, PP. 9.

Swami, K.N. (1985), Gavon Main Aushadh Ratna, Kalera Krishana Gopal, Kalera (Raj.), Vol. 2, PP. 284.

387. *Prosopis spicigera* Linn.

Family: Mimosaceae.

Synonym: *P. cineraria.*

Other similar plants: *P. stephaniana-* small var.

Name: Sanskrit: *Shami, Tungaa, Kashahantri, Shaktuphalaa, Shivaaphalaa, Mangalyaa, Laxmi,* **Hindi:** *Khejaraa,* **Local:** *Khejaraa.*

Botanical characteristics: Habit: A medium sized tree, height 9-18 m. **Stem:** Bark grey, rough, branches slender, glabrous, armed with nearly straight, scattered, somewhat compressed prickles 3-6 mm long. **Leaf:** 2-pinnate; main rachis glabrous or puberlous; pinnae usually 2 pairs, opposite, 2.5-7.5 cm long, often with roundinsect-galls on their rhachises. Leaflets 7-12 pairs, 10-16 by 3-5-4.5 mm, sub-sessile, oblong, obliquely rounded and mucronate at the apex, very unequal-sided, the upper side much smaller, reticulately veined, grey, glabrous, base rounded and very oblique. Shape like leaves of *Acacia nilotica.* **Flower:** Small, yellowish, sessile or nearly so, in short peduncle axillary spikes and terminal panicles; bracts small, membranous. **Fruit:** Pods, 10-20 cm long, turgid, straight, slender, cylindrical, torulose, glabrous, narrowed gradually into a short stalk and filled with a brown farinaceous edible substance. **Seed:** 10-15, dull brown, oblong.

Flowering and fruiting period: January-February and June-July.

Habitat: Dry and acrid regions of India, Punjab, Rajasthan, Bundelkhand and Gujarat.

Parts used: Bark, fruit. **Dosage:** 3-6 g.

Collection period: May-June.

Ayurvedic properties: ***Ras:*** *tikta, katu, kashaaya,* ***Gun:*** *laghu, rukhsa,* ***Veerya:*** *sheeta,* ***Vipaka:*** *katu,* ***Tridosha* Effect:** alleviates ***Kapha: +++, Pitta: +***.

Chemical constituents: The **stem bark** contains vitamin K, n-octacosyl acetate, the long chain aliphatic acid, glucose, rhamnose, sucrose and starch.

Action and disease indications: The **stem bark** is cooling, anti-inflammatory, anti-rheumatic, anthelmintic, purgative, and tonic, used for leprosy, vertigo, skin diseases, bronchitis, dysentery, asthma, leucoderma, piles, tremors of the muscles, wandering of the mind and diarrhea.

Clinical uses: Miscarriage: Fruit powder of described plant, 5 g, with honey water 10 g, three times a day, is useful. **Diarrhea:** Inner bark and leaves powder of described plant 1 g, *Piper nigrum* 0.5 g, with water, two times a day, is beneficial. **Helminthiasis:** Decoction of bark of described plant, 6 g, with honey 10 g, is beneficial. **Piles:** Decoction of bark of described plant 6 g, *'Triphala churna'* 5 g, is beneficial. **Vertigo:** Decoction of bark of described plant 6 g, *Cinamomum verum* 1 g, with sugar candy powder 10 g, two times a day, is beneficial.

Formulations: *Khadiraadi taila.*

Recommended readings:

Bhutya, R.K. (2007), Vanaspati Aushadha Vigyana, Scientific Publishers (India), Jodhpur, PP. 81.

Brahmavarchas (2003), Ayurved Ka Pran Vanoshadhi Vigyan, Shanti Kunj, Haridwar, PP. 363.

Chunekar, K.C. (2004), Bhava Prakash Nighantu, Chaukhambha Bharti Academy, Varanasi, PP. 546.

Khare, C.P. (2007), Indian Medicinal Plants, Springer (India) P.L. New Delhi, PP. 518.

Kirtikar, K.R. & Basu, B.D. (1998), Indian Medicinal Plants, L.M Basu, Allahabad, Vol. 2, PP. 910.

Misra, B.L. (2005), Dravya Guna Hastamalaka, Publication scheme, Jaipur, PP. 484.

Pareek, G.N. (2005), Sudhanidhi, Vanoshadhi Ratnakar, Dhanvantari Karyalaya, Aligarh, Vol. 9, PP. 302.

Sharma, P.V. (1981), Dravya gun vigyana, Chaukhambha Bharti Academy, Varanasi, Vol. 1, PP. 481.

388. *Prunus amygdalus* Batsch.

Family: Rosaceae.

Other similar plant: *Terminalia catappa- Jangali Baadaam* (Combretaceae).

Name: English: Almond, **Sanskrit:** *Vaataad, Vaataveri, Netropamaphalaa,* **Hindi:** *Baadaam,* **Local:** *Badaam.*

Botanical characteristics: Habit: A medium sized tree, height 8-10 m. **Stem:** Branches glabrous, light ash coloured. **Leaf:** Simple, alternate, greyish when fully grown, oblong-lanceolate, minutely serrete, petioled. **Flower:** White, tinged with red, showy, appearing before the leaves or with the early foliage from scaly buds, peduncles much shorter than the campanulate calyx. **Fruit:** drupes, velvety, 3-6 cm long, separating into 2 valves on maturity exposing the compressed stones having minute holes. **Seed:** The stone enclose the valuable kernel.

Flowering and fruiting period: December-January and March-May.

Habitat: Cultivated in Kashmir, Punjab, Himachal Pradesh and Uttar Pradesh, at an altitude of 760-2400 m.

Parts used: Seed, oil. **Dosage:** 5-10 g, oil 5-10 ml.

Collection period: May-June.

Ayurvedic properties: ***Ras:*** *madhur,* ***Gun:*** *guru, snigdha,* ***Veerya:*** *sheeta,* ***Vipaka:*** *madhur,* ***Tridosha* Effect:** alleviates ***Vaata: ++, Pitta: +***, aggrevates ***Kapha: +***.

Chemical constituents: The **kernel** contains protein is a globulin, amandin an albumin. The essential amino acid make-up of amandin is; arginine, histidine, lysine, phenylalanine, leucine and valine, tryptophan methionone and cystine. The sweet kernel yield 44-55% oil.

Action and disease indications: The **kernels** are thermogenic, emollient, aphrodisiac, nutritious, demulcent, laxative, diuretic, lithontriptic, stimulant nervine tonic, used for burning sensation, cephalgia, neuralgia, dysopia, cough, amenorrhoea, otalgia, obstruction of the liver and spleen, skin diseases, pharyngodynia, pruritus, inflammations, ascitis, colic, peptic ulcer, strangury, renal and vesical calculi and general debility. The **oil** is nutritive, demulcent, slightly laxative, cooling, anti-spasmodic, sedative, laxative, vulnerary and rejuvenating, used for liver diseases, delirium, cough, pharyngodynia, colic, wounds, ulcers, renal colic, gleet, otalgia, burning sensation amentia and cracked skin.

Contraindication: The oil of bitter almond variety is highly poisonous due to hydrocyanic acid. So beware of it.

Clinical uses: Diabetes mellitus, headache: Seed powder of described plant, 20 g, with milk, two times a day, is beneficial. **Otalgia:** Seed oil of described plant, 4-4 drops, two times a day, is beneficial. **For rejuvenating, weakness of female, lumbego:** Seed powder of described plant 2o g, *Withania somnifera* 2 g, *Piper longum* 1 g, with milk and clarified butter 10 g, two times a day, is beneficial. **Chronic constipation:** Seed oil of described plant, 5 ml, with milk, two times a day, is beneficial. **Pyorrhea, gingivitis:** Mix powder of black ash of fruit rind of described plant 10 parts, *Quercus infectoria*, seeds of *Elettaria cardamomum, Syzygium aromaticum, Hedycium spicatum,* Alum powder, 1-1 part, use this powder as tooth powder, three times a day, is useful. **Rhinitis:** Roasted seeds of described plant 20 g, at night, without any liquid, do not take cold water or liquid, after this medication. **Seminal weakness, amnesia:** Seed powder of described plant 20 g, *Elettaria cardamomum, Piper cubeba* 1-1 g, with clarified butter of cow 10 g and milk, two times a day, is beneficial.

Formulations: *Vaataad madhur sandhaan, Saalam paka, Badaam paka, Lupari.*

Recommended readings:

Bhutya, R.K. (2007), Vanaspati Aushadha Vigyana, Scientific Publishers (India), Jodhpur, PP. 161.

Brahmavarchas (2003), Ayurved Ka Pran Vanoshadhi Vigyan, Shanti Kunj, Haridwar, PP. 365.

Chunekar, K.C. (2004), Bhava Prakash Nighantu, Chaukhambha Bharti Academy, Varanasi, PP. 588.

Khare, C.P. (2007), Indian Medicinal Plants, Springer (India) P.L. New Delhi, PP. 518.

Kirtikar, K.R. & Basu, B.D. (1998), Indian Medicinal Plants, L.M Basu, Allahabad, Vol. 2, PP. 953.

Misra, B.L. (2005), Dravya Guna Hastamalaka, Publication scheme, Jaipur, PP. 375.

Nair, R.Vasudevan, (2007), Indian Medicinal Plants, Orient Longman P.L. Chennai, Vol. 4, PP. 363.

Prajapati, N.D., Purohit, S.S., Sharma, A.K. & Tarun Kumar (2003), A Hand Book of Medicinal Plants, Agrobios India, Jodhpur, PP. 423.

Singh, R.S. (2002), Vanoshadhi Nirdeshika, Uttar Pradesh Hindi Sansthan, Lucknow, PP. 269.

Swami, K.N. (1985), Gavon Main Aushadh Ratna, Kalera Krishana Gopal, Kalera (Raj.), Vol. 3, PP. 86.

389. *Prunus cerasoides* D.Don.

Family: Rosaceae.

Synonym: *P. puddum.*

Other similar plants: *P. rubeus-ingram, P. majestica.*

Name: English: Wild Himalayan Cherry, Bird Cherry, **Sanskrit:** *Padmaaka, Padmagandhi, Padmakaastha, Padam,* **Hindi:** *Padmakha,* **Local:** *Padamkatha.*

Botanical characteristics: Habit: A medium sized or large deciduous tree, height 10 m. **Stem:** Bark smooth, brown, peeling off in horizontal strips exposing a shining copper coloured surface; heartwood pale red. **Leaf:** Simple, alternate, glossy, nearly glabrous, ovate-lanceolate or elliptic-lanceolate, long-acuminate, sharply serrate, 7.5-12.5 by 2.5-3.5 cm; petiole 1.3 cm long, one or more conspicuous glands on the petiole, stipules long, 3-5 parted, glandular, fringed. **Flower:** White, pink or crimson, 2.5 cm in diam., appearing before the leaves, in umbellate fascicles, approximate near the end of branchlets, fragrance like flower of Lotus; peduncle long, pedicels slender, as long as or longer than the calyx. **Fruit:** Drupes, ovoid or globose, yellow or red, 1.25-2 cm long, obtuse at both ends. **Seed:** One, stone ovoid, rugose and furrowed, wrinkled, supported by the calyx-base, from which the tube separates after flowering, pulp very little. Walking-sticks are made by straight branchlets of this tree.

Flowering and fruiting period: October-December and February-March.

Habitat: The temperate Himalayas from Garhwal to Sikkim, at an altitude of 900-2300 m, also in Utakamand, often cultivated.

Parts used: Heartwood, seed. **Dosage:**1-3 g.

Collection period: April-May.

Ayurvedic properties: ***Ras:*** *kashaaya, tikta,* ***Gun:*** *laghu, rukhsa,* ***Veerya:*** *sheeta,* ***Vipaka:*** *katu,* ***Tridosha*** **Effect:** alleviates ***Kapha:*** ***++***, ***Pitta:*** ***+***, aggrevates ***Vaata:*** ***+***.

Chemical constituents: The **heartwood** contains dihydrotectochrysin, dihydrowogonin, pinocembrin, chrysin, naringenin, kaempferol, aromedendrin, quercetin, taxifolin, 7-hydroxy-5, 2', 4,-trimethoxy flavanone (carasinone), 2'-hydroxy 2, 4, 6'-tetramethoxy chalcone (carasidin), 2', 4'-dihydroxy-2, 4', 6'-trimethoxy-chalcone (carasin). The plant contains a flavone glucoside, puddumin-A.

Action and disease indications: The **heartwood** is refrigerant, anodyne, vulnerary, demulcent, digestive, diuretic, constipating, emmenogogue, depurative, hamostatic, febrifuge, anti-pyretic and tonic and prevents abortions, prescribed for neuralgia, burning sensation, sprains, wounds, ulcers, skin decolourations, strangury, diarrhea, pruritis, dyspepsia, dysmenorrhea, amenorrhea, erysipelas, asthma, hiccough, dipsesis, skin diseases, vomiting, cephalgia, ophthmopathy, cardiac debility, hallucinations and intermittent fevers.

Clinical uses: Hiccough, asthma, bronchitis, mitral regurgitation: Bark of described plant 2 g, with honey 10 g, three times a day, is useful. **Epistaxis:** Bark of described plant 2 g, *Santalum album* 1 g, with rice water and sugar 10 g, two times a day, is beneficial. **Scabies, pruritis:** Local application of paste of bark of described plant is beneficial.

Formulations: *Laxaadi taila, Chandanaasava, Ushiraasava, Arimedaadi taila, Kumkumaadi taila, Dashamoolaarista, Sarivaadhyaasava, Mahaa kalyaanaka ghrita, Sudarshan churna, Chandanaadi taila, Jaatyaadi taila, Balaa taila, Khadiraadi gutika, Guduchyaadi taila* .

Recommended readings:

Bhutya, R.K. (2007), Vanaspati Aushadha Vigyana, Scientific Publishers (India), Jodhpur, PP. 143.

Chunekar, K.C. (2004), Bhava Prakash Nighantu, Chaukhambha Bharti Academy, Varanasi, PP. 202.

Dhiman, A.K. (2006), Ayurvedic Drug Plants, Daya Publishing House, Delhi, PP. 283.

Khare, C.P. (2007), Indian Medicinal Plants, Springer (India) P.L. New Delhi, PP. 520.

Kirtikar, K.R. & Basu, B.D. (1998), Indian Medicinal Plants, L.M Basu, Allahabad, Vol. 2, PP. 959.

Nair, R.Vasudevan, (2007), Indian Medicinal Plants, Orient Longman P.L. Chennai, Vol. 4, PP. 353.

Namjoshi, A.N. (2001), The Ayurvedic Pharmacopoeia of India, Government of India, Department of Indian Systems of Medicine & Homoeopathy, New Delhi, Part-1, Volume- 3, PP. 145.

Prajapati, N.D., Purohit, S.S., Sharma, A.K. & Tarun Kumar (2003), A Hand Book of Medicinal Plants, Agrobios India, Jodhpur, PP. 424.

Sharma, P.C., Yelne, MB. & Denis, T.J. (2000), Database on medicinal plants used in ayurveda, Central Council for research in Ayurveda and siddha, Vol. 8, PP. 283.

Sharma, P.V. (1981), Dravya gun vigyana, Chaukhambha Bharti Academy, Varanasi, Vol. 1, PP. 43.

Singh, R.S. (2002), Vanoshadhi Nirdeshika, Uttar Pradesh Hindi Sansthan, Lucknow, PP. 223.

Swami, K.N. (1985), Gavon Main Aushadh Ratna, Kalera Krishana Gopal, Kalera (Raj.), Vol. 3, PP. 4.

390. *Psidium guajava* Linn.

Family: Myrtaceae.

Other similar plants: *P. guineense*-small var., found in Tripura, *P. cattleyanum*- found in tamilnadu and Bengal.

Name: English: Common Guava, **Sanskrit:** *Amaruphala, Peruka, Aamaruda,* **Hindi:** *Amarood,* **Local:** *Amarood, Jaamphala.*

Botanical characteristics: Habit: A Large shrub or small tree up to 10 m height and 90 cm girth. **Stem:** Bark quite smooth, pale pinkish brown or buff with grey patches, exfoliating in very thin woody flakes, blaze 2.5-5 mm, cheesy, not fibrous, whitish or pinkish-brown. **Leaf:** Simple, opposite, 10-15 by 6-8 cm, light green, oblong or elliptic-oblong, entire, glabrous above, pubescent beneath, pellucid-punctate, lateral nerves 10-20 pairs, prominent beneath, strongly curved near the edge, joined by intra marginal veins, petioles 2.5-7.5 cm long. Shape like leaves of *Terminalia arjuna.* **Flower:** White, fragrant, 2.5-3.8 cm in diam., in axillary 1-3 flowered cymes, peduncle 1.3-3.8 cm long. **Fruit:** Berry, fleshy, globose or pyriform, 5 cm long or more, often varying in size and shape, pulp yellowish white or pink, edible. **Seed:** Numerous, small, white, hard.

Flowering and fruiting period: September-October and November-December.

Habitat: Cultivated and naturalized throughout India, up to 1500 m.

Parts used: Fruit. leaves.

Dosage: Fruit 25-100 g, leaves 10-20 g.

Collection period: November-December.

Ayurvedic properties: ***Ras:*** *madhur, tikta,* ***Gun:*** *snigdha,* ***Veerya:*** *sheeta* ***Vipaka:*** *madhur* ***Tridosha*** **Effect:** alleviates ***Pitta:*** **++**, ***Vaata:*** ++, aggrevates ***Kapha:*** ++.

Chemical constituents: The **fruits** contain protein 1.5, fat 1.2, minerals 1.8, carbohydrates 14-9, calcium 0.01, phosphorus 0.04%, iron 1 mg/100g. Vitamin C content of the ripe fruit ranges from 100-1000 mg/100g. It is much higher then Lemon, Apple or Orange.

Action and disease indications: The **leaves** are astringent, anodyne, anti-spasmodic, febrifuge and tonic, used for wounds, ulcers, gingivitis, stomatitis, cholera, diarrhea, vomiting, nephritis, cachexia, epilepsy and odontalgia. The **fruits** are refrigerant, aphrodisiac, laxative and tonic, used for dipsia, burning sensation, colic, ulemorrhagia, diarrhea, dysentery and general debility.

Clinical uses: Gingivitis, stomatitis, dentalgia: Gargles of decoction of leaves of described plant, 50 g, is beneficial. **Anal prolapse:** Leaves powder of described plant 5 g, *Mesua ferrea* 2 g, with water, two times a day, and poultice of leaves of described plant, is beneficial. **Or** Decoction of root bark of described plant 10 g, with *Mesua ferrea* 3 g, two times a day, is beneficial. **Hemicrenia:** Local application of paste of fruit of described plant is beneficial. **Chronic diarrhea:** Decoction of bark of described plant, 10 g, with honey 10 g, two times a day, is useful.

Recommended readings:

Acharya, B.K. (2008), Ayurveda Jadi-buti Rahasya, Patanjali Yogapitha, Haridwar, PP. 59.

Bhutya, R.K. (2007), Vanaspati Aushadha Vigyana, Scientific Publishers (India), Jodhpur, PP. 13.

Brahmavarchas (2003), Ayurved Ka Pran Vanoshadhi Vigyan, Shanti Kunj, Haridwar, PP. 370.

Khare, C.P. (2007), Indian Medicinal Plants, Springer (India) P.L. New Delhi, PP. 522.

Kirtikar, K.R. & Basu, B.D. (1998), Indian Medicinal Plants, L.M Basu, Allahabad, Vol. 2, PP. 1046.

Nair, R.Vasudevan, (2007), Indian Medicinal Plants, Orient Longman P.L. Chennai, Vol. 4, PP. 371.

Pareek, G.N. (2005), Sudhanidhi, Vanoshadhi Ratnakar, Dhanvantari Karyalaya, Aligarh, Vol. 1, PP. 134.

Prajapati, N.D., Purohit, S.S., Sharma, A.K. & Tarun Kumar (2003), A Hand Book of Medicinal Plants, Agrobios India, Jodhpur, PP. 427.

Sharma, P.C., Yelne, MB. & Denis, T.J. (2000), Database on medicinal plants used in ayurveda, Central Council for research in Ayurveda and siddha, Vol. 6, PP. 296.

Sharma, P.V. (1981), Dravya gun vigyana, Chaukhambha Bharti Academy, Varanasi, Vol. 2, PP. 244.

Swami, K.N. (1985), Gavon Main Aushadh Ratna, Kalera Krishana Gopal, Kalera (Raj.), Vol. 1, PP. 36.

391. *Psoralea corylifolia* Linn.

Family: Papilionaceae; Fabaceae.

Name: English: Babchi, Fleabane, Psorlea Seed, **Sanskrit:** *Avalgujaa, Krishnaphalaa, Baakuchi, Somaraaji, Suparnikaa, Shashilekhaa, Somaa, Putiphali, Somavalli, Kushthaghni,* **Hindi:** *Baakuchi,* **Local:** *Baavachi, Mali Bavachaa.*

Botanical characteristics: Habit: A herbaceous erect annual herb, height 60-120 cm. **Stem:** Stem and branches are grooved, studded with conspicuous glands and with a few appressed and spreading hairs. **Leaf:** Simple, 3.8-7.5 by 2.5-5 cm, broadly-elliptic, rounded and mucronate at the apex, inciso-dentate, clothed with white hairs on both surfaces, covered with numerous black dots, main nerve 5, springing from the base and 4-6 pairs of lateral nerves higher up from the midrib; petioles 6-25 mm long, hairy and gland - dotted, stipules lanceolate, persistent. **Flower:** Bluish-purple, in dense, axillary 10-30 flowered racemes; peduncle 2.5-5 cm long, hairy; pedicels very short. **Fruit:** Pods, 5 mm long, 2.5 mm broad, sub-globose or ovoid-oblong, slightly compressed, closely pitted, black, mucronate, glabrous, beaked, without hairs. **Seed:** One, smooth, oblong, flattened, adhering to the pericarp, dark brown with an agreeable aromatic odour and taste.

Flowering and fruiting period: November-December and February-March.

Habitat: Throughout India, mostly in Rajasthan, Punjab, Uttar Pradesh and Bihar, as a weed in waste places, also cultivated.

Parts used: Seed, seed oil.

Dosage: Seed 1-3 g, oil 2-5 drops.

Collection period: March-April.

Ayurvedic properties: ***Ras:*** *madhur, tikta,* ***Gun:*** *rukhsa,* ***Veerya:*** *sheeta* ***Vipaka:*** *katu,* ***Tridosha*** **Effect:** alleviates ***Kapha:*** ++, ***Vaata:*** +, aggrevates ***Pitta:*** +.

Chemical constituents: The **seeds** contain chalcones, flavones, isoflavones, furano-coumarins and coumesterol group of compound. These include psoralene, isopsoralene, bavachinin, corylifolean, corylifolin, corylifolinin, psoralidin, isopsoralidin, backuchiol, bavachin, isobavachin, 7-0-methyl bavachin, 4-0-methylbavachalcone, isobavachalcone, neobavaisoflavone, bavachromene, triacontane, beta-sitosterol-D-glucoside, corylidin, bavachalcone, isobavachalcone, neobavachalcone, bukachalcone, isoneobavachalcone, psorilidin-2,3,-oxide, diacetate, stigmesterol, psoralone, isopsoralone, corylin, isoflavone, corylidin, corylinal and psoralenol.

Action and disease indications: The **seeds** are laxative, anthelmintic, stomachic, stimulant, aphrodisiac, diuretic, diaphoretic, rejuvenating, good for hairs and skin, used for leucoderma, ulcers, scabies, leprosy, asthma, anorexia, epistaxis, excessive and turbid micturation, fevers, helminthiasis, inflammations, bronchitis, anaemia, muco-membranous disorders of skin and dermatitis.

Clinical uses: Leucoderma: (1) Seed powder of described plant, 3 g, with water, two times a day is useful. (2) Soak and dry the seeds of described plant, in urine of cow, for seven times, dose 2 g, two times a day, is beneficial. (3) Use above seeds, by *'Kalpa prayoga',* from 5 seeds to 30 seeds, and 30 to 5 seeds, with water, is very beneficial. (4) Local application of paste of seeds, by water or urine of cow, is very beneficial. (5) Local application of paste, made by seed powder of described plant, *Plumbego zeylanica, Ocimum sanctum,* with the juice of the leaves of *Lagenaria siceria,* oil of *Sesamum orientale* and Vinegar, is beneficial. (6) Boil seed powder of described plant, bark of *Ficus hispida,* seed powder of *Casia tora,* in milk, then make curd of this milk. Separate butter and whey. Use this clarified butter locally on the spot of leucoderma and use whey throughout the day, in diet, and do not take any other thing to eat and common salt for 3 days. (7) Decoction of mix powder of described plant, bark of *Acacia catechu,* fruits of *Phylanthus emblica,* 10 g, with honey 10 g, two times a day, should be given for 1-2 months, is beneficial.(8) Local application of paste of seed powder of described plant, flowers of *Argemone maxicana,* new leaves of *Azadirachta indica* 3-3 parts, seeds of *Citrus aurintifolia* 1 part, powder of Ivory 2 parts, in *'Triphala'* decoction, is beneficial. (9) Local application of oil, made by seed powder of described plant, *Jatropha curcus,* Lac of *Ficus religiosa,* is beneficial. Take massage with this oil in sunlight. **Dysentery:** Leaves powder of described plant 5 g, with curd and juice of *Punica grantum,* 50 ml, two times a day, is beneficial. **Skin diseases:** Local application of oil of seeds of described plant is beneficial. **Intestinal worms:** Decoction of seeds of described plant 10 g, with honey 10 g, two times a day, is useful. **Urticaria:** Mix powder of seeds of described plant 3 parts, *Phylanthus emblica, Terminalia belliarica, Terminalia belliarica, Rubia cordifolia, Hemidesmus indicus,* sugar candy powder, 1-1 part, dose 10 g, two times a day, is beneficial.

Formulations: *Baakuchi taila, Baakuchyaadi churna, Panchanimba churna, Nimbaadi churna, Khadiraarista, Sarvaangasundari gutikaa, Triphalaa modaka, Bhallatakaavaleha, Dhaatryaavaleha, Panchaanan taila, Somaraaji ghrita, Mahaa bhallataka guda, Ayorajaadi lepa.*

Recommended readings:

Acharya, B.K. (2008), Ayurveda Jadi-buti Rahasya, Patanjali Yogapitha, Haridwar, PP. 125.

Bhutya, R.K. (2007), Vanaspati Aushadha Vigyana, Scientific Publishers (India), Jodhpur, PP. 160.

Brahmavarchas (2003), Ayurved Ka Pran Vanoshadhi Vigyan, Shanti Kunj, Haridwar, PP. 368.

Chunekar, K.C. (2004), Bhava Prakash Nighantu, Chaukhambha Bharti Academy, Varanasi, PP. 124.

Dhiman, A.K. (2006), Ayurvedic Drug Plants, Daya Publishing House, Delhi, PP. 65.

Khare, C.P. (2007), Indian Medicinal Plants, Springer (India) P.L. New Delhi, PP. 523.

Kirtikar, K.R. & Basu, B.D. (1998), Indian Medicinal Plants, L.M Basu, Allahabad, Vol. 1, PP. 718.

Misra, B.L. (2005), Dravya Guna Hastamalaka, Publication scheme, Jaipur, PP. 263.

Nair, R.Vasudevan, (2007), Indian Medicinal Plants, Orient Longman P.L. Chennai, Vol. 4, PP. 374.

Namjoshi, A.N. (2001), The Ayurvedic Pharmacopoeia of India, Government of India, Department of Indian Systems of Medicine & Homoeopathy, New Delhi, Part-1, Volume- 2, PP. 25.

Pareek, G.N. (2005), Sudhanidhi, Vanoshadhi Ratnakar, Dhanvantari Karyalaya, Aligarh, Vol. 6, PP. 148.

Prajapati, N.D., Purohit, S.S., Sharma, A.K. & Tarun Kumar (2003), A Hand Book of Medicinal Plants, Agrobios India, Jodhpur, PP. 428.

Sharma, P.C., Yelne, MB. & Denis, T.J. (2000), Database on medicinal plants used in ayurveda, Central Council for research in Ayurveda and siddha, Vol. 2, PP. 89.

Sharma, P.V. (1981), Dravya gun vigyana, Chaukhambha Bharti Academy, Varanasi, Vol. 1, PP. 175.

Singh, R.S. (2002), Vanoshadhi Nirdeshika, Uttar Pradesh Hindi Sansthan, Lucknow, PP. 268.

Swami, K.N. (1985), Gavon Main Aushadh Ratna, Kalera Krishana Gopal, Kalera (Raj.), Vol. 3, PP. 89.

392. *Pterocarpus marsupium* Roxb.

Family: Papilionaceae; Fabaceae.

Name: English: Indian Kino Tree, Malabar Kino Tree, **Sanskrit:** *Bijaka, Peetasaara, Peetasaalaka, Bandookapushpa, Priyaka, Sarjaka, Asana,* **Hindi:** *Vijaysar,* **Local:** *Bijak, Bija.*

Botanical characteristics: Habit: A medium sized to large deciduous tree, 10-15 m high. **Stem:** Stout, 2-3 m girth, crooked and widely spreading branches; bark thick, yellowish-grey or dark brown having shallow cracks, exfoliating in thin flakes and exuding a red gummy substance (Gum kino) on injury. **Leaf:** Compound, imperipinnate, 15-23 cm long, leaflets 5-7, coriaceous, 6.3-10 by 3.8-5 cm, oblong, obtuse, rounded, truncate or more or less retuse or emarginated or even bilobed at the apex, glabrous on both surfaces, shining above, base sub-acute, main nerves numerous, close prominent; petiolules 6-10 mm long. **Flower:** Yellow in short lateral and terminal fuscopubescent paniculate racemes, usually shorter than the leaves, corolla with crisped margins; pedicels short, articulated beneath the flower. **Fruit:** Pods, 2.5-5 cm diam., nearly circular, glabrous or nearly so, flat, winged, convexly curved between stipe and style, wings veined. **Seed:** Small, 1-2, convex bony, separated by hard dissepiments. The **Heartwood** is stronge, tough, very hard and moderately heavy and is golden brown or reddish brown on exposure with darker streaks. Aqueous extract of wood is yellowish blue and fluorescent.

Flowering and fruiting period: November-December and February-March.

Habitat: Throughout the tropical zones of India, in the hilly regions, in deciduous and evergreen forests.

Parts used: Heartwood, gum.

Dosage: Heartwood 3-6 g, gum 1-3 g.

Collection period: May-June.

Ayurvedic properties: ***Ras:*** *kashaaya, tikta,* ***Gun:*** *laghu, rukhsa,* ***Veerya:*** *sheeta* ***Vipaka:*** *katu,* ***Tridosha*** **Effect:** alleviates ***Kapha:*** *++,* ***Pitta:*** +.

Chemical constituents: The **heartwood** and **roots** contain isoflavonoids, terpenoids and tannins. Tannins include the hypoglycaemic principle (-)-epicatechin. Stilbenes, such as pterostilbene; flavonoids, including liquiritigenin, isoliquiritigenin, 7-hydroxyflavanone, 7,4-dihydroxyflavanone, 5-deoxykaempferol and pterosupin; a benzofuranone marsupsin and propterol, *p*-hydroxy-benzaldehyde are active principles of therapeutic importance. The **gum-kino** contents a non-glucisidal tannin, Kinotannic acid (25-80%). The (-)-epicatechin increases the AMP content of the islets which is associated with the increased insulin release, conversion of proinsulin to insulin and cathepsin B activity. Oral administration of ethylacetate extract of the heartwood and its flavonoid constituents, marsupin, pterosupin and liquiritigenin, exhibited a significant reduction of serum triglyceride, total cholesterol and LDL-and VLDL-cholesterol levels. The ethanolic and methanolic extracts of the heartwood exhibited significant in *vitro* antimicrobial activity against Gram-positive and Gram-negative becteria and some strains of fungi.

Action and disease indications: The **heartwood** is refrigerant, anti-inflammatory, depurative, urinary astringent, union-promotor, haemostatic, revulsive, anthelmintic, anodyne, constipating, alterant and rejuvenating, used for inflammations, fractures, skin diseases, bruises, elephantiasis, diabetes, leucoderma, erysipelas, urethrorrhea, rectalgia, rectitis, haemorrhages, diarrhea, dysentery, verminosis, odontalgia, ophthalmopathy, gout, rheumatoid arthritis, cough, asthma, bronchitis and greyness of hairs. The **gum-kino** is astringent, styptic, vulnerary, anti-pyretic, anthelmintic and liver tonic, used for diarrhea, dysentery, helminthiasis, intermittent fevers, spasmodic gastralgia, boils, gleet, urethrorrhea, odontalgia, psoriasis, wounds, ulcers, hepatopathy and ophthalmia.

Clinical uses: Dysentery, diarrhea: Gum of described plant 2 g, with water, three times a day, is useful. **Dentalgia:** Local application of gum of described plant, is beneficial. **Excess and turbid micturition:** Decoction of heartwood of described plant 6 g, two times a day, is beneficial. **Inflammation, skin diseases, erysipelas, urticaria, leucoderma:** Local application of paste of leaves of described plant is beneficial. **Canities, alopecia:** Local application of medicated oil, made by heartwood of described plant, is beneficial. **Pain, fractures:** Decoction of heartwood of described plant 6 g, with milk, two times a day, is beneficial. **Diabetes mellitus:** (1) Decoction of heartwood of described plant 6 g, two times a day, is beneficial. (2) Decoction of mix powder of described plant, *Symplocos racemosa, Terminalia arjuna, Pongamia pinnata, Acacia catechu, Delbergia sisso, Santalum album, Pterocarpus santalinus,* bark of *Butea monosperma, Areca catechu,* seeds of *Holarrhena antidysentrica,* 20-30 g, two times a day, is beneficial. **Gonorrhea:** Decoction of heartwood of described plant 6 g, gum of *Commiphora mukul* 1g, with *'Triphalaa'* powder 3 g, two times a day, is beneficial.

Formulations: *Dashamoolaarista, Vrihat manjisthaadi kwaatha.*

Recommended readings:

Bhutya, R.K. (2007), Vanaspati Aushadha Vigyana, Scientific Publishers (India), Jodhpur, PP. 206.

Brahmavarchas (2003), Ayurved Ka Pran Vanoshadhi Vigyan, Shanti Kunj, Haridwar, PP. 371.

Chunekar, K.C. (2004), Bhava Prakash Nighantu, Chaukhambha Bharti Academy, Varanasi, PP. 524.

Dhiman, A.K. (2006), Ayurvedic Drug Plants, Daya Publishing House, Delhi, PP. 406.

Khare, C.P. (2007), Indian Medicinal Plants, Springer (India) P.L. New Delhi, PP. 524.

Kirtikar, K.R. & Basu, B.D. (1998), Indian Medicinal Plants, L.M Basu, Allahabad, Vol. 1, PP. 828.

Misra, B.L. (2005), Dravya Guna Hastamalaka, Publication scheme, Jaipur, PP. 265.

Nair, R.Vasudevan, (2007), Indian Medicinal Plants, Orient Longman P.L. Chennai, Vol. 4, PP. 381.

Namjoshi, A.N. (2001), The Ayurvedic Pharmacopoeia of India, Government of India, Department of Indian Systems of Medicine & Homoeopathy, New Delhi, Part-1, Volume- 2, PP. 12 and 3-15.

Pareek, G.N. (2005), Sudhanidhi, Vanoshadhi Ratnakar, Dhanvantari Karyalaya, Aligarh, Vol. 9, PP. 70.

Prajapati, N.D., Purohit, S.S., Sharma, A.K. & Tarun Kumar (2003), A Hand Book of Medicinal Plants, Agrobios India, Jodhpur, PP. 429.

Sharma, P.V. (1981), Dravya gun vigyana, Chaukhambha Bharti Academy, Varanasi, Vol. 1, PP. 682.

Singh, R.S. (2002), Vanoshadhi Nirdeshika, Uttar Pradesh Hindi Sansthan, Lucknow, PP. 274.

393. *Pterocarpus santalinus* Linn. f.

Family: Papilionaceae; Fabaceae.

Name: English: Red Sandalwood, Red Sanders, **Sanskrit:** *Rakta chandan, Raktaangam, Khsudra chandanam, Tilparna, Raktasaara, Pravaalphalaa,* **Hindi:** *Rakta Chandan,* **Local:** *Laal Chandan.*

Botanical characteristics: Habit: A very pretty, small to medium sized deciduous tree, height 7.5-12 m. **Stem:** 1.5 min girth, bark blackish-brown, deeply cleft into rectangular plates and with extremely hard, dark purple or blackish-red, fibrous, heavy heartwood. **Leaf:** Compound, 3-foliolate, alternate, imparipinnate, leaflets 3, rarely 5, broad-elliptic orovate-orbicular, obtuse, 3.8-7.5 cm long, rounded at both ends, emarginated, under surface pale, clothed with fine appressed hairs. **Flower:** Yellow, few, bisexual, in short simple or sparingly branched axillary or terminal racemes. **Fruit:** Pods, oblique, 3.8 cm diam., gradually narrowed into a short stalk, beaked, narrowly winged with hard central portion containing the seed. **Seed:** Reddish-brown, smooth, leathery, shape like seed of *Abrus precatorius.*

Flowering and fruiting period: April-May and February-March.

Habitat: Found in Cuddapah district in Andhra Pradesh and adjoining areas of Tamilnadu and Karnataka, up to 900 m.

Parts used: Heartwood. **Dosage:** 3-6 g.

Collection period: May-June.

Ayurvedic properties: *Ras:* *madhur, tikta,* ***Gun:*** *guru, rukhsa,* ***Veerya:*** *sheeta,* ***Vipaka:*** *katu,* ***Tridosha* Effect:** alleviates ***Kapha:* +++, *Pitta:* ++.**

Chemical constituents: The **heartwood** contains terpanoids-eudesmol, *iso*-pterocarpolone, pterocarpol, cryptomeridiol, pterocarptriol and pterocarpdiolone; pigments santalins A and B.

Action and disease indications: The **heartwood** is cooling, constipating, depurative, anti-inflammatory, haemostatic, febrifuge, ophthalmic, diaphoretic, anthelmintic, aphrodisiac, alexeteric and tonic, prescribed for burning sensation, vomiting, diarrhea, dysentery, cephalgia, odontalgia, hemicrania, dipsia, skin diseases, ulcers, haemorrhage, haemoptysis, inflammations, fevers, verminisis, piles, blooding piles, ophthalmopathy, mental aberrations and general debility.

Clinical uses: Inflammation, boils, headache, wounds, burning sensation, skin diseases: Local application of paste of heartwood of described plant, is beneficial. **Diarrhea, dysentery:** Powder of heartwood of described plant 5 g, with water, two times a day, is beneficial. **Bleeding piles:** Powder of heartwood of described plant 5 g, with milk, two times a day, is beneficial, and local application of paste of heartwood of described plant, made with milk, is beneficial. **Leucoderma:** Local application of mix paste of heartwood of described plant, seeds of *Punica grantum* and *Vernonia cinerea,* is beneficial. **Acne vulgaris:** Local application of paste heartwood of described plant, *Symplocos racemosa, Sausurea costus, Valeriana jatamansi,* leaves of *Jasminum grandiflorum,* tender leaves of *Ficus bengalensis,* with water, two times a day, is beneficial.

Formulations: *Dashaanga lepa, Laxaadi taila, Pusyaanuga churna, Pathyaadi kwaatha, Triphalaadhya ghrita, Mahaa tikta ghrita, Kumkumaadi taila, Chandanaadi lauha, Aswagandhaarista.*

Recommended readings:

Bhutya, R.K. (2007), Vanaspati Aushadha Vigyana, Scientific Publishers (India), Jodhpur, PP. 92.

Chunekar, K.C. (2004), Bhava Prakash Nighantu, Chaukhambha Bharti Academy, Varanasi, PP. 191.

Dhiman, A.K. (2006), Ayurvedic Drug Plants, Daya Publishing House, Delhi, PP. 313.

Khare, C.P. (2007), Indian Medicinal Plants, Springer (India) P.L. New Delhi, PP. 525.

Kirtikar, K.R. & Basu, B.D. (1998), Indian Medicinal Plants, L.M Basu, Allahabad, Vol. 1, PP. 826.

Misra, B.L. (2005), Dravya Guna Hastamalaka, Publication scheme, Jaipur, PP. 268.

Nair, R.Vasudevan, (2007), Indian Medicinal Plants, Orient Longman P.L. Chennai, Vol. 4, PP. 384.

Namjoshi, A.N. (2001), The Ayurvedic Pharmacopoeia of India, Government of India, Department of Indian Systems of Medicine & Homoeopathy, New Delhi, Part-1, Volume- 3, PP. 155.

Pareek, G.N. (2005), Sudhanidhi, Vanoshadhi Ratnakar, Dhanvantari Karyalaya, Aligarh, Vol. 3, PP. 314.

Prajapati, N.D., Purohit, S.S., Sharma, A.K. & Tarun Kumar (2003), A Hand Book of Medicinal Plants, Agrobios India, Jodhpur, PP. 430.

Sharma, P.C., Yelne, MB. & Denis, T.J. (2000), Database on medicinal plants used in ayurveda, Central Council for research in Ayurveda and siddha, Vol. 7, PP. 361.
Sharma, P.V. (1981), Dravya gun vigyana, Chaukhambha Bharti Academy, Varanasi, Vol. 1, PP. 718.
Singh, R.S. (2002), Vanoshadhi Nirdeshika, Uttar Pradesh Hindi Sansthan, Lucknow, PP. 143.

394. *Pterospermum acerifolium* Willd.

Family: Sterculiaceae.

Other similar plants: *P.canescens.*

Name: English: Hathipaila, **Sanskrit:** *Muchakunda, Khsatravrikhsa, Chitraka, Prativishnuka,* **Hindi:** *Muchakunda,* **Local:** *Muchakunda.*

Botanical characteristics: Habit: An evergreen large tree, height 30 m. **Stem:** 3.25 m in girth, bark smooth, ash-coloured; young parts clothed with floccose pubescence. **Leaf:** Variable in shape and size, 15-35.5 by 12.5-30 cm, orbicular or oblong, entire or variously lobed, cordate and sometimes peltate, coriaceous, dark green, at length glabrous above, clothed beneath with whitish floccose tomentum; petioles 10-30 cm long, terete, tomentose, stipules multifid, caduceus. **Flower:** Yellowish-white, very fragrant, large, 12.5-15 cm diam., axillary, solitary or in pairs, pedicels 12.5 cm long, calyx 7.5-12.5 cm long, linear-oblong, obtuse, densely tomentose outside. **Fruit:** Capsule, 10-15 cm long, oblong, 5-angled, clothed outside with furfuraceous pubescence. **Seed:** Obliquely ovoid, compressed; wing large thin. The ripe fruit remains for a long time on the tree.

Flowering and fruiting period: February-March and November-December.

Habitat: Sub-Himalayan tracts and Outer Himalayan valleys and hills, up to 1600 m, Maharastra, Manipur, North Bengal, Bihar, Assam, Western Ghats and Andaman Islands.

Parts used: Flower. **Dosage:** flower 3-6 g.

Collection period: February-March.

Ayurvedic properties: ***Ras:*** *kashaya, katu, tikta,* ***Gun:*** *Pichhala,* ***Veerya:*** *ushna,* ***Vipaka:*** *katu,* ***Tridosha*** **Effect:** alleviates ***Pitta:*** **++,** ***Kapha:*** **+,** ***Vaata:*** **+.**

Chemical constituents: The **flowers** contain kaempferol-3-0-beta-D-galactoside, along with luteolin and its 7-0-glucoside. The **leaves** also contain betulin, lupeol, bauerenol, friedelin and beta-sitosterol.

Action and disease indications: The **flowers** are laxative, mucilaginous, anodyne, depurative, alexeteric, anthelmintic, tonic, used for inflammations, abdominal pains, ascitis, ulcers, leprosy, hemicrania, cephalgia, pharyngitis, bronchitis, skin diseases, excessive and turbid micturation and tumours.

Clinical uses: Headache: Local application of paste of flowers of described plant, with *'Kanji',* is beneficial. **Bleeding piles:** Local application of paste of flowers of described plant, with water, and oral use of *'Halva'* of flowers of described plant, two times a day, is beneficial. **Epistaxis:** Oral use of *'Halva'* of flowers of described plant, two times a day, is beneficial.

Formulations: *Himaanshu taila.*

Recommended readings:

Bhutya, R.K. (2007), Vanaspati Aushadha Vigyana, Scientific Publishers (India), Jodhpur, PP. 181.
Chunekar, K.C. (2004), Bhava Prakash Nighantu, Chaukhambha Bharti Academy, Varanasi, PP. 504.
Khare, C.P. (2007), Indian Medicinal Plants, Springer (India) P.L. New Delhi, PP. 525.
Kirtikar, K.R. & Basu, B.D. (1998), Indian Medicinal Plants, L.M Basu, Allahabad, Vol. 1, PP. 374.
Misra, B.L. (2005), Dravya Guna Hastamalaka, Publication scheme, Jaipur, PP. 420.
Nair, R.Vasudevan, (2007), Indian Medicinal Plants, Orient Longman P.L. Chennai, Vol. 4, PP. 388.
Sharma, P.V. (1981), Dravya gun vigyana, Chaukhambha Bharti Academy, Varanasi, Vol. 1, PP. 80.
Singh, R.S. (2002), Vanoshadhi Nirdeshika, Uttar Pradesh Hindi Sansthan, Lucknow, PP. 305.

395. *Pueraria tuberosa* D.C.

Family: Papilionaceae; Fabaceae.

Other similar plants: *P.lobata, Ipomoea digitata, Trichosanthus cordata, Lettsomia setosa.*

Ayurvedic Groups: Charak: *Balya, Vrinhaniya, Varnya, Kanthya, Snehopaga, Madhura skandha,* **Sushruta:** *Vidaarigandhaadi, Vallipanchamoola, Pittashamana.*

Name: English: Tropical Kudze, **Sanskrit:** *Vidaari, Swadukandaa, Sitaa, Ikhsugandhaa, Khsiravalli, Khsirashuklaa, Payaswini, Gajavaajipriyaa, Kandapalaasha, Bhumikushmaanda,* **Hindi:** *Vidaarikand,* **Local:** *Bilaikand, Bhuikumhadaa, Patalkoharaa, Sural, Ghodbel, Khankarbel, Fagiyo, Fagadano.*

Botanical characteristics: Habit: A large spreading perennial tuberous herbaceous twining shrub. **Tuber:** Very large, tuberous roots, colour reddish to dark-brown, creamy white inside, many, large tubers usually globose, or spindle shaped, 30-6- by 25-30 cm, up to 35 kg. **Stem:** Shrubby, woody, porous, up to 12 cm in diam., **Leaf:** 3-foliate; petioles 10-15 cm long, more or less pubescent; stipules 4 mm long, ovate-oblong, cordate, leaflets sub-coriaceous, 12.5-20 by 11.5-18 cm, the terminal large, broadly ovate, oval-rounded, acuminate, equal sided, cuneate at the base, the lateral ovate-oblong, inequilateral, truncate at the base, glabrescent above, silky beneath; petiolules 4.5-6 mm long; stipels small subulet. **Flower:** Blue or purplish-blue, in lax leafless racemes 15-30 cm long; pedicels 2-3 mm long, silky-pubescent, bracteoles 1.5 mm long, oblong, silky. **Fruit:** Pods, 5-7.5 cm long, membranous, linear, flat, constricted between the seeds, clothed with long, silky bristly brown hairs. **Seed:** 3-6, reddish-brown, ellipsoid-oblong.

Flowering and fruiting period: February-April and May-June.

Habitat: Almost throughout India, in deciduous forests, from Western Himalaya to Sikkim, up to an altitude of 1200 m.

Parts used: Tuber. **Dosage:** 3-6 g.

Collection period: April-May.

Ayurvedic properties: ***Ras:*** *madhur,* ***Gun:*** *guru, snigdha,* ***Veerya:*** *sheeta,* ***Vipaka:*** *madhur,* ***Tridosha*** **Effect:** alleviates ***Pitta:*** **++++,** ***Vaata:*** **+++.**

Chemical constituents: The **tuber** contains puerarin, diadzein, tuberosin, beta-sitosterol, stigmasterol, isoflavone C-glycoside-4'-6'-diacetyl-puerarin and pterocarpan-tuberosin.

Action and disease indications: The **tubers** are spasmolytic, refrigerant, emollient, laxative, hypoglycaemic, anti-inflammatory, aphrodisiac, galactagogue, diuretic, emetic, rejuvenating, cardio tonic, alterant, expectorant, febrifuge, tonic, oestrogenic, progestrogenic and anti-implantation, used for seminal weakness, burning sensation, constipation, arthritis, agalactia, strangury, emaciation, cardiac debility, intermittent fevers, pharyngitis, dyspepsia, tuberculosis, heptomegaly, spleenomegaly, cough, spermatorrhea and general debility.

Clinical uses: Inflammation: Local application of paste of tuber of described plant, with water, is beneficial. **Malaria, burning sensation, bleeding diasthesis:** Tuber powder of described plant 5 g, with water, two times a day, is beneficial. **Spermatorrhea, hypogalactia, spermacresia:** (1) Tuber powder of described plant 5 g, with milk, two times a day, is beneficial. (2) Soak and dry the tuber powder of described plant, by juice of tuber, by 21 times, dose 3 g, with milk, two times a day, is beneficial. **Dusuria:** Medicated clarified butter, made by tuber of described plant, 10 g, with milk, two times a day, is beneficial. **Billary colic:** Juice of tuber of described plant, 10 ml, with sugar candy powder 10 g, two times a day, is beneficial.

Formulations: *Chyavanpraasha, Dashamoolaarista, Saaraswataarista, Navajivan yoga, Naarsingha churna, Vidaari ghrita, Vrihat aswagandhaa ghrita, Nityaananda rasa, Manmatha-abhra rasa, Amritaprasha ghrita, Mahaamaayur ghrita.*

Recommended readings:

Acharya, B.K. (2008), Ayurveda Jadi-buti Rahasya, Patanjali Yogapitha, Haridwar, PP. 419.

Bhutya, R.K. (2007), Vanaspati Aushadha Vigyana, Scientific Publishers (India), Jodhpur, PP. 207.

Brahmavarchas (2003), Ayurved Ka Pran Vanoshadhi Vigyan, Shanti Kunj, Haridwar, PP. 373.

Chunekar, K.C. (2004), Bhava Prakash Nighantu, Chaukhambha Bharti Academy, Varanasi, PP. 388.

Dhiman, A.K. (2006), Ayurvedic Drug Plants, Daya Publishing House, Delhi, PP. 404.

Khare, C.P. (2007), Indian Medicinal Plants, Springer (India) P.L. New Delhi, PP. 527.

Kirtikar, K.R. & Basu, B.D. (1998), Indian Medicinal Plants, L.M Basu, Allahabad, Vol. 1, PP. 792.

Misra, B.L. (2005), Dravya Guna Hastamalaka, Publication scheme, Jaipur, PP. 274.

Nair, R.Vasudevan, (2007), Indian Medicinal Plants, Orient Longman P.L. Chennai, Vol. 4, PP. 391.

Namjoshi, A.N. (2001), The Ayurvedic Pharmacopoeia of India, Government of India, Department of Indian Systems of Medicine & Homoeopathy, New Delhi, Part-1, Volume- 1, PP. 173.

Prajapati, N.D., Purohit, S.S., Sharma, A.K. & Tarun Kumar (2003), A Hand Book of Medicinal Plants, Agrobios India, Jodhpur, PP. 430.

Sharma, P.C., Yelne, MB. & Denis, T.J. (2000), Database on medicinal plants used in ayurveda, Central Council for research in Ayurveda and siddha, Vol. 6, PP. 441.

Sharma, P.V. (1981), Dravya gun vigyana, Chaukhambha Bharti Academy, Varanasi, Vol. 1, PP. 738.

Singh, R.S. (2002), Vanoshadhi Nirdeshika, Uttar Pradesh Hindi Sansthan, Lucknow, PP. 346.

396. *Punica grantum* Linn.

Family: Punicaceae.

Name: English: Pomegranate, **Sanskrit:** *Daadim, Karaka, Dantabeja, Lohitapushpaka,* **Hindi:** *Anaar,* **Local:** *Anar, Daadyun.*

Botanical characteristics: Habit: A large deciduous shrub or small tree, height 5-10 m. **Stem:** With smooth, dark grey, thin bark and often spinescent branchlets, girth 1 m. **Leaf:**

Opposite, 2.5-6.3 cm, oblong-lanceolate, oblong-elliptic, or oblong-oblanceolate, glabrous, acute, entire, minutely pellucid-punctate, shining above, bright green beneath, base narrowed into a very short petiole. **Flower:** Scarlet red, orange or sometimes yellow, 3.8-5 cm long and as much across, mostly solitary, sometimes 2-4 together, terminating short shoots, sometimes apparently axillary, sessile or nearly so, stamens very numerous, inserted on the calyx below the petals at various levels. **Fruit:** Globose, 3.8-7.5 cm diam., crowned by the persistent calyx, rind coriaceous and woody, interior septate with membranous walls containing numerous seeds. **Seed:** Angular with red, pink or whitish fleshy testa, with a watery outer coat containing pink juice and a horny inner coat.

Flowering and fruiting period: Almost throughout year, mostly in April-May and July-September.

Habitat: Apparently wild in warm valleys in outer parts of Western Himalaya, hilly tracts of Punjab, cultivated throughout India.

Parts used: Fruit, fruit rind, root bark.

Dosage: fruit juice 20-50 ml, fruit rind, root bark 1-3 g.

Collection period: August-September.

Ayurvedic properties: ***Ras:*** *madhur, kashaaya,* ***Gun:*** *laghu, snigdha,* ***Veerya:*** *anushna,* ***Vipaka:*** *madhur,* ***Tridosha* Effect:** alleviates ***Vaata:*** *++,* ***Pitta:*** *++,* ***Kapha:*** *+.*

Chemical constituents: The **fruits** contain nicotinic acid, pectin, protein, riboflavin, thiamine, vitamin C, delphinidin, diglycoside; aspartic, citric, ellagic, gallic and malic acids; glutamine, isoquercetin. The **rind** contains an ellagitannin (grantin B), pentose glycoside of malvidin and pentunidin. The **leaves** contain granatins A and B, and punicafolin; punicalagin-punicalin and ellagic acid. The **flower** contain pelargonidin-3,5-diglucoside; also sitosterol, ursolic acid, maslinic acid, asiatic acid, sitosterol-beta-D-glucoside and gallic acid.

Action and disease indications: The **fruits** are refrigerant, tonic, aphrodisiac, laxative, diuretic, cardio-tonic, brain tonic, semeniferous, used for cardiac debility, anaemia, biliousness, inflammation of stomach, palpitation, dipsia, fevers, hyperdipsia, pharyngodynia, spleenomegaly, bronchitis, ozostomia, seminal weakness, burning sensation, fevers, lack of memory and otalgia. The **Flowers** are styptic to gums, used for vomiting, ophthalmodynia, ulcers, pharyngodynia, hydrocele and epistaxis. The **rind of fruit** is astringent, stomachic, digestive, used for diarrhea, dysentery, colitis, dyspepsia and uterine disorders.

Clinical uses: Tapeworms: Decoction of mix powder of fruit rind of described plant 15 g, seeds of *Butea monosperma* 2 g, *Embelia ribes* 2 g, at morning, empty stomach, and give any purgative drug, with this medication. **Stomatitis:** Gargles by decoction of powder of fruit rind 15 g, or leaves juice of described plant, two times a day, is beneficial. **Diarrhea of children:** Flower bud of described plant, 3 g, with water, two times a day, is beneficial. **Dry cough, bronchitis:** Flower bud or fruit rind powder of described plant, 3 g, with honey 10 g, three times a day, is useful. Sucking of fruit rind of described plant is also useful. **Epistaxis:** Juice sour fruit of described plant, 50 ml, with sugar candy powder 10 g, two times a day, is beneficial. **or** Cold infusion of mix powder of leaves of described plant, tender leaves of *Acacia nilotica, Phylanthus emblica, Coriandrum sativum,* 20 g, with sugar candy powder 10 g, two times a day, is beneficial. **Or** Nasal drops of juice of flowers of bud of described plant, 4-4 drops, is useful. **Piles, bleeding piles:** Local application of paste of leaves of described plant 50 g, fried in clarified butter 10 g, two times a day, is beneficial. **Burning sensation:** Fruit juice of described plant 50 ml, with *Mesua ferrea* 3 g, two times a day, is beneficial. **Or** Local application of paste of fruit rind of described plant and fruit of *Tamarindus indica,* two times a day, is beneficial. **Or** Local application of juice of fruits of described plant and juice of fresh fruits of *Phylanthus emblica,* two times a day, is beneficial. **Vaginal laxity:** Use vaginal tablet of 10 g of mix powder of fruit rind of described plant, *Quercus infectoria, Symplocos racemosa* and Alum, at night, is beneficial. **Acne vulgaris:** Local application of paste of fruit rind, *Symplocos racemosa, Curcuma longa,* with fresh milk, is very beneficial. **Alopecia:** Local application of paste of leaves of described plant, two times a day, is beneficial. **Anorexia:** Mix powder of seeds of described plant 80 g, sugar candy powder 120 g, *Cinamomum verum, Elettaria cardamomum, Cinamomum tamala,* 10-10 g, dose 4-4 g, with water, two times a day, is beneficial. **Hiccough:** Juice of fruits of described plant 30 ml, rock salt 2 g, two times a day, is beneficial. **Intestinal worms:** Root bark powder of described plant 15 g, with water, two times a day, is beneficial. **Polyuria:** Mix powder of flower buds of described plant, gum of *Acacia nilotica,* gum of *Bambusa arundinacea, Santalum album,* 2-2 parts, seeds of *Syzygium* *cumini,* seeds of *Mangifera indica,* 5-5 parts, *Coriandrum sativum, Trigonella foenum-graecum* 3-3 parts, *Cinamomum camphora* 1 part, dose 5 g, with juice of fruits of described plant 50 g, two times a day, is very beneficial.

Formulations: *Daadimaavaleha, Daadimaastaka churna, Daadimaadhya ghrita, Daadima-chatusama churna, Kutajaastaka churna.*

Recommended readings:

Acharya, B.K. (2008), Ayurveda Jadi-buti Rahasya, Patanjali Yogapitha, Haridwar, PP. 62.

Bhutya, R.K. (2007), Vanaspati Aushadha Vigyana, Scientific Publishers (India), Jodhpur, PP. 123.

Brahmavarchas (2003), Ayurved Ka Pran Vanoshadhi Vigyan, Shanti Kunj, Haridwar, PP. 374.

Chunekar, K.C. (2004), Bhava Prakash Nighantu, Chaukhambha Bharti Academy, Varanasi, PP. 582.

Dhiman, A.K. (2006), Ayurvedic Drug Plants, Daya Publishing House, Delhi, PP. 108.

Khare, C.P. (2007), Indian Medicinal Plants, Springer (India) P.L. New Delhi, PP. 527.

Kirtikar, K.R. & Basu, B.D. (1998), Indian Medicinal Plants, L.M Basu, Allahabad, Vol. 2, PP. 1084.

Misra, B.L. (2005), Dravya Guna Hastamalaka, Publication scheme, Jaipur, PP. 467.

Nair, R.Vasudevan, (2007), Indian Medicinal Plants, Orient Longman P.L. Chennai, Vol. 4, PP. 396.

Namjoshi, A.N. (2001), The Ayurvedic Pharmacopoeia of India, Government of India, Department of Indian Systems of Medicine & Homoeopathy, New Delhi, Part-1, Volume- 1, PP. 33.

Pareek, G.N. (2005), Sudhanidhi, Vanoshadhi Ratnakar, Dhanvantari Karyalaya, Aligarh, Vol. 4, PP. 301.

Prajapati, N.D., Purohit, S.S., Sharma, A.K. & Tarun Kumar (2003), A Hand Book of Medicinal Plants, Agrobios India, Jodhpur, PP. 432.

Sharma, P.C., Yelne, MB. & Denis, T.J. (2000), Database on medicinal plants used in ayurveda, Central Council for research in Ayurveda and siddha, Vol. 2, PP. 177.

Sharma, P.V. (1981), Dravya gun vigyana, Chaukhambha Bharti Academy, Varanasi, Vol. 1, PP. 340.

Singh, R.S. (2002), Vanoshadhi Nirdeshika, Uttar Pradesh Hindi Sansthan, Lucknow, PP. 16.

Swami, K.N. (1985), Gavon Main Aushadh Ratna, Kalera Krishana Gopal, Kalera (Raj.), Vol. 1, PP. 18.

397. *Pyrus communis* Linn.

Family: Rosaceae.

Synonym: *P.pyrifolia.*

Other similar plants: *P.sinensis.*

Name: English: Common Pear, European Pear, **Sanskrit:** *Amritaphala,* **Hindi:** *Naashapati,* **Local:** *Naashapati, Bagu ghosa.*

Botanical characteristics: Habit: A medium sized deciduous tree, height 6-10 m. **Stem:** Glabrous, branchlets on young trees often spinescent. **Leaf:** Broadly ovate, 6.25 cm long, slightly dentate, entire or obtusely serrate, petiole slender, nearly as long as leaf. **Flower:** White, 2.5 cm diam., style 5, free. **Fruit:** More or less tuberbinate, not intruded at the base, light green, crowned with the persistent calyx.

Flowering and fruiting period: March-April and July-September.

Habitat: Largely cultivated in Punjab and Kashmir.

Parts used: Fruit. **Dosage:** 25-50 g.

Collection period: July-Septenber.

Ayurvedic properties: ***Ras:*** *madhur,* ***Gun:*** *guru, snigdha,* ***Veerya:*** *sheeta,* ***Vipaka:*** *madhur,* ***Tri-dosha*** **Effect:** alleviates ***Vaata:*** ++, ***Pitta:*** ++.

Chemical constituents: The **leaves** contain arbutin, *iso*-quercetin, sorbitol, ursolic acid, astragalin and tannin (0.8-2.9%). The **bark** contains friedelin, epifriedelanol and beta-sitosterol. The **fruits** contain pectin, gallic and tartaric acids, also contains protein 0.1, carbohydrates 2.7, calcium2, iron 0.1/per ounce, vitamin A 3 units, B1-2 units, B2-2mg per ounce.

Action and disease indications: The **fruits** are refrigerant, aphrodisiac, semeniferous, febrifuge, rejuvenating, used for seminal weakness, dyspepsia, fevers, neuralgia, burning sensation, vomiting, anorexia, leucorrhea, diarrhea, dysentery and diarrhea with bleeding.

Clinical uses: Spermacresia, general debility: Fruit pulp of described plant 100 g, two times a day, is beneficial.

Recommended readings:

Bhutya, R.K. (2007), Vanaspati Aushadha Vigyana, Scientific Publishers (India), Jodhpur, PP. 137.

Chunekar, K.C. (2004), Bhava Prakash Nighantu, Chaukhambha Bharti Academy, Varanasi, PP. 590.

Khare, C.P. (2007), Indian Medicinal Plants, Springer (India) P.L. New Delhi, PP. 529.

Kirtikar, K.R. & Basu, B.D. (1998), Indian Medicinal Plants, L.M Basu, Allahabad, Vol. 2, PP. 988.

Swami, K.N. (1985), Gavon Main Aushadh Ratna, Kalera Krishana Gopal, Kalera (Raj.), Vol. 2, PP. 381.

398. *Quercus infectoria* Oliv.

Family: Fagaceae.

Other similar plants: *Q.incana, Q.ilex, Q.robur.*

Name: English: Oak galls, Aleppo galls, Mecca galls, **Sanskrit:** *Maayaphala,* **Hindi:** *Manju-phala,* **Local:** *Manjuphala.*

Botanical characteristics: Habit: An evergreen shrub or small tree, height 2-5 m. **Stem:** With many spreading branches and grey bark. **Leaf:** Very excrescence on the young twigs, alternate, very rigid, often glabrescent with spinous teeth and are 4-6 cm long, yellowish in colour. **Flower:** Unisexual, male flowers in pendulous catkins, bracts small, 1-flowered; perianth campanulate, 4-8 lobed, female flowers with an involucre of small scales, solitary, axillary or in few flowered spikes; perianth-tube adnate to the ovary. **Fruit:** (Acorn), a 1-seeded nut seated on a cup formed from the and hardened involucral scales, globose, 6 mm long, lemon coloured and are tinged with yellow. The **galls** arise as excrescences on the young twigs, consequent on the deposition of eggs by a small hymenopterous insect known as *Adeleria gallae-tinctoriae.* The galls are spherical or pear-shaped with a smooth and shining surface bearing spinous projections. It is chestnut brown in colour. The galls collected before the emergence of the insects are the best, Such galls have inner soft tissue of a deep greenish yellow colour. Those collected after the escape of the insects will have perforations. The galls generally vary in size, colour and appearance.

Flowering and fruiting period: March-April and October-January.

Habitat: Found in Kumaon, Garhwal and Bijanor forests.

Parts used: Gall. **Dosage:** 1-3 g.

Collection period: May-June.

Ayurvedic properties: ***Ras:*** *kashaaya,* ***Gun:*** *laghu, rukhsa,* ***Veerya:*** *sheeta,* ***Vipaka:*** *katu,* ***Tridosha*** **Effect:** alleviates ***Kapha: +++, Pitta:*** +.

Chemical constituents: The **galls** contain 50-70% gallo tannic acid, gallic acid 2-4%, ellagic acid, nycthanthic acid, rubric acid, along sugars, starch, an essential oil and anthocyanins. Galls were also found tocontain beta-sitosterol, amentoflavone, hexamethyl ether and isocryptomerin.

Action and disease indications: The **galls** are astringent, refrigerant, haemostatic, constipating, expectorant, vulnerary, digestive, febrifuge, trichogenous and tonic, used for haemoptysis, internal haemorrhages, diarrhea, dysentery, cough, asthma, bronchitis, ulcerative stomatitis, dyspepsia, leucorrhea, menorrhagia, piles, proleps of uterus and rectum, diseases of gums and oral cavity, nasal catarrh and sore throat. fever, gonorrhea, impetigo, eczema, pharyngodynia, diabetes, tonsillitis, hyperhydrosis and general debility, also very useful in blackening the hairs and antidote of poisoning by Aconite, Datura, Nux-vomica and Antimony and included in breast and vaginal firming creams.

Clinical uses: Piles: Local application of paste of galls of described plant, with cream, is beneficial. **Chronic diarrhea, sprue:** Galls of described plant, 2 g, *Cinamomum verum* 1 g, with honey 10 g, two times a day, is useful. **Bleeding piles:** Galls of described plant 2 g, *Zingiber officinale* 1 g, with clarified butter 10 g and sugar candy powder 10 g, two times a day, is beneficial. **Chronic leucorrhea:** Galls of described plant, 2 g, with honey 10 g, two times a day, is useful. **Vaginal prolapse:** Put powder of galls of described plant 10 g, Alum 2 g, in vagina, in a small, thin piece of cotton cloth, at night. **Gingivitis:** Gargles of powder of galls of described plant, *Quercus infectoria, Cinamomum camphora,* extract of *Acacia catechu,* 5 g, two times a day, or use this powder as tooth powder, 10 g, is beneficial.

Formulations: *Vajradanta manjan, Maayaaphalaadi malahar, Dantaprabhaakar manjan, Pradaraantaka churna, Maayikaa vati.*

Recommended readings:

Bhutya, R.K. (2007), Vanaspati Aushadha Vigyana, Scientific Publishers (India), Jodhpur, PP. 177.

Chunekar, K.C. (2004), Bhava Prakash Nighantu, Chaukhambha Bharti Academy, Varanasi, PP. 834.

Dhiman, A.K. (2006), Ayurvedic Drug Plants, Daya Publishing House, Delhi, PP. 260.

Khare, C.P. (2007), Indian Medicinal Plants, Springer (India) P.L. New Delhi, PP. 532.

Kirtikar, K.R. & Basu, B.D. (1998), Indian Medicinal Plants, L.M Basu, Allahabad, Vol. 3, PP. 2357.

Misra, B.L. (2005), Dravya Guna Hastamalaka, Publication scheme, Jaipur, PP. 445.

Nair, R.Vasudevan, (2007), Indian Medicinal Plants, Orient Longman P.L. Chennai, Vol. 4, PP. 403.

Sharma, P.V. (1981), Dravya gun vigyana, Chaukhambha Bharti Academy, Varanasi, Vol. 1, PP. 483.

Singh, R.S. (2002), Vanoshadhi Nirdeshika, Uttar Pradesh Hindi Sansthan, Lucknow, PP. 301.

Swami, K.N. (1985), Gavon Main Aushadh Ratna, Kalera Krishana Gopal, Kalera (Raj.), Vol. 3, PP. 180.

399. *Randia dumetorum* Poir.

Family: Rubiaceae.

Synonym: *R. spinosa, R. brandisii, R. longispina, R. tomentosa, Xeromphis spinosa.*

Name: English: Common Emetic Nut, **Sanskrit:** *Madan, Chardan, Pinda, Nut, Pinditaka,*

Karhaat, Maruvaka, Shalyaka, Vishapushpaka, **Hindi:** *Madanphala,* **Local:** *Mainphala.*

Botanical characteristics: Habit: A deciduous armed rigid large shrub or small tree, height up to 9 m. **Stem:** Girth 1 m, bark dark brown or grey rough scaly bark, branches horizontal, rigid, numerous, with strong, straight, nearly opposite, decussate spines 1.3-3.2 cm long, coming off from above the branchlets. **Leaf:** Simple, usually fascicled on the suppressed branches, 3.2-5.7 by 2-3.2 cm, obovate, obtuse, wrinkled, shining or more or less pubescent above and on nerves beneath, main nerves 6-10 pairs, petioles 1-3 mm long, densely pubescent; stipules ovate, acuminate. **Flower:** White, later turning yellow, fragrant, solitary or 2-3 together at the ends of short leaf bearing branchlets, peduncles short. **Fruit:** Berry, like a small crab-apple, 2-3 cm long and 2.5 cm broad, yellowish, globose or broadly ovoid, smooth, or obscurely longitudinally ribbed, crowned with the large calyx-limb, fleshy, 2-celled, glabrous; 4 round masses of black seeds in a fruit, just like Greater Cardamom, pericarp thick. **Seed:** Numerous, black, flat, ovoid, angular, embedded in pulp.

Flowering and fruiting period: May-June and November-December.

Habitat: Throughout India, in deciduous forests, up to an altitude of 1350 m, mostly in Assam, Sikkim, Deharadun, Bengal, Bihar, coastal districts of South India and Andamans.

Parts used: Fruit.

Dosage: 1-2 g, for induction vomiting 3-6 g.

Collection period: December-January.

Ayurvedic properties: ***Ras:*** *kashaaya, madhur, tikta, katu,* ***Gun:*** *laghu, rukhsa,* ***Veerya:*** *ushna,* ***Vipaka:*** *katu,* ***Tridosha*** **Effect:** alleviates ***Kapha: ++, Vaata: +, Pitta: +.***

Chemical constituents: The **fruits** contain mainly saponins about 10%, a mixture of two saponins, *viz.* randialic or neutral saponin and randialic acid or acid saponins has been isolated from pulp. On complete hydrolysis both the saponins yield oleanolic acid as sapogenin. Ursosaponin, isolated from the ethannolic extract of the dried whole fruit, gave ursolic acid and glucose. Randianin, isolated from the fruit, gave a haemolytic triterpenoid saponin.

Action and disease indications: The **fruits** are thermogenic, emetic, anodyne, anti-inflammatory, anthelmintic, carminative, depurative, vulnerary, emmenogogue, expectorant, febrifuge, sudorofic, abortifacient and anti-spasmodic, used for inflammations, pains, sprains, gout, helminthiasis, leprosy, skin diseases, abscess, wounds, ulcers, tumours, dysmenorrhea, ameno-rrhea, cough, asthma, bronchitis, flatulence, colic, constipation and fever.

Clinical uses: Asthma, bronchitis: Mix powder of fruit powder of described plant, *Glycyrrhiza glabra,* 250-750 mg, with honey 10 g, three times a day, is useful. **Rheumatism, boils, hurt:** Local application of paste of bark of described plant is beneficial. **Colic:** Local application of paste of bark of described plant, with Vinegar or *'Kanji',* around the umbilicus is beneficial. **Diarrhea, diarrhea with bleeding, dysentery:** Seed powder of described plant, 0.5-1 g, with honey 10 g, two times a day, is useful. **Whooping cough:** Tincture of the fruits of described plant, 15-30 drops, two times a day, is beneficial. **For induction of vomiting:** Cold infusion of fruit powder of described plant 6 g, *Piper longum* 1 g, with honey 10 g, in empty stomach.

Formulations: *Utphullikaankusha, Malashodhaka basti, Phala varti, Siddhasanbhara, Madanaadi lepa, Durlabhaadya khsara, Vrihat saindhavaadi taila.*

Recommended readings:

Acharya, B.K. (2008), Ayurveda Jadi-buti Rahasya, Patanjali Yogapitha, Haridwar, PP. 278.

Bhutya, R.K. (2007), Vanaspati Aushadha Vigyana, Scientific Publishers (India), Jodhpur, PP. 172.

Brahmavarchas (2003), Ayurved Ka Pran Vanoshadhi Vigyan, Shanti Kunj, Haridwar, PP. 380.

Chunekar, K.C. (2004), Bhava Prakash Nighantu, Chaukhambha Bharti Academy, Varanasi, PP. 77.

Khare, C.P. (2007), Indian Medicinal Plants, Springer (India) P.L. New Delhi, PP. 535.

Kirtikar, K.R. & Basu, B.D. (1998), Indian Medicinal Plants, L.M Basu, Allahabad, Vol. 2, PP. 1273.

Misra, B.L. (2005), Dravya Guna Hastamalaka, Publication scheme, Jaipur, PP. 261.

Nair, R.Vasudevan, (2007), Indian Medicinal Plants, Orient Longman P.L. Chennai, Vol. 2, PP. 33.

Namjoshi, A.N. (2001), The Ayurvedic Pharmacopoeia of India, Government of India, Department of Indian Systems of Medicine & Homoeopathy, New Delhi, Part-1, Volume- 2, PP. 84.

Pareek, G.N. (2005), Sudhanidhi, Vanoshadhi Ratnakar, Dhanvantari Karyalaya, Aligarh, Vol. 7, PP. 54.

Prajapati, N.D., Purohit, S.S., Sharma, A.K. & Tarun Kumar (2003), A Hand Book of Medicinal Plants, Agrobios India, Jodhpur, PP. 434.

Sharma, P.C., Yelne, MB. & Denis, T.J. (2000), Database on medicinal plants used in ayurveda, Central Council for research in Ayurveda and siddha, Vol. 2, PP. 380.

Sharma, P.V. (1981), Dravya gun vigyana, Chaukhambha Bharti Academy, Varanasi, Vol. 1, PP. 376.

Singh, R.S. (2002), Vanoshadhi Nirdeshika, Uttar Pradesh Hindi Sansthan, Lucknow, PP. 321.

Swami, K.N. (1985), Gavon Main Aushadh Ratna, Kalera Krishana Gopal, Kalera (Raj.), Vol. 3, PP. 227.

400. *Ranunculus sceleratus* Linn.

Family: Ranunculaceae. **Synonym:** *R.umbellatus* roxb., *R.digitatus* gibb., *R.carnosus* wall.

Name: English: Blister butter cup, Celery leaved crowfoot, **Sanskrit**: *Kaandeera, Kaandkadama, Nasasamvedana, Toyvalli, Sukandaka, Kandkatuka,* **Hindi name**: *Kaandeer, Devkaandar,* **Local name**: *Jal dhaniaa.*

Botanical characteristics: Habit: An erect glabrous, much branched, annual herb, height up to 80cm. **Stem:** Herbaceous, erect, angular, aerial, fistular, smooth, nodes and internodes are very prominent, green in colour. **Leaf:** Shape like leaves of *Coriandrum sativum* , cauline and ramal, alternate, exstipulate, simple, petiolate, lamina much dissected, each lobe ovate, entire, obtuse, glabrous, multicostate reticulate, smell like *Brassica juncea* seeds. **Flower:** Bracteate , bracteolate, pedicelate, complete, actinomorfic, hermaphrodite, pentamerous, hypogynous, thalamus prominent and convex, Spiro cyclic, yellow coloured. **Fruit:** Etaerio of achenes, many long, round shaped, like a fruit of *Piper longum.*

Flowering and fruiting period: January to March and March to April.

Habitat: Wet plain of Northern India and warm valley of the Himalayas, from Kashmir to Assam, at banks of rivers, up to 2000m.

Parts used: Whole plant.

Dosage: Dried powder: 1-3 g.

Collection period: September to October.

Ayurvedic properties: ***Ras:*** *katu, tikta,* ***Gun:*** *laghu, rukhsa, tikhasna,* ***Veerya:*** *usna,* ***Vipaka:*** *katu,* ***Tridosha*** **effect:** alleviates ***Kapha:*** *++,* ***Vaata:*** *+.*

Chemical constituents: **Plants** contains anemonin, prota-a nemonin, ranunculine, seretonin and other triptamine derivatives.

Action and diseases indications: **Fresh plant** is highly acrid, rubefacient, vesicant and toxic; causes inflammation of the digestive tract. Use after drying the plant. It has blistering effect. It is anti septic, digestive, appetizer, deobstruent, anthelmintic, and emmenagogue. Seretonin is potent vaso constrictor. Protoanemonin is strong anti-bacterial, anti-viral, cytopathogenic and vermicidal properties. It is effective against both gram-positive and gram-negative bacteria, similar to penicillic acid. It inhibits the growth of *E.coli, Staphylococcus aureus* and *Candida albicans.*

Contra-indication: Fresh plant is toxic. So dry it and control the over dose.

Clinical uses: Inflammation of lymphatic glands, bubo of plague, skin diseases, and rheumatoid arthritis, leucoderma: Local application of poultice of *R.sceleratus* is beneficial. **Amenorrhea and hypomenorrhea:** 30 ml decoction of *R.sceleratus* 3 g, with honey 10 g, from 4 days before the menstrual period, till it ends. **Prohibition of plague:** Pills of *R.sceleratus* 2 g, twice a day. **Eczema, skin diseases:** Local application of paste of the plant and leaves of *Ocimum sanctum* is useful.

Recommended readings:

Bhutya, R.K. (2007), Vanaspati Aushadha Vigyana, Scientific Publishers (India), Jodhpur, PP. 59.

Khare, C.P. (2007), Indian Medicinal Plants, Springer (India) P.L. New Delhi, PP. 536.

Kirtikar, K.R. & Basu, B.D. (1998), Indian Medicinal Plants, L.M Basu, Allahabad, Vol. 1, PP. 14.

Misra, B.L. (2005), Dravya Guna Hastamalaka, Publication scheme, Jaipur, PP. 477.

Pareek, G.N. (2005), Sudhanidhi, Vanoshadhi Ratnakar, Dhanvantari Karyalaya, Aligarh, Vol. 5, PP. 122.

Prajapati, N.D., Purohit, S.S., Sharma, A.K. & Tarun Kumar (2003), A Hand Book of Medicinal Plants, Agrobios India, Jodhpur, PP. 435.

Sharma, P.V. (1981), Dravya gun vigyana, Chaukhambha Bharti Academy, Varanasi, Vol. 1, PP. 237.

Swami, K.N. (1985), Gavon Main Aushadh Ratna, Kalera Krishana Gopal, Kalera (Raj.), Vol. 2, PP. 303.

401. *Raphanus sativus* Linn.

Family: Cruciferae; Brassicaceae.

Other similar plant: *R.caudatus.*

Name: English: Radish, **Sanskrit:** *Mulaka, Shaalaamarkata, Vishra, Shaaleya, Marushambhava,* **Hindi:** *Mooli,* **Local:** *Mooli.*

Botanical characteristics: Habit: An annual or biennial herb, height 0.2-1 m. **Root:** White or brightly coloured, tuberous tap root. **Stem:** Flexuose, short condensed, branched in upper part, glabrous or hispid, often purple. **Leaf:** Basal leaves long, lyrately pinnate, coarsely toothed, petioles 5-5.3 cm long, hairy 3-4, subcordate at the base, upper leaves shorter petiolate, margin coarsely dentate, upper most simple, sub-linear, narrowed at the base, all roughly pilose bright green, often obscurely red-margined, often also red-nerved. **Flower:** White or lilac scented in lax racemes. **Fruit:** Pods, erect, cylindric, inflated, 3-9 cm long, 0.8-1.4 cm diam., yellow or pale purple, spongy, 2-8 seeded, continuous or more or less constricted, longitudinally sulcate-nervose, beak green. **Seed:** Sessile, pendulous, ovoid, light brown, testa reticulate.

Flowering and fruiting period: September-October and December-January.

Habitat: Cultivated in plains throughout India, and up to an altitude of 3500 m in Himalaya.

Parts used: Root tuber, seed, Alkali of plant.

Dosage: Root juice 15-30 ml, dried roots for decoction 6 g, seed 1-3 g, alkali 0.5-1.5 g.

Collection period: December-January.

Ayurvedic properties: ***Ras:*** *katu,* ***Gun:*** *laghu,* ***Veerya:*** *ushna,* ***Vipaka:*** *katu,* ***Tridosha* Effect:** alleviates ***Vaata:*** ***++,*** ***Kapha:*** ++, aggravates ***Pitta:*** ++.

Chemical constituents: The **fleshy roots** and **Seeds** contain trans-4-methyl-tuiobutenyl isothio-cyanate glucoside (the pungent principle), cyaniding-5-glucoside-3-sophoroside, pelargonidin diglycoside, cyaniding diglycoside, 5-methyl-L-cysteine-sulphoxide (methiin), steroidal sapogenins and sulphorophene. The enzymes are phosphatase, catalase, sucrase, amylase, alcohol dehydrogenase and pyruvic carboxylase. **Radish** contains caffeic acid and ferulic acid which exhibit hepatoprotective and choleretic properties. It contains choline which prevents deposition of fat in liver. Amino acids, ornithine, citrilline, arginine, glutamic acid and aspartic acid remove toxins from the body and urea accumulation. It is good source of ascorbic acid (15-40 mg/100g) and ascorbigen. The **roots, leaves, flowers and pods** are active against Gram-positive bacteria. The **seeds** contain a broad spectrum antibiotic, machrolysin, specific against *Mycobacterium tuberculosis.* Raphanin, extracted from the **seeds,** is active against Gram-positive and Gram-negative bacteria.

Action and disease indications: The **roots** are thermogenic, appetizer, digestive, depurative, laxative, stomachic, anti-inflammatory, anodyne, good for throat, refreshing and anti-bacterial, used for peptic disorders, especially those related to dyskinesia of the bile ducts; and in catarrhs of the upper respiratory tract, piles, hiccough, influenza, dysentery, colic and liver, gall bladder and urinary complaints, neuralgia, nausea, dyspepsia, flatulence, fevers, asthma, jaundice, ophthalmopathy, helminthiasis, skin diseases, cephalgia, inflammations, insomnia and chronic diarrhea. The **seeds** are diuretic, expectorant, carminative, laxative and emmenogogue, used for cough, strangury, flatulence, dyspepsia, amenorrhea, spleenomegaly and paralysis.

Clinical uses: Chronic urticaria: Juice of roots of described plant, 50 ml, two times a day, is beneficial. **Piles:** poultice of root powder of described plant, is beneficial. Juice of described plant, 30 ml, two times a day, is beneficial. **Bleeding piles:** Soak and dry the extract of *Aloe barbadensis,* By rootjuice of described plant 7 times, and make pills of 250 mg, dose 1 pill, with butter, and juice of leaves of described plant 25 ml, two times a day, is beneficial. **Hiccough:** Decoction of small roots of described plant, 50-100 ml, by 1-1 hour, is beneficial. **Hyperacidity:** Root or leaves juice of described plant, with sugar candy powder 10 g, two times a day, is beneficial. **Inflammation:** Root powder of described plant and seed powder of *Sesamum orientale,* 100 g, two times a day, is beneficial. **Ptyresis versicolor:** Local applic-ation of paste of seeds of described plant with juice of *Achyranthus aspera,* is beneficial. **Anuria, dysuria:** Local application of paste of leaves juice of described plant 50 ml and Salt petre 2 g, is beneficial. **Slip disc:** Seed powder of described plant 3 g, with water, two times a day, and local application of paste of leaves of *Datura inoxia,* is beneficial.

Formulations: *Khsaara taila, Chandanabalaa-lakhsaadi taila, Punarnavaasava, Udaraamrita yoga, Sauramoolaka, Hajaralyahooda bhasma, Shothaari churna, Sushkamulakaadhya taila.*

Recommended readings:

Acharya, B.K. (2008), Ayurveda Jadi-buti Rahasya, Patanjali Yogapitha, Haridwar, PP. 295.

Bhutya, R.K. (2007), Vanaspati Aushadha Vigyana, Scientific Publishers (India), Jodhpur, PP. 182.

Brahmavarchas (2003), Ayurved Ka Pran Vanoshadhi Vigyan, Shanti Kunj, Haridwar, PP. 381.

Chunekar, K.C. (2004), Bhava Prakash Nighantu, Chaukhambha Bharti Academy, Varanasi, PP. 697.

Khare, C.P. (2007), Indian Medicinal Plants, Springer (India) P.L. New Delhi, PP. 537.

Kirtikar, K.R. & Basu, B.D. (1998), Indian Medicinal Plants, L.M Basu, Allahabad, Vol. 1, PP. 178.

Misra, B.L. (2005), Dravya Guna Hastamalaka, Publication scheme, Jaipur, PP. 319.

Nair, R.Vasudevan, (2007), Indian Medicinal Plants, Orient Longman P.L. Chennai, Vol. 4, PP. 407.

Namjoshi, A.N. (2001), The Ayurvedic Pharmacopoeia of India, Government of India, Department of Indian Systems of Medicine & Homoeopathy, New Delhi, Part-1, Volume- 1, PP. 109 and 3-125.

Prajapati, N.D., Purohit, S.S., Sharma, A.K. & Tarun Kumar (2003), A Hand Book of Medicinal Plants, Agrobios India, Jodhpur, PP. 436.

Sharma, P.C., Yelne, M. B. & Denis, T.J. (2000), Database on medicinal plants used in ayurveda, Central Council for research in Ayurveda and siddha, Vol. 4, PP. 443.

Sharma, P.V. (1981), Dravya gun vigyana, Chaukhambha Bharti Academy, Varanasi, Vol. 2, PP. 271.

Singh, R.S. (2002), Vanoshadhi Nirdeshika, Uttar Pradesh Hindi Sansthan, Lucknow, PP. 316.

Swami, K.N. (1985), Gavon Main Aushadh Ratna, Kalera Krishana Gopal, Kalera (Raj.), Vol. 3, PP. 216.

402. *Rauvolfia serpentina* Benth. Ex Kurz.

Family: Apocynaceae.

Other similar plants: *R.tetraphylla*- bigger var., *R.beddomei, R.densiflora, R.micrantha.*

Name: English: Rauvolfia Root, Serpentina Root, Indian Snakeroot, **Sanskrit:** *Sarpagandhaa, Naakuli, Surasaa, Naagasugandhaa, Gandhan-aakuli, Bhujangaakhsi, Sarpaangi, Dhawal vitapa,* **Hindi:** *Sarpagandhaa,* **Local:** *Chhota Chand, Dhaval Barua.*

Botanical characteristics: Habit: A small erect perennial shrub or undershrub, height 30-90 cm. **Root:** Soft, stout, thick, tortuous, terete, frequently curved and twisted, brownish, tuberous, about 30 cm long, 2 cm diam., zig-zag with irregular nodes, bark separates easily in fresh condition, very hard in dry condition. **Stem:** Bark pale brown, corky, longitudinally fissured. **Leaf:** Simple, 3 in a whorl, thin, 7.5-18 by 2.5-6.3 cm, lanceolate, acute or acuminate, glabrius, bright green above, pale beneath, base tapering; main nerves 8-10 pairs, slender; petioles 8 mm long. **Flower:** Bisexual, white, often tinged with violate, in 5-10 cm long peduncled irregular corymbose cymes; pedicels stout bright red. **Fruit:** Drupes of 2 pyrenes, single, connate at base, purplish-black when ripe. **Seed:** Pyrenes rugose, hard.

Flowering and fruiting period: Almost throughout year, chiefly February-March and April-May.

Habitat: Sub-Himalayan tracts from Punjab to Nepal, Sikkim, Bhutan, Assam, Western Ghats and Andamans, as forest undergrowth.

Parts used: Root. **Dosage:** 1-2 g.

Collection period: May-June.

Ayurvedic properties: ***Ras:*** *tikta,* ***Gun:*** *laghu, rukhsa,* ***Veerya:*** *ushna,* ***Vipaka:*** *katu,* ***Tridosha*** **Effect:** alleviates ***Kapha:* ++, *Vaata:* ++.**

Chemical constituents: The **roots** are rich in alkaloids, the most important being reserpine, others, around 30, which include ajmaline, ajmalicine (raubasine), yohimbine, coryanthine, iso-ajmaline, neo-ajmaline, papaverine, raubasine, rauwolscine, rescinnamine, reserpine, sarpagine, serpentine, serpentinine, serpinine and deserpidine. Resrpine is hypotensive and tranquilizer, used for certain forms of mental disorders. Ajmalicine and rescinnamine are also hypotensive and tranquilizer. Deserpidine is sedative, as well as hypotensive. Ajmaline exhibits anti-arrhythmic activity. While selecting the raw material (root) care should be taken to see that the bark is intact. If the bark is peeled off the quality of the root is severely affected as the bark contains more alkaloid than the woody portion.

Action and disease indications: The **roots** are thermogenic, anthelmintic, hypotensive, laxative and sedative, induced bradycardia, prescribed for hypertension, strangury, fever, wounds, colic, insomnia, epilepsy, giddiness, dyspepsia. Key application in essential hypertension, borderline hypertension, especially with elevated tension of the sympathetic nervous system, as sinus tachycardia, anxiety, tension and psychomotor irritation, when dietetic measures alone are not sufficient, hypochondria, neuropsychiatric disorders, psychosis and schizophrenia. The **root** decoction is employed toincrease uterine contractions and for expulsion of foetus in difficult cases. The juice of **leaves** is used as a remedy for the removal of opacities of the cornea.

Contraindication: Contraindicated in depression, bleeding disorders, gastric and duodenal ulcers, also in pregnancy, since it has both teratogenic and abortifacient potential. Treatment should be administered with a diuretic to prevent fluid retention which may develop if Rauvolfia root is given alone.

Clinical uses: Alcoholism, insomnia, hyposmnia, hysteria: Make decoction of described plant 10 parts, *Hyoscyamus niger* 2 parts, *Nardostachys jatamansi* 1 part, *Canabis sativa* 1 part, filter it and make it thick, add powder of root powder of *Piper longum* 0.25 part, then make tablets of 250 mg, dose 1-2 tablets, with milk, at night, is beneficial. **Bacillary dysentery:** Root powder of described plant, 250 mg, with decoction of bark of *Holarrhena antidysentrica* 10 g, or *'Kutajarista'* 25 ml, two times a day, is beneficial. **Chronic fever, dysmenorrhea:** Mix powder of root powder of described plant, *Piper nigrum, Acorus calamus,*

Gardenia gummifera, Swertia chirata, rock salt, 3 g, with water, two times a day, is beneficial. **Hypertension:** (1) Root powder of described plant 250-500 mg, with milk or water or rose water or *'Saaraswataaristaa' or 'Phalaasava'* 20 ml, two times a day, is beneficial. (2) Mix powder of root powder of described plant, *Hyoscyamus niger,* 1.25 g, sugar candy powder 5 g, with water, two times a day, is beneficial. (3) Root powder of described plant 300 mg, seeds of *Elettaria cardamomum* 250 mg, Bitumen 500 mg, with milk, two times a day, is beneficial. (4) Root powder of described plant 500 mg, *Tinospora cordifolia* 1 g, *Phylanthus emblica,* 2 g, with water, two times a day, is beneficial. (5) Mix powder of described plant, *Bacopa monnieri, Celestrus paniculatus,* 2-2 parts, *Acorus calamus, Nardostachys jatamansi,* 1-1 part, dose 1-2 g, with cold infusion of *Convolvulus pluricaulis* 5 g, two times a day, is beneficial. (6) Mix powder of root powder of described plant 20 parts, *'Ras sindoora', 'Mukta sukti pisti', 'Jahar moharaa khatai pisti'* extract of *Tinospora cordifolia,* 1-1 part, dose 1 g, with water or rose water 20 ml, two times a day, is beneficial. (7) Mix powder of described plant, *'Sweta parpati'* 1 g, with water, as required. **Epilepsy:** Mix powder of root powder of described plant, seeds of *Elettaria cardamomum, Bacopa monnieri,* gum of *Bambusa arundinacea,* 4 g, with water, two times a day, is beneficial. **Hysteria:** Mix powder of described plant, *Bacopa monnieri, Acorus calamus, Cinamomum verum,* 2 g, with cold water, two times a day, is beneficial. **Headache:** Root powder of described plant 250 mg, *'Godanti bhsama'* 500 mg, with honey 10 g, two times a day, is useful. **Somatalgia:** Mix powder of described plant, *Zingiber officinale, Foeniculum vulgare, Withania somnifera,* root bark of *Vitex negundo,* root powder of *Ricinus communis,* roots of *Piper longum,* 2 g with warm milk, two times a day, is beneficial. **Hiccough:** Root powder of described plant 500 mg, with cold infusion of *Trachy spermum-ammi,* 2 g, as required. **Mania:** Mix powder of root powder of described plant, *Bacopa monnieri, Convolvulus pluricaulis,* 2 g, with milk, two times a day, is beneficial. **Insomnia:** Mix powder of roots of described plant, *Piper nigrum,* 1-2 g, with milk, at night, is beneficial.

Formulations: *Sarpagandhaadi churna, Sarpagandhaa yoga, Sarpagandhaa vati, Sarpagandhaaghana vati, Khsaaraagada.*

Recommended readings:

Bhutya, R.K. (2007), Vanaspati Aushadha Vigyana, Scientific Publishers (India), Jodhpur, PP. 225.

Brahmavarchas (2003), Ayurved Ka Pran Vanoshadhi Vigyan, Shanti Kunj, Haridwar, PP. 383.

Chunekar, K.C. (2004), Bhava Prakash Nighantu, Chaukhambha Bharti Academy, Varanasi, PP. 82.

Dhiman, A.K. (2006), Ayurvedic Drug Plants, Daya Publishing House, Delhi, PP. 343.

Khare, C.P. (2007), Indian Medicinal Plants, Springer (India) P.L. New Delhi, PP. 538.

Kirtikar, K.R. & Basu, B.D. (1998), Indian Medicinal Plants, L.M Basu, Allahabad, Vol. 2, PP. 1550.

Misra, B.L. (2005), Dravya Guna Hastamalaka, Publication scheme, Jaipur, PP. 305.

Nair, R.Vasudevan, (2007), Indian Medicinal Plants, Orient Longman P.L. Chennai, Vol. 4, PP. 409.

Pareek, G.N. (2005), Sudhanidhi, Vanoshadhi Ratnakar, Dhanvantari Karyalaya, Aligarh, Vol. 8, PP. 235.

Prajapati, N.D., Purohit, S.S., Sharma, A.K. & Tarun Kumar (2003), A Hand Book of Medicinal Plants, Agrobios India, Jodhpur, PP. 436.

Sharma, P.C., Yelne, MB. & Denis, T.J. (2000), Database on medicinal plants used in ayurveda, Central Council for research in Ayurveda and siddha, Vol. 7, PP. 386.

Sharma, P.V. (1981), Dravya gun vigyana, Chaukhambha Bharti Academy, Varanasi, Vol. 1, PP. 36.

Singh, R.S. (2002), Vanoshadhi Nirdeshika, Uttar Pradesh Hindi Sansthan, Lucknow, PP. 363.

Swami, K.N. (1985), Gavon Main Aushadh Ratna, Kalera Krishana Gopal, Kalera (Raj.), Vol. 3, PP. 310.

403. *Rheum emodi* Wall.ex Meissn.

Family: Polygonaceae.

Synonym: *R. australe.*

Other similar plants: *R. webbianum, R. palmatum, R. moorcroftianum, R. spiciforme, R. rhaponticum, R. nobile.*

Name: English: Indian Rhubarb, Himalayan Rhubarb, **Sanskrit:** *Amlaparni, Peetamooli, Revatikaa, Khiripi, Hemadugdhaa,* **Hindi:** *Revandchini,* **Local:** *Revandchini, Revandkhatai.*

Botanical characteristics: Habit: A robust perennial stout herb, height 1.5-3 m, grows on rocky lands. **Roots** are very stout and thick. **Stem:** Leafy, hollow, very stout, streaked green and brown. **Leaf:** Sour, redical leaves very large, often 30-60 cm diam., orbicular or broadly ovate, obtuse, base cordate, 5-7 nerved, sub-scaberulous above, papillose beneath; petioles 30-45 cm long, very stout, scaberulous, panicles 60-90 cm, papillosely puberulous, branched and leafy. **Flower:** Small, 3 mm diam., dark purple or pale red in axillary tall penicles. The plant has three to five years of juvenile phase, followed by reproductive phase. **Fruit:** Ovoid-oblong, 13 mm long, purple, base cordate, apex notched, wings narrower than the disk. **Seed:** Dark brown.

Flowering and fruiting period: June-July and August-September.

Habitat: Temperate Himalaya from Kashmir to Sikkim, at an altitude of 2800-4000 m, found in alpine zone on rocky soil, moraines and crevices, between boulders and near streams in specific pockets, also cultivated in North-eastern states for its leaves, which are used as vegetable.

Parts used: Root. **Dosage:** 0.2-1 g.

Collection period: September-October.

Ayurvedic properties: ***Ras:*** *tikta, katu,* ***Gun:*** *laghu, rukhsa, tikhsna,* ***Veerya:*** *ushna,* ***Vipaka:*** *katu,* ***Tridosha*** **Effect:** alleviates ***Kapha:*** *++.*

Chemical constituents: The **roots** contain emodin, emodin-3-monomethyl ether, chropophenol, aloe-emodin, rhein, sennoside, engenol, rutin and glucoglatin. These occur free and as quinine, anthrone or dianthrone glycosides. The astringent principle consists of gallic acid together with small amounts of tannin, also contain cinnamic and rheinolic acids, volatile oil, starch and calcium oxalate, Two major principles, sennoside A and B, are presentalong with free anthraquinones.

Action and disease indications: The **roots** are mild purgative, astringent, tonic, laxative, stomachic, anti-inflammatory, liver stimulant, sialogogue, mild diuretic, emmenogogue, anthelmintic, febrifuge and aperient, used for inflammations, constipation, atonic dyspepsia, fever and helminthiasis.

Contraindicated: Not advised for patients suffering from gout, rheumatism and epilepsy. It should not be use alone, but with Ginger, Lesser Cardamom and Soda bi carb.

Clinical uses: Diarrhea of children: Root powder of described plant, 250 mg, with water or honey 5 g, three times a day, is useful. **Foul ulcer:** dusting of root powder of described plant is beneficial. **Strangury:** Mix powder of root powder of described plant, Salt petre, *Piper cubeba, Elettaria cardamomum,* 6 g, with cold milk, three times a day, is useful. **Jaundice:** Root powder of described plant, 1 g, with milk, two times a day, is beneficial.

Formulations: *Revandachinyaadi vati, Revandachinyaadi churna, Usnavaataghna churna, Mutravirechaka churna.*

Recommended readings:

Bhutya, R.K. (2007), Vanaspati Aushadha Vigyana, Scientific Publishers (India), Jodhpur, PP. 194.

Chunekar, K.C. (2004), Bhava Prakash Nighantu, Chaukhambha Bharti Academy, Varanasi, PP. 624.

Dhiman, A.K. (2006), Ayurvedic Drug Plants, Daya Publishing House, Delhi, PP. 30.

Khare, C.P. (2007), Indian Medicinal Plants, Springer (India) P.L. New Delhi, PP. 543.

Kirtikar, K.R. & Basu, B.D. (1998), Indian Medicinal Plants, L.M Basu, Allahabad, Vol. 3, PP. 2108.

Misra, B.L. (2005), Dravya Guna Hastamalaka, Publication scheme, Jaipur, PP. 440.

Prajapati, N.D., Purohit, S.S., Sharma, A.K. & Tarun Kumar (2003), A Hand Book of Medicinal Plants, Agrobios India, Jodhpur, PP. 439.

Sharma, P.V. (1981), Dravya gun vigyana, Chaukhambha Bharti Academy, Varanasi, Vol. 1, PP. 444.

Singh, R.S. (2002), Vanoshadhi Nirdeshika, Uttar Pradesh Hindi Sansthan, Lucknow, PP. 329.

Swami, K.N. (1985), Gavon Main Aushadh Ratna, Kalera Krishana Gopal, Kalera (Raj.), Vol. 3, PP. 250.

404. *Rhus parviflora* Roxb.

Family: Anacardiaceae.

Name: English: Sumach, **Sanskrit:** *Tintidika,* **Hindi:** *Tintideek,* **Local:** *Samaakdaanaa.*

Botanical characteristics: Habit: An evergreen or sub-deciduous shrub, height 1.2-2.4 m, but attaining 90 cm girth and 4.5 m high. **Stem:** Bark dark brown roughish, exfoliating in small woody scales. Blaze 7.6-9 mm, pink or red. Twigs pale reddish brown, rusty-tomentose. **Leaf:** Alternate, trifoliate, petioles 2.5-5 cm long, tomentose, leaflets 2.5-12.5 by 1.5-7.5 cm, the terminal largest, obovate, the basal portion entire and cuneately attenuate, the upper coarsely and irregularly crenate, rather thick, hairy on the nerves, especially beneath; the lateral relatively broader and more round at the base, sessile. **Flower:** 2.5 mm diam., yellowish-green, in terminal panicles 10-20 cm long, the lower branches axillary, pediceles minute. **Fruit:** Drupes, 5 mm long, ovoid, brown, glabrous, shining. **Seed:** Pendulous from the funicles, testa membranous.

Flowering and fruiting period: May-June and July-August.

Habitat: Dry hot slopes of the North-west Himalaya, up to an altitude of 600-2150 m, from Punjab to Nepal and in the hills of Madhya Pradesh and South India.

Parts used: Fruit. **Dosage:** 3-6 g.

Collection period: July-August.

Ayurvedic properties: ***Ras:*** *amla,* ***Gun:*** *laghu, rukhsa,* ***Veerya:*** *ushna,* ***Vipaka:*** *amla,* ***Tridosha*** **Effect:** alleviates ***Vaata:*** **++,** ***Kapha:*** ++, aggrevates ***Pitta:*** **+.**

Chemical constituents: The **leaves** contain the flavonoids, myricetin, quercetin and kaempferol and their 3-0-rhmnosides; the **stems** and **leaves** also gave henitriacontane, henitriacontanol, beta-sitosterol, lignoceric acid and iso-rhamnetin-3-alpha-L-arvinoside.

Action and disease indications: The **fruits** are appetizer, astringent, anti-inflammatory, anodyne, used for anorexia, dyspepsia, inflammations, dipsia, sprue, dysentery, diarrhea, nausea, vomiting and burning sensation.

Clinical uses: Dentalgia: Gargles of decoction of fruits of described plant 10 g, two times a day, is beneficial. **Inflammation:** Local application of paste of fruit of described plant is beneficial. is beneficial. **Diarrhea, diarrhea with bleeding, nausea, vomiting, dipsesis, burning sensation:** Fruit powder of described plant 3 g, common salt 250 mg, with water, three times a day, is useful.

Formulations: *Khsudabodhana rasa, Tintidipanchaka, Ruchikara churna, Vrikhsaamla yoga.*

Recommended readings:

Bhutya, R.K. (2007), Vanaspati Aushadha Vigyana, Scientific Publishers (India), Jodhpur, PP. 116.

Chunekar, K.C. (2004), Bhava Prakash Nighantu, Chaukhambha Bharti Academy, Varanasi, PP. 598.

Khare, C.P. (2007), Indian Medicinal Plants, Springer (India) P.L. New Delhi, PP. 549.

Kirtikar, K.R. & Basu, B.D. (1998), Indian Medicinal Plants, L.M Basu, Allahabad, Vol. 1, PP. 645.

Misra, B.L. (2005), Dravya Guna Hastamalaka, Publication scheme, Jaipur, PP. 406.

Namjoshi, A.N. (2001), The Ayurvedic Pharmacopoeia of India, Government of India, Department of Indian Systems of Medicine & Homoeopathy, New Delhi, Part-1, Volume- 3, PP. 49.

Sharma, P.V. (1981), Dravya gun vigyana, Chaukhambha Bharti Academy, Varanasi, Vol. 1, PP. 349.

Singh, R.S. (2002), Vanoshadhi Nirdeshika, Uttar Pradesh Hindi Sansthan, Lucknow, PP. 178.

405. *Ricinus communis* Linn.

Family: Euphorbiaceae.

Variety: White and red flower var.

Name: English: Castor seed, **Sanskrit:** *Eranda, Chitrabeeja, Triputi, Tribeeja, Vaatari, Gandharvahasta, Panchaangula, Vardhamaana, Urubuka, Rubuka, Deerghadandaa,* **Hindi:** *Eranda.* **Local name:** *Andoli.*

Ayurvedic groups: Charaka: *bhedaniya, swedopaga, angamard prashamana, madhur skandha,* **Sushruta:** *vidarigandhadi, adhobhaghara, vaata sanshamana.*

Botanical characteristics: Habit: A tall glabrous and glucose annual or perennial soft wooded shrub or small tree, with a thin grayish brown bark, height 2.5-7m. **Stem:** Herbaceous, erect, cylindrical, branched, older portion fistular, younger portion solid, glabrous, green-purple. **Leaf:** Palmetly lobed, broad, alternate, serete30-60cm diam, 5-11 lobed, petiole 25-35cm long. **Flower:** Monoecious, rather large, in terminal sub paniculate racemes, male Flowers crowded in the upper portion of inflorescence, the females below. **Fruit:** A prickly capsule of three 2-valved cocci, 3 seeded, **Seed:** Oblong, with smooth, hard, spotted, mottled crutaceous testa, with white, flashy, oily endosperm, 4-12 mm long, 8 mm wide, 6 mm thick, one side flat and other side round.

Flowering and fruiting period: February-March and March-April.

Habitat: Throughout India, upto 2150 m, cultivated in peninsular India.

Parts used: Seeds, seed oil, roots, leaves.

Dosage: Seeds 5-10 g, seed oil 5-20 ml, root 10-20 g.

Collection period: March-April.

Ayurvedic properties: ***Ras:*** *madhur, katu, kashaaya,* ***Gun:*** *snigdha,tikhsna,sukhsama,* ***Veerya:*** *ushna,* ***Vipaka:*** *madhur* ***Tridosha*** **Effect:** alleviates ***Vaata:*** ++++, ***Kapha:*** +++, have special effect on '*Saam vaata*'.

Chemical constituents: Castor **seeds** contain 2.8-3% toxic component which is highly poisonous, these are albumin, risin, allergens and a feebly toxic alkaloid, ricinine. Seeds have 50% oil. Toxic elements are not present in oil, but in seeds or oilless substance. **Seed oil** contains ricinoleic acid, stearic acid, oleic-linoleic and dihydroxystearic acid, hexadecanoic, hydrocyanic and uric acids. Roots contain germinicolester derivative and an unidentified triterpene.

Action and disease indications: Roots are thermogenic, carminative, astringent, purgative, anthelmintic, diuretic, emollient, aphrodisiac, sudorofic, galactagogue, expectorant, depurative and are used for rheumatism, pain of urinary bladder, lumbago, inflammations, diseases of abdomen as flatulance, abdominal colic, '*Aam dosha*', constipation, fevers, ascitis, strangury, bronchitis, cough, leprosy, skin diseases and coxalgia. **Leaves** are diuretic, galactagogue, anthelmintic, useful to cure burns, nyctalopia, strangury, helminthiasis, dysurea, arthritis, urinary bladder pain, abscess and bathing, fomentation to cure rheumatoid arthritis, urodynia, arthralgia. **Flowers** are good for urodynia and glandular tumours. **Seeds** are thermogenic, digestive, cathartic, aphrodisiac, useful to cure arthralgia as poultice and dyspepsia. **Oil** is anti pyretic, thermogenic, viscous, purgative, depurative, or deobstuent, emollient, and useful to cure neuritis, neuralgia, diseases of nervous system, scrotocele, ascitis, intermittent fevers, lumbago, coxalgia, colonitis, coxitis, skin diseases, anti ageing, aphrodisiac, vaginal diseases and promotes counting of spermatozoa and motility, good for brain and complexion, asthma, bronchitis, lower abdomen colic and remove obstruction of intestines.

Contra indication: Seeds contain toxic components (2.8-3%) which are highly poisonous. Ricin and ricinine are toxic elements. Do not use seeds by mouth. Fatal dose of seeds are 25 g, so for oral use pick out the middle germination part of seed and purify the seeds by putting in hot milk or lightly boiling in water or milk.

Toxic symptoms: Pain in the throat, abdominal pain, severe vomiting, diarrhea, cold skin and cardiac arrest.

Treatment and antidote: 1. wash the stomach. 2. Keep the body hot by hot water bags. 3. If pulse rate comes down, use *'Siddha makaradhvaja rasa'* or *'Vrihata kastoori bherava rasa'* 100 mg with honey 10 g. 4. Use analgesic drugs for pain. 5.Use G.N.S. fluid intravenous for dehydration. 6. Lemon juice with glucose and common salt with gum of *Bambusa arundinacea,* 5-10 g. 7. Use fruit juice of *Punica grantum,* 50-100 ml by mouth. 8. Use gum of *Pistacia lentiscus* or gum of *Cochlospermum religiosum* 2-5 g.

Note: Seed oil should not be used with fat soluble vermifuge, it may increase it's absorption and toxicity. There are no toxicity in oil, can be used with any fear. For oral use oil should be obtain by compressed and cold process.

Clinical uses: Chronic appendicitis: Add Castor oil 15 g, with the wheat-flour before making *'Roti'* or *'Chapati'.* Give enema of Castor oil 20 g, fried gum of *Ferula narthex* 250 mg, luke warm water 200 ml. Use seed powder of *Hyoscyamus niger* 250 mg, with any medicine made of *Strychnos nux vomica* as *'Agnitundi vati'* 250 mg, or *'Tinduka vati'* 125 mg, with honey 10g, or water, 2 times a day, for 1-2 months. **Neuralgia, sciatica, rheumatoid arthritis, backache, ribs pain, chest pain, rheumatic arthritis, myalgia (special for calf muscles):** Decoction of root powder of the described plant 15 g, dry rhizome powder of *Zingiber officinale* 1 g, and Bitumen 1g, with honey 10 g, 2 times a day. For local application massage of Castor oil and sprinkle powder of *Zingiber officinale,* then put warmed leaves on effected area, put some cotton and tie loose bandage. It gives quick relief. Or massage of medicated oil, made with juice of Castor leaves, decoction of *Zingiber officinale*, and leaves of *Vitex negundo*, and keep warm by hot water bag. **Piles:** Local application of Castor oil and juice of *Aloe barbadensis.* **Foreign body in the eye:** Use 4 drops of Castor oil. **Constipation**: Seed oil of the plant 20-30 ml, with decoction of *Zingiber officinale* 1 g, at morning, take 1-1 draught of warm water by 5 minuts. Do not take lunch but dinner of early digestive food. Or enema of oil 50 ml in lukewarm water. **Acute and Chronic rheumatism:** Add Castor oil 15 g, with the wheat-flour before making *'Roti'* or *'Chapati'.* **Hypogalactia, and gland in breast:** Massage of seed oil, and put a warm leaf of plant on breast, put some cotton and wear a bra. **Cracked nipples and cracked heel:** Local application of seed oil. **Burning sensation in palm and sole:** Massage of seed oil or local application of pulp of seeds in milk of she goat. **Dysuria, urinary bladder pain:** Use seed oil 10 ml, in Luke warm water and massage of oil, is beneficial. **Penile dysfunction:** Root powder of the described plant 2-4 g, with milk 250 ml. **Inflammation, pain of knee:** Seed oil 10 ml, Bitumen 1 g, with milk 250 ml, 2 times a day. **Jaundice, jaundice of pregnancy**: Juice of leaves of the described plant 12 ml, with honey 10 g, at morning, for 5 days. **Enlargement of spleen:** Decoction of root powder of the described plant 10 g, with honey 10 g, and apply warm leaf on left abdominal area. **Insect entry in ear:** Use Luke warm oil as ear drops, 4 drops. **For remove fat on abdomen:** Cold infusion of root powder of the described plant 20 g, with honey 10 g, at morning only. **Bronchitis, asthma, rhinitis:** 4-4 drops of luke warm Castor oil, 2 times a day.

Formulations: *Erandapaaka, Eranda taila, Punarnavaasava, Mahaa raasnaadi kwaatha, Vrihatyadi kwaatha, Aamvaatari rasa, Vaatari guggulu, Saindhavaadhya taila, Gandharvahasta taila.*

Recommended readings:

Acharya, B.K. (2008), Ayurveda Jadi-buti Rahasya, Patanjali Yogapitha, Haridwar, PP. 187.

Bhutya, R.K. (2007), Vanaspati Aushadha Vigyana, Scientific Publishers (India), Jodhpur, PP. 38.

Brahmavarchas (2003), Ayurved Ka Pran Vanoshadhi Vigyan, Shanti Kunj, Haridwar, PP. 385.

Chunekar, K.C. (2004), Bhava Prakash Nighantu, Chaukhambha Bharti Academy, Varanasi, PP. 299.

Dhiman, A.K. (2006), Ayurvedic Drug Plants, Daya Publishing House, Delhi, PP. 131.

Khare, C.P. (2007), Indian Medicinal Plants, Springer (India) P.L. New Delhi, PP. 551.

Kirtikar, K.R. & Basu, B.D. (1998), Indian Medicinal Plants, L.M Basu, Allahabad, Vol. 3, PP. 2274.

Misra, B.L. (2005), Dravya Guna Hastamalaka, Publication scheme, Jaipur, PP. 342.

Nair, R.Vasudevan, (2007), Indian Medicinal Plants, Orient Longman P.L. Chennai, Vol. 5, PP. 1.

Namjoshi, A.N. (2001), The Ayurvedic Pharmacopoeia of India, Government of India, Department of Indian Systems of Medicine & Homoeopathy, New Delhi, Part-1, Volume- 2, PP. 34.

Pareek, G.N. (2005), Sudhanidhi, Vanoshadhi Ratnakar, Dhanvantari Karyalaya, Aligarh, Vol. 2, PP. 93.

Prajapati, N.D., Purohit, S.S., Sharma, A.K. & Tarun Kumar (2003), A Hand Book of Medicinal Plants, Agrobios India, Jodhpur, PP. 443.

Sharma, P.C., Yelne, MB. & Denis, T.J. (2000), Database on medicinal plants used in Ayurveda, Central Council for research in Ayurveda and siddha, Vol. 4, PP. 122.

Sharma, P.V. (1981), Dravya gun vigyana, Chaukhambha Bharti Academy, Varanasi, Vol. 1, PP. 58.

Singh, R.S. (2002), Vanoshadhi Nirdeshika, Uttar Pradesh Hindi Sansthan, Lucknow, PP. 55.

Swami, K.N. (1985), Gavon Main Aushadh Ratna, Kalera Krishana Gopal, Kalera (Raj.), Vol. 1, PP. 84 or 90.

406. *Rosa centifolia* Linn.

Family: Rosaceae.

Other similar plant: *R. alba, R. bourboniana, R. chinensis, R. damascene, R. macrophylla.*

Name: English: Rose, Cabbage rose, Provence rose, Hundred-leaved rose, **Sanskrit:** *Taruni, Shatapatri, Karnikaa, Mahaakumaari, Gandha-adyaa, Lakhsaapushpaa, Atimanjulaa, Chaaru-kesaraa,* **Hindi:** *Gulab,* **Local:** *Gulab.*

Botanical characteristics: Habit: A small erect prickly shrub, height 1.5-2 m. **Stem:** With unequal, large, hooked prickles and many bristles. **Leaf:** Compound, alternate, leaflets usually five, rachis not prickly. **Flower:** Usually pink, very fragrant, very double on long slender pedicles, terminal, solitary, calyx tube globose, ovoid, petals numerous, stamens many, inserted on the mouth of the calyx tube, sepal persistent. **Fruit:** A fleshy hip enclosing bony achenes. **Seed:** Small, pendulous.

Flowering and fruiting period: Almost throughout year, mostly November-December and January-February.

Habitat: Cultivated throughout India, mostly in Uttar Pradesh and Bihar.

Parts used: Flower-petals, distillate of petals.

Dosage: 3-6 g, 20-40 ml.

Collection period: February-March.

Ayurvedic properties: ***Ras:*** *katu, tikta, madhur,* ***Gun:*** *laghu, snigdha,* ***Veerya:*** *sheeta,* ***Vipaka:*** *madhur* ***Tridosha*** **Effect:** alleviates, ***Pitta:*** +++, ***Vaata:*** ++, ***Kapha:*** +.

Chemical constituents: The **flowers** contain 1.3% of saponin respectively, also methionine sulphoxide, also a volatile oil 0.2% consisting mainly of citronellol, geraniol, nerol, phenylethanol, linalool and citral. It contain 15% tannins (oligomeric proanthocysnidins).

Action and disease indications: The **flowers** are refrigerant, emollient, aromatic, anti-inflammatory, cardio-tonic, expectorant, digestive, carminative, aphrodisiac, depurative, febrifuge, styptic, intellect promoting, rejuvenating and tonic, used for burning sensation, cough, asthma, bronchitis, inflammations, wound, ulcers, halitosis, dyspepsia, flatulence, amentia, colic, skin diseases, hyperhidrosis, fever, cardiac debility and general debility. The rose water is cooling, fragrant, emollient and ophthalmic, used for hyperhidrosis, halitosis and ophthalmopathy.

Clinical uses: Hyperhydrosis: Dusting of petals of described plant is useful. **Burning sensation, tachycardia:** Cold infusion of petals of described plant 6 g, with sugar candy powder 10 g, or use of *'Gulkanda'* 20 g, two times a day, is beneficial. **Constipation:** *'Gulkanda'* of described plant 20 g, fruit pulp of *Cassia fistula* 20 g, with water, at night, is useful. **Cloasma:** (1) Local application of paste of petals of described plant, *Santalum album, Prunus amyadalus,* with water, is useful. (2) Local application of paste of petals of described plant, curd, seed powder of *Cicer arietinum,* fruit rind of Orange, is useful.

Formulations: *Gulkanda, Gulaab jal, Pravaal pisti, Shatapatryaadi churna, Saarivaadi shaarkar.*

Recommended readings:

Bhutya, R.K. (2007), Vanaspati Aushadha Vigyana, Scientific Publishers (India), Jodhpur, PP. 87.

Brahmavarchas (2003), Ayurved Ka Pran Vanoshadhi Vigyan, Shanti Kunj, Haridwar, PP. 387.

Chunekar, K.C. (2004), Bhava Prakash Nighantu, Chaukhambha Bharti Academy, Varanasi, PP. 488.

Dhiman, A.K. (2006), Ayurvedic Drug Plants, Daya Publishing House, Delhi, PP. 377.

Khare, C.P. (2007), Indian Medicinal Plants, Springer (India) P.L. New Delhi, PP. 554.

Kirtikar, K.R. & Basu, B.D. (1998), Indian Medicinal Plants, L.M Basu, Allahabad, Vol. 2, PP. 981.

Misra, B.L. (2005), Dravya Guna Hastamalaka, Publication scheme, Jaipur, PP. 372.

Nair, R.Vasudevan, (2007), Indian Medicinal Plants, Orient Longman P.L. Chennai, Vol. 5, PP. 8.

Namjoshi, A.N. (2001), The Ayurvedic Pharmacopoeia of India, Government of India, Department of Indian Systems of Medicine & Homoeopathy, New Delhi, Part-1, Volume- 3, PP. 195.

Pareek, G.N. (2005), Sudhanidhi, Vanoshadhi Ratnakar, Dhanvantari Karyalaya, Aligarh, Vol. 3, PP. 253.

Prajapati, N.D., Purohit, S.S., Sharma, A.K. & Tarun Kumar (2003), A Hand Book of Medicinal Plants, Agrobios India, Jodhpur, PP. 444.

Sharma, P.V. (1981), Dravya gun vigyana, Chaukhambha Bharti Academy, Varanasi, Vol. 1, PP. 214.

Singh, R.S. (2002), Vanoshadhi Nirdeshika, Uttar Pradesh Hindi Sansthan, Lucknow, PP. 133.

Swami, K.N. (1985), Gavon Main Aushadh Ratna, Kalera Krishana Gopal, Kalera (Raj.), Vol. 2, PP. 245.

407. *Roscoea alpina* Wall.

Family: Zingiberaceae.

Synonym: *R. procera.*

Ayurvedic Groups: Charak: *Astavarga, Jivaniya gana.*

Name: Sanskrit: *Kaakoli, Vaayasoli, Veraa, Kayasthikaa,* **Hindi:** *Kakoli,* **Local:** *Kakoli.*

Substitute: *Withania somnifera-Aswagandha.*

Botanical characteristics: Habit: An annual erect herb, height 50 cm long. **Tuber:** Curved, outer surface blackish, inner portion white, like *Asparagus racemosus,* sweet in taste **Stem:** Erect, strong. **Leaf:** 2-6, lanceolate, 12.5-15 by 2.5-3 cm. **Flower:** Purple or white, numerous, fragrant, pedicles small, corolla tube longer than calyx.

Flowering and fruiting period: June-July and August-September.

Habitat: It found in Himalayas, at altitudes of 1500-2700 m, in grassy slopes.

Parts used: Tuberous root. **Dosage:** 3-6 g.

Collection period: September-October.

Ayurvedic properties: ***Ras:*** *madhur, tikta,* ***Gun:*** *guru, snigdha,* ***Veerya:*** *sheeta,* ***Vipaka:*** *madhur* ***Tridosha*** **Effect:** alleviates ***Vaata:*** ++, ***Pitta:*** ++.

Action and disease indications: The **Tuberous roots** are cooling, revitalizing, age-sustainer and restorative, aphrodisiac, galactagogue, expectorant, diuretic, febrifuge, used for epistaxis, seminal weakness, burning sensation, inflammations, fever, agalactia, bronchitis and general debility.

Clinical uses: Burning sensation, general debility, oligogalactia, spermacresia: Root powder of described plant 3 g, *Withania somnifera* 2 g, with milk, two times a day, is beneficial.

Formulations: *Chyavanpraasha.*

Recommended readings:

Acharya, B.K. & Sharma, B.D. (2005), Jivani Shaktivardhak Astavarga Padapa, Divya Yoga Mandir, Haridwar, PP. 38.

Bhutya, R.K. (2007), Vanaspati Aushadha Vigyana, Scientific Publishers (India), Jodhpur, PP. 59.

Khare, C.P. (2007), Indian Medicinal Plants, Springer (India) P.L. New Delhi, PP. 557.

M.R. Uniyal (1966), Upalabdha Astavarga ka Vanspatika Adhyana, Sachitra Ayurveda Patrika.

M.R. Uniyal (1967), Botanical Study of Astavarga, Nagarjun Patrika.

408. *Rubia cordifolia* Linn.

Family: Rubiaceae.

Synonym: *R. munjesta.*

Name: English: Indian Madder, Bengal Madder **Sanskrit:** *Manjisthaa, Vikashaa, Samangaa, Kaalmeshikaa, Mandookaparni, Bhandi, Bhandiri, Yojanvalli, Raktaangi, Arunaa, Kaalaa, Vastraranjini, Manjushaa,* **Hindi:** *Manjisthaa,* **Local:** *Majithaa.*

Botanical characteristics: Habit: A very variable prickly or scabrous perennial climbing herb. **Root:** Long, cylindric, flexuose, smooth, with thin red bark. **Stem:** 4-angled, rough, very long, grooved stem and branches, bark white. **Leaf:** 3.8-9 by 1.6-3.5 cm, usually in whorls of 4, one pair of each whorl often larger and longer petioles than the other, sometimes 2-8, cordate-ovate to ovate-lanceolate, acute, the lower leaves larger than the upper, all scabrous above, on the nerve beneath, base rounded or slightly cordate, 5-nerved from the base, on the margins with minute white prickles; petioles very long, triangular, with many sharp recurved prickles on the edges, often deflexed, stipules 0. **Flower:** Small, greenish or white, sweet-scented, in terminal panicled glabrous cymes. **Fruit:** 4-6 mm diam., globose or slightly 2-lobed, fleshy, smooth, purplish black when ripe. **Seed:** Two, small.

Flowering and fruiting period: July-September and November-December.

Habitat: Throughout India, In North west Himalaya, ascending up to an altitude of 3750 m.

Parts used: Root. **Dosage:** 1-3 g.

Collection period: October-November.

Ayurvedic properties: ***Ras:*** *madhur, tikta, kashaaya,* ***Gun:*** *rukhsa, guru,* ***Veerya:*** *ushna,* ***Vipaka:*** *katu,* ***Tridosha*** **Effect:** alleviates ***Kapha:*** *+++,* ***Pitta:*** *++.*

Chemical constituents: The **roots** are rich in anthraquinones and their glycosides (around 20), the important ones include purpurin (trihydroxy anthraquinone), munjistin (xanthopurpurin-2-carboxylic acid); besides xanthopurpurin, pseudopurpurin (purpurin-3-carboxylic acid), free alizarinas well as its glucoside. The whole plant contains pentacyclic tritrepenic acids-rubicoumaric and rubifolic acids.

Action and disease indications: The **roots** are blood purifier, astringent, thermogenic, anti-inflammatory, anodyne, digestive, carminative, constipating, anthelmintic, depurative, vulnerary, galacto-purifier, ophthalmic, febrifuge, rejuvenating diuretic, emmenogogue, deobstruent, anti-dysenteric, anti-septic, alterative and tonic, used for skin diseases, urinogenital disorders, inflammations, piles, ulcers, dysentery, neuralgia, cephalgia, rheumatoid arthritis, erysipelas, rheumatism, dyspepsia, flatulence, colic, diarrhea, dysentery, helminthiasis, leucoderma, pruritis, wounds, dysmenorrhea, amenorrhea, strangury, ophthalmopathy, intermittent fevers, pharyngitis, cough, diabetes, discolouration of skin, tubercular conditions, otorrhea, urethrorrhea, piles, jaundice, hepato and spleen disorders, arthralgia, leucorrhea and general debility.

Clinical uses: Burning sensation, general debility, oligogalactia, spermacresia: Root powder of described plant 3 g, *Withania somnifera* 2 g, with milk, two times a day, is beneficial. **skin diseases:** (1) Mix powder of root powder of described plant, *Terminalia chebula, Terminalia belliarica, Phylanthus emblica,* pure Sulphur, sugar candy powder, dose 10 g, with water, three times a day, is beneficial. (2) Mix powder of roots of described plant, *Pterocarpus santalinus, Mesua ferrea,* 5 g, with water, two times a day, is beneficial. (3) Decoction of mix powder of roots of described plant, *Picrorhiza kurroa, Tinospora cordifolia,* bark of *Azadirachta indica,* 10 g, with honey 10 g, two times a day, is useful. **Bronchitis, disphonia:** Decoction of mix powder of roots of described plant, *Glycyrrhiza glabra, Justisia adhatoda,* 5 g, with honey 10 g, three times a day, is useful. **Bone fractures:** Mix powder of roots of described plant, *Glycyrrhiza glabra, Withania somnifera, Curcuma longa,* 4 g, with milk, two times a day, is beneficial. **Bleeding piles:** Mix powder of roots of described plant, *Santalum album, Symplocos racemosa, Nelumbo nusifera,* gum of *Bombax ceiba,* 5 g, with milk of she goat, two times a day, is beneficial. **Allergy:** Mix powder of roots of described plant, *Hemidesmus indicus, Acacia catechu, Smilax china,* 4 g, with water, two times a day, is beneficial. **Allergic bronchitis, asthma:** Decoction of mix powder of roots of described plant, *Hemidesmus indicus, Acacia catechu, Smilax china, Curcuma longa, Justisia adhatoda,* 5 g, with honey 10 g, two times a day, is useful. **Diarrhea:** Decoction of mix powder of roots of described plant, *Woodfordia fruticosa, Aegle marmelos, Cyperus scarissus, Cissampelos pariera,* 6 g, with honey 10 g, two times a day, is useful. **Acne vulgaris, chloasma:** (1) Local application of paste of roots of described plant, *Pterocarpus santalinus, Sausurea costus,* with water, is beneficial. (2) Local application of paste of roots of described plant, fruit of *Myristica fragrans, Lens culinaris,* with milk, is beneficial. (3) Local application of paste of roots of described plant, seeds of *Buchanania lanzan,* with milk, is beneficial.

Formulations: *Manjisthaadi kwaatha, Manjisthaadi churna, Manjisthaadi taila, Guduchyaadi taila, Vyaghri taila, Arvindaasava, Chandanaasava, Aswagandhaarista, Ushiraasava, Manjisthaadi lepa, Khadiraadi gutikaa.*

Recommended readings:

Bhutya, R.K. (2007), Vanaspati Aushadha Vigyana, Scientific Publishers (India), Jodhpur, PP. 169.

Brahmavarchas (2003), Ayurved Ka Pran Vanoshadhi Vigyan, Shanti Kunj, Haridwar, PP. 389.

Chunekar, K.C. (2004), Bhava Prakash Nighantu, Chaukhambha Bharti Academy, Varanasi, PP. 110.

Dhiman, A.K. (2006), Ayurvedic Drug Plants, Daya Publishing House, Delhi, PP. 252.

Khare, C.P. (2007), Indian Medicinal Plants, Springer (India) P.L. New Delhi, PP. 559.

Kirtikar, K.R. & Basu, B.D. (1998), Indian Medicinal Plants, L.M Basu, Allahabad, Vol. 2, PP. 1303.

Misra, B.L. (2005), Dravya Guna Hastamalaka, Publication scheme, Jaipur, PP. 260.

Nair, R.Vasudevan, (2007), Indian Medicinal Plants, Orient Longman P.L. Chennai, Vol. 5, PP. 17.

Pareek, G.N. (2005), Sudhanidhi, Vanoshadhi Ratnakar, Dhanvantari Karyalaya, Aligarh, Vol. 7, PP. 40.

Prajapati, N.D., Purohit, S.S., Sharma, A.K. & Tarun Kumar (2003), A Hand Book of Medicinal Plants, Agrobios India, Jodhpur, PP. 448.

Sharma, P.C., Yelne, MB. & Denis, T.J. (2000), Database on medicinal plants used in Ayurveda, Central Council for research in Ayurveda and Siddha, Vol. 5, PP. 171.

Sharma, P.V. (1981), Dravya gun vigyana, Chaukhambha Bharti Academy, Varanasi, Vol. 1, PP. 800.

Singh, R.S. (2002), Vanoshadhi Nirdeshika, Uttar Pradesh Hindi Sansthan, Lucknow, PP. .

409. *Ruta graveolens* Linn.

Family: Rutaceae.

Other similar plant: *R.chalepensis.*

Name: English: Garden Rue, **Sanskrit:** *Sarpadamstraa,* **Hindi:** *Sitaab,* **Local:** *Sitaab.*

Botanical characteristics: Habit: An aromatic perennial herb, height up to 75 cm. **Stem:** Herbaceous, cylindrical, branched, soft. **Leaf:** Alternate, compound, shortly petioled, ultimate segments oblong or obovate-oblong, characteristic smell, oil glands present. **Flower:** Yellow, in divaricated spreading corymbs; pedicles longer than the capsule; bracts lanceolate. **Fruit:** Capsules, obtuse, 4-5 lobed, many seeded, shortly pediclled. **Seed:** Angled, brown, testa pitted.

Flowering and fruiting period: August-September and September-October.

Habitat: Cultivated throughout India, in gardens.

Parts used: Whole plant, oil.

Dosage: 1-3 g, oil 1-5 drops.

Collection period: December-January.

Ayurvedic properties: ***Ras:*** *tikta,* ***Gun:*** *laghu, rukhsa, tikhsna,* ***Veerya:*** *ushna,* ***Vipaka:*** *katu,* ***Tridosha*** **Effect:** alleviates ***Kapha: ++, Vaata: +.***

Chemical constituents: The **herb** contain a volatile oil, with 2-undecanone (30.73), 2-nonanone (18.06%, 2-nonyl acetate (11.03), psoralene (1.28), and bergapten and xanthotoxin (7.24%); rutin about 2%.The flavonoids include quercetin; coumarins including bergaptendaphnoretin, isoimperatorin, naphthoherniarin, psoralen, pengelin, rutamarin, scopoletin and umbelliferone. Tissue culture of plant gavefuracridone alkaloids. Tissue culture of the root gave gravacridondiol and its glucoside. The spasmolytic activity of the herb is attributed to the bergapten, xanthotoxin and the essential oil. Anti-inflammatory and anti-tumour activity is due to rutin. The furo-coumarins are responsible for the herb's phototoxicity.

Action and disease indications: The **plant** is stimulating, stomachic, anti-spasmodic, thermogenic, diuretic, laxative, aphrodisiac, febrifuge, digestive, carminative, irritant, abortifacient, emmenogogue and tonic, used for hysteria, cough, colic, flatulence, strangury, fever, flatulence, atonic amenorrhea, menorrhea, sciatica, headache, muscular chest pain, bronchitis, arthritic condition, The oil is anti-spasmodic, anti-epileptic, emmenogogue, and rubefacient and toxic in large doses.

Contraindication: The herb is hepatotoxic, and it contraindicated in kidney and bleeding disorders.

Clinical uses: Paralysis: Local application of paste of leaves of described plant, with wine, is beneficial. **Convulsion, epilepsy, hysteria:** Whole plant of described plant 3 g, with water, two times a day, is beneficial. **Whooping cough:** Whole plant of described plant 3 g, roasted gum of *Ferula narthex* 100 mg, Alum 125 mg, with water, two times a day, is beneficial. **Hookworm:** Oil of described plant 3-5 drops, with milk, two times a day, is beneficial. **Dysmenorrhea:** Juice of whole plant of described plant 10-20 ml, with honey 10 g, two times a day, is useful. **Fever:** Cold infusion of described plant, 3 g, with honey 10 g, two times a day, is useful.

Formulations: *Pidaashaamaka taila.*

Recommended readings:

Bhutya, R.K. (2007), Vanaspati Aushadha Vigyana, Scientific Publishers (India), Jodhpur, PP. 227.

Chunekar, K.C. (2004), Bhava Prakash Nighantu, Chaukhambha Bharti Academy, Varanasi, PP. 840.

Khare, C.P. (2007), Indian Medicinal Plants, Springer (India) P.L. New Delhi, PP. 566.

Kirtikar, K.R. & Basu, B.D. (1998), Indian Medicinal Plants, L.M Basu, Allahabad, Vol. 1, PP. 453.

Misra, B.L. (2005), Dravya Guna Hastamalaka, Publication scheme, Jaipur, PP. 362.

Nair, R.Vasudevan, (2007), Indian Medicinal Plants, Orient Longman P.L. Chennai, Vol. 5, PP. 22.

Prajapati, N.D., Purohit, S.S., Sharma, A.K. & Tarun Kumar (2003), A Hand Book of Medicinal Plants, Agrobios India, Jodhpur, PP. 452.

Sharma, P.V. (1981), Dravya gun vigyana, Chaukhambha Bharti Academy, Varanasi, Vol. 1, PP. 609.

Singh, R.S. (2002), Vanoshadhi Nirdeshika, Uttar Pradesh Hindi Sansthan, Lucknow, PP. 377.

Swami, K.N. (1985), Gavon Main Aushadh Ratna, Kalera Krishana Gopal, Kalera (Raj.), Vol. 3, PP. 322.

410. *Saccharum bengalense* Retz.

Family: Gramineae; Poaceae.

Synonym: *S.sara, S.munja, Erianthus munja.*

Other similar plants: *S.arundinaceum.*

Name: Sanskrit: *Bhadramunja, Shara, Baana, Tejan, Ikhsuvestana,* **Hindi:** *Sharpat,* **Local:** *Munja, Baan, Sarpat, Raamsar.*

Botanical characteristics: Habit: An erect perennial grass, height 5.5 m, kooks like plant of Sugarcane. **Stem:** Erect, 12 mm diam., pale straw-coloured, smooth, striate, solid. **Leaf:** Upper leaf of flowering clum 22-70 cm by 5-10 mm, flat, tapering from the base, long acuminate, lower leaves up to 2 and 2.4 m by 18-25 mm, colour glaucous, midrib white, margin scabrid, densely white villous at the base behind the ligule, Ligule truncate. **Flower:** Flowering panicle 30-90 cm long, usually lanceolate, pale cream-coloured to dark reddish-purple, branches spreading and whorled. **Fruit:** Fruiting panicle oblong, branches appressed to the axis, white to grayish white. Primary rachis glabrous, sulcate, more or less scabrid on the ridges.

Flowering and fruiting period: October-November and December-January.

Habitat: Throughout India, in the plains and lower hills, along river-beds.

Parts used: Root. **Dosage:** 3-6 g.

Collection period: December-January.

Ayurvedic properties: ***Ras:*** *madhur, kashaaya,* ***Gun:*** *laghu, snigdha,* ***Veerya:*** *sheeta,* ***Vipaka:*** *madhur* ***Tridosha*** **Effect:** alleviates ***Vaata:*** ++, ***Pitta:*** ++, ***Kapha:*** +.

Chemical constituents: The **stem** contain furfural 5.67%, it yields 19.5%of reducing sugars; glucose, xylose, galactose and rhamnosehave been identified in thehydrolysate which contains34.5% fermentable sugars.

Action and disease indications: The **roots** are aphrodisiac, diuretic, demulcent, depurative, cooling, used for burning sensation, dipsia, erysipelas, skin diseases, ophthalmopathy, dysuria, anuria and general debility.

Clinical uses: Dysuria: Root powder of described plant, 6 g, with water, two times a day, is beneficial. **Leucorrhea, oligogalactia, spermacresia:** Root powder of described plant, 6 g, with milk, two times a day, is beneficial. **Piles, dispesis:** Decoction of roots of described plant, 6 g, two times a day, is beneficial.

Formulations: *Trinapanchamoola kwaatha, Brahmarasaayana, Chandanaadi taila, Sharakurcha kwaatha.*

Recommended readings:

Bhutya, R.K. (2007), Vanaspati Aushadha Vigyana, Scientific Publishers (India), Jodhpur, PP. 212.

Chunekar, K.C. (2004), Bhava Prakash Nighantu, Chaukhambha Bharti Academy, Varanasi, PP. 380.

Dhiman, A.K. (2006), Ayurvedic Drug Plants, Daya Publishing House, Delhi, PP. 336.

Khare, C.P. (2007), Indian Medicinal Plants, Springer (India) P.L. New Delhi, PP. 567.

Kirtikar, K.R. & Basu, B.D. (1998), Indian Medicinal Plants, L.M Basu, Allahabad, Vol. 4, PP. 2666.

Misra, B.L. (2005), Dravya Guna Hastamalaka, Publication scheme, Jaipur, PP. 352.

Nair, R.Vasudevan, (2007), Indian Medicinal Plants, Orient Longman P.L. Chennai, Vol. 5, PP. 26.

Namjoshi, A.N. (2001), The Ayurvedic Pharmacopoeia of India, Government of India, Department of Indian Systems of Medicine & Homoeopathy, New Delhi, Part-1, Volume- 3, PP. 187.

Sharma, P.V. (1981), Dravya gun vigyana, Chaukhambha Bharti Academy, Varanasi, Vol. 1, PP. 637.

Singh, R.S. (2002), Vanoshadhi Nirdeshika, Uttar Pradesh Hindi Sansthan, Lucknow, PP. 359.

411. *Saccharum officinale* Linn.

Family: Gramineae; Poaceae.

Ayurvedic Groups: *Trinapanchamoola.*

Name: English: Sugarcane, Noble cane, **Sanskrit:** *Ikhsu, Dirghachchada, Bhurirasa, Gudamoola, Asipatra, Madhutrina,* **Hindi:** *Ikha,* **Local:** *Gannaa, Saanthaa, Ganderi.*

Botanical characteristics: Habit: A tall perennial herb, height 6.5 m. **Stem:** Varying in thickness and colours, with many distinct nodes and internodes, 2-4 cm in diam., cylindrical, solid juicy, glabrous or pubescent below the panicle, more or less coated with wax below the nodes and with sweet juice in clum who is the source of sugar. **Leaf:** Leaf sheaths tight, terete, smooth, glabrous, ligules very short, membranous, ciliate; leaves 1.6 m by 6 cm, erect or drooping, green above, glaucous below, more or less scribed along the margins, midrib very stout, rounded on the back, more or lees flat above. **Flower:** Panicles pyramidal, up to 1 m, long, dense silvery; primary rhachis glabrous. Raceme up to 10 cm long, fragile, pedicel shirt. Spikelets lanceolate, up to 0.1 cm long, usually surrounded by long silky hairs from their base. **Seed:** Grains oblong or sub-globose, sub-terete, flesh covered, embryo 1/6 the length of the grain.

Flowering and fruiting period: Almost througHout year, mostly in November-December and January-February.

Habitat: Extensively cultivated throughout India, mostly in Uttar Pradesh, Punjab, Maharastra and Bihar.

Parts used: Root, stem.

Dosage: Root 10-20g, stem juice 200-400 ml.

Collection period: December-March.

Ayurvedic properties: ***Ras:*** *madhur,* ***Gun:*** *guru, snigdha,* ***Veerya:*** *sheeta,* ***Vipaka:*** *madhur* ***Tridosha*** **Effect:** alleviates ***Vaata: ++, Pitta: ++,*** aggrevates ***Kapha:*** ++.

Chemical constituents: The **stem juice** contains sucrose 70-80%, glucose, and fructose. Non-sugar constituents present in the cane juice are carbohydrates other than sugars. Asparagine and glutamine are prominent amino acids in the juice. Other amino acids include alanine, gamma-amino butyric acid, aspartic acid and glutamic acids, glycine, leucine, lycine, serine and tyrosine, also phenylalanine, hitidine, valine, praline, threonine, arginine, pipecolic acid, methionine and triptophan. Vitamins are thiamine, riboflavin, niacin, pantothenic acid, biotin, and vitamin D; enzymes include diastase, invertase, lactase, peroxidase and tyrosinase. Phenols in the cane juice are mainly polyphenols from tannin and anthro-cyanin from the rind. Cane juice contains glycolic acid which improves skin complexion as it has anti-wrinkle effect, prevents scaly growth and increases natural collagen and elastin in the skin.

Action and disease indications: The **roots** are cooling, demulcent, stimulant and diuretic, used for uropathy. The **stems** are refrigerant, emollient, laxative, cardio-tonic, diuretic, galac-tagogue, aphrodisiac, expectorant, haemostatic and tonic, used for cardiac debility, fatigue, jaundice, dipsia, gastropathy, haematemesis, cough, bronchitis, anaemia, erysipelas, ulcers of skin and mucous membrane, fistula in ano, hiccough, diarrhea, delirium, gonorrhea, agalactia, seminal weakness, emaciation and general debility.

Clinical uses: Hiccough: Nasal drops 4-4 drops, of juice of described plant, or water of raw sugar and powder of *Zingiber officinale,* in ratio of 20:1, two or three times a day, is useful. **Migraine:** Raw sugar 20 g, clarified butter 10 g, with milk, two times a day, and local application of paste of seeds of *Sesamum orientale,* is beneficial. **Dehydration due to diarrhea, or intoxication of *Croton tinglium* or *Euphorbia ligularia*:** Syrup of sugar candy powder 25 g, with extract of *Acacia catechu* 500 mg, two times a day, is beneficial. **Burning sensation of throat:** Gargles of juice of described plant, 200 ml and Vinegar 10 ml, two times a day, is beneficial. **Dysuria:** Juice of described plant 250 ml, fruit juice of *Phylanthus emblica* 20 ml, with honey 10 g, two times a day, is useful. **Epistaxis:** Nasal drops of juice of described plant, 5-5 drops, is beneficial. **Indigestion:** Raw sugar 25 g, *Piper longum* 1 g, with warm water, two times a day, is beneficial. **Piles, indigestion:** Raw sugar 25 g, fruit powder of *Terminalia chebula* 3 g, with warm water, two times a day, is beneficial. **Dysmenorrhea:** Decoction of seeds of *Sesamum orientale* 50 g, with raw sugar 25 g, two times a day, 3 days before menstrual period to it's end, is beneficial. **Asthma, bronchitis:** Raw sugar 25 g, oil of *Brassica campestris* 20 ml, with warm water, at morning, is beneficial. **Rheumatism, dysentery:** Raw sugar 25 g, *Zingiber officinale* 1.5 g, with warm water, two times a day, is beneficial. **Stomatitis:** Suck the piece of sugar candy 10 g, and extract of *Acacia catechu* 2 g, two times a day, is beneficial. **Nocturnal emission:** Sugar candy powder 20 g, Borax 250 mg, with water, three times a day, is useful. **Acidity:** (1) Sugar candy powder 10 g, fried powder of *Piper nigrum* 1 g, with milk, two times a day, is beneficial. (2) Sugar candy powder 10 g, seeds of *Elettaria cardamomum* 1.5 g, with milk cream 20 g, two times a day, is beneficial.

Formulations: *Chyavanpraasha, Brahmarasaayana, Vasantakusumaakar rasa, Draakhsaadi ghrita, Panchanimba churna, Mushali churna, Balaa taila, Trinapanchamoola kwaatha, Vasant tilaka rasa, Navaratnaraajamrigaanka rasa, Samasharkara churna, Raktapittaantaka lauha.*

Recommended readings:

Acharya, B.K. (2008), Ayurveda Jadi-buti Rahasya, Patanjali Yogapitha, Haridwar, PP. 181.

Bhutya, R.K. (2007), Vanaspati Aushadha Vigyana, Scientific Publishers (India), Jodhpur, PP. 29.

Brahmavarchas (2003), Ayurved Ka Pran Vanoshadhi Vigyan, Shanti Kunj, Haridwar, PP. 390.

Chunekar, K.C. (2004), Bhava Prakash Nighantu, Chaukhambha Bharti Academy, Varanasi, PP. 792.

Khare, C.P. (2007), Indian Medicinal Plants, Springer (India) P.L. New Delhi, PP. 567.

Kirtikar, K.R. & Basu, B.D. (1998), Indian Medicinal Plants, L.M Basu, Allahabad, Vol. 4, PP. 2662.

Misra, B.L. (2005), Dravya Guna Hastamalaka, Publication scheme, Jaipur, PP. 355.

Nair, R.Vasudevan, (2007), Indian Medicinal Plants, Orient Longman P.L. Chennai, Vol. 5, PP. 31.

Namjoshi, A.N. (2001), The Ayurvedic Pharmacopoeia of India, Government of India, Department of Indian Systems of Medicine & Homoeopathy, New Delhi, Part-1, Volume- 1, PP. 48.

Pareek, G.N. (2005), Sudhanidhi, Vanoshadhi Ratnakar, Dhanvantari Karyalaya, Aligarh, Vol. 9, PP. 96.

Prajapati, N.D., Purohit, S.S., Sharma, A.K. & Tarun Kumar (2003), A Hand Book of Medicinal Plants, Agrobios India, Jodhpur, PP. 453.

Sharma, P.C., Yelne, MB. & Denis, T.J. (2000), Database on medicinal plants used in ayurveda, Central Council for research in Ayurveda and siddha, Vol. 4, PP. 187.

Sharma, P.V. (1981), Dravya gun vigyana, Chaukhambha Bharti Academy, Varanasi, Vol. 1, PP. 638.

Singh, R.S. (2002), Vanoshadhi Nirdeshika, Uttar Pradesh Hindi Sansthan, Lucknow, PP. 48.

Swami, K.N. (1985), Gavon Main Aushadh Ratna, Kalera Krishana Gopal, Kalera (Raj.), Vol. 2, PP. 111.

412. *Saccharum spontaneum* Linn.

Family: Gramineae; Poaceae.

Ayurvedic Groups: Charak: *Mutravirechaniya, Stanyajanan,* **Sushruta:** *Trinapanchamoola.*

Name: English: Thatch Grass, **Sanskrit:** *Kaasa, Kaasekhsu, Ikhsurasa, Ikhsavaalikaa, Ikhsugandhaa, Potagal.* **Hindi:** *Kaasa,* **Local:** *Kaasa.*

Botanical characteristics: Habit: A tall erect gregarious perennial grass, height up to 6 m. **Stem:** Erect, slender, from a stout rootstock, solid, smooth, polished, silky beneath the panicle, bearing extensive roots. **Leaf:** Simple, 30-75 cm by 3-6 mm, sheathing, narrowly linear, finely acuminate, rigid, coriaceous, usually glabrous, often with convolute margins; ligule ovate, membranous. **Flower:** Spikelets in pairs, on silky, hairy panicles 20-60 cm long, pale or grayish-white to purplish grey in colour; in each spikelet pair one is pediceled and the other sessile, glumes 4, coriaceous and brown below, obscurely keeled, one-nerved. **Seed:** Grain oblong to sub-globose.

Flowering and fruiting period: October-November and December-January.

Habitat: Throughout India, up to 1800 m.

Parts used: Root. **Dosage:** 3-6 g.

Collection period: December-January.

Ayurvedic properties: ***Ras:*** *madhur, tikta,* ***Gun:*** *laghu, snigdha,* ***Veerya:*** *sheeta,* ***Vipaka:*** *madhur,* ***Tridosha*** **Effect:** alleviates ***Vaata:*** *+++,* ***Pitta:*** ++.

Action and disease indications: The **roots** are cooling, astringent, diuretic, emollient, laxative, lithotriptic, aphrodisiac, galactagogue and tonic, used for burning sensation, dysuria, anuria, dyscrasia, strangury, dyspepsia, menorrhagia, agalactia, phthisis, renal and vesical calculi, skin diseases, dysentery, bleeding piles, haemorrhagic diseases and general debility.

Clinical uses: Oligogalactia, dysuria, renal and vesical calculus, bleeding piles, menorrhagia, metrorrhagia, tuberculosis, burning sensation: Decoction of roots of described plant, 10 g, with honey 10 g, two times a day, is useful.

Formulations: *Brahmarasaayan, Pancha trinamoola kwaatha, Vrihatyaadi kwaatha.*

Recommended readings:

Bhutya, R.K. (2007), Vanaspati Aushadha Vigyana, Scientific Publishers (India), Jodhpur, PP. 63.

Chunekar, K.C. (2004), Bhava Prakash Nighantu, Chaukhambha Bharti Academy, Varanasi, PP. 380.

Dhiman, A.K. (2006), Ayurvedic Drug Plants, Daya Publishing House, Delhi, PP. 205.

Khare, C.P. (2007), Indian Medicinal Plants, Springer (India) P.L. New Delhi, PP. 568.

Kirtikar, K.R. & Basu, B.D. (1998), Indian Medicinal Plants, L.M Basu, Allahabad, Vol. 4, PP. 2668.

Misra, B.L. (2005), Dravya Guna Hastamalaka, Publication scheme, Jaipur, PP. 353.

Nair, R.Vasudevan, (2007), Indian Medicinal Plants, Orient Longman P.L. Chennai, Vol. 5, PP. 44.

Namjoshi, A.N. (2001), The Ayurvedic Pharmacopoeia of India, Government of India, Department of Indian Systems of Medicine & Homoeopathy, New Delhi, Part-1, Volume- 3, PP. 88.

Prajapati, N.D., Purohit, S.S., Sharma, A.K. & Tarun Kumar (2003), A Hand Book of Medicinal Plants, Agrobios India, Jodhpur, PP. 453.

Sharma, P.V. (1981), Dravya gun vigyana, Chaukhambha Bharti Academy, Varanasi, Vol. 1, PP. 636.

Singh, R.S. (2002), Vanoshadhi Nirdeshika, Uttar Pradesh Hindi Sansthan, Lucknow, PP. 96.

413. *Salacia chinensis* Linn.

Family: Hippocrateaceae; Celastraceae.

Name: English: Saptarangi, **Sanskrit:** *Saptachakraa, Swarnaamoolaa, Saptarangi,* **Hindi:** *Saptachakra,* **Local:** *Satarangi.*

Botanical characteristics: Habit: A large climbing shrub or small tree. **Root:** Outer surface golden yellow, in transverse section seven folds present, in fresh cut many colours appears like Rainbow. **Leaf:** Opposite cordate to lanceolate, 7.5-15 by 2-5 cm, entire or dentate, petioled, coriaceous, shining above. **Flower:** Yellowish, small, 3-6, axillary. **Fruit:** Baccate, small, globose, 1.25-2.5 cm in diam., 1-3 celled, red when ripe, pulp white, mucilaginous, edible. **Seed:** Large, angular, 1-4 in a fruit.

Flowering and fruiting period: December-January and March-April.

Habitat: Throughout India, up to 900 m, Malabar to Kurga, including Andaman Islands.

Parts used: Root. **Dosage:** 10-20 g.

Collection period: December-January.

Ayurvedic properties: ***Ras:*** *kashaaya, tikta,* ***Gun:*** *laghu, rukhsa, tikhsna,* ***Veerya:*** *ushna,* ***Vipaka:*** *katu,* ***Tridosha* Effect:** alleviates ***Kapha:*** ++, ***Pitta:*** +.

Chemical constituents: The **root bark** contains proantho-cyanidins, consisting of monomeric leucopelargonidin, its monomer, dimer and tetramer; triterpenoids (friedelin and its derivatives), mangiferine, phlobatannin and glucosidal tannins. The **stem** contains gutta, ducitol and proanthocyanidin consisting of dimmer of leucopelargonidin.

Action and disease indications: The **Roots** are thermogenic, anti-inflammatory, anodyne, appetizer, liver stimulant, emmenogogue, uterine stimulant, used for diabetes, gonorrhea, inflammations, anorexia, skin diseases, dysmenorrhea, amenorrhea, piles and hyper hydrosis.

Clinical uses: Piles: Local application of paste of roots of described plant is beneficial. **Hyperhydrosis, piles, dysmenorrhea:** Root powder of described plant, 10 g, with water, two times a day, is beneficial.

Recommended readings:

Bhutya, R.K. (2007), Vanaspati Aushadha Vigyana, Scientific Publishers (India), Jodhpur, PP. 222.

Khare, C.P. (2007), Indian Medicinal Plants, Springer (India) P.L. New Delhi, PP. 569.

Kirtikar, K.R. & Basu, B.D. (1998), Indian Medicinal Plants, L.M Basu, Allahabad, Vol. 1, PP. 582.

Sharma, P.V. (1981), Dravya gun vigyana, Chaukhambha Bharti Academy, Varanasi, Vol. 1, PP. 686.

414. *Salix caprea* Linn.

Family: Salicaceae.

Other similar plants: *S.daphnoides.*

Name: English: Weeping Willow, Goat Willow, **Hindi:** *Vetas,* **Local:** *Vedmuska.*

Botanical characteristics: Habit: A small deciduous tree, height 4-8 m. **Stem:** Girth 1 m. **Leaf:** 5-10 cm long, simple, alternate, acute, ultimately glabrous and more or less rugose above, more or less grey-tomentose beneath, crenate or nearly entire; stipules usually conspicuous, sub-reniform. **Flower:** Yellow, appears before the leaves, male flowers sweet scented. Male catkins 2.5-5 cm long, sessile, stout and densely silky with long bract hairs, on leafy peduncles; bracts oblong, ciliate, yellow. Female catkins a little longer than the male. **Fruit:** Capsules, 2-valved, when ripe the valves usually rolled back, glabrous, sub-sessile, downy and stiptate. **Seed:** With a tuft of silky hairs.

Flowering and fruiting period: September-October and November-December.

Habitat: Kashmir, Punjab, Himachal Pradesh and Uttar Pradesh, cultivated in gardens in various parts of India, for its sweet-scented flowers.

Parts used: Bark, flower.

Dosage: Bark 5-10 g, flower Distillate 25-50 ml.

Collection period: October-November.

Ayurvedic properties: ***Ras:*** *kashaaya, tikta,* ***Gun:*** *laghu,* ***Veerya:*** *sheeta,* ***Vipaka:*** *katu,* ***Tridosha* Effect:** alleviates ***Kapha:*** ++, ***Vaata:*** +.

Chemical constituents: The **bark** contains phenol glycosides as delphinidin, cyaniding, pipecolic, fragilin, picein, salicin, salicortin, salireproside, triandrin and vimalin, tannin is to be 8-13%. The **male racemes** contain flavonoids as diometin, isorhamnetin, capreoside and salicapreoside. Alkaloids, glycosides and saponins of male racemes increase the amplitude and slow the heartbeat and act more rapidly than digitalis.

Action and disease indications: The **bark** is cooling, aphrodisiac, expectorant, febrifuge, cardiac tonic laxative, used for pains, inflammations, hepatitis, dipsia, biliousness, headache, fevers, tremors of limbs, muscular pain, burning sensation, piles, erysipelas, dysuria, epistaxis, penile dysfunction, calculus, ophthalmia, enlargement of spleen. The distilled water from **flowers**- cordial, stimulant; externally applied to headache.

Clinical uses: Malaria, bilious fever, acute rheumatism, burning sensation, arthritis, arthralgia: Decoction of bark of described plant, 10 g, with honey 10 g, two times a day, is useful. **Piles:** Local application of paste of bark of described plant, is beneficial. **Fever, palpitation:** Distillate of flowers of described plant, 20 ml, two times a day, is beneficial. **Spermatorrhea, nocturnal emission, spermacresia:** Liquid extract of described plant 10 drops, with water 30 ml, at night, is beneficial.

Formulations: *Chandanaadi taila, Ark vedmusk, Rogan ibid.*

Recommended readings:

Bhutya, R.K. (2007), Vanaspati Aushadha Vigyana, Scientific Publishers (India), Jodhpur, PP. 208.

Chunekar, K.C. (2004), Bhava Prakash Nighantu, Chaukhambha Bharti Academy, Varanasi, PP. 361.

Dhiman, A.K. (2006), Ayurvedic Drug Plants, Daya Publishing House, Delhi, PP. 75.

Khare, C.P. (2007), Indian Medicinal Plants, Springer (India) P.L. New Delhi, PP. 571.

Kirtikar, K.R. & Basu, B.D. (1998), Indian Medicinal Plants, L.M Basu, Allahabad, Vol. 3, PP. 2364.

Misra, B.L. (2005), Dravya Guna Hastamalaka, Publication scheme, Jaipur, PP. 471.

Prajapati, N.D., Purohit, S.S., Sharma, A.K. & Tarun Kumar (2003), A Hand Book of Medicinal Plants, Agrobios India, Jodhpur, PP. 455.

Sharma, P.V. (1981), Dravya gun vigyana, Chaukhambha Bharti Academy, Varanasi, Vol. 1, PP. 45.

Singh, R.S. (2002), Vanoshadhi Nirdeshika, Uttar Pradesh Hindi Sansthan, Lucknow, PP. 277.

Swami, K.N. (1985), Gavon Main Aushadh Ratna, Kalera Krishana Gopal, Kalera (Raj.), Vol. 3, PP. 103.

415. *Salix tetrasperma* Roxb.

Family: Salicaceae.

Name: English: Indian Willow, **Sanskrit:** *Jal vetasa, Nikunchaka, Parivyaadha, Naadeya,* **Hindi:** *Jalvetas,* **Local:** *Vaanira, Benta, Ved Lailaa, Ved Saadaa.*

Botanical characteristics: Habit: A medium sized deciduous tree, height 15-20 m. **Stem:** Girth 3 m, bark brown or blackish, with longitudinal furrows, rough, young shoots silky.

Leaf: 5-12.5 by 1.5-4.5 cm, lanceolate or ovate-lanceolate, caudate-acuminate, entire or more usually serrulate, green and glabrous above, pale or white beneath and more or less silky when quite young; petioles 7.5-18 mm long, red; stipule on vigourous shoots semicordate, conspicuous, with gland-tipped teeth. **Flower:** Appearing before leaves, Male catkins 5-12.5 cm long, sweet scented, sessile or on leafy shoots, rhachis hairy; bracts obovate, concave, yellowish-brown, villous, not crowded, tip rounded or sub-acute. Female catkins 2.5 cm long, on leafy shoots, rhachis hairy, bracts as in the male but rather smaller. **Fruit:** Fruiting catkins about 5 cm long, capsules, glabrous, 3.8-5 mm long, on a slender distinct stipe. **Seed:** 4-6, brown-blackish.

Flowering and fruiting period: September-October and November-December.

Habitat: Throughout tropical and sub-tropical India, along the banks of rivers and streams.

Parts used: Bark, leaves.

Dosage: 5-10 g, juice 25-50 g, distillate 25-50 ml.

Collection period: October-November.

Ayurvedic properties: ***Ras:*** *kashaaya, tikta,* ***Gun:*** *laghu,* ***Veerya:*** *sheeta,* ***Vipaka:*** *katu,* **Tridosha Effect:** alleviates ***Kapha:*** +, ***Pitta:*** +, Aggravates ***Vaata:*** ++.

Chemical constituents: The **bark** contains tannins 8.2-8.8% and phenol glycosides, fragilin, picein, salicin 0.13%, salicortin, salireposide, triandrin and vimalin, salicin A, salicase, calcium and potassium nitrates.

Action and disease indications: The **bark** is febrifuge, tonic, used for fevers, hydrophobia, blood in diarrhea, dysentery, hepatitis, spleenomegaly and jaundice.

Clinical uses: Hepatitis, jaundice: Juice of leaves of described plant 20 ml, with honey 10 g, two times a day, is beneficial.

Formulations: *Laxmivilaasa rasa, Dhaatakyaadi taila.*

Recommended readings:

Bhutya, R.K. (2007), Vanaspati Aushadha Vigyana, Scientific Publishers (India), Jodhpur, PP. 105.

Chunekar, K.C. (2004), Bhava Prakash Nighantu, Chaukhambha Bharti Academy, Varanasi, PP. 361.

Khare, C.P. (2007), Indian Medicinal Plants, Springer (India) P.L. New Delhi, PP. 572.

Kirtikar, K.R. & Basu, B.D. (1998), Indian Medicinal Plants, L.M Basu, Allahabad, Vol. 3, PP. 2362.

Sharma, P.V. (1981), Dravya gun vigyana, Chaukhambha Bharti Academy, Varanasi, Vol. 1, PP. 48.

Swami, K.N. (1985), Gavon Main Aushadh Ratna, Kalera Krishana Gopal, Kalera (Raj.), Vol. 3, PP. 104.

416. *Salvadora persica* Linn.

Family: Salvadoraceae.

Synonym: *S. persica,* var. *wightiana, S. indica.*

Other similar plant: *S. oleoides- Raj pilu*-bigger var.

Name: English: Mustard Tree, Salt Bush Tree, Tooth Brush Tree, **Sanskrit:** *Pilu, Gudaphala, Sranshi, Sheetaphala,* **Hindi:** *Pilu,* **Local:** *Sandodiyaa.*

Botanical characteristics: Habit: A large much branched evergreen shrub or small tree, height 4-13.5 m. **Stem:** Girth 1.25-1.85 m, hollow, crooked, short, with soft whitish yellow wood, bark of old stem rugose; branches numerous, dropping, glabrous, terete, finely striate, shining, almost white. **Leaf:** Somewhat fleshy, glaucous, opposite, 3.8-6.3 by 2-3.2 cm, greyish green, elliptic-lanceolate or ovate, oblong, often mucronate at the apex, base usually acute, less commonly rounded, characteristic smell in crushed leaves; main nerves 5-6 pairs; petioles 1.3-2.2 cm long, glabrous. **Flower:** Small, greenish-yellow, in axillary and terminal compound lax panicles 5-12.5 cm long, numerous in the upper axils; pedicels 1.5-3 mm long; bracts beneath the pedicels ovate, very caducous. **Fruit:** Drupes, 3 mm diam., globose, smooth, red when ripe, mucilaginous, smell like Black Mustard, edible. **Seed:** Small, one seed in a fruit.

Flowering and fruiting period: January-February and April-May.

Habitat: Arid and drier parts of India, on saline lands and in coastal regions, mostly in Rajasthan, Gujarat, Punjab and Kacch.

Parts used: Fruit, seed, seed oil, leaves, root bark.

Dosage: Fruit 3-6 g, seed 1-3 g, leaves 1-3 g, root bark 1-3 g, seed oil for external use.

Collection period: May-June.

Ayurvedic properties: ***Ras:*** *madhur, tikta,* ***Gun:*** *laghu, snigdha, tikhsna,* ***Veerya:*** *ushna,* ***Vipaka:*** *katu,* ***Tridosha*** **Effect:** alleviates ***Kapha: ++, Vaata: ++, Pitta: +.***

Chemical constituents: The **roots** contain elemental gamma-monoclinic sulphur, benzyl glucosinolate, salvadourea, *m*-anisic acid and sitosterol, benzyl isothiocyanate, isolated from the root, exhibits antiviral activity against *Herpes simplex virus-1* which affects oral region, The **root bark** and **stem bark** contain trimethylamine, Myristic, lauric and palmitic acids are the major acid components of the **seed** fat. The root is used as a tooth brush.

Action and disease indications: The **leaves** are anthelmintic, anti-scorbutic, deobstruant, diuretic, astringent, expectorant and tonic, used for cough, asthma, bronchitis, strangury, painful tumours, scurvy, constipation, verminosis and piles. The **flowers** are stimulant, laxative, used for rheumatic conditions. The **fruits** are thermogenic, aphrodisiac, emollient, alexeteric, stomachic, purgative, carminative, deobstruent, diuretic, lithontriptic and digestive, used for seminal weakness, flatulence, rheumatism, tumours, spleenomegaly, biliousness, constipation and gastropathy. The **root bark** is stimulant, emmenogogue and tonic, used for spleenalgia. The root bark is good for gastropathy. The **seeds** are diuretic, purgative. The **stem bark** is emmenogogue, ascarifuge, febrifuge, spasmolytic, anti-inflammatory, hypoglycaemic and anti-bacterial, used for inflammations, fevers and diabetes.

Clinical uses: Tumour, rheumatism, piles: Local application of paste of leaves of described plant, is beneficial. **Bronchitis:** Leaves powder of described plant 1-3 g, with honey 10 g, two times a day, is useful. **Piles:** Fruits of described plant 20 g, with whey, two times a day, is beneficial. **Rheumatism:** Local application and massage of seed oil of described plant, is beneficial. **Delirium:** Decoction of root bark of described plant, 5 g, two times a day, is beneficial. **Neuralgia, pains:** Local application of medicated oil, made by leaves and root bark of described plant, is beneficial. **Dentalgia:** Brush with stick of root of described plant, is beneficial.

Formulations: *Piluparnyaadi taila.*

Recommended readings:

Bhutya, R.K. (2007), Vanaspati Aushadha Vigyana, Scientific Publishers (India), Jodhpur, PP. 153.

Chunekar, K.C. (2004), Bhava Prakash Nighantu, Chaukhambha Bharti Academy, Varanasi, PP. 591.

Khare, C.P. (2007), Indian Medicinal Plants, Springer (India) P.L. New Delhi, PP. 574.

Kirtikar, K.R. & Basu, B.D. (1998), Indian Medicinal Plants, L.M Basu, Allahabad, Vol. 2, PP. 1537.

Misra, B.L. (2005), Dravya Guna Hastamalaka, Publication scheme, Jaipur, PP. 465.

Nair, R.Vasudevan, (2007), Indian Medicinal Plants, Orient Longman P.L. Chennai, Vol. 5, PP. 49.

Prajapati, N.D., Purohit, S.S., Sharma, A.K. & Tarun Kumar (2003), A Hand Book of Medicinal Plants, Agrobios India, Jodhpur, PP. 455.

Sharma, P.V. (1981), Dravya gun vigyana, Chaukhambha Bharti Academy, Varanasi, Vol. 1, PP. 450.

Singh, R.S. (2002), Vanoshadhi Nirdeshika, Uttar Pradesh Hindi Sansthan, Lucknow, PP. 248.

Swami, K.N. (1985), Gavon Main Aushadh Ratna, Kalera Krishana Gopal, Kalera (Raj.), Vol. 3, PP. 23.

417. *Salvia plebeia* R. Br.

Family: Labiatae; Lamiaceae.

Name: Sanskrit: *Samudrashosha,* **Hindi:** *Samudrashosha,* **Local:** *Bhutulasi, Kammarakasa.*

Botanical characteristics: Habit: An annual erect herb, height 15-50 cm. **Stem:** Hoary-pubescent, obtusely quandrangular, grooved. **Leaf:** 5-10 by 2-4.5 cm, oblong-lanceolate, obtuse or sub-acute, irregularly crenate, simplem exstipulate, sparsely hairy or nearly glabrous base usually acute, often decurrent into the petiole, petioles 2.5-5 cm long. **Flower:** White, in paniculate interrupted pubescent spicate racemes; floral leaves 2.5 mm long, broadly ovate, sub-acute, shortly petiolate, petioles 6.25 mm long; bracts small, linear-spathulate. **Fruit:** Nutlets 1 mm long, ovoid, the inner face slightly angular, the dorsal face rounded, smooth, brown. **Seed:** Mucilaginous when wetted.

Flowering and fruiting period: August-September and October-November.

Habitat: Throughout the plains of India, up to an altitude of 1500 m in hills.

Parts used: Seed. **Dosage:** 1-3 g.

Collection period: November-December.

Ayurvedic properties: ***Ras:*** *kashaaya, tikta,* ***Gun:*** *snigdha, pichhala,* ***Veerya:*** *ushna,* ***Vipaka:*** *katu,* ***Tridosha*** **Effect:** alleviates ***Vaata:*** **++**, ***Pitta:*** +.

Chemical constituents: The **seeds** contain secoisolari-ciresinol diester, fix oil 18%, protein 11.75%, gum 44%, fibrous tissue and ash 15%. The **plant** contains flavones-nepetin and hispulidin and their glucosides, The **flowers** also contain nepetin, sitosterol and oleanolic acid.

Action and disease indications: The **seeds** are mucilaginous, tonic, used for premature ejaculation, spermatorrhea, diarrhea, leucorrhea, menorrhagia and piles.

Clinical uses: Premature ejaculation, somasthenia: Seed powder of described plant, 3 g, with milk, two times a day, is beneficial.

Formulations: *Madan modaka, Kauncha paaka, Pramehaprahaara churna, Sukrastambhan gutikaa.*

Recommended readings:

Bhutya, R.K. (2007), Vanaspati Aushadha Vigyana, Scientific Publishers (India), Jodhpur, PP. 223.

Chunekar, K.C. (2004), Bhava Prakash Nighantu, Chaukhambha Bharti Academy, Varanasi, PP. 838.

Khare, C.P. (2007), Indian Medicinal Plants, Springer (India) P.L. New Delhi, PP. 577.

Kirtikar, K.R. & Basu, B.D. (1998), Indian Medicinal Plants, L.M Basu, Allahabad, Vol. 3, PP. 1998.

Misra, B.L. (2005), Dravya Guna Hastamalaka, Publication scheme, Jaipur, PP. 500.

Singh, R.S. (2002), Vanoshadhi Nirdeshika, Uttar Pradesh Hindi Sansthan, Lucknow, PP. 357.

418. *Sansevieria roxburghiana* J. & J. Schultes

Family: Liliaceae.

Synonym: *S. zeylanica.*

Other similar plant: *S.hyacinthoides.*

Name: English: Indian Bowstring Hemp, **Sanskrit:** *Naagadaman,* **Hindi:** *Nagdaman,* **Local:** *Nagdaman.*

Botanical characteristics: Habit: A perennial herb, height 30-60 cm. **Stem:** Absent. **Rootstock:** Creeping. **Leaf:** 6-24 in number, radical, smooth above, slightly rough beneath, 10-20 by 2.5-3.8 cm, flat, strap-shaped or narrowly lanceolate; inner or adult leaves ascending and slightly recurving, somewhat stiff, 20-60 by 1.25-2.54 cm, 3-4 mm thick, linear, blackish-green, deeply concave channeled down the face, rounded or very obtusely keeled on the back, gradually tapering into a stout subulate soft green point 0.6-5 cm long, transversely marked with darker green rather regular bars on both sides and with 6-11 longitudinal dark green lines on the scarcely paler under-surface and often1-3 on the upper. **Flower:** White or light green, flower stem 30-75 cm long, with 4-5 erect acuminate sheaths 2.5-3.8 cm long, on the lower part and a spike-like raceme 30-45 cm long of flower-clusters above; bracts 3-4 mm long, lanceolate-attenulate, membranous. Flowers about 4 in a cluster; pedicels 5-8.4 mm long; jointed near the middle, with the persistent part 3-4 mm long; tube 6.3-7.3 mm long; lobes 8.4-9.5 mm long, linear, obtuse. **Fruit:** Membranous, indehiscent. **Seed:** 1-3 ripening outside the pericarp, globose, all large, or 1-2 imperfect, testa long, fleshy or succulent.

Flowering and fruiting period: June-July and November-December.

Habitat: The eastern coast of India, from West Bengal to Tamilnadu.

Parts used: Root, leaves. **Dosage:** Juice 10-20 ml.

Collection period: November-December.

Ayurvedic properties: ***Ras:*** *madhur,* ***Gun:*** *snigdha, pichhala,* ***Veerya:*** *sheeta,* ***Vipaka:*** *madhur* ***Tridosha*** **Effect:** alleviates ***Vaata:*** ++, ***Pitta:*** +.

Action and disease indications: The **rhizomes** are expectorant, mucilaginous, used for cough, constipation, piles, dysuria, bronchitis and tuberculosis.

Clinical uses: Lumbago, whitlow, inflammation, insect stings: Local application of warm paste of leaves of described plant, with castor oil, is beneficial.

Recommended readings:

Bhutya, R.K. (2007), Vanaspati Aushadha Vigyana, Scientific Publishers (India), Jodhpur, PP. 134.

Khare, C.P. (2007), Indian Medicinal Plants, Springer (India) P.L. New Delhi, PP. 579.

Kirtikar, K.R. & Basu, B.D. (1998), Indian Medicinal Plants, L.M Basu, Allahabad, Vol. 4, PP. 2457.

Sharma, P.V. (1981), Dravya gun vigyana, Chaukhambha Bharti Academy, Varanasi, Vol. 1, PP. 769.

419. *Santalum album* Linn.

Family: Santalaceae.

Ayurvedic Groups: Charak: *Daahaprashamana, Angamardaprashamana, Trishnaanigrahana, Varnya, Kandughna, Vishaghna,* **Sushruta:** *Patolaadi, Saarivaadi, Priyangvadi, Guduchyaadi, Pittasanshamana varga.*

Name: English: White Sandalwood, **Sanskrit:** *Chandan, Shreekhanda, Bhadrashree, Tailaparnika, Gaandhasaara, Malayaja,* **Hindi:** *Chandan-Sweta,* **Local:** *Safed Chandan.*

Botanical characteristics: Habit: A small to medium sized evergreen semi-parasitic, glabrous tree, height up to 18 m. **Stem:** Girth 2.4 m, bark dark grey or brownish-black, rough with short vertical cracks, with slender drooping branches, the sapwood white and odourless, the heartwood yellowish-brown, strongly scented, mature after 50 years. **Leaf:** 3.8-6.3 by 1.6-3.2 cm, sometimes larger, simple, opposite, elliptic-lanceolate, subacute, thin, base acute, glabrous, entire; petioles 1-1.3 cm long, slender. **Flower:** Brownish-purple, reddish-purple or violate, unscented, in terminal and axillary paniculate cymes; perianth campanulate; limb of 4 valvate triangular segments. **Fruit:** Drupes, globose, 1.3 cm diam., purple-black; endocarp hard, ribbed. **Seed:** Hard, globose or obovoid.

Flowering and fruiting period: June-September and November-February.

Habitat: Dry regions of Peninsular India, from Vindhyachal Mountains southwards, especially in Karnataka, Tamilnadu and Kerala, up to an altitude of 1200 m.

Parts used: Heartwood, oil.

Dosage: Heartwood 3-6 g, oil 5-15 drops.

Collection period: May-June.

Ayurvedic properties: ***Ras:*** *tikta, madhur,* ***Gun:*** *guru,* ***Veerya:*** *sheeta,* ***Vipaka:*** *madhur,* ***Tridosha*** **Effect:** alleviates ***Kapha:*** **+++,** ***Pitta:*** **++.**

Chemical constituents: The **essential oil** of **heartwood** contains chiefly alpha and beta santalol. Other constituents are sesquiterpene hydrocarbons-alpha-beta-*epi*-beta-santalene and alpha and beta curcumene and beta-farnesene and droagarofuran.

Action and disease indications: The **heartwood** is refrigerant, aromatic, deodorant, disinfectant, depurative, intellect promoting, cardio-tonic, diaphoretic, diuretic, tranquilizer, anti-septic, bacteriostatic against gram positive, expectorant, aphrodisiac, haemostatic, anodyne, anti-pyretic, restorative and tonic, prescribed for burning sensation, dipsia, cephalgia, fatigue, skin diseases, forgetfulness, amentia, psychopathy, cardiac debility, haemoptysis, hyperacidity, jaundice, strangury, cough, bronchitis, gastric irritability, menorrhagia, leucorrhea, spermatorrhea, inflammations, cystitis, sexually transmitted diseases, dysentery, intermittent fever and general debility. The essential oil is anti-bacterial, anti-fungal, used for dysuria, urethral discharges and diseases of gall bladder.

Contraindication: Do not apply in the diseases of the parenchyma of the kidney.

Clinical uses: Dipsesis: Heart wood powder of described plant 2 g, with milk of coconut 50 ml, two times a day, is beneficial. **Burning sensation of urine, haematuria, dipsrsis, excess and turbid micturition, diarrhea with bleeding, burning sensation:** Heart wood powder of described plant 2 g, with rice water 50 ml, sugar candy powder 10 g and honey 10 g, two times a day, is beneficial. **Nausea, vomiting, sun stroke:** Heart wood powder of described plant 2 g, with fruit juice of *Phylanthus emblica* 20 ml, two times a day, is beneficial. **Dermatitis, erysipelas, scabies, hyperhydrosis, furunculosis:** Local application of paste of heart wood of described plant, 10 parts, *Cinamomum camphora* 1 part, with rose water, is beneficial. **Leucorrhea, menorrhagia, metrorrhagia, excess and turbid micturition:** Cold infusion of heart wood of described plant 5 g, with honey 10 g, two times a day, is useful. **Headache due to heat:** Local application of paste of heartwood of described plant, *Coriandrum sativum,* with rose water, is beneficial. **Gonorrhea, nephritis, chronic bronchitis:** Heart wood powder of described plant 2 g, with *Elettaria cardamomum* 1 g, gum of *Bambusa arundinacea* 2 g, with water **or** heart wood powder of described plant 2 g, with *Zingiber officinale* 1 g, with water, **or** heart wood powder of described plant 2 g, with cold infusion of *Trachy spermum-ammi* 2 g, two times a day, is beneficial. **Chronic cystitis, infection of urinary tract, chronic bronchitis:** Sandal wood oil 3 drops, in roundish sugar cake, two times a day, is beneficial. **Eczema:** Local application of sandal wood oil, with lemon juice, in ratio of 10:1, or sandal wood oil and seed oil of *Hydnocarpus laurifolia,* in ratio of 10:2, is beneficial. *Stiria gravidarum* local application of heart wood powder of described plant and root powder of

Vetiveria zizanoiodes, with water, two times a day, is beneficial. **Epistaxis:** Cold infusion of mix powder of heart wood powder of described plant, *Glycyrrhiza glabra,* flowers of *Madhuca longifolia,* fruits of *Grewia subinequalis,* fruit pulp of *Aegle marmelos,* 10 g, with honey 10 g, two times a day, is beneficial.

Formulations: *Chandanaadi lauha, Chandanaadi churna, Chandanaasava, Aswagandhaa taila, Vyaghri taila, Kutajaastaka churna.*

Recommended readings:

Bhutya, R.K. (2007), Vanaspati Aushadha Vigyana, Scientific Publishers (India), Jodhpur, PP. 93.

Brahmavarchas (2003), Ayurved Ka Pran Vanoshadhi Vigyan, Shanti Kunj, Haridwar, PP. 394.

Chunekar, K.C. (2004), Bhava Prakash Nighantu, Chaukhambha Bharti Academy, Varanasi, PP. 187.

Dhiman, A.K. (2006), Ayurvedic Drug Plants, Daya Publishing House, Delhi, PP. 95.

Khare, C.P. (2007), Indian Medicinal Plants, Springer (India) P.L. New Delhi, PP. 579.

Kirtikar, K.R. & Basu, B.D. (1998), Indian Medicinal Plants, L.M Basu, Allahabad, Vol. 3, PP. 2186.

Misra, B.L. (2005), Dravya Guna Hastamalaka, Publication scheme, Jaipur, PP. 453.

Nair, R.Vasudevan, (2007), Indian Medicinal Plants, Orient Longman P.L. Chennai, Vol. 5, PP. 57.

Namjoshi, A.N. (2001), The Ayurvedic Pharmacopoeia of India, Government of India, Department of Indian Systems of Medicine & Homoeopathy, New Delhi, Part-1, Volume- 3, PP. 207.

Pareek, G.N. (2005), Sudhanidhi, Vanoshadhi Ratnakar, Dhanvantari Karyalaya, Aligarh, Vol. 3, PP. 314.

Prajapati, N.D., Purohit, S.S., Sharma, A.K. & Tarun Kumar (2003), A Hand Book of Medicinal Plants, Agrobios India, Jodhpur, PP. 458.

Sharma, P.C., Yelne, MB. & Denis, T.J. (2000), Database on medicinal plants used in ayurveda, Central Council for research in Ayurveda and siddha, Vol. 3, PP. 184.

Sharma, P.V. (1981), Dravya gun vigyana, Chaukhambha Bharti Academy, Varanasi, Vol. 1, PP. 715.

Singh, R.S. (2002), Vanoshadhi Nirdeshika, Uttar Pradesh Hindi Sansthan, Lucknow, PP. 144.

420. *Sapindus mukorossi* Gaertn.

Family: Sapindaceae.

Other similar plant: *S.laurifolius,* Syn. *Trifoliatus, S.emarginatus.*

Name: English: Chinese Soap Berry, Soap Nut Tree of North India, **Sanskrit:** *Aristaka, Mangalya, Krishanavarna, Arthasaadhana, Raktabeeja, Peetafena, Fenil, Garbhapaatan,* **Hindi:** *Arithaa,* **Local:** *Rithaa.*

Botanical characteristics: Habit: A small or medium sized deciduous tree, height up to 18 m. **Stem:** Girth 1.8 m, bark dark or pale grey, somewhat rough, exfoliating in irregular woody scales. Blaze 1.3-7.5 mm, hard, not fibrous, pale orange-brown. **Leaf:** 23-50 cm long, leaflets 5-8 pairs, opposite or alternate, 9-18 by 2.5-5 cm, lanceolate, acuminate, glabrous, often slightly falcate or oblique, with 15-20 pairs or rather indistinct secondary nerves. Petiolules 2.5-5 mm long. **Flower:** White or purple, 5 mm diam., subsessile, very numerous, mostly bisexual, in large terminal pubescent, pyramidal panicles. **Fruit:** Drupes, of 1-3 distinct, fleshy, indehiscent carpels, 1.8-2.5 cm diam., smooth, pale brown, globose, wrinkled before falling. **Seed:** Solitary, 10-13 mm diam., globose, black, loosely contained in the fleshy pericarp.

Flowering and fruiting period: November-December and February-April.

Habitat: Distributed in the Himalaya from Himachal Pradesh to eastwards, up to 1220 m, Assam, Bihar and North-western India.

Parts used: Fruit. **Dosage:** 3-6 g.

Collection period: March-April.

Ayurvedic properties: ***Ras:*** *tikta, katu,* ***Gun:*** *laghu, tikhsna,* ***Veerya:*** *ushna,* ***Vipaka:*** *katu,* ***Tridosha*** **Effect:** alleviates ***Kapha: ++, Vaata: +, Pitta: +.***

Chemical constituents: The **plant** contains triterpenoid glycosides, derived from hederagenin. Saponins exhibit hypotensive, anticholesterolemic, spermicidal and anti-microbial properties. Saponin A and C, sapindoside A and B, extracted from the fruit rind, showed antifungal acivity. Hederagenin, isolated from the fruit rind or pericarp, is used in skin-lightening and anti-inflammatory cosmetics. Other constituents from the plant are flavonoids-quercetin, kaempferol, apigenin and rutin.

Action and disease indications: The **fruits** are emetic, expectorant, demulcent, thermogenic, anthelmintic, abortifecient, hypotensive, anticholesterolemic, spermicidal and anti-microbial, used for hypersalivation, chlorosis, epilepsy, inflammations, skin diseases, asthma, diarrhea, lumbago, verminosis and dyspepsia,

Clinical uses: Hemicrenia, asthma: Snuff of fruit powder of described plant, 500 mg, two times a day, is beneficial. **Scabies, skin diseases, arthritis and insect stings:** Local application of paste of fruit of described plant is beneficial. **Intoxication of opium:** Make vomit by decoction of described plant, 3 g, is beneficial. **Alopecia:** Wash hairs with cold infusion of mix powder of fruits of described plant, *Phylanthus emblica, Acacia sinuta,* leaves powder of *Zizyphus jujuba,* is very beneficial.

Formulations: *Chandanaadi taila, Keshamanjan powder.*

Recommended readings:

Acharya, B.K. (2008), Ayurveda Jadi-buti Rahasya, Patanjali Yogapitha, Haridwar, PP. 362.

Bhutya, R.K. (2007), Vanaspati Aushadha Vigyana, Scientific Publishers (India), Jodhpur, PP. 18.

Brahmavarchas (2003), Ayurved Ka Pran Vanoshadhi Vigyan, Shanti Kunj, Haridwar, PP. 397.

Chunekar, K.C. (2004), Bhava Prakash Nighantu, Chaukhambha Bharti Academy, Varanasi, PP. 529.

Khare, C.P. (2007), Indian Medicinal Plants, Springer (India) P.L. New Delhi, PP. 581.

Kirtikar, K.R. & Basu, B.D. (1998), Indian Medicinal Plants, L.M Basu, Allahabad, Vol. 1, PP. 632.

Misra, B.L. (2005), Dravya Guna Hastamalaka, Publication scheme, Jaipur, PP. 459.

Nair, R.Vasudevan, (2007), Indian Medicinal Plants, Orient Longman P.L. Chennai, Vol. 5, PP. 66.

Prajapati, N.D., Purohit, S.S., Sharma, A.K. & Tarun Kumar (2003), A Hand Book of Medicinal Plants, Agrobios India, Jodhpur, PP. 459.

Sharma, P.C., Yelne, MB. & Denis, T.J. (2000), Database on medicinal plants used in ayurveda, Central Council for research in Ayurveda and siddha, Vol. 6, PP. 20.

Sharma, P.V. (1981), Dravya gun vigyana, Chaukhambha Bharti Academy, Varanasi, Vol. 1, PP. 384.

Singh, R.S. (2002), Vanoshadhi Nirdeshika, Uttar Pradesh Hindi Sansthan, Lucknow, PP. 328.

421. *Saraca asoca* (Roxb.) De Wilde.

Family: Caesalpiniaceae.

Synonym: *Saraca indica.*

Name: English: Ashoka Tree, **Sanskrit:** *Ashok, Hempushpa, Vanjul, Taamrapallava, Pindapushpa, Gaandhapushpa, Nata,* **Hindi:** *Ashok,* **Local:** *Ashok, Sitaa Ashok.*

Botanical characteristics: Habit: A Medium sized handsome evergreen tree, height 6-9m. **Stem:** Erect, bark dark-brown to grey or black, with a warty surface, 5 mm to 1 cm thick, branches numerous, spreading, drooping, glabrous. **Leaf:** Pinnate, 15-20 cm long, rhachis glabrous, corky at the base; leaflets 4-6 pairs, 7.5-20 by 3-5.7 cm, oblong-lanceolate, obtuse or acute, quite glabrous, base rounded or cuneate, slightly oblique; petiolules 4.5-6.5 mm long, stout, wrinkled; stipules deciduous. **Flower:** Orange or orange-yellow, fragrant, numerous, in dense axillary corymbs 7.5-10 cm across; peduncle stout; pedicles 8-13 mm long, red, glabrous; bracts ovate, sub-acute; bracteoles 2, appearing like a calyx, 4 mm long, spathulate-oblong, sub-acute, ciliolate, amplexicaul, coloured. **Fruit:** Pods, black, 7.5-25 by 4.5-5 cm, linear-oblong, tapering to both ends, compressed, glabrous, woody, veined. **Seed:** 4-8 per pods, ellipsoid-oblong, 3.8 long, slightly compressed.

Flowering and fruiting period: March-April and August-September.

Habitat: Throughout India, except North-Western India, also in Central and East Himalaya, up to an altitude of 750 m, also cultivated.

Parts used: Bark, seed, flower.

Dosage: Bark 15-30 g (boiled in milk), seed, flower 3-6 g.

Collection period: November-December.

Ayurvedic properties: ***Ras:*** *kashaaya, tikta,* ***Gun:*** *laghu, rukhsa,* ***Veerya:*** *sheeta,* ***Vipaka:*** *katu,* ***Tridosha*** **Effect:** alleviates, ***Kapha:*** ***+++,*** ***Pitta:*** *++.*

Chemical constituents: The **bark** contains alkanes, esters and primary alcohoks. It gave *n*-octacosanol, tannin 6%, catechin, (+)-catechol, (-) -epicatechin, (-)-epicatechol, leucocyanidin, leucopelargonidin, procyanidin, derivatives, methyl- and ethyl cholesterol derivatives. The **leaves** and **stem** contains quercetin and its 3-0-rhamnoside, kaempfreol-3-0-alpha-L-rhamnoside, amyrin, ceryl alcohol and beta-sitosterol. The **flowers** contain fatty acids and gallic acid; apigenin-7-0-beta-D-glucoside, cyaniding-3,5-diglucoside, kaempferol, 3-0-beta-D-glucoside, pelargonidin-3,5-diglucoside, quercetin and its 3-0-beta-D-glucoside and sitosterol. Alcoholic extract of the bark is reported to be active against a wide range of bactria. Pure phenolic glucoside (P2), isolated from stem bark, exhibited highly potent oxytocic activity and was similar in nature topitocin and ergometrine.

Action and disease indications: The **Bark** is refrigerant, anthelmintic, styptic, stomachic, demulcent, constipating, febrifuge, uterine tonic, corrects tone of uterus, used for suppressed menses, leucorrhea, menstrual pain, menorrhagia, complaints of menopause, dyspepsia, boliousness, colic, burning sensation, fever, dipsia, visceromegaly, ulcers and pimples. The **flowers** are uterine tonic, used for haemorrhagic dysentery, bleeding piles, cervical adenitis, hyperdipsia, inflammations, scabies, diabetes and retention of urine. The **seeds** are treating bone fractures, strangury and vesical calculi.

Clinical uses: Leucorrhea, strangury, renal and vesical calculus: : *'Khsira paka'* of stem bark of described plant 15 g, two times a day, is beneficial. **Menorrhagia, metrorrhagia:** Stem bark of described plant 5 g, root powder of *Amaranthus spinosus, Berberis aristata,* 3-3 g, *Cinamomum verum* 1 g, with rice water, two times a day, is beneficial. **Diarrhea, dysentery, intestinal worms, dipsesis:** Seed powder of described plant 4 g, with water, two times a day, is beneficial. **Epistaxis:** Flower powder of described plant 5 g, with distillate of *Foeniculum vulgare,* 20 ml, two times a day, is beneficial. **Inflammation, pains:** Local application of paste of bark of described plant, with water, is beneficial. **Gout:** Decoction of stem bark of described plant 15 g, with Castor oil 10 ml, two times a day, is beneficial. **Acne vulgaris:** Local application of paste of stem bark of described plant, fruits of *Buchanania lanzan,* seed powder of *Lens culinaris, Brassica campestris,* with fresh milk, is beneficial. **Stomatitis:** Gargles by decoction of stem bark of described plant 15 g, bark of *Bauhinia racemosa,* 15 g, two times a day, is beneficial.

Formulations: *Ashoka ghrita, Ashokaarista, Devadaarvyaadhyarista, Madhukaadyavaleha, Mahaa marichyaadi taila, Kaasisaadi taila, Pradaraari rasa.*

Recommended readings:

Acharya, B.K. (2008), Ayurveda Jadi-buti Rahasya, Patanjali Yogapitha, Haridwar, PP. 97.

Bhutya, R.K. (2007), Vanaspati Aushadha Vigyana, Scientific Publishers (India), Jodhpur, PP. 21.

Brahmavarchas (2003), Ayurved Ka Pran Vanoshadhi Vigyan, Shanti Kunj, Haridwar, PP. 398.

Chunekar, K.C. (2004), Bhava Prakash Nighantu, Chaukhambha Bharti Academy, Varanasi, PP. 500.

Dhiman, A.K. (2006), Ayurvedic Drug Plants, Daya Publishing House, Delhi, PP. 48.

Khare, C.P. (2007), Indian Medicinal Plants, Springer (India) P.L. New Delhi, PP. 583.

Kirtikar, K.R. & Basu, B.D. (1998), Indian Medicinal Plants, L.M Basu, Allahabad, Vol. 2, PP. 883.

Misra, B.L. (2005), Dravya Guna Hastamalaka, Publication scheme, Jaipur, PP. 277.

Nair, R.Vasudevan, (2007), Indian Medicinal Plants, Orient Longman P.L. Chennai, Vol. 5, PP. 66.

Namjoshi, A.N. (2001), The Ayurvedic Pharmacopoeia of India, Government of India, Department of Indian Systems of Medicine & Homoeopathy, New Delhi, Part-1, Volume- 2, PP. 14.

Pareek, G.N. (2005), Sudhanidhi, Vanoshadhi Ratnakar, Dhanvantari Karyalaya, Aligarh, Vol. 1, PP. 239.

Prajapati, N.D., Purohit, S.S., Sharma, A.K. & Tarun Kumar (2003), A Hand Book of Medicinal Plants, Agrobios India, Jodhpur, PP. 460.

Sharma, P.C., Yelne, MB. & Denis, T.J. (2000), Database on medicinal plants used in ayurveda, Central Council for research in Ayurveda and siddha, Vol. 3, PP. 76.

Sharma, P.V. (1981), Dravya gun vigyana, Chaukhambha Bharti Academy, Varanasi, Vol. 1, PP. 617.

Swami, K.N. (1985), Gavon Main Aushadh Ratna, Kalera Krishana Gopal, Kalera (Raj.), Vol. 1, PP. 47.

422. *Sarcostema brevistigma* W. & A.

Family: Asclepiadaceae.

Synonym: *S. acidum.*

Name: English: Moon Plant, Soma Plant, **Sanskrit:** *Somalataa, Somavalli, Somakhsiri, Saumyaa, Dwijpriyaa,* **Hindi:** *Somalataa,* **Local:** *Baghadudha.*

Botanical characteristics: Habit: A leafless perennial, jointed trailing shrub. **Stem:** 3-6 mm diam., joints 10-20 cm long, branches green, cylindrical, fleshy, glabrous, pendulous, twining branches having milky white latex. **Leaf:** Temporary, reduced to scales, opposite. **Flower:** White or pale greenish white, 1 cm diam., fragrant, in sessile many flowered terminal umbels; pedicles 6-8 mm long, slender, pubescent; bracts minute, lanceolate. **Fruit:** Follicles, 10-12.5 by 0.8 cm, lanceolate, tapering at both ends, straight. **Seed:** 5 by 3 mm, flat, ovate, comose, coma 2 mm long.

Flowering and fruiting period: August-September and September-October.

Habitat: Dry rocky places in West Bengal, Bihar and Peninsular India, up to an altitude of 1350 m.

Parts used: Milky exudate. **Dosage:** 1-3 drops.

Collection period: February-March.

Ayurvedic properties: ***Ras:*** *katu, tikta,* ***Gun:*** *laghu, snigdha,* ***Veerya:*** *ushna,* ***Vipaka:*** *katu,* ***Tridosha*** **Effect:** alleviates ***Vaata:*** **+,** ***Kapha:*** +, ***Pitta:*** +.

Chemical constituents: The **plant** contains mallic acid, succinic acid, reducing sugars, surcosa, trace of tannin, an alkaloid, a phytosterol, alpha and beta-amyrins, luoeol and lupeol acetate, and beta-sitotosterol. The milky **exudates** from the stem contains 4.1% of caoutchouc. Coagulum contains caoutcaouc 16, resins 68.1, and insolubles 15.9%.

Action and disease indications: The **plant** is bitter, acrid, refrigerant, alterant, emetic, narcotic, anti-viral and rejuvenating, used for viral infections, hydrophobia, dipsia, psychopathy and general debility.

Clinical uses: Dipsesis, general debility: Milky exudate 3 drops, with honey 10 g, two times a day, is useful.

Recommended readings:

Chunekar, K.C. (2004), Bhava Prakash Nighantu, Chaukhambha Bharti Academy, Varanasi, PP. 446.

Khare, C.P. (2007), Indian Medicinal Plants, Springer (India) P.L. New Delhi, PP. 584.

Kirtikar, K.R. & Basu, B.D. (1998), Indian Medicinal Plants, L.M Basu, Allahabad, Vol. 3, PP. 1622.

Nair, R.Vasudevan, (2007), Indian Medicinal Plants, Orient Longman P.L. Chennai, Vol. 5, PP. 73.

Prajapati, N.D., Purohit, S.S., Sharma, A.K. & Tarun Kumar (2003), A Hand Book of Medicinal Plants, Agrobios India, Jodhpur, PP. 461.

423. *Saussurea costus* (Falc.) Lipsch.

Family: Compositae; Asteraceae.

Synonym: *S. lappa.*

Ayurvedic Groups: Charak: *Sukrashodhana, Lekhaniya, Aasthaapanopaga,* **Sushruta:** *Elladi gana.*

Other similar plants: *S. hypoleuca,* syn. *auriculata.*

Name: English: Cuth, Costus, **Sanskrit:** *Kushtha, Vaapya, Paaribhavya,* **Hindi:** *Kustha, Kutha,* **Local:** *Kutha, Sugandha, Kutha.*

Botanical characteristics: Habit: A tall, robust, perennial herb, height up to 2 m. **Root:** Stout, up to 60 cm long, having a penetrating characteristic odour. It is brown with longitudinal ridges and a rough reticulated surfaces. It is brittle, the fractured surface having a resinous appearance and dirty white colour. **Stem:** Erect, fibrous, 1.2-2 m high, simple. **Leaf:** Membranous, Simple, alternate, scaberulous above, glabrous beneath, irregularly toothed, basal ones very large, 0.6-1.2 m long, triangular, with a long lobately winged stalk, end lobe often 30 cm diam. Stem leaves smaller stalked or stalk less, with two- half-stem clasping lobes at the base. **Flower:** Heads stalk less, hard, rounded, 2.5-3.8 cm diam., dark bluish-purple or almost black, 2-5, in axillary and terminal heads; bracts many, ovate-lanceolate, long pointed, rigid, bent back, hairless. **Fruit:** Achens, 3-8 mm long, compressed, curved, tip narrowed, with 1 rib on each face, top contracted, cupped.

Flowering and fruiting period: June-July and August-September.

Habitat: Kashmir, Himachal Pradesh and Garhwal, at 2500-3000 m, also cultivated.

Parts used: Root. **Dosage:** 0.25-1g.

Collection period: September-October.

Ayurvedic properties: ***Ras:*** *tikta, katu, madhur,* ***Gun:*** *laghu, rukhsa, tikhsna,* ***Veerya:*** *ushna,* ***Vipaka:*** *katu,* ***Tridosha*** **Effect:** alleviates ***Kapha:*** *+++,* ***Vaata:*** *++.*

Chemical constituents: The **roots** contain resinoids 6%, essential oil 1.5%, alkaloids 0.05%-mainly saussurine, inulin 18%, saussurea lactone 20-25%, a fixed oil and minor constituents like tannin and sugars. Others are costunolide, dehydrocostuslactone, costic acid, palmitic and linoleic acids, beta-sitosterol and alpha-cyclocostunolide.alantolactone, beta-cyclocostunolide ans *iso*-alantolactone. The root containing saussurine, is used for asthma, oarticularly of vagotonic type and it produces a definite relaxtion of the bronchioles. The relief obtained is comparable to that of conventional bronchodilators with out side effects, like a rise of blood pressure, sweating or headache even on repeated administration. Saussurine depresses parasympathetic nervous system. The amino-acids-sesquiterpene adducts, saussureamines A, B and C show anti-ulcer effect. The aqueous extract of the root exhibits anti-anginal activity. The **essential oil** inhibits peristaltic movement of the gut. It is absorbed from the gastro-intestinal tract and partly excreted by lungs or producing an expectorant action and partly by the kidneys producing diuretic effect.

Action and disease indications: The **roots** are thermogenic, aromatic, deodorant, anti-spasmodic, expectorant, carminative, anti-septic, aphrodisiac, anodyne, digestive, stomachic, diaphoretic, stimulant, alterant, depurative, galactagogue, diuretic, disinfectant, febrifuge, rejuvenating and tonic, used for dyspepsia, asthma, cough, chronic rheumatism, skin diseases, wounds, ulcers, prurigo of scalp, bronchitis, headache, odontalgia, flatulence, colic, erysipelas, leucoderma, pruritus, ringworm, diarrhea, dysentery, fever, seminal weakness, hiccough, hysteria, strangury, dysmenorrhea, amenorrhea, cardiac diseases, gout and general debility.

Clinical uses: Diarrhea: Cold infusion of root powder of described plant, 500 mg, *Elettaria cardamomum* 1 g, two times a day, is beneficial. **Bronchitis:** Root powder of described plant, 1 g, with honey 10 g, two times a day, is useful. **Asthma:** Root powder of described plant, 1 g, with honey 10 g, clarified butter 5 g, two times a day, is beneficial. **Hiccough:** Snuff or fumigation of root powder of described plant and gum of *Shorea robusta* 2 g, two times a day, is beneficial. **Epilepsy:** Root powder of described plant 1 g, *Acorus calamus* 1 g, with honey 10 g, two times a day, is useful. **Dysmenorrhea:** Root powder of described plant, 1.5 g, *Cinamomum camphora* 250 mg, with honey 10 g, two times a day, is beneficial. Use this medication 7 days before menstrual period. **Alopecia:** Local application of paste of root of described plant, with Vinegar, is beneficial. **Leucoderma:** Local application of paste of root of described plant, seeds of *Abrus precatorious,* roots of *Plumbego zeylanica, Acorus calamus,* with lemon juice is beneficial.

Formulations: *Shaileyaadi churna, Kalyaan ghrita, Naaraayan churna, Jaatyaadi taila, Balaa taila, Mahaa naaraayan taila, Khsaara taila, Phala ghrita, Dashamoolarista, Saaras-wataarista, Saarivaadhyasava, Rodhraasava, Kumaaryaasava, Yogaraja guggulu, Dashaanga lepa, Chadrodayaa varti, Chyavanpraasha, Kushthaadi churna.*

Recommended readings:

Bhutya, R.K. (2007), Vanaspati Aushadha Vigyana, Scientific Publishers (India), Jodhpur, PP. 73.

Chunekar, K.C. (2004), Bhava Prakash Nighantu, Chaukhambha Bharti Academy, Varanasi, PP. 91.

Dhiman, A.K. (2006), Ayurvedic Drug Plants, Daya Publishing House, Delhi, PP. 223.

Khare, C.P. (2007), Indian Medicinal Plants, Springer (India) P.L. New Delhi, PP. 586.

Kirtikar, K.R. & Basu, B.D. (1998), Indian Medicinal Plants, L.M Basu, Allahabad, Vol. 2, PP. 1420.

Misra, B.L. (2005), Dravya Guna Hastamalaka, Publication scheme, Jaipur, PP. 295.

Nair, R.Vasudevan, (2007), Indian Medicinal Plants, Orient Longman P.L. Chennai, Vol. 5, PP. 80.

Namjoshi, A.N. (2001), The Ayurvedic Pharmacopoeia of India, Government of India, Department of Indian Systems of Medicine & Homoeopathy, New Delhi, Part-1, Volume- 2, PP. 76.

Pareek, G.N. (2005), Sudhanidhi, Vanoshadhi Ratnakar, Dhanvantari Karyalaya, Aligarh, Vol. 3, PP. 107.

Prajapati, N.D., Purohit, S.S., Sharma, A.K. & Tarun Kumar (2003), A Hand Book of Medicinal Plants, Agrobios India, Jodhpur, PP. 462.

Sharma, P.C., Yelne, MB. & Denis, T.J. (2000), Database on medicinal plants used in ayurveda, Central Council for research in Ayurveda and siddha, Vol. 7, PP. 244.

Sharma, P.V. (1981), Dravya gun vigyana, Chaukhambha Bharti Academy, Varanasi, Vol. 1, PP. 572.

Singh, R.S. (2002), Vanoshadhi Nirdeshika, Uttar Pradesh Hindi Sansthan, Lucknow, PP. 115.

Swami, K.N. (1985), Gavon Main Aushadh Ratna, Kalera Krishana Gopal, Kalera (Raj.), Vol. 2, PP. 202.

424. *Schrebera swientenioides* Roxb.

Family: Oleaceae.

Name: English: Weaver's Beam Tree, **Sanskrit:** *Mokhsa, Mokhsaka, Golidha, Khsaarshrestha, Khsaarvrikhsa,* **Hindi:** *Muskaka,* **Local:** *Mokhaa, Eksira.*

Botanical characteristics: Habit: A moderate sized deciduous tree, height up to 20 m. **Stem:** With thick grey bark, branches grey. **Leaf:** Imparipinnate, leaflets opposite, 3-4 pairs, ovate, entire, unequal-sided, blade 7.5-12.5 cm; petioles 6-13 mm, thickened at the insertion of leaflets. **Flower:** Yellowish-brown or whitish, fragrant at night, in terminal trichotomous, corymbose, compound cymes. **Fruit:** Capsules, 5 by 7.5 cm long, pendulous, pear-shaped, 2-valved, 8-seeded. **Seed:** Angular, ending in long wings.

Flowering and fruiting period: March-April, June-July.

Habitat: Throughout India, in deciduous forests, up to an altitude of 1200 m, tropical and sub-tropical Himalayas from Kumaun to eastward, also in West Bengal, Bihar and Rajasthan.

Parts used: Root, Alkali.

Dosage: Root 3-6 g, Alkali 250-500 mg.

Collection period: May-June

Ayurvedic properties: ***Ras:*** *katu, tikta,* ***Gun:*** *laghu, rukhsa,* ***Veerya:*** *ushna,* ***Vipaka:*** *katu,* ***Tridosha*** **Effect:** alleviates ***Kapha:*** **++,** ***Vaata:*** +.

Chemical constituents: The **roots** contain charcoal, acetic acid, formic acidand methyl alcohol. The **fruit** contains betulinic and oleanolic acids.

Action and disease indications: The **leaves, flowers** and **roots** are thermogenic, stomachic, appetizer, digestive, depurative, constipating, urinary astringent and anthelmintic, used for dyspepsia, colic, flatulence, skin diseases, diarrhea, urethrorrhea, anaemia, spleenomegaly, helminthiasis, boils, burns, rectal disorders and obesity.

Clinical uses: Skin diseases: Medicated clarified butter, made by root powder of described plant, 10 g with milk, two times a day, is beneficial. **Sprue:** Alkali of described plant, 500 mg, with clarified butter 10 g, two times a day, is beneficial.

Recommended readings:

Bhutya, R.K. (2007), Vanaspati Aushadha Vigyana, Scientific Publishers (India), Jodhpur, PP. 182.

Chunekar, K.C. (2004), Bhava Prakash Nighantu, Chaukhambha Bharti Academy, Varanasi, PP. 544.

Khare, C.P. (2007), Indian Medicinal Plants, Springer (India) P.L. New Delhi, PP. 589.

Kirtikar, K.R. & Basu, B.D. (1998), Indian Medicinal Plants, L.M Basu, Allahabad, Vol. 2, PP. 1531.

Nair, R.Vasudevan, (2007), Indian Medicinal Plants, Orient Longman P.L. Chennai, Vol. 5, PP. 88.

Prajapati, N.D., Purohit, S.S., Sharma, A.K. & Tarun Kumar (2003), A Hand Book of Medicinal Plants, Agrobios India, Jodhpur, PP. 465.

425. ***Scindapsus officinalis*** Schott.

Family: Araceae.

Name: Sanskrit: *Kapivalli, Kolavalli, Shreyasi, Vasir, Gajakrishnaa, Hastipippali,* **Hindi:** *Gajapipal,* **Local:** *Gajapipal.*

Botanical characteristics: Habit: A large epiphytic climber. **Stem:** As thick as little finger, with adventitious aerial roots growing on trees and rocks, branches wrinkled when dry. **Leaf:** Dark green, very large, 12.5-25 by 6.3-15 cm, ovate, elliptic-ovate, or nearly orbicular, caudate - acuminate,base rounded or slightly cordate, leathery, primary nerves distinct; petioles 7.5-15 cm long, penducles solitary, terminal, much shorter than the petioles. **Flower:** Densely arranged in the spadix which is cylindric, spathe 10-15 cm long, oblong, sub-cylindrical, slender-beaked, green outside and yellow with in. **Fruit:** Berries, confluent, few only ripening fleshy, fruiting spadix sometimes a span long. **Seed:** Ovate-cordate.

Flowering and fruiting period: March-April and may-June or almost throughout year.

Habitat: Tropical Himalayas, at 330-1000 m, from Sikkim eastwards, Bengal and Andaman islands.

Parts used: Dried pieces of mature female spadix.

Dosage: 2-5 g. **Collection period:** April-May.

Ayurvedic properties: ***Ras:*** *katu,* ***Gun:*** *laghu, tikhsna,* ***Veerya:*** *ushna,* ***Vipaka:*** *katu,* ***Tridosha*** **Effect:** alleviates ***Vaata:*** ***++,*** ***Kapha:*** ***++.***

Chemical constituents: The **fruits** contain two glycosidic substances-scindapsin A and B, which on hydrolysis yield the aglucons, scindapsin A and B. Free sugars, rhmnose, fructose, glucose and xylose together with some di and tri-saccharides have been identified in the plant.

Action and disease indications: The **fruits** are stimulant, thermogenic, aphrodisiac, carminative, hypoglycaemic, diaphoretic, anthelmintic, anti-diarrhoeal, expectorant, used for asthma, hyperglycemia, rheumatism, cough, bronchitis, diarrhea, helminthiasis and pharyngopathy.

Clinical uses: Rheumatism, osteo-arthritis: Local application of paste of fruit of described plant, is beneficial. **Fever:** Fruit powder of described plant 5 g, with warm water, two times a day, is useful. **For expectoration:** Cold infusion of fruits of described plant 6 g, with honey 10 g, two times a day, is useful.

Formulations: *Vrahat yogaraaja guggulu, Astaadashaanga kwaatha, Gulmakaalaanala rasa.*

Recommended readings:

Bhutya, R.K. (2007), Vanaspati Aushadha Vigyana, Scientific Publishers (India), Jodhpur, PP. 82.

Chunekar, K.C. (2004), Bhava Prakash Nighantu, Chaukhambha Bharti Academy, Varanasi, PP. 21.

Dhiman, A.K. (2006), Ayurvedic Drug Plants, Daya Publishing House, Delhi, PP. 133.

Khare, C.P. (2007), Indian Medicinal Plants, Springer (India) P.L. New Delhi, PP. 590.

Kirtikar, K.R. & Basu, B.D. (1998), Indian Medicinal Plants, L.M Basu, Allahabad, Vol. 4, PP. 2621.

Nair, R.Vasudevan, (2007), Indian Medicinal Plants, Orient Longman P.L. Chennai, Vol. 5, PP. 92.

Namjoshi, A.N. (2001), The Ayurvedic Pharmacopoeia of India, Government of India, Department of Indian Systems of Medicine & Homoeopathy, New Delhi, Part-1, Volume- 1, PP. 40.

Prajapati, N.D., Purohit, S.S., Sharma, A.K. & Tarun Kumar (2003), A Hand Book of Medicinal Plants, Agrobios India, Jodhpur, PP. 465.

Sharma, P.C., Yelne, MB. & Denis, T.J. (2000), Database on medicinal plants used in ayurveda, Central Council for research in Ayurveda and siddha, Vol. 4, PP. 182.

Singh, R.S. (2002), Vanoshadhi Nirdeshika, Uttar Pradesh Hindi Sansthan, Lucknow, PP. 127.

426. ***Scirpus grossus*** Linn. f.

Family: Cyperacae.

Synonym: *S.kysoor, Schoenoplectus grosus.*

Other similar plants: *S.tuberosus- Raj kaseruka* (bigger var.), *S.articulatus.*

Name: English: Water chestnut, **Sanskrit:** *Chichor,* **Hindi:** *Kasheruka,* **Local:** *Kashoriaa, Chichodaa, Kasheru.*

Botanical characteristics: Habit: A perennial stoloniferous sedge or herb, height 1-3 m. **Root:** Tuber hard, globose, 1.2-2 cm in diam., 1.6-2.4 cm in length, clothed with matted fibers. **Stem:** Erect, stout, triquetrous, 1.2.8 m high, as thick as little finger, spongy, with concave sides and smooth angles. **Leaf:** Several, radical, linear, finely acuminate, 60-90 cm by 13 mm, much keeled, coriaceous with smooth or scaberulous margins; sheath long, open. **Flower:** Inflorescence, terminal, compound corymbs; spikelets sub-globosely ovoid, brown or reddish-brown. **Fruit:** Nuts, obovoid, trigonous, smooth, yellow.

Flowering and fruiting period: September-October and November-December.

Habitat: More or loss throughout India, up to an altitude of 700 m, especially in swamps, marshy areas, in river beds, banks of streams, lakes and ditches.

Parts used: Rhizome. **Dosage:** 5-10g.

Collection period: February-March.

Ayurvedic properties: ***Ras:*** *madhur, kashaaya,* ***Gun:*** *rukhsa, guru,* ***Veerya:*** *sheeta,* ***Vipaka:*** *madhur,* ***Tridosha*** **Effect:** alleviates ***Pitta:*** +++, aggrevates ***Vaata:*** +, ***Kapha:*** +.

Chemical constituents: The **tubers** contain progesterone, sugars, tannins, starch and saponins, carbohydrate, amino acids and fatty acids-caprylic, capric, lauric, myristic, pentadecanoic, heptadecanoic, palmitic, stearic, oleic, linoleic, arachidic, gadoleic acids.

Action and disease indications: The **tubers** are cooling, astringent, laxative, alexiteric, diuretic, ophthalmic, galactagogue, hypotensive, anti-viral, anti-spasmodic, aphrodisiac and tonic, used for burning sensation, anorexia, biliousness, vomiting, diarrhea, strangury, eye diseases, seminal weakness and miscarriage.

Clinical uses: Habitual abortion, hypogalactia, burning sensation, general debility, spermacresia: Rhizome of described plant 10 g, with milk, two times a day, is beneficial.

Formulations: *Vrihat naarikela khanda, Chandanaadi taila.*

Recommended readings:

Bhutya, R.K. (2007), Vanaspati Aushadha Vigyana, Scientific Publishers (India), Jodhpur, PP. 56.

Chunekar, K.C. (2004), Bhava Prakash Nighantu, Chaukhambha Bharti Academy, Varanasi, PP. 701.

Khare, C.P. (2007), Indian Medicinal Plants, Springer (India) P.L. New Delhi, PP. 591.

Kirtikar, K.R. & Basu, B.D. (1998), Indian Medicinal Plants, L.M Basu, Allahabad, Vol. 4, PP. 2644.

Misra, B.L. (2005), Dravya Guna Hastamalaka, Publication scheme, Jaipur, PP. 432.

Namjoshi, A.N. (2001), The Ayurvedic Pharmacopoeia of India, Government of India, Department of Indian Systems of Medicine & Homoeopathy, New Delhi, Part-1, Volume- 2, PP. 68.

Sharma, P.C., Yelne, MB. & Denis, T.J. (2000), Database on medicinal plants used in ayurveda, Central Council for research in Ayurveda and siddha, Vol. 6, PP. 80.

Sharma, P.V. (1981), Dravya gun vigyana, Chaukhambha Bharti Academy, Varanasi, Vol. 1, PP. 586.

Singh, R.S. (2002), Vanoshadhi Nirdeshika, Uttar Pradesh Hindi Sansthan, Lucknow, PP. 87.

427. *Semecarpus anacardium* Linn. f.

Family: Anacardiaceae.

Ayurvedic Groups: Charak: *Kushthaghna, Deepanita, Mutrasangrahaniya,* **Sushruta:** *Nyagrodhadi, Mustaadi gana.*

Other similar plants: *S.kurzi*- bigger var.

Name: English: Marking Nut, **Sanskrit:** *Bhallaataka, Aruska, Aruskara, Agnika, Agnimukhi, Bhalli, Veeravrikhsa, Shofakrita,* **Hindi:** *Bhallaataka,* **Local:** *Bhilaavaa.*

Botanical characteristics: Habit: A medium to large sized, dioecious, deciduous tree, height 15-25 m. **Stem:** With rough, grey bark 2.54 cm thick, exfoliating in small irregular flakes, a blackish juice, exudates from bark on cut, which is caustic, inflammatory and burning. **Leaf:** Simple, alternate, obovate-oblong, rounded at apex, coriaceous, glabrous above and more or less pubescent beneath and cartilaginous margins, base rounded, cordate or cuneate, main nerves 15-25 pairs, making a large angle with the costa, sometimes nearly horizontal, prominent on both surfaces; petioles 1.2-3.8 cm long. **Flower:** Greenish-white, 8.3-12.5 mm in diam., sub-sessile, fascicled in pubescent panicles, the female panicles shorter than the male; pedicles short; bracts lanceolate, pilose. **Fruit:** Drupes, 2.5 by 2 cm, shape more or less like Mango, obliquily ovoid or oblong, smooth and shining, black when ripe, a acrid, burning, inflammatory and caustic juice or oil is present in fruit, seated on a fleshy receptacle or hypocarp about 2 cm long, smooth and yellow when ripe, edible. **Seed:** Ovate, shape like Almond, one in a fruit.

Flowering and fruiting period: May-June and November-February.

Habitat: Throughout India, in semi-evergreen and moist deciduous forests, sub-Himalayan tract from Bias eastwards, up to an altitude of 1000 m, also in Punjab, Assam, Khassi Hills, Madhya Pradesh and Peninsular India.

Parts used: Fruit, oil.

Dosage: Detoxified fruit 1-2 g, in milk confection, oil 10-20 drops.

Collection period: May-June.

Ayurvedic properties: ***Ras:*** *kashaaya, madhur,* ***Gun:*** *laghu, snigdha,* ***Veerya:*** *ushna,* ***Vipaka:***

madhur, ***Tridosha*** **Effect:** alleviates ***Kapha: +++, Vaata: +++,*** aggrevates ***Pitta: ++.***

Chemical constituents: The **fruits** contain nicotinic acid, riboflavin, thiamine and the essential amino acids-arginine, histidine, isoleucine, leucine, lycine, methionine, pheynylalanine, threonine, triptophan and valine. The **oil** and **seed** contain bhilawanol and anacardioside. The **nut shell** also contain biflavonoids, including tetrahydrobustaflavone, tetrahydroamentoflavone and anacarduflavonone; nallaflavone; anacardic acid; aromatic amines and bhilawanol.

Action and disease indications: The **fruits** are thermogenic, emollient, digestive, carminative, anthelmintic, purgative, expectorant, liver tonic, alterant, aphrodisiac, anti-arthritic, depurative, anti-carcinomic, stimulant, febrifuge, sudorofic, urinary astringent, anti-septic, anti-inflammatory, cardio-tonic, rejuvenating and tonic, prescribed for sciatica, neuritis, cough, asthma, dyspepsia, constipation, flatulence, colic, piles, helminthiasis especially hookworm, beriberi, cancer, hepatopathy, spleenomegaly, leprosy, leucoderma, scaly skin eruptions, inflammations, cardiac-diseases, fevers, diabetes, dysmenorrhea, amenorrhea, scorphula, tumours, ulcers, seminal weakness, erectile dysfunction and general debility.

Clinical uses: Bronchial asthma: Oil of the fruit of described plant 10 drops, *Curcuma longa* 2 g, sugar candy powder 10 g, with milk, as required. **Piles, bronchitis, asthma, fever, spleen enlargement:** Mix powder or tablet of detoxified fruit of described plant, *Terminalia chebula, Sesamum orientale,* raw sugar, 3 g, with milk, two times a day, is beneficial. **For rejuvenating:** Detoxified fruit of described plant 3 g, with milk, at morning, is very beneficial. **Neuritis, sciatica, bell's palsy, paralysis:** Mix paste of detoxified fruit of described plant, leaves of *Tamarindus indica, Allium sativum, Embelia ribes,* 10 g, with milk of coconut and sugar candy powder 10 g, two times a day, is beneficial. **Acute or chronic rheumatism:** Detoxified fruit of described plant 1.5 g, *Anacardium occidantale* 6 g, with honey 10 g, two times a day, is useful. **Chronic skin diseases, ringworm, leucoderma, arthralgia, sprain:** Local application of paste of fruit oil of described plant and butter, in ratio of 1:20, is beneficial. **Penile dysfunction:** (1) Seeds of described plant 2 g, *Buchanania lanzan* 20 g, with milk, two times a day, is beneficial. (2) Mix powder of detoxified fruit of described plant, *Sesamum orientale, Prunus amyadalus, Withania somnifera, Anacyclus pyrenthrum,* 6 g, with honey 10 g, two times a day, is useful. **Alopecia:** Local application of paste of leaves of described plant and honey is beneficial. **Leucoderma:** Local application of paste of fruit of described plant, *Picrorhiza kurroa, 'Trikatu churna', Saussurea costus, Psorlalea corylifolia, Brassica campestris,* Blue vitriol, Orpimint, is very beneficial.

Contraindication: Taken in large dose, it acts as poison, so beware of large dose. Follow these precautions. (1) Do not use in summer. (2) Avoid children, old men, women, pregnant women, hot natured person, patient of chronic stomatitis, kidney diseases, nephritis, hyperhydrosis, dipsesis, insomnia, burning sensation and hematuria. (3) Give purgation before use, if feel constipation. (4) Test of urine complete is necessary. (5) Start with very small dose for particular allergy. (6) In the period of use of this medication, use of clarified butter, milk, oil, rice, is preferable. (7) Do not use salt, chilli and meat. (8) Hot meal, sharp sun light, to sit by the fireside, is not preferable. (9) Use detoxified fruit of described plant. **Detoxification:** (1) Remove the cap, rub with powder of brick, and wash with warm water. (2) Boil in milk of coconut and milk of cow. **Symptoms:** It produces blisters on the tongue and in the throat, causes severe gastrointestinal irritation, and may cause fever, vomiting, diarrhea, hematuria, collapse and death. Its external application causes blisters and an exzematous eruption on the skin.

Fatal time: 12 to 24 hours. **Fatal dose:** 5 ml. **Treatment:** It is purely symptomatic. Use under mentioned treatment. (1) Leaves juice of *Tamarindus indica* 10-20 ml, two times a day, is beneficial. (2) Clarified butter 20 g, with milk and sugar, two times a day, is beneficial. (3) Seed powder of *Tamarindus indica* 20 g, with milk, two times a day, is beneficial. (4) *Sesamum orientale, Cocos nusifera, Buchanania lanzan,* 50-100 g, two times a day, is beneficial. (5) Local application of paste of seeds of *Sesamum orientale* with butter and milk of she goat, **or** *Sesamum orientale, Glycyrrhiza glabra* with milk, **or** Seed powder of *Terminalia belliarica* with milk, **or** Gum of *Shorea robusta* with butter, **or** Coconut oil, **or** Juice of *Raphanus sativus* and *Amaranthus spinosus,* **or** Leaves juice of *Cassia occidantalis,* is beneficial.

Formulations: *Amrit bhallaataka, Naarsingha churna, Kaankaayan vati, Chinchaa bhallaataka vati, Bhallataka rasaayana, Sanjivani vati, Bhallaataka ghrita, Bhallaatakaavaleha.*

Recommended readings:

Bhutya, R.K. (2007), Vanaspati Aushadha Vigyana, Scientific Publishers (India), Jodhpur, PP. 165.

Chunekar, K.C. (2004), Bhava Prakash Nighantu, Chaukhambha Bharti Academy, Varanasi, PP. 139.

Dhiman, A.K. (2006), Ayurvedic Drug Plants, Daya Publishing House, Delhi, PP. 79.

Khare, C.P. (2007), Indian Medicinal Plants, Springer (India) P.L. New Delhi, PP. 597.

Kirtikar, K.R. & Basu, B.D. (1998), Indian Medicinal Plants, L.M Basu, Allahabad, Vol. 1, PP. 667.

Misra, B.L. (2005), Dravya Guna Hastamalaka, Publication scheme, Jaipur, PP. 404.

Nair, R.Vasudevan, (2007), Indian Medicinal Plants, Orient Longman P.L. Chennai, Vol. 5, PP. 98.

Namjoshi, A.N. (2001), The Ayurvedic Pharmacopoeia of India, Government of India, Department of Indian Systems of Medicine & Homoeopathy, New Delhi, Part-1, Volume- 1, PP. 19.

Pareek, G.N. (2005), Sudhanidhi, Vanoshadhi Ratnakar, Dhanvantari Karyalaya, Aligarh, Vol. 6, PP. 291.

Prajapati, N.D., Purohit, S.S., Sharma, A.K. & Tarun Kumar (2003), A Hand Book of Medicinal Plants, Agrobios India, Jodhpur, PP. 470.

Sharma, P.C., Yelne, MB. & Denis, T.J. (2000), Database on medicinal plants used in ayurveda, Central Council for research in Ayurveda and siddha, Vol. 5, PP. 9.

Sharma, P.V. (1981), Dravya gun vigyana, Chaukhambha Bharti Academy, Varanasi, Vol. 1, PP. 166.

Singh, R.S. (2002), Vanoshadhi Nirdeshika, Uttar Pradesh Hindi Sansthan, Lucknow, PP. 288.

Swami, K.N. (1985), Gavon Main Aushadh Ratna, Kalera Krishana Gopal, Kalera (Raj.), Vol. 3, PP. 144.

428. *Sesamum orientale* Linn.

Family: Pedaliaceae.

Synonym: *S.indicum.*

Name: English: Sesame, Gingelly, **Sanskrit:** *Til,* **Hindi:** *Til, Tilli,* **Local:** *Tilli.*

Botanical characteristics: Habit: An erect, annual, foetid-glandular-pubescent herb, height 0.3-1.5 m. **Stem:** Branching from the base, quadrangular, pubescent. **Leaf:** Simple, large, thin, the lower ones deeply 3-lobed; lobes lanceolate, 3-15 by 1.5-6 cm, serrate, puberlous beneath, sparsely hairy, uppermost entire, linear and intermediate usually ovate and toothed. **Flower:** White or pink or purplish with yellow marks, in racemes in the leaf axils, sub-erect or drooping, 2.5-3.2 cm long, pubescent. **Fruit:** Capsules, 2.5 cm long, oblong, bluntly 4-gonous, deeply 4-grooved, compressed, erect, dehiscent from above downwards, but rarely to the base. **Seed:** Many, obovoid, compressed, pointed at one end, 3-4 by 2 mm, 1 mm thick, three varieties of seeds are known, white, black and red.

Flowering and fruiting period: September-October and November-December.

Habitat: Cultivated throughout India, in the plains and up to an altitude of 1200 m, mostly in Uttar Pradesh, Madhya Pradesh, Rajasthan, Orissa, Gujarata and Maharastra.

Parts used: Seed, Seed oil, alkali.

Dosage: Seed 10-25 g, oil 10-20 ml, alkali 0.5-1.5 g.

Collection period: December-January.

Ayurvedic properties: *Ras:* *madhur, katu, tikta, kashaaya,* ***Gun:*** *guru, snigdha,* ***Veerya:*** *ushna,* ***Vipaka:*** *madhur,* ***Tridosha* Effect:** alleviates ***Vaata:* ++++, *Kapha:* ++, *Pitta:* +.**

Chemical constituents: The **seeds** are important source of protein, also rich in thiamin, niacin, also contain riboflavin, nicotinic acid, pentothenic acid, folic acid, biotin, pyridoxine, inositol, choline, *p*-aminobenzoic acid, ascorbic acid, vitamin A, alpha and beta tocoferol. Sugars present are glucose, sucrose, galactose, planteose, raffinose. Fatty acid in the seeds are myristic, palmitic, stearic, arachidic, hexadecenoic, oleic, linoleic and lignoceric acids. Non-saponifiable fraction of the **seed oil** gave sterols, a lignans, sesamin and a nitrolactone, sesamolin. Sesamin and sesamolin are not found in any other vegetable. Sesamol, a phenolic antioxidant, is present in trace.

Action and disease indications: The **seeds** are thermogenic, emollient, laxative, aphrodisiac, galactagogue, digestive, diuretic, emmenogogue, hair-restorer, brain tonic and tonic, used for strangury, skin diseases, migraine, alopecia, piles, ulcers, burns, dysentery, dysmenorrhea, amenorrhea, ophthalmopathy and obesity. The **oil** is thermogenic, digestive, anthelmintic, constipating, emollient, used for ophthalmopathy, burning sensation of the legs, gonorrhea, otalgia, headache, obesity and emaciation, externally it is used for dryness of the skin and leucoderma.

Clinical uses: Piles: Seed powder of described plant 6 g, leaves of *Dalbergia sisso* 3 g, with butter 10 g, two times a day, is beneficial. **Bronchitis:** Decoction of seed powder of described plant, 25 g, with sugar candy powder 10 g, two times a day, is beneficial. **Dry bronchitis:** Cold infusion of fresh leaves of described plant 10 ml, with honey 10 g, two times a day, is useful. **Renal and vesical calculus:** Alkali of described plant 1 g, *Achyranthus aspera* 500 mg, *Hordium vulgare* 500 mg, with honey 20 g and clarified butter 10 g, two times a day, is beneficial. **Amenorrhea, dysmenorrhea:** Decoction of seed powder of described plant 25 g, seeds of *Anthum graveolens* 10 g, with old raw sugar 20 g, two times a day, is beneficial. Use this medication 5 days before the menstrual period. **Polyuria, enuresis, prostatitis:** (1) Seed powder of described plant 25 g, raw sugar 15 g, two times a day, is beneficial. (2) Seed powder of described plant 10 g, *Trachy spermum-ammi* 1.5 g, raw sugar 10 g, water, at night, is beneficial. (3) Mix roasted powder of seeds of described plant, *Trachy spermum-ammi,* seeds of *Papaver somniferum,* 6 g, two times a day, is beneficial. **Osteo arthritis:** Seed powder of described plant 10 g, *Zingiber officinale* 1 g, with warm water, two times a day, is beneficial. **Alopecia, dandruff:** Local application of paste of flowers of described plant, *Tribulus terrestris,* with honey and clarified butter, is beneficial. **Diarrhea with bleeding:** Seed powder of described plant 15 g, with milk of she goat, two times a day, is beneficial. **Amebiasis:** Mucilage of leaves of described plant 10 g, two times a day, is benef-icial. **Intestinal worms:** Seed oil of described plant 20 ml, with milk, at night, is beneficial. **Inflammation due to use of *Semecarpus anacardium*:** Local application of paste of seeds of described plant, with butter, is beneficial. **Somasthenia, spermacresia:** Mix powder of seeds of described plant and *Juglans regia* 5-5 parts, *Piper longum, Piper nigrum* and *Zingiber officinale,* 1-1 part, sugar candy powder 10 parts, dose 10 g, with honey 10 g, two times a day, is useful. **General debility, tuberculosis:** Mix powder of seed powder of described plant, *Withania somnifera,* seed powder of *Phaseolus mungo,* 6 g, with clarified butter 10 g, honey 20 g, two times a day, is useful. **Cracked heel:** Local application of paste of flowers of described plant, rock salt, oil of *Sesamum orientale* and urine of cow, is beneficial.

Formulations: *Tilaadi lepa, Tilaastaka, Labooba kabir, Til bhallaataka, Lupari, Til prayoga, Tilaadi gudikaa, Tilaastaka.*

Recommended readings:

Acharya, B.K. (2008), Ayurveda Jadi-buti Rahasya, Patanjali Yogapitha, Haridwar, PP. 401.

Bhutya, R.K. (2007), Vanaspati Aushadha Vigyana, Scientific Publishers (India), Jodhpur, PP. 117.

Brahmavarchas (2003), Ayurved Ka Pran Vanoshadhi Vigyan, Shanti Kunj, Haridwar, PP. 401.

Chunekar, K.C. (2004), Bhava Prakash Nighantu, Chaukhambha Bharti Academy, Varanasi, PP. 652.

Khare, C.P. (2007), Indian Medicinal Plants, Springer (India) P.L. New Delhi, PP. 599.

Kirtikar, K.R. & Basu, B.D. (1998), Indian Medicinal Plants, L.M Basu, Allahabad, Vol. 3, PP. 1858.

Misra, B.L. (2005), Dravya Guna Hastamalaka, Publication scheme, Jaipur, PP. 466.

Nair, R.Vasudevan, (2007), Indian Medicinal Plants, Orient Longman P.L. Chennai, Vol. 5, PP. 104.

Pareek, G.N. (2005), Sudhanidhi, Vanoshadhi Ratnakar, Dhanvantari Karyalaya, Aligarh, Vol. 10, PP. 258.

Prajapati, N.D., Purohit, S.S., Sharma, A.K. & Tarun Kumar (2003), A Hand Book of Medicinal Plants, Agrobios India, Jodhpur, PP. 472.

Sharma, P.C., Yelne, MB. & Denis, T.J. (2000), Database on medicinal plants used in ayurveda, Central Council for research in Ayurveda and siddha, Vol. 5, PP. 417.

Sharma, P.V. (1981), Dravya gun vigyana, Chaukhambha Bharti Academy, Varanasi, Vol. 1, PP. 120.

Singh, R.S. (2002), Vanoshadhi Nirdeshika, Uttar Pradesh Hindi Sansthan, Lucknow, PP. 179.

429. *Sesbania grandiflora* (L.) Poir.

Family: Papilionaceae; Fabaceae.

Synonym: *Agati grandiflora.*

Name: English: Agati Sesban, Swamp Pea, **Sanskrit:** *Agatsya, Vangasen, Munipushpa, Agatsi, Munidruma, Vakrapushpa,* **Hindi:** *Agatsya,* **Local:** *Agathiyaa, Hathiyaa.*

Botanical characteristics: Habit: A short lived, quick growing, slender, small tree, height 6-9 m. **Stem:** Soft wooded, 0.6 m in girth, with spreading branches. **Leaf:** 15-30 cm long, abruptly pinnate; leaflets 16-30 pairs, linear-oblong or oblong-elliptic, glabrous above, thinly pubescent beneath, deciduous. **Flower:** 6-10 cm long, showy, fleshy, white, pink or crimson, in lax, 2-4 flowered racemes 2.5 cm long. **Fruit:** Pods, 30-50 cm long, pendulous, rather flat and somewhat 4-cornered, non-torulose, septate with swollen margins. **Seed:** 15-50 per pod, pale coloured.

Flowering and fruiting period: October-November and December-January.

Habitat: Cultivated throughout India, mostly in Assam, Bengal, Punjab, Andhra Pradesh and Tamilnadu.

Parts used: Bark, leaves, flower, root.

Dosage: Powder 3-6 g, Juice 10-20 ml.

Collection period: October-November.

Ayurvedic properties: ***Ras:*** *tikta,* ***Gun:*** *laghu, rukhsa,* ***Veerya:*** *sheeta,* ***Vipaka:*** *katu,* ***Tridosha*** **Effect:** alleviates ***Pitta:*** ++, ***Kapha:*** ++, aggrevates ***Vaata:*** +.

Chemical constituents: The **bark** contain gum and tannin. A saponin present in the **leaves** on hydrolysis gave an acid sapogenin, oleanoic acid, galactose, rhamnose and glucuronic acid. Besides saponin, the **leaves** contain an aliphatic alcohol, grandiflorol. The aqueous extract of **flowers** has been found to produce haemolysis of human and sheet erythrocytes even at low concentrationdue to methyl ester of oleanolic acid, also gave nonacosan-6-one and kaempferol-3-rutinoside.

Action and disease indications: The **leaves** are cooling, aperient, tonic and diuretic, used for nasal catarrh, nyctalopia, cephalgia, mouth and throat diseases and colic. The **flowers** are cooling, anti-pyretic, used for nyctalopia, intermittent fevers. The **fruits** are laxative and alexiteric, used for flatulence, colic, anaemia and emaciation. The **bark** is cooling, tonic, anthelmintic and febrifuge, used for scabies, dyspepsia, diarrhea and gastralgia.

Clinical uses: Night blindness, amenorrhea, dysmenorrhea: Vegetable of flowers of described plant 50 g, fried with oil of *Brassica campestris* 25 ml, or medicated clarified butter, made with leaves of described plant, 10 ml, with milk, two times a day, is beneficial. **Excess and turbid micturition, gout:** Flower powder of described plant 10-15 g, fried with clarified butter 10 g, two times a day, is beneficial. **Arthritis:** Local application of paste of flowers of described plant, roots of *Datura inoxia,* is beneficial. **Cough, bronchitis of children:** Leaves juice of described plant, 2-4 drops, with honey 10 g, two times a day, is useful. **Headache, hemicrenia:** Nasal drops of leaves juice of described plant, 5-5 drops, in opposite nostril, two times a day, is beneficial. **Bronchitis:** Decoction of flowers of described plant and *Justisia adhatoda*, 5-5 g, juice of fresh tubers of *Curcuma longa,* 5 ml, powder of seeds of *Elettaria cardamomum* 250 mg, two times a day, is beneficial. **Colic:** Decoction of bark of described plant, 6 g, with rock salt 1 g, two times a day, is beneficial. **Amensia:** Seed powder of described plant, 3-3 g, with milk, two times a day, is beneficial. **Dental carries:** Fill the hole with gum of described plant is beneficial. **Abscess:** Poultice of leaves of described plant, is beneficial.

Formulations: *Prataplankeswara rasa, Ratnaagiri rasa, Pittakaasaantaka rasa, Grahanikapaata rasa* (Fifth method).

Recommended readings:

Acharya, B.K. (2008), Ayurveda Jadi-buti Rahasya, Patanjali Yogapitha, Haridwar, PP. 25.

Bhutya, R.K. (2007), Vanaspati Aushadha Vigyana, Scientific Publishers (India), Jodhpur, PP. 4.

Chunekar, K.C. (2004), Bhava Prakash Nighantu, Chaukhambha Bharti Academy, Varanasi, PP. 508.

Khare, C.P. (2007), Indian Medicinal Plants, Springer (India) P.L. New Delhi, PP. 600.

Kirtikar, K.R. & Basu, B.D. (1998), Indian Medicinal Plants, L.M Basu, Allahabad, Vol. 1, PP. 735.

Misra, B.L. (2005), Dravya Guna Hastamalaka, Publication scheme, Jaipur, PP. 267.

Nair, R.Vasudevan, (2007), Indian Medicinal Plants, Orient Longman P.L. Chennai, Vol. 5, PP. 117.

Pareek, G.N. (2005), Sudhanidhi, Vanoshadhi Ratnakar, Dhanvantari Karyalaya, Aligarh, Vol. 9, PP. 29.

Prajapati, N.D., Purohit, S.S., Sharma, A.K. & Tarun Kumar (2003), A Hand Book of Medicinal Plants, Agrobios India, Jodhpur, PP. 473.

Sharma, P.C., Yelne, MB. & Denis, T.J. (2000), Database on medicinal plants used in ayurveda, Central Council for research in Ayurveda and siddha, Vol. 3, PP. 1.

Sharma, P.V. (1981), Dravya gun vigyana, Chaukhambha Bharti Academy, Varanasi, Vol. 1, PP. 289.

Swami, K.N. (1985), Gavon Main Aushadh Ratna, Kalera Krishana Gopal, Kalera (Raj.), Vol. 2, PP. 284.

430. *Sesbania sesban* (Linn.) Merr.

Family: Papilionaceae; Fabaceae.

Synonym: *S. aegyptica.*

Variety: *S. typtica* (yellow var.), *S. picta* (purple var.), *S. bicolor, S. ciliabicolor* (dark brown).

Name: English: Common sesban, Egyption rattle pod, **Sanskrit:** *Jayanti, Jayaa, Sukhsma moola, Sukhsma patra, Jwaalaamukhi, Kesha ruhaa, Balamota, Harita,* **Hindi:** *Jayanti.* **Local:** *Dhaadoona, Jainta.*

Botanical characteristics: Habit: An annual herb, height up to 4.5 m. **Stem:** Cylindrical, branched, solid, glabrous and green. **Leaf:** Alternate, compound, unipinnate and paripinnate, oblong, entire, glabrous, 10-15 cm long, leaflets 8-20 pairs and 1.8-2.5 cm long, special smell in crushed leaves. **Flower:** Small, group of 8-10 flowers, yellow or red, purple dotted and complete. **Fruit:** Legume, 15-22 cm long, beaked, lean, bent, 20-30 seeded. **Seed:** Oblong, slightly reniform, shiny, hard and special smelled.

Flowering and fruiting period: November-December and February-March.

Habitat: Throughout India, wild and cultivated, up to an altitude of 1200 m.

Parts used: Seeds, leaves, flower and root.

Dosage: Seeds, roots 2-6 g, leaves, flowers 3-6 g.

Collection period: March-April.

Ayurvedic properties: ***Ras:*** *katu, tikta,* ***Gun:*** *laghu, rukhsa,* ***Veerya:*** *ushna,* ***Vipaka:*** *katu,* ***Tridosha*** **Effect:** alleviates ***Kapha:*** ++, ***Pitta:*** +.

Chemical constituents: The **pods** and **leaves** contain cholesterol, xampesterol and beta-sitosterol. **Flowers** contain cyanidin, delfinidin, alfa-ketoglutaric, oxoloaxetic and pyruvic acids.

Action and disease indications: Seeds and **bark** are emmenogogue and astringent, useful to cure menorrhagia, spleen enlargement and diarrhea. **Leaves** are anti-inflammatory, useful to cure dysuria. **Bark** is useful in skin diseases. **Seeds** are cardiac depressant, anti-bacterial, anti-poison, anti-ageing, anodyne, are beneficial to hairs and skin diseases.

Clinical uses: For contraception: Flower sauce prepare with *'Kanji'* added old raw sugar, 10 g, at morning, after menstrual period for 3 days, for 3 months. **Glycosuria, polyuria:** Decoction of leaves powder of the described plant 10 g, 3 times a day. **Dysuria:** Leaves powder of the described plant 2 g, 2 times a day, with water.

Leukoderma, skin diseases: Root powder of the described plant 2 g, 2 times a day, with milk.

Inflammations, pains, skin diseases: Tropical use of paste of plant is Beneficial. **Dysmenorrhea, amenorrhea:** Seed powder of the described plant 2 g, 2 times a day, 3 days before the menstrual period starts.

Formulations: *Jayaa vati, Ratnagiri rasa, Ratnaprabhaa vatika, Rasbhadra vati,* useful for purification of various metals for preparing medicines.

Recommended readings:

Bhutya, R.K. (2007), Vanaspati Aushadha Vigyana, Scientific Publishers (India), Jodhpur, PP. 103.

Khare, C.P. (2007), Indian Medicinal Plants, Springer (India) P.L. New Delhi, PP. 601.

Misra, B.L. (2005), Dravya Guna Hastamalaka, Publication scheme, Jaipur, PP. 275.

Namjoshi, A.N. (2001), The Ayurvedic Pharmacopoeia of India, Government of India, Department of Indian Systems of Medicine & Homoeopathy, New Delhi, Part-1, Volume- 1, PP. 60.

Pareek, G.N. (2005), Sudhanidhi, Vanoshadhi Ratnakar, Dhanvantari Karyalaya, Aligarh, Vol. 10, PP. 167.

Sharma, P.C., Yelne, MB. & Denis, T.J. (2000), Database on medicinal plants used in ayurveda, Central Council for research in Ayurveda and siddha, Vol. 7, PP. 158.

Sharma, P.V. (1981), Dravya gun vigyana, Chaukhambha Bharti Academy, Varanasi, Vol. 1, PP. 154.

431. *Shorea robusta* Gaertn. f.

Family: Dipterocarpaceae.

Ayurvedic Groups: Charak: *Vedanaasthaapaka, Kashaayaskandha, Aasava yoni,* **Sushruta:** *Saalsaaraadi, Rodhraadi gana.*

Name: English: Sal Tree, **Sanskrit:** *Shaal, Sarja, Kaarsya, Aswakarnaka, Sasyasambhara,* **Hindi:** *Shaal,* **Local:** *Shaal.*

Botanical characteristics: Habit: A large deciduous tree, but seldom quite leafless, height 18-30 m. **Stem:** Girth 2-3 m, bark grayish, reddish-brown or dark brown, smooth or with a few longitudinal cracks. **Leaf:** Simple, large, 10-30 by 5-18 cm, ovate-oblong, acuminate, tough, thinly, coriaceous, glabrous, shining when mature, base cordate or rounded, lateral nerves 12-15 pairs; petioles 1.2-2 cm long, branches grey-tomentos; stipules pubescent, falcate. **Flower:** Pale-yellow or cream coloured, in lax axillary or terminal panicles, velvety pubescent. **Fruit:** 1-1.5 cm long, ovoid with 5 equal wings, acute, indehiscent, pubescent, with wing like persistent sepals, 5-7 cm long, wing linear, 10 nerved, obtuse. **Seed:** One, ovoid, with fleshy unequal cotyledons. On tapping the trees exudes a white liquid, an oleo-resin which turns brown on drying. Heart wood pale-brown to dark reddish-brown.

Flowering and fruiting period: January-March and April-June.

Habitat: North, east and central India, up to an altitude of 1700 m.

Parts used: Bark, resin.

Dosage: Bark 10-20 g, resin 1-3 g.

Collection period: November-December.

Ayurvedic properties: ***Ras:*** *kashaaya,* ***Gun:*** *laghu, rukhsa,* ***Veerya:*** *sheeta* ***Vipaka:*** *katu,* ***Tridosha*** **Effect:** alleviates ***Kapha:*** ++, ***Pitta:*** +.

Chemical constituents: The **bark** contains 7-12% tannin and oleanolic acid. The **resin** contains several triterpenoids. Hydroxy-hopanone, dammarenediol-2 and dammarenolic acid are reported toexhibit anti-viral activity against *Herpes simplex.* The **resin** on dry distillation yields an essential oil, known as Chuoo Oil. It consists of 96% neutral and 3% and 1.9%phenolic portion of the oil is reported to have a depressing effect on the central nervous system, the phenolic portion is less effective. The young **leaves** contain 20, **twigs** and **leaves** 22, and powder dust 12% tannin.

Action and disease indications: The **leaves** and **bark** are refrigerant, anthelmintic, anodyne, alexiteric, constipating, urinary astringent, union promoter, depurative and tonic, used for diarrhea, dysentery, ulcers, wounds, otalgia, gonorrhea, leucorrhea, pruritis, cough, hyperhydrosis, piles and anemia. The **resin** is cooling, anodyne, deodorant, constipating, detergent, vulnerary, anti-bacterial, carminative, stomachic, aphrodisiac, expectorant, ophthalmic and tonic, prescribed for neuralgia, hyperhidrosis, wounds, ulcers, birns, pruritis, fractures, fever, diarrhea, dysentery, piles, gonorrhea, menorrhagia, spleenomegaly, obesity, headache, odontalgia, burning of eyes and ophthalmodynia.

Clinical uses: Inflammation, pains: Local application of paste of bark and gum of described plant is beneficial. **Wounds, ulcers, boils, burn, chilblains, skin diseases:** Ointment of gum of described plant, in Cream or Vaseline, is beneficial. **Diarrhea, diarrhea with bleeding, bleeding piles:** Bark of described plant 6 g, with water, two times a day, is beneficial. **Burn:** Ointment of gum of described plant, wax and oil of *Linum usitatissimum,* in ratio of 1:2:10, and washed with water by 100 times, is very beneficial.

Formulations: *Saalasaaraadi kwaatha, Sarjarasaadi malham, Atsyaadi lepa, Mamaayikaa, Chandanaadi lepa, Panchagun taila.*

Recommended readings:

Bhutya, R.K. (2007), Vanaspati Aushadha Vigyana, Scientific Publishers (India), Jodhpur, PP. 213.

Brahmavarchas (2003), Ayurved Ka Pran Vanoshadhi Vigyan, Shanti Kunj, Haridwar, PP. 403.

Chunekar, K.C. (2004), Bhava Prakash Nighantu, Chaukhambha Bharti Academy, Varanasi, PP. 520.

Dhiman, A.K. (2006), Ayurvedic Drug Plants, Daya Publishing House, Delhi, PP. 324.

Khare, C.P. (2007), Indian Medicinal Plants, Springer (India) P.L. New Delhi, PP. 602.

Kirtikar, K.R. & Basu, B.D. (1998), Indian Medicinal Plants, L.M Basu, Allahabad, Vol. 1, PP. 288.

Misra, B.L. (2005), Dravya Guna Hastamalaka, Publication scheme, Jaipur, PP. 456.

Nair, R.Vasudevan, (2007), Indian Medicinal Plants, Orient Longman P.L. Chennai, Vol. 5, PP. 124.

Prajapati, N.D., Purohit, S.S., Sharma, A.K. & Tarun Kumar (2003), A Hand Book of Medicinal Plants, Agrobios India, Jodhpur, PP. 474.

Sharma, P.C., Yelne, MB. & Denis, T.J. (2000), Database on medicinal plants used in ayurveda, Central Council for research in Ayurveda and siddha, Vol. 7, PP. 423.

Sharma, P.V. (1981), Dravya gun vigyana, Chaukhambha Bharti Academy, Varanasi, Vol. 1, PP. 671.

Singh, R.S. (2002), Vanoshadhi Nirdeshika, Uttar Pradesh Hindi Sansthan, Lucknow, PP. 326.

432. *Sida cordifolia* Linn.

Family: Malvaceae.

Name: English: Country mellow, **Sanskrit:** *Balaa, Vatyalikaa, Kharyastika, Vaatyaa, Samanganaa, Balini, Bhadrabalaa, Bhadraudani, Balaadhya, Audanikaa, Kanakaa,* **Hindi:** *Balaa,* **Local:** *Kharenti, Beejband, Bariyaar.*

Ayurvedic groups: Charak: *Balya, brahaniya, prajasthan, madhur skandha.* **Sushruta**: *Vata sansamana.*

Botanical characteristics: Habit: Herb, 60-150 cm high, branched and hairy, annual or perennial, grayish-green, woody. **Stem:** Herbaceous, aerial, erect, cylindrical, branched solid, green, puberlous. **Leaf:** Simple, very downy, cauline and ramal, alternate, stipulate, orbicular, ovate, ovate-oblong or cordate, serrete, acute, pubescent, unicostate reticulate, length 2.5- 6 cm, width 2.5-5cm, hairy, petioles 1.2-3.8 cm long. **Flower:** Diameter 2.5 cm, yellow or white, bracteate, pedicilate, complete, actinomorphic, hermaphrodite, pentamerous, hypogynous and cyclic. **Fruit:** Schizocarpic, depressed, globose, 6-8 mm diameter, shape like green gram. **Seed:** Dark brown or black, smooth, flattened, reniform, called *Beej band.*

Flowering and fruiting period: August-October and November-January.

Habitat: Throughout the tropical and subtropical regions of India, in moist places, up to 1800m in Himachal Pradesh.

Parts used: Root and seeds.

Dosage: Roots and seeds 3-6 g, juice or decoction of whole plant 20 ml.

Collection period: February-March.

Ayurvedic properties: Ayurvedic properties: ***Ras:*** *madhur,* ***Gun:*** *laghu, snigdha,picchil,* ***Veerya:*** *sheet,* ***Vipaka:*** *madhur,* ***Tridosha*** **Effect:** alleviates ***Vaata:*** ++++, ***Pitta:*** ++.

Chemical constituents: Plant contains Ephedrine and pseudo-ephedrine are the major alkaloids in the aerial parts. Total alkaloid is 0.085%. The **seeds** contain fatty oil (3.23%), steroids, proteins, ephedrine, pseudoephedrine, linoleic acid, malvalic acid, aterculic acid, coronaric acid, phytosterols, resin, resin acids, mucin and pottacium nitrate. The **root** contains alkaloids-ephedrine, pseudoephedrin, beta phenethylamine, carboxilated triptamines and hypaphorine, quinazoline alkaloids- vasicinon, vasicinin, vasicimol, choline and betaine.

Action and disease indications: The **plant** is vigorating, spermatopoietic, used for cure spermatorrhea, fever, fits, leucorrhoea, micturition, gonorrhea, colic, nervous disorders, general debility and heart irregularity. **Seeds** are nervine tonic, aphrodisiac, used for sexual debility, tonic, bleeding diathesis, spermatorrhea, leucorrhoea, paralysis, facial paralysis, increases semen quantity and promotes conception. The **roots** useful to cure rheumatism, neurological disorders, hemiplegia, facial paralysis, sciatica, polyuria, dysuria, cystitis, strangury, hematuria, leucorrhea, urinary tract infection, fevers and general debility. The **leaves** are demulcent and febrifuge, useful to cure dysentery, bloody flux, opthalmia and rheumatism.

Clinical uses: For anti ageing, tuberculosis, leucorrhea, metrorrhagia, polyuria, spermaturia: Powder of root of the plant 3 g, 2 times a day, with milk. **Bleeding piles, bleeding diathesis:** Medicated milk, made by root powder of described plant and *Uraria picta* 10 g, 2 times a day, is very useful. **Hemiplegia, facial paralysis, frozen shoulder, sciatica:** Root powder 5 g, roasted gum of *Ferula foetida* 125 mg, Rock salt 250 mg, lukewarm water, 2-3 times a day. **Spermaturia:** Juice or decoction of whole plant 20 ml, 2 times a day, or seed powder of *Sida cordifolia, Mucana pruriens* and *Blepheris edelis*, 5 g, 2 times a day, with milk. It shows remarkable effect. **Hoarseness:** Root powder 3g, 3 times a day, with honey 10 g. **Erysipelas:** Rubbing of paste of leaves of plant, is beneficial. **Inguinal and umblical hernia:** Decoction of root powder 20 ml, Caster oil 10 ml, 2 times a day. **General debility, sexual debility, hypotension and for spermatogenesis:** Mixed powder of seeds of plant, *Asparagus recemosus, Phoenix sylvestris, Withania somnifera* and *Pueraria tuberosa* 10g, with sugar candy and milk, 2 times a day. **Intermittent fever, pyrexia with rigor:** Root powder of plant 4 g, *Zingiber officinale* 1 g, 2 times a day, with tea of leaves of *Ocimum sanctum* 2 g, is beneficial. **Epilepsy:** Stem bark of plant, root of *Aristilochia indica, Cyperus scarissus, Selaginella bryopteris* and *Phylanthus fraternus,* mix powder of all plants and make pills of 500 mg, with water. 3 pills, 3 times a day, for 15 days. **Headache:** Tropical use of the paste of Mix powder of the plant, *Santalum album, Vativeria zizanoiodes, Glycyrrhiza glabra, Cynodon dactylon* made with water. **Pyrexia with diarrhea:** Decoction of rough root powder of described plant, *Aegle marmelos, Coriandrum sativum, Cyperus scarissus, Fumaria indica,* 10-20 g, in 200 ml water, remaining 100 ml, with honey 10 g, 3 times a day. **Bronchitis:** Decoction of half grounded root powder of plant and *Solunum surattense* 6 g, in 100 ml water, remaining 50 ml, with honey 10 g, 3-4 times a day. **Hiccough:** Decoction of root powder of *Sida cordifolia,* root powder of *Ricinus cumonis,*root powder of *premna corymbosa, Clerodendrum serretum,* 10 g, 3 times a day. **General debility and for spermatogenesis:** Mix powder of seeds of plant, root of *Abutilon indicum,* seeds of *Mucana pruriens,* roots of *Withania somnifera Asparagus recemosus, Glycyrrhiza glabra, Pueraria tuberosa,* 6-10 g, added *'Ras sindoor'* or *'Makardhwaja'* 100 mg, with milk, 2 times a day. **Polyuria, Metrorrhagia, leukorrhea:** Mix powder of root of the plant, *Dactylorhiza hatagirea, Eulophia dabia, Asparagus recemosus, Mucana oruriens, Elettaria cardamomum,* gum of *Bambusa orundinacea, Rosa centifolia, Smilax china,* add sugar in equal quantity. Dose 5-10 g, 2 times a day, with milk.

Formulations: *Balaa taila, Balaarista, Ucchataadi churna, Mahaa raasnaadi kwaatha, Chandanbalaalaakshaadi taila, Manmathaabhra rasa, Chyavanpraasa, Manikya rasa, Mahaa vaatgajaankush rasa, Agatshya haritaki, Brahmarasaayan, Kumaryaasava, Sarivadhyaasava.*

Recommended readings:

Acharya, B.K. (2008), Ayurveda Jadi-buti Rahasya, Patanjali Yogapitha, Haridwar, PP. 128.

Bhutya, R.K. (2007), Vanaspati Aushadha Vigyana, Scientific Publishers (India), Jodhpur, PP. 159.

Brahmavarchas (2003), Ayurved Ka Pran Vanoshadhi Vigyan, Shanti Kunj, Haridwar, PP. 405.

Chunekar, K.C. (2004), Bhava Prakash Nighantu, Chaukhambha Bharti Academy, Varanasi, PP. 367.

Dhiman, A.K. (2006), Ayurvedic Drug Plants, Daya Publishing House, Delhi, PP. 270.

Khare, C.P. (2007), Indian Medicinal Plants, Springer (India) P.L. New Delhi, PP. 603.

Kirtikar, K.R. & Basu, B.D. (1998), Indian Medicinal Plants, L.M Basu, Allahabad, Vol. 1, PP. 312.

Misra, B.L. (2005), Dravya Guna Hastamalaka, Publication scheme, Jaipur, PP. 306.

Nair, R.Vasudevan, (2007), Indian Medicinal Plants, Orient Longman P.L. Chennai, Vol. 5, PP. 129.

Pareek, G.N. (2005), Sudhanidhi, Vanoshadhi Ratnakar, Dhanvantari Karyalaya, Aligarh, Vol. 6, PP. 117.

Prajapati, N.D., Purohit, S.S., Sharma, A.K. & Tarun Kumar (2003), A Hand Book of Medicinal Plants, Agrobios India, Jodhpur, PP. 475.

Sharma, P.C., Yelne, MB. & Denis, T.J. (2000), Database on medicinal plants used in ayurveda, Central Council for research in Ayurveda and siddha, Vol. 4, PP. 82.

Sharma, P.V. (1981), Dravya gun vigyana, Chaukhambha Bharti Academy, Varanasi, Vol. 1, PP. 734.

Singh, R.S. (2002), Vanoshadhi Nirdeshika, Uttar Pradesh Hindi Sansthan, Lucknow, PP. 264.

Swami, K.N. (1985), Gavon Main Aushadh Ratna, Kalera Krishana Gopal, Kalera (Raj.), Vol. 2, PP. 230.

433. *Sida rhombifolia* Linn.

Family: Malvaceae.

Name: Sanskrit: *Pitapushpaa, Sahadevi, Khsetrabalaa,* **Hindi:** *Mahabalaa,* **Local:** *Peelaa Bariyaar.*

Botanical characteristics: Habit: An erect, woody, very variable annual or perennial undershrub, height about 1.5 m. **Stem:** With strong wiry flexuose branches with stellate hairs. **Leaf:** Very variable in shape, rhomboid-lanceolate or lanceolate, serrated towards the top, entire towards the base, up to 2.5-5 cm by 18 mm, glabrous or sub-glabrous above, grey-pubescent or hoary beneath, 3-5-nerved; petioles up to 6 mm long, pubescent, swollen in the upper third. **Flower:** Yellow or white, axillary, solitary or in pairs, leaves are reduced on the flowering branches. **Fruit:** Schizocarp, depressed, globose, enclosed within the calyx, separating into one seeded indehiscent unit. **Seed:** Black, smooth.

Flowering and fruiting period: August-September and October-November.

Habitat: Throughout India, in moist places.

Parts used: Root, leaves. **Dosage:** 5-10 g.

Collection period: November-December.

Ayurvedic properties: ***Ras:*** *madhur,* ***Gun:*** *laghu, snigdha,* ***Veerya:*** *sheeta,* ***Vipaka:*** *madhur,* ***Tridosha*** **Effect:** alleviates ***Vaata:*** **+++**, ***Pitta:*** **++.**

Chemical constituents: The **roots** contain 0.054% alkaloids, beta-phenethylamine, N-methyl-beta-phenethylamine, vasicinol, vasicinone, vasicine, choline and betaine. These alkaloids are also present in the aerial parts. The **aerial parts** contain alkaloids, ephedrine, *si*-ephedrine and cryptolepine. The **seeds** contain proteins, linoleic, malvic and culic acid.

Action and disease indications: The **aerial parts** are diuretic, febrifuge, demulcent, emollient, used for skin diseases. The **roots** are cooling, diuretic, constipating and anthelmintic, used for deficient spermatogenesis, oedema, diarrhea, tuberculosis, leucorrhea, strangury, burning sensation and dipsia.

Clinical uses: Elephantiasis: Local application of decoction of roots of described plant and Orpimint, with water is beneficial. **Anuria, dysuria:** Distillate of described plant, 20 ml, or decoction of described plant 10 g, two times a day, is beneficial. **Rheumatism:** Decoction of roots of described plant 6 g, *Zingiber officinale* 1 g, with honey 10 g, two times a day, is useful. **Wounds, ulcers:** Local application of juice of roots of described plant, is beneficial.

Formulations: *Chandrakalaa rasa (Pitta Jwara).*

Recommended readings:

Bhutya, R.K. (2007), Vanaspati Aushadha Vigyana, Scientific Publishers (India), Jodhpur, PP. 176.

Brahmavarchas (2003), Ayurved Ka Pran Vanoshadhi Vigyan, Shanti Kunj, Haridwar, PP. 407.

Chunekar, K.C. (2004), Bhava Prakash Nighantu, Chaukhambha Bharti Academy, Varanasi, PP. 368.

Khare, C.P. (2007), Indian Medicinal Plants, Springer (India) P.L. New Delhi, PP. 604.

Kirtikar, K.R. & Basu, B.D. (1998), Indian Medicinal Plants, L.M Basu, Allahabad, Vol. 1, PP. 310.

Misra, B.L. (2005), Dravya Guna Hastamalaka, Publication scheme, Jaipur, PP. 308.

Nair, R.Vasudevan, (2007), Indian Medicinal Plants, Orient Longman P.L. Chennai, Vol. 5, PP. 132.

Namjoshi, A.N. (2001), The Ayurvedic Pharmacopoeia of India, Government of India, Department of Indian Systems of Medicine & Homoeopathy, New Delhi, Part-1, Volume- 3, PP. 112.

Pareek, G.N. (2005), Sudhanidhi, Vanoshadhi Ratnakar, Dhanvantari Karyalaya, Aligarh, Vol. 6, PP. 141.

Prajapati, N.D., Purohit, S.S., Sharma, A.K. & Tarun Kumar (2003), A Hand Book of Medicinal Plants, Agrobios India, Jodhpur, PP. 476.

Sharma, P.V. (1981), Dravya gun vigyana, Chaukhambha Bharti Academy, Varanasi, Vol. 1, PP. 737.

Singh, R.S. (2002), Vanoshadhi Nirdeshika, Uttar Pradesh Hindi Sansthan, Lucknow, PP. 264.

434. *Sisymbrium irio* Linn.

Family: Cruciferae; Brassicaceae.

Other similar plants: *S.loeselii.*

Name: English: London Rocket, **Sanskrit:** *Khubakalaan,* **Hindi:** *Khubakalaan,* **Local:** *Khaakasi.*

Botanical characteristics: Habit: An annual or biennial herb, height 30-90 cm. Plant looks like the plant of Mustard. **Stem:** Erect, glabrous or slightly pubescent below. **Leaf:** Runicate or pinnatifid; lobes not auricled, remote, spreading, toothed; terminal large, sometimes hastate; petioled. **Flower:** Yellow, minute on slender pedicels. **Fruit:** 3.8-5 cm long, slender, erect, glabrous, sub-torulose; valves 3-nerved; pedicels ascending, curved. **Seed:** Numerous, minute, reddish-yellow, 2 mm long, ovate, one surface convex and one groove on back surface ending in a notch, mucilaginous with water, after sometimes seeds become rancid.

Flowering and fruiting period: November-December and January-February.

Habitat: Kashmir, Punjab, Hariyana, Rajasthan and Uttar Pradesh, in moist soils.

Parts used: Seed. **Dosage:** 3-6 g.

Collection period: January-February.

Ayurvedic properties: ***Ras:*** *katu,* ***Gun:*** *guru, snigdha, pichhala,* ***Veerya:*** *ushna,* ***Vipaka:*** *katu,* ***Tridosha*** **Effect:** alleviates ***Vaata:*** ++, ***Pitta:*** +, ***Kapha:*** +.

Chemical constituents: The **leaves** are rich in vitamin C (176mg/100g), beta-carotene (10000 IU100g) and minerals, used for throat and chest infections. The **aerial parts** contain beta-sitosterol, 3-beta-D-glucoside, isorhmnetin and quercetin. The **seeds** contain a flavonoid, *iso*-rhamnetin, Fatty oils from seeds contain linolenic and oleic, along with erucic, palmitic and stearic acids. Ethanolic extract of seeds exhibited marked anti-bacterial action, also anti-pyretic and analgesic effects.

Action and disease indications: The **seeds** are expectorant, restorative, febrifuge, rubefacient, anti-bacterial and tonic, used for asthma, inflammations, vomiting and general debility.

Clinical uses: Typhoid fever: Decoction of mix powder of described plant, *Elephantopus scaber, Viola odorata, Ocimum sanctum, Bacopa monnieri, Tinospora cordifolia, Solanum nigrum,* 12 g, with honey 10 g, two times a day, is useful. **Chicken pox:** Decoction of mix powder of described plant, *Bacopa monnieri, Tinospora cordifolia, Fegonia indica, Fumaria indica, Swertia chirata, Picrorhiza kurroa,* 6 g, with honey 10 g, two times a day, is useful. **Boils, abscess:** Poultice of seeds of described plant, is beneficial. **Asthma, bronchitis:** Fried seeds powder of described plant, 4 g, with syrup of *Viola odorata* 4 g, two times a day, is beneficial. **General debility:** Seed powder of described plant, 3 g, with milk, two times a day, is beneficial.

Formulations: *Gojihvaadi kwaatha, Drakhsaadi kwaatha.*

Recommended readings:

Bhutya, R.K. (2007), Vanaspati Aushadha Vigyana, Scientific Publishers (India), Jodhpur, PP. 81.

Chunekar, K.C. (2004), Bhava Prakash Nighantu, Chaukhambha Bharti Academy, Varanasi, PP. 820.

Dhiman, A.K. (2006), Ayurvedic Drug Plants, Daya Publishing House, Delhi, PP. 214.

Khare, C.P. (2007), Indian Medicinal Plants, Springer (India) P.L. New Delhi, PP. 607.

Kirtikar, K.R. & Basu, B.D. (1998), Indian Medicinal Plants, L.M Basu, Allahabad, Vol. 1, PP. 153.

Misra, B.L. (2005), Dravya Guna Hastamalaka, Publication scheme, Jaipur, PP. 320.

Pareek, G.N. (2005), Sudhanidhi, Vanoshadhi Ratnakar, Dhanvantari Karyalaya, Aligarh, Vol. 9, PP. 310.

Sharma, P.V. (1981), Dravya gun vigyana, Chaukhambha Bharti Academy, Varanasi, Vol. 1, PP. 783.

Singh, R.S. (2002), Vanoshadhi Nirdeshika, Uttar Pradesh Hindi Sansthan, Lucknow, PP. 120.

Swami, K.N. (1985), Gavon Main Aushadh Ratna, Kalera Krishana Gopal, Kalera (Raj.), Vol. 1, PP. 167.

435. *Smilax china* Linn.

Family: Liliaceae.

Other similar plants: *S. glabra-* bigger var., *S. lanceifolia, S. ovalifolia, S.macrophylla, S. zeylanica.*

Name: English: China Root, **Sanskrit:** *Dwipaantara vachaa,* **Hindi:** *Chopchini,* **Local:** *Topchini.*

Botanical characteristics: Habit: A hard tendril climber. **Stem:** Sparsely prickled or unarmed and with thick tuberous rhizomes. **Leaf:** Simple, alternate, elliptic, rounded at base, prominently nerved. **Flower:** White in umbels, small, numerous. **Fruit:** Berries, red.

Habitat: Japan, China and Cochin China.

Parts used: Root. **Dosage:** 3-5 g.

Ayurvedic properties: ***Ras:*** *tikta,* ***Gun:*** *laghu, rukhsa,* ***Veerya:*** *ushna,* ***Vipaka:*** *katu,* ***Tridosha*** **Effect:** alleviates ***Vaata:*** ++, ***Pitta:*** +, ***Kapha:*** +.

Chemical constituents: The **rhizomes** contain steroidal saponins, pro-sapogenin-A-of dioscin, dioscin, gracillin. Me-protogracillin, Me-protogracillin and its 22-hydroxy-analog; besides beta-sitosterol glucoside, smilaxin, two furastan and one spirostane glycosides.

Action and disease indications: The **rhizomes** are alterative, thermogenic, anodyne, anti-inflammatory, digestive, laxative, depurative, aphrodisiac, diuretic, sudorofic, febrifuge, tonic, gentle circulatory stimulant and with mild testosterone activity, used for venereal diseases, rheumatic affections, chronic skin diseases, syphilis, epilepsy, insanity, scrofula, flatulence, dyspepsia, colic, neuralgia, constipation, helminthiasis, psoriasis, fever, strangury, seminal weakness and general debility.

Clinical uses: Chronic headache: Tuber of described plant 3 g, *Hemidesmus indicus* 5 g, with milk two times a day, is beneficial.

Rheumatism, gout, epilepsy, somasthenia, spermacresia, general debility, penile dysfunction, osteo arthritis: Mix powder of tuber of described plant, *Pistacia lentiscus, Elettaria cardamomum, Cinamomum verum,* 5 g, with milk, two times a day, is beneficial. **Skin diseases:** Tuber powder of described plant, 3 g, with water, two times a day, is beneficial.

Formulations: *Maajoon chopachini, Chopachini paaka.*

Recommended readings:

Bhutya, R.K. (2007), Vanaspati Aushadha Vigyana, Scientific Publishers (India), Jodhpur, PP. 99.

Brahmavarchas (2003), Ayurved Ka Pran Vanoshadhi Vigyan, Shanti Kunj, Haridwar, PP. 408.

Chunekar, K.C. (2004), Bhava Prakash Nighantu, Chaukhambha Bharti Academy, Varanasi, PP. 48.

Khare, C.P. (2007), Indian Medicinal Plants, Springer (India) P.L. New Delhi, PP. 608.

Kirtikar, K.R. & Basu, B.D. (1998), Indian Medicinal Plants, L.M Basu, Allahabad, Vol. 4, PP. 2496.

Misra, B.L. (2005), Dravya Guna Hastamalaka, Publication scheme, Jaipur, PP. 324.

Nair, R.Vasudevan, (2007), Indian Medicinal Plants, Orient Longman P.L. Chennai, Vol. 5, PP. 143.

Prajapati, N.D., Purohit, S.S., Sharma, A.K. & Tarun Kumar (2003), A Hand Book of Medicinal Plants, Agrobios India, Jodhpur, PP. 477.

Sharma, P.V. (1981), Dravya gun vigyana, Chaukhambha Bharti Academy, Varanasi, Vol. 1, PP. 802.

Singh, R.S. (2002), Vanoshadhi Nirdeshika, Uttar Pradesh Hindi Sansthan, Lucknow, PP. 154.

Swami, K.N. (1985), Gavon Main Aushadh Ratna, Kalera Krishana Gopal, Kalera (Raj.), Vol. 2, PP. 285.

436. *Solanum ferox* Linn.

Family: Solanaceae.

Synonym: *S. indicum.*

Other similar plants: *S. torvum*- White flowered var.

Ayurvedic Groups: Charak: *Kanthya, Hikkanigrahana, Shothahara, Angamardaprashamana,* **Sushruta:** *Vrihatyaadi, Laghu panchamoola.*

Name: English: Poison Berry, **Sanskrit:** *Vrihati, Vaartaaki, Khsudrabhantaaki, Mahati, Kuli, Hinguli, Raastrikaa, Mahostri, Dushpragharshini,* **Hindi:** *Vrihati, Badi Kantakari,* **Local:** *Badi Kateli, Vanbhantaa.*

Botanical characteristics: Habit: An erect, stellate-tomentose, armed herb or undershrub, height 60-120 cm, plants looks like the plant of Brinjal. **Stem:** Herbaceous, stout, densely clothed with long, coarse, often stalked, usually fulvous stellate hairs, and copiously armed with straight slender prickles. **Leaf:** 15-28 by 10-20 cm, usually 2 at a node and unequal, broadly elliptic in outline, sinutely or pinnately cut into few short triangular lobes, softly stellately fulvous-hairy on both sides, armed with long, erect, yellow slender prickles on the nerves on both sides, base cordate, truncate or more or less acute, often unequal-sided; main nerves 6-8 pairs; petioles 3.8-6.3 cm long, prickly and densely fulvous-hairy. **Flower:** Blue or purple, sometimes white, 18.75 mm in diam., solitary or in 2-6-flowered leaf-opposed densely hairy cymes; peduncles very short; pedicles 6-13 mm long, densely stellately fulvous-hairy and usually with a few prickles. **Fruit:** Berry, globose, 2-3.2 cm diam., densely covered with long fulvous hairs, green with white lines when unripe and yellow when ripe. **Seed:** 2.5 mm diam., numerous, glabrous, like Brinjal, faintely rugose with concentric rings.

Flowering and fruiting period: Almost throughout year,

Habitat: Throughout hotter parts of India, up to an altitude of 1500 m, mostly in Assam, Konkan and Western Ghats.

Parts used: Root, fruit. **Dosage:** 3-6 g.

Collection period: April-May.

Ayurvedic properties: ***Ras:*** *katu, tikta,* ***Gun:*** *laghu, rukhsa, tikhsna,* ***Veerya:*** *ushna,* ***Vipaka:*** *katu,* ***Tridosha*** **Effect:** alleviates ***Kapha:*** ***+++,*** ***Vaata:*** ***++.***

Chemical constituents: The **fruit** and **leaves** contain solanin; 0.3 and 0.43 of total alkaloids respectively.

Action and disease indications: The **roots** are thermogenic, anodyne, digestive, carminative, resolvent, anthelmintic, expectorant, stomachic, constipating, demulcent, depurative, diuretic, aphrodisiac, emmenogogue, febrifuge and cardiotonic, used for anorexia, inflammations, hiccough, cough, asthma, bronchitis, dysmenorrhea, amenorrhea, odontalgia, dyspepsia, flatulence, colic, helminthiasis, diarrhea, pruritis, skin diseases, strangury, fever, cardiac diseases and vomiting.

Clinical uses: Alopecia: Local application of juice of roots or paste of roots of described plant is beneficial. **Penile dysfunction:** Local application of paste of seeds of described plant, with water, is beneficial. **Pruritis of vulva:** Fumigation by mix powder of fruits of described plant, *Curcuma longa, Berberis aristata,* is useful. **Anuria, dysuria:** Root powder of described plant, 3 g, with lukewarm water, two times a day, is beneficial. **Headache:** Local application of paste of roots of described plant, with water, is beneficial. **Cough, asthma, bronchitis:** Decoction of roots of described plant, 6 g, with honey 10 g, two times a day, is useful. **Colic, gripping, dysuria:** Decoction of roots of described plant, 6 g, two times a day, is beneficial. **Skin diseases:** Local application of paste of leaves of described plant is beneficial. **Nausea, vomiting:** Leaves juice of described plant, 10 ml, juice of fresh tuber of *Zingiber officinale,* 5 ml, with honey 10 g, two times a day, is useful. **Asthma:** Decoction of mix powder of roots of described plant, roots of *Solanum surattense, Glycyrrhiza glabra, Tinospora cordifolia, Solanum nigrum, Piper longum, Zingiber officinale,* 6 g, with Nitrate of potash 500 mg, two times a day, is beneficial.

Formulations: *Dashamoola kwaatha, Chyavanpraasha, Anu taila, Sirahsoolaadivajra rasa, Naaraayan taila, Vrihachhaagalaadhya ghrita, Amritapraasha ghrita, Agatsyaharitaki, Brahmarasaayana, Bhaarangi guda, Punarnavaasava, Mritasanjivani suraa, Dantyarista, Amritaarista, Dashamoolaarista.*

Recommended readings:

Bhutya, R.K. (2007), Vanaspati Aushadha Vigyana, Scientific Publishers (India), Jodhpur, PP. 43.

Brahmavarchas (2003), Ayurved Ka Pran Vanoshadhi Vigyan, Shanti Kunj, Haridwar, PP. 409.

Chunekar, K.C. (2004), Bhava Prakash Nighantu, Chaukhambha Bharti Academy, Varanasi, PP. 288.

Dhiman, A.K. (2006), Ayurvedic Drug Plants, Daya Publishing House, Delhi, PP. 407.

Khare, C.P. (2007), Indian Medicinal Plants, Springer (India) P.L. New Delhi, PP. 611.

Kirtikar, K.R. & Basu, B.D. (1998), Indian Medicinal Plants, L.M Basu, Allahabad, Vol. 3, PP. 1754.

Misra, B.L. (2005), Dravya Guna Hastamalaka, Publication scheme, Jaipur, PP. 314.

Nair, R.Vasudevan, (2007), Indian Medicinal Plants, Orient Longman P.L. Chennai, Vol. 5, PP. 151.

Namjoshi, A.N. (2001), The Ayurvedic Pharmacopoeia of India, Government of India, Department of Indian Systems of Medicine & Homoeopathy, New Delhi, Part-1, Volume- 1, PP. 27.

Pareek, G.N. (2005), Sudhanidhi, Vanoshadhi Ratnakar, Dhanvantari Karyalaya, Aligarh, Vol. 2, PP. 233.

Prajapati, N.D., Purohit, S.S., Sharma, A.K. & Tarun Kumar (2003), A Hand Book of Medicinal Plants, Agrobios India, Jodhpur, PP. 478.

Sharma, P.C., Yelne, MB. & Denis, T.J. (2000), Database on medicinal plants used in ayurveda, Central Council for research in Ayurveda and siddha, Vol. 8, PP. 59.

Sharma, P.V. (1981), Dravya gun vigyana, Chaukhambha Bharti Academy, Varanasi, Vol. 1, PP. 282.

Singh, R.S. (2002), Vanoshadhi Nirdeshika, Uttar Pradesh Hindi Sansthan, Lucknow, PP. 64.

Swami, K.N. (1985), Gavon Main Aushadh Ratna, Kalera Krishana Gopal, Kalera (Raj.), Vol. 2, PP. 138.

437. *Solanum melongena* Linn.

Family: Solanaceae.

Other similar plants: *S.melongena* var. *incanum* syn. *coagulans*-wild var.

Name: English: Egg Plant, Brinjal, **Sanskrit:** *Vaartaaka, Bhantaaki, Vrintaaka, Bhantikaa,* **Hindi:** *Begun,* **Local:** *Began, Bhatta.*

Botanical characteristics: Habit: An erect or suffrutescent, herbaceous, armed or unarmed perennial herb, height 1.2-2 m. **Stem:** Young parts closely tomentose. **Leaf:** Simple, large, entire, lobed, large elliptic, 10-18 cm long. **Flower:** Blue or purple, 2.5 cm diam., in clusters of 2-5. **Fruit:** Berry, large, glabrous, dark purple, white or yellow, varying in shape and size, capped with thick persistent calyx. **Seed:** Numerous, yellow or cream, discoid.

Flowering and fruiting period: September-October and November-December, or almost throughout year.

Habitat: Cultivated throughout India.

Parts used: Fruit. **Dosage:** 20-50 g.

Collection period: November-December.

Ayurvedic properties: ***Ras:*** *madhur,* ***Gun:*** *laghu, rukhsa,* ***Veerya:*** *ushna,* ***Vipaka:*** *madhur,* ***Tridosha*** **Effect:** alleviates ***Vaata:* +++,** ***Kapha:* ++,** aggravates ***Pitta:* ++.**

Chemical constituents: The **fruits** contain solasodin, arginine and aspartic acid. The **seeds** contain steroidal saponins, tigogenin, diosgenin and melongosides. The **leaves** contain quercetin, 3-0-rhmnoside and kaempferol-3-0-rutinoside.

Action and disease indications: The **leaves** are sialogogue, narcotic and anti-herpetic, used for bronchitis, asthma, odontalgia and fever. The unripe fruits are aphrodisiac, appetizer, cardiotonic and haematinic, used for obesity, piles and anorexia. The **roots** are laxative, analgesic and cardio-tonic, used for inflammations, neuralgia, cardiac-debility and ulcers of the nose.

Clinical uses: Burning sensation of sole: Local application of paste of unripe fruit of described plant, or massage of juice of unripe fruits, is beneficial.

Formulations: *Aakallaka vati.*

380. *Polyalthia longifolia* - Aashaapaalaa

381. *Polygonatum cirrhifolium*-Mahameda

382. *Polygonatum verticillatum*-Meda

385. *Portulaca oleracea*-Lona

383. *Polygonum aviculare*-Granthiparni

384. *Pongamia pinnata*-Karanja

386. *Premna integrifolia*-Agnimantha

388. *Prunus amygdalus*-Baadaam

390. *Psidium guajava*-Amarooda

387. *Prosopis spincigera*-Khejaraa

389. *Prunus cerasoides*-Padamaakh

391. *Psoralea corylifolia* - Bakuchi

392. *Pterocarpus marsupium*-Vijayasar

395. *Pueraria tuberosa*-Vidarikanda

399. *Randia dumetorum*-Madanphala

400. *Ranunculus sceleratus*-Kaandeer

403. *Rheum emodi*-Revandachini

393. *Pterocarpus santalinus*-Chandan rakta

397. *Pyrus communis*-Naashapaati

401. *Raphanus sativus*-Mooli

394. *Pterospermum acerifolium*-Muchakund

396. *Punica grantum*-Anaar

398. *Quercus infectoria* - Maajuphala

402. *Rauvolfia serpentina*-Sarpagandha

404. *Rhus parviflora*-Tintidik

405. *Ricinus communis*-Eranda

406. *Rosa centifolia*-Gulab

407. *Roscoia alpina*-Kaakoli

408. *Rubia cordifolia*-Manjistha

409. *Ruta graveolens* - Sitaab

410. *Saccharum bengalense*-Sharapata

411. *Saccharum officinanale*-Ikhsu

412. *Saccharum spontaneum*-Kaas

413. *Salacia chinensis*-Saptachakra

414. *Salix caprea*-Vetas

415. *Salix tetrasperma*-Jalvetas

416. *Salvadora persica*-Pilu

417. *Salvia plebeia*-Samudrashosha

418. *Sansevieria roxburghiana* - Naagadaman

419. *Santalum album* - Chandan sweta

420. *Sapindus mukorossi*-Aritha

421. *Saraca asoca*-Ashoka

422. *Sarcostemma brevistigma*-Somlata

423. *Sausurea costus*-Kustha

425. *Scindapsus officinalis*-Gajapipal

424. *Schrebera swietenioides*-Mushkaka

426.*Scirpus grosus*-Kasheru

427. *Semecarpus anacardium*-Bhallataka

428. *Sesamum orientale*-Til

429. *Sesbania grandiflora*-Agatsya

430. *Sesbenia sesben*-Jayanti

431. *Shorea robusta*-Saal

432. *Sida cordifolia*-Balaa

433. *Sida rhombifolia*-Mahabalaa

434. *Sisybrium ireo*-Khubakalan

435. *Smilax china*-Chopachini

436. *Solunum ferox*-Bari Kantakaari

437. *Solunum melongena*-Begun

438. *Solunum nigrum*-Makoya

439. *Solunum surattense* - Choti Kantakaari

440. *Soymida febrifuga*-Mansarohini

441. *Sphyeranthus indicus*-Gorakhamundi

442. *Spilanthes oleracea*-Akarkaraa-Desi

443. *Spinacea oleracea*-Paalak

445. *Sterospermum suaveolens*-Paatalaa

444. *Spondias pinnata*-Aamaraa

446. *Streblus asper*-Shakhotak

447. *Strychnos nux-vomica* - Tinduk

448. *Strychnos potatorum*-Nirmali

449. *Styrax benzoin*-Loban

450. *Swertia chiryata* - Chirayata

451. *Symplocos racemosa*-Lodhra

452. *Syzygium aromaticum*-Lavanga

453. *Syzygium cumini*-Jamun

454. *Tagetes erecta*-Genda

455. *Tamarindus indica*-Imali

456. *Taraxcum officinale*-Dugdhapheni

457. *Tecomela undulata*-Rohida

458. *Tectona grandis* - Saagavan

459. *Tephrosia purpurea*-Sharpunkhaa

460. *Teramnus labialis*-Maashaparni

461. *Terminalia arjuna*-Arjun

462. *Terminalia belliarica*-Bahera

463. *Terminalia chebula*-Harad

464. *Terminalia tomentosa*-Aswakarna

465. *Thespesia populnea*-Paaras pipal

466. *Thevertia neriifolia*-Kaner

468. *Tinospora cordifolia*-Giloya

467. *Thuja orientalis*-Mayurpankhi

Recommended readings:

Bhutya, R.K. (2007), Vanaspati Aushadha Vigyana, Scientific Publishers (India), Jodhpur, PP. 164.

Brahmavarchas (2003), Ayurved Ka Pran Vanoshadhi Vigyan, Shanti Kunj, Haridwar, PP. 410.

Chunekar, K.C. (2004), Bhava Prakash Nighantu, Chaukhambha Bharti Academy, Varanasi, PP. 690.

Khare, C.P. (2007), Indian Medicinal Plants, Springer (India) P.L. New Delhi, PP. 612.

Kirtikar, K.R. & Basu, B.D. (1998), Indian Medicinal Plants, L.M Basu, Allahabad, Vol. 3, PP. 1757.

Nair, R.Vasudevan, (2007), Indian Medicinal Plants, Orient Longman P.L. Chennai, Vol. 5, PP. 157.

Prajapati, N.D., Purohit, S.S., Sharma, A.K. & Tarun Kumar (2003), A Hand Book of Medicinal Plants, Agrobios India, Jodhpur, PP. 480.

Sharma, P.V. (1981), Dravya gun vigyana, Chaukhambha Bharti Academy, Varanasi, Vol. 2, PP. 209.

438. *Solanum nigrum* Linn.

Family: Solanaceae.

Synonym: *S.rubrum.*

Name: English: Black night shade, Garden night shade, **Sanskrit:** *Kaakamaachi, Kaakaahvaa, Waayasi, Dhvaangamaachi, Kaakamaataa,* **Hindi:** *Makoya,* **Local:** *Makoya.*

Ayurvedic groups: Charaka: *Tiktaskandha.*

Botanical characteristics: Habit: An unarmed erect, variable annual, divaricately branched, suffrutescent, annual herb, 30-90 cm high. **Stem:** Herbaceous, aerial, cylindrical, solid, smooth or puberulous, green with terete or angular. **Leaf:** Dark green, 2.5-10 cm long, 2.5-3 cm wide, thin, ovate, oblong or ovate-lanceolate, entire or remotely dentate, petiole 1.25-2.5 cm long, **Flower:** White, small, pentamerous, 3-8 flowered pendulous cyme, **Fruit:** Berry, 5-8 mm across, green when unripe and purplish-black or reddish or yellow when ripe, **Seed:** Many, discoid, smooth, ovoid, 1.5 mm diam, yellow, minutely pitted.

Flowering and fruiting period: November-December and January- February.

Habitat: Throughout dry parts of India, as a weed, up to 2100 m.

Parts used: Whole plant, fruit.

Dosage: Juice 10-20 ml, fruit powder 1-3 g, distillate 20-25 ml.

Collection period: March-April.

Ayurvedic properties: ***Ras:*** *tikta, katu,* ***Gun:*** *laghu, snigdha,* ***Veerya:*** mild *ushna,* ***Vipaka:*** *katu,* ***Tridosha*** **Effect:** alleviates ***Vaata:*** ++, ***Pitta:*** +, ***Kapha:*** +.

Chemical constituents: The **plant** contains steroidal alkaloid glycosides, solasoline, alpha and beta-solanigrine, alpha and beta-solamargine; steroidal sapogenins, diosgenin and tigogenin; solasodine. Solamargine and solasonine are present also in leaves. The total alkaloid contain of **fruit** is 0.101% and **leaves** is 0.431%.

Action and disease indications: Plant is anti-inflammatory, anti-spasmodic, sedative, diuretic, laxative, anti-septic, expectorant, anodyne, vulnerary, digestive, cardio-tonic, depurative, febrifuge and tonic. It is useful to cure inflammatory swelling, enlargement of liver and spleen, cirrhosis of lever, rheumatalgia, cough, asthma, piles, bronchitis, wounds, skin diseases, hoarseness, hiccough, vomiting, heart diseases, lack of semen quantity, urinary tract diseases, hemoptysis, flatulence, dyspepsia, strangury, otalgia, opthalmopathy, nephropathy, dropsy and general debility. A decoction of the plant depresses the central nervous system and reflexes of the spinal card and has influence on cardiac activity and in the regulation of blood pressure. **Leaves** applied hot to swollen testicles, paste used as a poultice to gout, rheumatic swelling and skin diseases and gastro helcosis. **Fruits and flowers** are prescribed in cough, cold, erysipelas, rat-bite, bronchitis, pulmonary tuberculosis, fever, diarrhea and hydrophobia. Seeds are useful to cure giddiness, dipsia, skin diseases and inflammations. **Root bark** is useful to cure rhinopathy, hepatitis, otopathy and opthalmopathy.

Clinical uses: Chronic skin diseases, pruritis, psoriasis, ring worm: Use leaves and soft stem of plant 50 g, as vegetable in the food. **Inflammations:** Use fresh juice of plant 20 ml, 2 times a day, and local application also. **Ascitis:** Use fresh juice 20-50 ml, 3 times a day.

Osteo arthritis, ulcers, swelling of testicles, enlargement of liver and spleen: Local application of warm poultice of whole plant is beneficial. **Diseases of mouth and throat:** Gargles of decoction of described plant, 3 times a day. **Otalgia:** Use hot juice, 4-4 drops, as ear drops. **Leukoderma:** Use local application of paste of described plant is beneficial. **Hoarseness, bronchitis, asthma, hiccough:** Fruit powder of plant 5 g, with honey 10 g, 2 times a day. **Any metallic toxicity:** Use 20 ml fresh juice, 3 times a day, for seven days.

Formulations: *Arka makoya, Saarivadi vati, Draakhsaadi kwaatha, Rasaraaj rasa, Kalkoota rasa, Vrihat sarvajwarantaka lauha, Mahat maahaavishagarbha taila.*

Recommended readings:

Acharya, B.K. (2008), Ayurveda Jadi-buti Rahasya, Patanjali Yogapitha, Haridwar, PP. 275.

Bhutya, R.K. (2007), Vanaspati Aushadha Vigyana, Scientific Publishers (India), Jodhpur, PP. 170.

Brahmavarchas (2003), Ayurved Ka Pran Vanoshadhi Vigyan, Shanti Kunj, Haridwar, PP. 411.

Chunekar, K.C. (2004), Bhava Prakash Nighantu, Chaukhambha Bharti Academy, Varanasi, PP. 438.

Dhiman, A.K. (2006), Ayurvedic Drug Plants, Daya Publishing House, Delhi, PP. 247.

Khare, C.P. (2007), Indian Medicinal Plants, Springer (India) P.L. New Delhi, PP. 613.

Kirtikar, K.R. & Basu, B.D. (1998), Indian Medicinal Plants, L.M Basu, Allahabad, Vol. 3, PP. 1748.

Misra, B.L. (2005), Dravya Guna Hastamalaka, Publication scheme, Jaipur, PP. 315.

Nair, R.Vasudevan, (2007), Indian Medicinal Plants, Orient Longman P.L. Chennai, Vol. 5, PP. 160.

Namjoshi, A.N. (2001), The Ayurvedic Pharmacopoeia of India, Government of India, Department of Indian Systems of Medicine & Homoeopathy, New Delhi, Part-1, Volume- 1, PP. 66.

Pareek, G.N. (2005), Sudhanidhi, Vanoshadhi Ratnakar, Dhanvantari Karyalaya, Aligarh, Vol. 9, PP. 205.

Prajapati, N.D., Purohit, S.S., Sharma, A.K. & Tarun Kumar (2003), A Hand Book of Medicinal Plants, Agrobios India, Jodhpur, PP. 480.

Sharma, P.C., Yelne, MB. & Denis, T.J. (2000), Database on medicinal plants used in Ayurveda, Central Council for research in Ayurveda and siddha, Vol. 3, PP. 347.

Sharma, P.V. (1981), Dravya gun vigyana, Chaukhambha Bharti Academy, Varanasi, Vol. 1, PP. 540.

Singh, R.S. (2002), Vanoshadhi Nirdeshika, Uttar Pradesh Hindi Sansthan, Lucknow, PP. 292.

439. *Solanum surattense* Burm. f.

Family: Solanaceae.

Synonym: *S.xanthocarpum, S.virginianum, S. maccanni.*

Other similar plants: *S.suratanse.*

Name: English: Wild Egg plant, Yellow-Berried Nightshade, **Sanskrit:** *Kantakaari, Duhsparshaa, Khsudraa, Vyaghree, Nidigdhikaa, Kantaalikaa, Kantakini, Dhaavani, Vrihati,* **Hindi:** *Kantakari,* **Local:** *Choti Kateli, Pasar Kateli, Began Kateli, Bhatta Kateli.*

Botanical characteristics: Habit: A very prickly diffuse bright green suffrutescent, perennial herb, spreading in 30-120 cm diam. **Root:** 10-45 cm long and up to 2 cm in diam., almost cylindrical and tapering, outer surface showing a number of fine longitudinal and few transverse wrinkles. **Stem:** Woody at base, with zigzag numerous branches that spread close to the ground cover over with strong, broad, sharp, compressed, glabrous, shining, straight, yellowish white prickles, often exceeding 1.3 cm long. **Leaf:** 5-10 by 2.5-7.5 cm, ovate or ovate-oblong, elliptic, sinute or sub-pinnatified, obtuse or sub-acute, stellately hairy on both sides, armed on the mid rib and often on the nerves with long yellow sharp prickles, base usually rounded and unequal-sided; petioles 1.3-2.5 cm long, stellately hairy and prickly. **Flower:** Purple or bluish-purple, in extra-axillary cymes, peduncles short; pedicles short curved, stellatey hairy. **Fruit:** Berry, 1.3-2 cm diam., glabrous, globular drooping, yellow or white with green veins, surrounded by the enlarged calyx. **Seed:** 2.5 mm diam., glabrous, numerous, reniform, smooth and yellowish- brown.

Flowering and fruiting period: December-February and march-June.

Habitat: Throughout India, up to an altitude of 2200 m on the Himalaya, abundant in dry situations as a weed by roadsides and on waste lands.

Parts used: Root, fruit.

Dosage: Powder 1-2 g, 5-10 g for decoction.

Collection period: April-May.

Ayurvedic properties: ***Ras:*** *tikta, katu,* ***Gun:*** *laghu, rukhsa,* ***Veerya:*** *ushna,* ***Vipaka:*** *katu,* ***Tridosha*** **Effect:** alleviates ***Kapha:*** +++, ***Vaata:*** ++.

Chemical constituents: The **fruits** contain solasonine, solamargine, beta-solamargine and solasodine; The glycol alkaloid content of fruits is 3.5%. The **roots** contain coumarins, scopolin, scopoletin, esculin and esculetin. The **flowers** contain apigenin, quercetin diglycoside and sitosterol. Both glycoalkaloid and fatty acid fractions of the plants extracts cause liberation of histamine from chopped lung tissue. The beneficial effect of the drug on bronchial asthma may be attributed to the depletion of histamine from bronchial and lung tissue.

Action and disease indications: The **plant** is thermogenic, anti-inflammatory, anthelmintic, anodyne, digestive, carminative, appetizer, stomachic, febrifuge, depurative, sudorofic, expectorant, laxative, stimulant, rejuvenating, diuretic, emmenogogue and aphrodisiac, prescribed for cough, asthma, bronchitis, helminthiasis, dental carries, inflammations, arthralgia, anorexia, dyspepsia, flatulence, colic, constipation, skin diseases, hypertension, rheumatoid arthritis, fever, hoarseness, phyringitis, hiccough, strangury, urolithiasis, dysmenorrhea, amenorrhea, piles lumbago, catarrh, epilepsy, cardiac disorders and rhinopathy.

Clinical uses: Rheumatism: Leaves juice of described plant, 10 ml, with *Solanum nigrum* 500 mg, two times a day, is beneficial. **Sterility:** Seed powder of white flowered var. of described plant, 1 g, with milk, for seven days, from menstrual period, repeat it for three months. Use rice and milk in this period. **Hiccough:** Decoction of roots of described plant, 5 g, with honey 10 g, by 1 hour, as required. **Attack of asthma:** Black ash of fruits 2 g, with honey 10 g, or decoction of fruits of described plant, 6 g, with fried gum of *Ferula narthex* 125 mg and rock salt 500 mg, or root powder of described plant, 5 g, with milk, or alkali of described plant 1.5 g, with leaves juice of *Piper betel* 10 ml, two times a day, is useful. (2) Mix powder flowers of described plant, flowers of *Calotropis procera,* extract of *Glycyrrhiza glabra, Piper longum,* 4 g, with honey 10 g, two times a day, is very useful. **Dental carries, ulcers, fistula:** Fumigation by fruits of described plant, two times a day, is useful. **Bronchitis:** (1) Root powder of described plant, 3 g, *Piper longum* 500 mg, with honey 10 g, two or three times a day, is useful. (2) Decoction or syrup of mix powder of described plant 5 g, *Justisia adhatoda* 1.5 g, *Glycyrrhiza glabra* 1 g, with honey 10 g, two times a day, is useful. **Chronic bronchitis:** Root powder of described plant, 3 g, roasted seeds of *Cuminum cyminum* 1 g, fruit powder of *Phylanthus emblica* 5 g, with honey 10 g, two times a day, is useful. **Alopecia:** Local massage of juice of plant with honey, two times a day, is useful. Use it for one month. **Dentalgia:** Gargles with decoction of described plant, is beneficial. **Mastoptosis:** Local application of paste of roots of described plant, root bark of *Punica grantum,* roots of *Trichosanthus cucurmerina,* is beneficial. Use tight bra at this time. **Paralysis:** Decoction of mix powder of roots of described plant, *Ricinus communis,* and *Mucana pruriens,* seeds of *Phaseolus mungo,* with fried gum of *Ferula narthex* 125 mg and rock salt 500 mg, two times a day, is beneficial. **Renal and vesical calculus:** Decoction of mix powder of roots of described plant, roots of *Moringa oleifera,* seeds of *Macrotyloma uniflorum*, 10 g, with honey 10 g, two times a day, is useful.

Formulations: *Kantakaaryaavaleha, Kantakaari ghrita, Vyaaghriharitaki, Dashamoola kwaatha, Vyaghri taila, Dashamoolaarista, Gojihvaadi kwaatha, Dashamoola taila, Mushikaadhya taila, Nidigdhikaadi kwaatha, Vishnu taila.*

Recommended readings:

Acharya, B.K. (2008), Ayurveda Jadi-buti Rahasya, Patanjali Yogapitha, Haridwar, PP. 253.

Bhutya, R.K. (2007), Vanaspati Aushadha Vigyana, Scientific Publishers (India), Jodhpur, PP. 42.

Brahmavarchas (2003), Ayurved Ka Pran Vanoshadhi Vigyan, Shanti Kunj, Haridwar, PP. 413.

Chunekar, K.C. (2004), Bhava Prakash Nighantu, Chaukhambha Bharti Academy, Varanasi, PP. 290.

Dhiman, A.K. (2006), Ayurvedic Drug Plants, Daya Publishing House, Delhi, PP. 192.

Khare, C.P. (2007), Indian Medicinal Plants, Springer (India) P.L. New Delhi, PP. 615.

Kirtikar, K.R. & Basu, B.D. (1998), Indian Medicinal Plants, L.M Basu, Allahabad, Vol. 3, PP. 1759.

Misra, B.L. (2005), Dravya Guna Hastamalaka, Publication scheme, Jaipur, PP. 314.

Nair, R. Vasudevan, (2007), Indian Medicinal Plants, Orient Longman P.L. Chennai, Vol. 5, PP. 164.

Namjoshi, A.N. (2001), The Ayurvedic Pharmacopoeia of India, Government of India, Department of Indian Systems of Medicine & Homoeopathy, New Delhi, Part-1, Volume- 2, PP. 59.

Pareek, G.N. (2005), Sudhanidhi, Vanoshadhi Ratnakar, Dhanvantari Karyalaya, Aligarh, Vol. 2, PP. 211.

Prajapati, N.D., Purohit, S.S., Sharma, A.K. & Tarun Kumar (2003), A Hand Book of Medicinal Plants, Agrobios India, Jodhpur, PP. 481.

Sharma, P.C., Yelne, MB. & Denis, T.J. (2000), Database on medicinal plants used in ayurveda, Central Council for research in Ayurveda and siddha, Vol. 4, PP. 269.

Sharma, P.V. (1981), Dravya gun vigyana, Chaukhambha Bharti Academy, Varanasi, Vol. 1, PP. 280.

Singh, R.S. (2002), Vanoshadhi Nirdeshika, Uttar Pradesh Hindi Sansthan, Lucknow, PP. 63.

Swami, K.N. (1985), Gavon Main Aushadh Ratna, Kalera Krishana Gopal, Kalera (Raj.), Vol. 2, PP. 138.

440. *Soymida febrifuga* A. Juss.

Family: Meliaceae.

Ayurvedic Groups: Charak: *Balya,* **Sushruta:** *Nyagrodhaadi gana.*

Name: English: Indian Redwood, Bastard Cedar, **Sanskrit:** *Maansarohini, Atiruhaa, Vritta, Charmakashaa, Vasaa, Prahaaravalli, Vikashaa, Rohini, Veeravati,* **Hindi:** *Maansarohini,* **Local:** *Rohan.*

Botanical characteristics: Habit: A tall tree, height up to 22 m. **Stem:** Girth 2.5-3 m, bark 0.8 cm thick, bluish-grey or blackish, heartwood reddish-brown. **Leaf:** 23-45 cm long, crowded towards the ends of the branches; leaflets 3-6 pairs, opposite, 5-11.3 by 2.5-6.3 cm, elliptic or oblong, obtuse, glabrous, penninerved, the nerves numerous and conspicuous beneath, base rounded, inequilateral; petiolules 3-6 mm long. **Flower:** Small, bisexual, greenish-white, in large terminal or axillary divercately branched panicles often equaling the leaves, the branches of the penicle alternate; pedicels very short; bracts minute, triangular, acute. **Fruit:** Capsules, 7.5 by 5 cm, very hard, brown-red, obovoid, 5-celled, 5-valved. **Seed:** Numerous, winged.

Flowering and fruiting period: March-April and May-June.

Habitat: Dry forests of Peninsular India, Rajasthan and Bihar.

Parts used: Bark. **Dosage:** 3-6 g.

Collection period: December-January.

Ayurvedic properties: ***Ras:*** *kashaaya, katu,* ***Gun:*** *laghu, rukhsa,* ***Veerya:*** *sheeta,* ***Vipaka:*** *katu,* ***Tridosha*** **Effect:** alleviates ***Kapha:*** *++,* ***Pitta:*** *+,* ***Vaata:*** *+.*

Chemical constituents: The **bark** contains tetranor-triterpenoids with modified furan ring. Petroleum ether extract of the bark yielded a steroid, methyl angolensate, ether extract yielded a steroid glycoside.

Action and disease indications: The **bark** is astringent, refrigerant, anthelmintic, union promoter, laxative, aphrodisiac, anti-pyretic, bitter tonic, used for malaria, sore throat, cough, asthma, ulcers, skin diseases, seminal weakness, leprosy, stomatitis, rheumatic swelling, diarrhea, dysentery and general debility.

Clinical uses: Chronic fever: Decoction of bark of described plant, 3 g, with honey 10 g, two times a day, is useful. **Amebic dysentery, diarrhea:** Bark powder of described plant, 3 g, with water, two times a day, is beneficial. **Inflammation, ulcer:** Local application of paste of bark of described plant is beneficial. **Dentalgia:** Gargles by decoction of described plant, 3 g, is beneficial.

Recommended readings:

Bhutya, R.K. (2007), Vanaspati Aushadha Vigyana, Scientific Publishers (India), Jodhpur, PP. 177.

Brahmavarchas (2003), Ayurved Ka Pran Vanoshadhi Vigyan, Shanti Kunj, Haridwar, PP. 415.

Chunekar, K.C. (2004), Bhava Prakash Nighantu, Chaukhambha Bharti Academy, Varanasi, PP. 358.

Khare, C.P. (2007), Indian Medicinal Plants, Springer (India) P.L. New Delhi, PP. 619.

Kirtikar, K.R. & Basu, B.D. (1998), Indian Medicinal Plants, L.M Basu, Allahabad, Vol. 1, PP. 559.

Misra, B.L. (2005), Dravya Guna Hastamalaka, Publication scheme, Jaipur, PP. 436.

Sharma, P.V. (1981), Dravya gun vigyana, Chaukhambha Bharti Academy, Varanasi, Vol. 1, PP. 825.

Singh, R.S. (2002), Vanoshadhi Nirdeshika, Uttar Pradesh Hindi Sansthan, Lucknow, PP. 300.

441. *Sphaeranthus indicus* Linn.

Family: Compositae; Asteraceae.

Synonym: *S. senegalensis, S. hirtus.*

Other similar plants: *S. africanus-* bigger var.- *Mahamundi- Mahashravani.*

Ayurvedic Groups: Charak: *Rasaayana.*

Name: Sanskrit: *Mundi, Bhikhsu, Shraavani, Tapodhanaa, Munditikaa,* **Hindi:** *Gorakhamundi,* **Local:** *Gorakhamundi.*

Botanical characteristics: Habit: An aromatic, visid, annual, prostrate or decumbent-ascending herb, height 30-60 cm and in same diam. **Stem:** Stem and branches are cylindrical, glandular, hairy, toothed winged. **Leaf:** Sessile, decurrent, 1-5 by 0.45-2.2 cm, obovate-oblong, rounded or sub-acute, glandular-hairy, spinous-serrate or dentate, at the base. **Flower:** Purple or pink, in close terminal, globose or ovoid, compound, ebracteate heads 1-15 cm across, on solitary and grandular peduncles, with toothed wings. Involucral bracts linear, acuminate, pubescent and ciliate near the ends. **Fruit:** Achenes, 1 mm long, glabrous, stalked.

Flowering and fruiting period: December-January and February-March.

Habitat: Distributed throughout India, up to an altitude of 1500 m, very common as a weed in dry rice fields and cultivated lands.

Parts used: Flower, whole plant.

Dosage: Flower 3-5 g, plant juice 10-20 ml.

Collection period: February-March.

Ayurvedic properties: ***Ras:*** *madhur, tikta, katu,* ***Gun:*** *laghu, rukhsa,* ***Veerya:*** *ushna,* ***Vipaka:*** *katu,* ***Tridosha*** **Effect:** alleviates ***Vaata:*** *+++,* ***Pitta:*** *++,* ***Kapha:*** *++.*

Chemical constituents: The **capitula** contain albumin, a fatty oil up to 5%, reducing sugars, tannins, mineral matter, a volatile oil 0.07%, and a glucoside. The glucoside on hydrolysis gave a aglycone, phenolic in nature. The unsaponifiable matter of the fatty oil showed beta-sitosterol, stigmasterol, *n*-triacontanol, *n*-pentacosane and hentriacontane. The **essential oil** contain methylchavicol, alpha-ionone, *d*-csdinene, *p*-methoxycinnamaldehyde as a major constituent, also a bitter alkaloid sphaeranthine. The **essential oil** is active against *Vibrio cholera* and *Micrococcus pyrogenes* var. *aureus*. The **flower**

heads contain beta-D-glucoside of beta-sitosterol, eudesmanolides, cryptomeridiol, 4-epicryptomeridiol, a sesquiterpene glycoside, sphaeranthanolide, which exhibited immune stimulating activity.

Action and disease indications: The **Capitulas** are blood purifier, alterative, aphrodisiac, depurative and tonic, used for skin diseases, seminal weakness and penile dysfunction. The **plant** is thermogenic, anti-inflammatory, diuretic, expectorant, nervine tonic, anodyne, appetizer, digestive, liver stimulant, good for brain, rejuvenating, febrifuge, stomachic, prescribed for epilepsy, hemicrania, jaundice, hepatomegaly, inflammations, strangury, diabtes, dysuria, anuria, vaginopathy, anemia, fileria, obesity, anal fissure and sinus, spleenomegaly, fever, scrofula, pectoralgia, cough, hernia, piles, dyspepsia and helminthiasis.

Clinical uses: Migraine, hemicrenia: Juice of described plant 10-20 ml, with *Piper nigrum* 500 mg, two times a day, is beneficial. **Prostatitis:** Juice of described plant, or distillate of described plant, 20 ml, two times a day, is beneficial. **Skin diseases, boils, Bromidiosis :** Local application of paste of leaves of described plant is beneficial. **Piles:** Root powder of described plant 3 g, with whey, two times a day, is beneficial. **Chronic rheumatism:** Flower powder of described plant 3 g, *Zingiber officinale* 1 g, with lukewarm water, two times a day, is beneficial. **Pain of piles:** Fumigation by described plant, is beneficial. **Penile dysfunction:** Mix powder of flowers of described plant, pure leaves of *Canabis sativa, Asparagus racemosus, Zingiber officinale, Tricholepsis glaberrima, Cinamomum cassia, Eclipta alba,* 6 g, with milk, two times a day, is beneficial. **Gout, skin diseases:** Flower powder of described plant 3 g, clarified butter 10 g, with decoction of bark of *Azadirachta indica,* 6 g, *Tinospora cordifolia* 10 g, two times a day, is beneficial. **Osteo arthritis:** Powder of described plant 5 g, with lukewarm water, three times a day, is useful. **Nocturnal emission, excess and turbid micturition:** Decoction of mix powder of described plant, inner bark of *Ficus religiosa,* new leaves of *Ficus bengalensis,* 10 g, two times a day, is beneficial. **Epilepsy:** Flower powder of described plant 3 g, *Acorus calamus* 1 g, with water, two times a day, is beneficial. **Mastoptosis:** Local massage by medicated oil of *Sesamum orientale,* made by described plant and *Piper longum,* is beneficial. Nasal drops by this oil, 4-4 drops, is also very beneficial. **Anuria, dysuria:** Fruit of *Vitis vinifera* 20 g, with juice of described plant 20 ml, two times a day, is beneficial. **Hypomnesia:** Mix powder of described plant, *Acorus calamus, Bacopa monnieri, Asparagus racemosus, Nardostachys jatamansi,* 6 g, with milk, two times a day, is beneficial. **For rejuvenating, spermacresia:** Mix powder of described plant, *Eclipta alba,* 5 g, with clarified butter 10 g, two times a day, is beneficial. Use rice and milk in meal.

Formulations: *Gorakhamundi arka, Chandanaadi arka, Raktashodhakaarista, Patumundi kwaatha, Guduchyaadi taila, Navaratnarajam-rigaanka rasa, Vaatagajaankusha rasa, Chandanaadi taila.*

Recommended readings:

Acharya, B.K. (2008), Ayurveda Jadi-buti Rahasya, Patanjali Yogapitha, Haridwar, PP. 212.

Bhutya, R.K. (2007), Vanaspati Aushadha Vigyana, Scientific Publishers (India), Jodhpur, PP. 90.

Chunekar, K.C. (2004), Bhava Prakash Nighantu, Chaukhambha Bharti Academy, Varanasi, PP. 413.

Dhiman, A.K. (2006), Ayurvedic Drug Plants, Daya Publishing House, Delhi, PP. 264.

Khare, C.P. (2007), Indian Medicinal Plants, Springer (India) P.L. New Delhi, PP. 620.

Kirtikar, K.R. & Basu, B.D. (1998), Indian Medicinal Plants, L.M Basu, Allahabad, Vol. 2, PP. 1347.

Misra, B.L. (2005), Dravya Guna Hastamalaka, Publication scheme, Jaipur, PP. 296.

Nair, R.Vasudevan, (2007), Indian Medicinal Plants, Orient Longman P.L. Chennai, Vol. 5, PP. 180.

Namjoshi, A.N. (2001), The Ayurvedic Pharmacopoeia of India, Government of India, Department of Indian Systems of Medicine & Homoeopathy, New Delhi, Part-1, Volume- 3, PP. 127.

Pareek, G.N. (2005), Sudhanidhi, Vanoshadhi Ratnakar, Dhanvantari Karyalaya, Aligarh, Vol. 10, PP. 81.

Prajapati, N.D., Purohit, S.S., Sharma, A.K. & Tarun Kumar (2003), A Hand Book of Medicinal Plants, Agrobios India, Jodhpur, PP. 484.

Sharma, P.C., Yelne, MB. & Denis, T.J. (2000), Database on medicinal plants used in ayurveda, Central Council for research in Ayurveda and siddha, Vol. 5, PP. 251.

Sharma, P.V. (1981), Dravya gun vigyana, Chaukhambha Bharti Academy, Varanasi, Vol. 1, PP. 804.

Singh, R.S. (2002), Vanoshadhi Nirdeshika, Uttar Pradesh Hindi Sansthan, Lucknow, PP. 307.

Swami, K.N. (1985), Gavon Main Aushadh Ratna, Kalera Krishana Gopal, Kalera (Raj.), Vol. 2, PP. 259.

442. *Spilanthes oleracea* Murr.

Family: Compositae; Asteraceae.

Other similar plants: *Spilanthes Calva* syn. *S.acmela, S.paniculata, S.pseudoacmela.*

Name: English: Brazilian Cress, Para Cress, **Sanskrit:** *Maharaastri, Marethi,* **Hindi:** *Akarakaraa-desi,* **Local:** *Akarkaraa, Marethi, Akalkhuro.*

Botanical characteristics: Habit: An annual, erect or ascending herb, height 30-60 cm, more or less pubescent, sometimes hairy. **Root:** 8-15 cm long, 1.25 cm diam. **Stem:** Usually decumbent near the base. **Leaf:** Opposite, 2.5-5 by 1.3-3.8 cm, ovate, acute or subobtuse, irregular ly crenate-serrate or sometimes entire, glabrous, or nearly so, base usually acute, petioles 0.6-1.6 cm, pubescent. **Flower:** Yellow, purple or white, heads, 0.6-1.3 cm long, ovoid, solitary or sub-panicled; peduncles 10 cm long, involucral bracts oblong-lanceolate, sub-acute, pubescent. **Fruit:** Achnes, oblong or slightly obovoid, truncate, much compressed, nearly glabrous.

Flowering and fruiting period: September-October and November-December.

Habitat: Throughout India, cultivated in gardens.

Parts used: Root. **Dosage:** 0.5-1 g.

Collection period: December-January.

Ayurvedic properties: ***Ras:*** *katu,* ***Gun:*** *laghu, rukhsa,* ***Veerya:*** *ushna,* ***Vipaka:*** *katu,* ***Tridosha*** **Effect:** alleviates ***Kapha: +++, Vaata: ++.***

Chemical constituents: The **plant** contains mainly spilanthol, also an **essential oil** consisting mainly of spilanthol and a hydro-carbons, spilanthene, cerotic acid, crystalline phytosterols, tannic acid, resin, potassium malate and large amounts of choline and potassium nitrate.

Action and disease indications: The **roots** are thermogenic, anti-inflammatory, anodyne, nervine tonic, aphrodisiac, sialagogue, diuretic, used for inflammations, seminal weakness, penile dysfunction, premature ejaculation, cough, asthma, bronchitis, hypo salivation and neuralgia.

Clinical uses: Shuttering: Root powder of described plant, 250 mg, with honey 10 g, two times a day, is useful. **Rhinitis:** Root powder of described plant, 500 mg, with juice of *Piper betel* 10 ml, two times a day, is beneficial.

Recommended readings:

Bhutya, R.K. (2007), Vanaspati Aushadha Vigyana, Scientific Publishers (India), Jodhpur, PP. 2.

Khare, C.P. (2007), Indian Medicinal Plants, Springer (India) P.L. New Delhi, PP. 622.

Kirtikar, K.R. & Basu, B.D. (1998), Indian Medicinal Plants, L.M Basu, Allahabad, Vol. 2, PP. 1368.

Prajapati, N.D., Purohit, S.S., Sharma, A.K. & Tarun Kumar (2003), A Hand Book of Medicinal Plants, Agrobios India, Jodhpur, PP. 43.

Sharma, P.V. (1981), Dravya gun vigyana, Chaukhambha Bharti Academy, Varanasi, Vol. 1, PP. 578.

Swami, K.N. (1985), Gavon Main Aushadh Ratna, Kalera Krishana Gopal, Kalera (Raj.), Vol. 1, PP. 1.

443. *Spinacea oleracea* Linn.

Family: Chenopodiaceae.

Synonym: *S. tetrandra.*

Name: English: Garden Spinach, **Sanskrit:** *Palakyaa, Vastukaakaaraa, Chhurikaa, Chiritachhadaa,* **Hindi:** *Paalak,* **Local:** *Paalak.*

Botanical characteristics: Habit: An erect annual herb, height 30-60 cm. **Stem:** Round, smooth, piped, angular, succulent, sometimes reddish. **Leaf:** Alternate, the lower ones very-long petioled, glabrous, fleshy, variously lobed with lobes of an acute triangular shape, smooth on both sides. **Flower:** Male: greenish, very numerous, sessile, on long terminal glomerate spikesand shorter ones from the axil. Female: axillary, sessile, crowded. **Fruit:** Capsules, 1-celled, 1-valved, armed, with 2 opposite short horns, and crowned with the small remaining calyx.

Flowering and fruiting period: October-November and December-January.

Habitat: Cultivated throughout India.

Parts used: Leaves. **Dosage:** 25-50 g.

Collection period: November-December.

Ayurvedic properties: ***Ras:*** *madhur,* ***Gun:*** *rukhsa,* ***Veerya:*** *sheeta,* ***Vipaka:*** *madhur,* ***Tridosha*** **Effect:** alleviates ***Pitta: +, Kapha: +,*** aggrevates ***Vaata: +.***

Chemical constituents: The **aerial parts** contains rutin, hyperoside, astragalin, and caffeic, chlorogenic, neochlorogenic and protocatechuic acids. The **seeds** contain glycoprotein-bound hexosamine. The **roots** contain spirasaponins.

Action and disease indications: The **leaves** are cooling, emollient, anti-pyretic, diuretic, maturant, laxative, digestible, anthelmintic, alexipharmic, prescribed for inflammation of lung and bowels, sore throat, arthralgia, dispesis, lumbago, cold, sore eyes, ringworm, scabies, leucoderma, scalding urin, vomiting, biliousness, flatulence, constipation, asthma and skin diseases.

Clinical uses: Fever: Decoction of described plant, 50 g, two times a day, is beneficial. **Hepatitis, jaundice, asthma:** Seed powder of described plant 3 g, with water, two times a day, is beneficial. **Abscess:** Poultice of seed powder of described plant, is beneficial.

Recommended readings:

Bhutya, R.K. (2007), Vanaspati Aushadha Vigyana, Scientific Publishers (India), Jodhpur, PP. 150.

Brahmavarchas (2003), Ayurved Ka Pran Vanoshadhi Vigyan, Shanti Kunj, Haridwar, PP. 417.

Chunekar, K.C. (2004), Bhava Prakash Nighantu, Chaukhambha Bharti Academy, Varanasi, PP. 668.

Khare, C.P. (2007), Indian Medicinal Plants, Springer (India) P.L. New Delhi, PP. 622.

Kirtikar, K.R. & Basu, B.D. (1998), Indian Medicinal Plants, L.M Basu, Allahabad, Vol. 5, PP. 2078.

Sharma, P.V. (1981), Dravya gun vigyana, Chaukhambha Bharti Academy, Varanasi, Vol. 2, PP. 194.

Swami, K.N. (1985), Gavon Main Aushadh Ratna, Kalera Krishana Gopal, Kalera (Raj.), Vol. 1, PP. 263.

444. *Spondias pinnata* (Linn. f.) Kurz.

Family: Anacardiaceae.

Synonym: *S.mangifera.*

Other similar plants: *S.cytherea,* syn. *S.dulcis.*

Name: English: Hog-Plum, Wild Mango, **Sanskrit:** *Aamraataka, Pitana, Markataamra, Kapitana,* **Hindi:** *Aamratak,* **Local:** *Aamaraa, Jangali Aam.*

Botanical characteristics: Habit: A medium sized, aromatic deciduous tree, height 9-12 m, sometimes up to 27 m. **Stem:** 2.5 in girth, straight; bark thick, smooth, ash-coloured; branches nearly horizontal. **Leaf:** Compound, 30-45 cm long, the common petioles slender, terete, smooth, straight; crowded at the ends of branches; leaflets large, 3-5 pairs and a terminal one, 7.5-18 by 3.8-7.5 cm, oblong or elliptic-oblong, acuminate, quite entire, more or less oblique; main nerves numerous, horizontal, straight, joined by a strong intramarginal one; petiolules 5-6 mm long. **Flower:** Mono or bisexual, sessile, numerous, pinkish-green, clustered in sparingly branched glabrous terminal panicles 25-38 cm long. **Fruit:** Drupes, fleshy, about 3.8 cm long, with woody endocarp surrounded by longitudinal interwoven fibres, young fruits green, turning light yellow or greenish-yellow on ripening. **Seed:** Stone woody, hard, rough with irregular furrows and cavities, fibrous outside, seed usually 1, more rarely 2 or 3.

Flowering and fruiting period: February-May and June-January.

Habitat: Throughout India, up to an altitude of 1600 m, in deciduous forests, as wild as cultivated.

Parts used: Unripe fruit. **Dosage:** 5-10 g.

Collection period: June-January.

Ayurvedic properties: ***Ras:*** *kashaaya, madhur,* ***Gun:*** *guru, snigdha,* ***Veerya:*** *sheeta,* ***Vipaka:*** *madhur,* ***Tridosha*** **Effect:** alleviates ***Vaata:*** **++,** ***Pitta:*** **+,** aggrevates ***Kapha:*** **+.**

Chemical constituents: The **fruits** contain beta-amyrin, oleanolic acid and amino acids-glycine, cystine, serine, alanine and leucine; and polysaccharides. The **aerial parts** contain lignoceric acid, 24-methyllenecycloartanone, stigmast-4-en-3-one, beta-sitosterol and its glucoside.

Action and disease indications: The **unripe fruits** are thermogenic, appetizer and aphrodisiac. The **ripe fruits** are cooling, emollient, constipating, anti-scorbutic and tonic, used for bilious dyspepsia, diarrhea and general debility.

Clinical uses: Anorexia, indigestion: Unripe fruit powder of described plant, 10 g, rock salt 1 g, with water, two times a day, is beneficial. **Diarrhea:** Unripe fruit powder of described plant, 10 g, with water, two times a day, is beneficial.

Recommended readings:

Chunekar, K.C. (2004), Bhava Prakash Nighantu, Chaukhambha Bharti Academy, Varanasi, PP. 553.

Khare, C.P. (2007), Indian Medicinal Plants, Springer (India) P.L. New Delhi, PP. 622.

Kirtikar, K.R. & Basu, B.D. (1998), Indian Medicinal Plants, L.M Basu, Allahabad, Vol. 1, PP. 673.

Nair, R.Vasudevan, (2007), Indian Medicinal Plants, Orient Longman P.L. Chennai, Vol. 5, PP. 186.

Prajapati, N.D., Purohit, S.S., Sharma, A.K. & Tarun Kumar (2003), A Hand Book of Medicinal Plants, Agrobios India, Jodhpur, PP. 486.

Sharma, P.C., Yelne, MB. & Denis, T.J. (2000), Database on medicinal plants used in ayurveda, Central Council for research in Ayurveda and siddha, Vol. 6, PP. 13.

Singh, R.S. (2002), Vanoshadhi Nirdeshika, Uttar Pradesh Hindi Sansthan, Lucknow, PP. 36.

445. *Streblus asper* Lour.

Family: Moraceae.

Synonym: *Epicarpurus orientalis.*

Name: English: Siamee Rough Brush. **Sanskrit:** *Shaakhota, Peetaphalaka, Bhutaavaasa, Kharachhada,* **Hindi:** *Shaakhotak,* **Local:** *Sihor.*

Botanical characteristics: Habit: A small rigid gnarled evergreen tree, height up to 15 m. **Stem:** With light grey or greenish rough bark, and hairy scabrid twigs, milky white latex. **Leaf:** Simple, alternate, 2.5-10 cm long, rhomboid-elliptic, obovate or elliptic-oblong, acute or acuminate, more or less sinuate or crenate, scbrid on both surfaces but especially beneath;

lateral nerves 4-6 pairs; prominent beneath, connected by intramarginal loops; petioles 1.3-3.8 mm long; stipules rather longer than the petiole, obliquily lanceolate, acuminate. **Flower:** Unisexual, dioecious, axillary, male flowers in globose pedunculate heads 7.5 mm diam.; peduncles 1-4 together, 7.5-13 mm long. Female flowers solitary, inconspicuous, long peduncled, 1-4 together, 5-13 mm long, bracts 2-3 below the perianth. **Fruit:** Berry, succulent, one seeded, loosely enclosed by the enlarged sepals, yellow when ripe, 5 mm diam. **Seed:** smooth, round, greenish white.

Flowering and fruiting period: January-February and May-July.

Habitat: Drier parts of India, from Rohilkhand eastwards and peninsular India, up to an altitude of 600 m.

Parts used: Bark, latex.

Dosage: Bark 3-5 g, latex for external use.

Collection period: December-January.

Ayurvedic properties: ***Ras:*** *tikta, kashaaya,* ***Gun:*** *laghu, rukhsa,* ***Veerya:*** *ushna,* ***Vipaka:*** *katu,* ***Tridosha*** **Effect:** alleviates ***Vaata:*** +, ***Kapha:*** +.

Chemical constituents: The **root bark** contains cardenolide glycosides, asperoside and strebloside, 6-deoxyallose. The **stem bark** contains alpha-amyrin acetate, lupeol acetate, lupeol and beta-sitosterol.

Action and disease indications: The **bark** is vulnerary, anti-inflammatory and constipating, used for foul ulcers, diarrhea, dysentery, inflammations and fever. The **latex** is antiseptic, sedative and styptic, used for sore heels, chapped hands, adenitis, neuralgia and haemorrhages. The roots are thermogenic, vulnerary, anti-inflammatory, haemostatic, anticonvulsant, constipating, febrifuge and antiseptic, used for inflammations, ulcers, sinusitis, elephantiasis, boils, haemorrhages, haemoptysis, cough, asthma, bronchitis, convulsions, diarrhea, dysentery, fever, syphilis and piles.

Clinical uses: Fever, diarrhea, dysentery: Decoction of bark of described plant, 6 g, two times a day, is beneficial. **Elephantiasis:** Decoction of bark of described plant, 6 g, with urine of cow, two times a day, is beneficial. **Foul ulcer, sinus:** Local application of paste of roots of described plant is beneficial. **Cracked heel:** Local application of latex of described plant is beneficial. **Leucoderma:** Local application of paste of seeds of described plant, is beneficial. **Epilepsy:** Root powder of described plant, 5 g, with water, two times a day, is beneficial.

Formulations: *Vrihat Manjisthaadi kwaatha, Saakhotaka bindu.*

Recommended readings:

Bhutya, R.K. (2007), Vanaspati Aushadha Vigyana, Scientific Publishers (India), Jodhpur, PP. 213.

Chunekar, K.C. (2004), Bhava Prakash Nighantu, Chaukhambha Bharti Academy, Varanasi, PP. 542.

Dhiman, A.K. (2006), Ayurvedic Drug Plants, Daya Publishing House, Delhi, PP. 352.

Khare, C.P. (2007), Indian Medicinal Plants, Springer (India) P.L. New Delhi, PP. 627.

Kirtikar, K.R. & Basu, B.D. (1998), Indian Medicinal Plants, L.M Basu, Allahabad, Vol. 3, PP. 2304.

Nair, R.Vasudevan, (2007), Indian Medicinal Plants, Orient Longman P.L. Chennai, Vol. 5, PP. 198.

Namjoshi, A.N. (2001), The Ayurvedic Pharmacopoeia of India, Government of India, Department of Indian Systems of Medicine & Homoeopathy, New Delhi, Part-1, Volume- 3, PP. 147.

Prajapati, N.D., Purohit, S.S., Sharma, A.K. & Tarun Kumar (2003), A Hand Book of Medicinal Plants, Agrobios India, Jodhpur, PP. 489.

Sharma, P.V. (1981), Dravya gun vigyana, Chaukhambha Bharti Academy, Varanasi, Vol. 1, PP. 233.

446. *Stereospermum suaveolens* D.C.

Family: Bignoniaceae.

Other similar plants: *S.personatum* syn. *chelonoides, tetragonum-Paatali*-white flowered var. *S.suaveolens-Tamrapushpi-* copper-red flowered var.

Ayurvedic Groups: Charak: *shothhara,* **Sushruta:** *Vrihat panchamoola, Dashamoola, Adhobhaagahar, Aaragvadhaadi gana.*

Name: English: Trumpet Flower Tree, **Sanskrit:** *Paatali, Patalaa, Amoghaa, Madhuduti, Phaleruhaa, Krisnavrintaa, Kuberaakhsi, Alivallabhaa, Taamrapushpi,* **Hindi:** *Paatalaa,* **Local:** *Paadhal, Adhakapaari.*

Botanical characteristics: Habit: A large deciduous tree, height 9-30 m, more or less pubescent. **Root:** Dull brown, cylindrical, hard and heavy with transversely extended lenticles. **Stem:** With a straight trunk and fairy smooth yellowish-brown bark; young parts viscous-hairy. **Leaf:** Imparipinnate, large, 30-60 cm long, clustered towards the end of the branchlets, leaflets 3-6 pairs and an odd one, 7.5-15 by 5-7.5 cm, broadly elliptic, usually acuminate, often serrulate, rough above, pubescent beneath, base usually rounded and unequal-sided; main nerves 6-8 pairs with reticulate venation between; petiolules of the lateral leaflets 2.5 mm or less long. **Flower:** Dull purple, infundibuliform, pubescent outside, sweetly fragrant, in large, lax, drooping, trichotomous viscidly-hairy, terminal cymose panicles. **Fruit:** Capsules, 30-60 cm by 1.7 cm, cylindric, slender, curved, somewhat rough with elevated white specks; valve thick, hard, pendulous for long time on tree. **Seed:** 3.2 by 1.3 cm, 12-30 per pod, with a long membranous wing at each end, the nucleus furrowed across the middle, sunk into the notches of the cylindric brown spongy dissepiment.

Flowering and fruiting period: March-April and December-January.

Habitat: Throughout India, in deciduous forests, especially in the moist regions, up to an altitude of 1200 m.

Parts used: Root bark, flower, seed, leaves, alkaline.

Dosage: Root bark 3-5 g, flower 1-3 g, alkaline 0-5-1g, seed and leaves for external use.

Collection period: December-January.

Ayurvedic properties: ***Ras:*** *kashaaya, tikta,* ***Gun:*** *laghu, rukhsa,* ***Veerya:*** *anushna,* ***Vipaka:*** *katu,* ***Tridosha*** **Effect:** alleviates ***Vaata:*** *+++,* ***Kapha:*** ++,***Pitta:*** +.

Chemical constituents: The **roots** and **root bark** contain beta-sitosterol, *n*-tricontanol, lapachol, dehydro-alpha-lapochone, dehydrotectol, ceryl alcohol oleic, palmitic and stearic acids.

Action and disease indications: The **roots** are anodyne, appetizer, constipating, diuretic, expectorant, lithontriptic, aphrodisiac, cardio tonic, anti-inflammatory, anti-bacterial, febrifuge and tonic, used for renal and vesical calculi, cough, asthma, bronchitis, hiccough, dyspepsia, diarrhea, strangury, hyperdisia, piles, hyperacidity, vomiting, dropsy, fever and general debility.

Clinical uses: Hemicrenia: Local application of paste of seeds of described plant is beneficial. **Hiccough:** Flower juice of described plant 5 ml, with honey 10 g, two times a day, is useful. **Diabetes mellitus, renal and vesical calculus, anuria:** Alkali of described plant 1.5 g, with oil of *Sesamum orientale* 10 g, two times a day, is beneficial. Use warm water after this medication. **Hyperacidity:** Cold infusion of bark of described plant 5 g, with honey 10 g, two times a day, is useful. **Somasthenia:** *'Gulkand'* of flowers of described plant, 10 g, with milk, two times a day, is beneficial. **Lumbego, Sciatica:** Decoction of *'Dashamoola kwatha'*, 15 g, *Sida cordifolia* 3 g, *Pluchea lanceolata* 2 g, *Zingiber officinale* 1 g, with castor oil 10 ml, at morning, is beneficial. **Burning sensation:** Local application of paste of roots of described plant, with water, is beneficial. **Pneumnia:** Decoction of mix powder of root bark of described plant, *Zingiber officinale, Trachy spermum-ammi, Clerodendron serratum, Inula racemosa, Piper longum,* 6 g, with honey 10 g, two times a day, is useful. **Abscess, inflammation, pains** Root bark powder of described plant, *Boerhavia diffusa, Zingiber officinale, Tinospora cordifolia, Moringa oleifera,* 10 g, with honey 10 g, two times a day, is useful. **Anuria, dysuria:** Mix powder of *Cinamomum verum, Elettaria cardamomum, Piper longum,* 1 g, with 50 ml solution of mix alkali of described plant, *Hordium vulgare, Sesamum orientale,* 1.5 g, two times a day, is beneficial. **Renal and vesical calculus:** Alkali of described plant, 500 mg, with urine of she goat, 20 ml, two times a day, is beneficial. **Obesity:** Mix powder of decoction of root bark of described plant, *Gmelina arboria, Orxylum indicum, Premna corymbosa, Aegle marmelos,* 10 g, with honey 10 g, two times a day, is useful. **Hyperacidity:** Decoction of roots of described plant 10 g, *Trichosanthus dioica* 5 g, with powder of *Coriandrum sativum* 3 g, **Asthma, bronchitis:** Decoction of root bark of described plant 10 g, with nitrate of potash 500 mg, rock salt 250 mg, two times a day, is beneficial. **Lumbego:** Decoction of *'Dashamoola kwatha'* 10 g, with powder of *Zingiber officinale* 1 g, two times a day, is beneficial. **Sciatic neuritis:** Decoction of *'Dashamoola kwatha'* 10 g, *Zingiber officinale* 1 g, *Pluchea lanceolata* 5 g, with castor oil 10 ml, at morning, is beneficial. **Inflammation:** Decoction of *'Dashamoola kwatha'* 10 g, *Boerhavia diffusa* 5 g, *cedrus deodara* 3 g, with urine of cow, two times a day, is beneficial.

Formulations: *Dashamoola kwaatha, Dantyaarista, Chyavanpraasha, Bhaarangi guda, Mushakaadhya taila, Brahmarasaayana, Dashamoolaarista, Amritaarista, Madhyama naaraayana taila, Dashamoola ghrita, Mahaa panchagavya ghrita, Lasunaadi ghrita, Agatsya haritaki rasaayana.*

Recommended readings:

Bhutya, R.K. (2007), Vanaspati Aushadha Vigyana, Scientific Publishers (India), Jodhpur, PP. 147.

Chunekar, K.C. (2004), Bhava Prakash Nighantu, Chaukhambha Bharti Academy, Varanasi, PP. 279.

Dhiman, A.K. (2006), Ayurvedic Drug Plants, Daya Publishing House, Delhi, PP. 295.

Khare, C.P. (2007), Indian Medicinal Plants, Springer (India) P.L. New Delhi, PP. 626.

Kirtikar, K.R. & Basu, B.D. (1998), Indian Medicinal Plants, L.M Basu, Allahabad, Vol. 3, PP. 1848.

Misra, B.L. (2005), Dravya Guna Hastamalaka, Publication scheme, Jaipur, PP. 409.

Nair, R.Vasudevan, (2007), Indian Medicinal Plants, Orient Longman P.L. Chennai, Vol. 5, PP. 192.

Namjoshi, A.N. (2001), The Ayurvedic Pharmacopoeia of India, Government of India, Department of Indian Systems of Medicine & Homoeopathy, New Delhi, Part-1, Volume- 3, PP. 147.

Pareek, G.N. (2005), Sudhanidhi, Vanoshadhi Ratnakar, Dhanvantari Karyalaya, Aligarh, Vol. 5, PP. 288.

Prajapati, N.D., Purohit, S.S., Sharma, A.K. & Tarun Kumar (2003), A Hand Book of Medicinal Plants, Agrobios India, Jodhpur, PP. 488.

Sharma, P.C., Yelne, MB. & Denis, T.J. (2000), Database on medicinal plants used in ayurveda, Central Council for research in Ayurveda and siddha, Vol. 6, PP. 288.

Sharma, P.V. (1981), Dravya gun vigyana, Chaukhambha Bharti Academy, Varanasi, Vol. 1, PP. 223.

Singh, R.S. (2002), Vanoshadhi Nirdeshika, Uttar Pradesh Hindi Sansthan, Lucknow, PP. 236.

447. *Strychnos nux-vomica* Linn.

Family: Loganiaceae; Strychnaceae.

Other similar plants: *Strychnos potatatorum.*

Name: English: Nux vomica, Strychnine tree, Snake-wood, Poison nut, **Sanskrit:** *Tinduka, Jalada, Dirghapatraka, Kupilu, Kulaka, Kaakatinduka, Kaakapiluka, Kaakendu, Vishatindu, Markatatindu,* **Hindi:** *Tinduka,* **Local:** *Kuchalaa.*

Botanical characteristics: Habit: A medium sized deciduous tree, 15-30 m high. **Stem:** 70 cm in diam., with a fairly straight and cylindrical bole, having thin, dark grey or yellowish grey bark and minute tubercles, often with sharp, strong, axillary spines. **Leaf:** 7.5-15 by 4.5-7.5 cm, broadly elliptic, acute, obtuse, or shortly acuminate, coriaceous, glabrous, shining, 5-nerved, base usually rounded; petioles 6-13 mm long. **Flower:** Greenish-white, numerous, in terminal pedunculate pubescent compound cymes; peduncles and pedicles short, pubescent. **Fruit:** Globose, 2.5-7.5 cm diam., orange-red when ripe, contains many discoid, compressed coin like seeds in fleshy white pulp. **Seed:** 2-5, about 2 cm diam., 3 mm thick, concave on one side and convex on the other side, very bitter, clothed on both sides very fine grey silky hairs, radiating from the centre, cotyledons cordate.

Flowering and fruiting period: March-April and November-December.

Habitat: Throughout tropical India, in deciduous forests, up to an altitude of 1360 m, mostly Bihar, Orissa, West Bengal, Uttar Pradesh, Andhra Pradesh and Karnataka. It is most common in the forests along the western coast.

Parts used: Seed.

Dosage: Detoxified seed 30-125 mg.

Collection period: December-January.

Ayurvedic properties: ***Ras:*** *tikta,* ***Gun:*** *laghu,* ***Veerya:*** *ushna,* ***Vipaka:*** *katu,* ***Tridosha*** **Effect:** alleviates ***Kapha:*** ***++,*** ***Vaata:*** ***++,*** ***Pitta:*** ***+.***

Chemical constituents: The **seeds** contain indole alkaloids, the major one is strychnine (50% of alkaloids); others include strychnine N-oxide, brucine and its N-oxide, alpha and beta colubrine, condylocarpine, diaboline, geissoschizine, icajine, isostrychnine, normocusine, nova-cine, pseudobrucine, pseudo-alpha-colubrine, pseudo-beta-colubrine, pseudostrychnine, vomicine and loganin. The alkaloidal content of the seeds ranges from 1.8-5.3%.

Action and disease indications: The **seeds** are alexiteric, appetizer, aphrodisiac, anthelmintic, anti-periodic, digestive, diuretic, emmenogogue, purgative, tonic, nervine tonic and stimulant, CNS stimulant, febrifuge and stomachic, used for neuralgia, anemia, cough, asthma, bronchitis, constipation, diabetes, intermittent and malarial fevers, insomnia, emotional disorders, hysteria, epilepsy, paralytic and neurological affections, retention of nocturnal incontinence of urine, spermatorrhea, sexual debility and impotence, gastro-intestinal tract disorders, skin diseases, cardiac diseases, paralysis, facial paralysis, sciatica, obesity, anorexia, hydrophobia, flatulence, night sweating of tuberculosis, and weakness of muscles.

Contraindication: Nux vomica is toxic. So beware to over dose. Use detoxified seeds.

Detoxification: 1. Put the seeds in urine of cow, for seven days, change the urine daily. After 7 days wash with fresh water, remove the silky hairy layer and pound it in wet condition. 2. Put seeds in *'Kanji'* for 3 days, repeat the above method. 3. Boil seeds in cow milk, in a piece of cloth in pendulous condition, for 3 hours at slight heat, repeat above method. 4. Fry the seeds in slight heat, until colour of seeds turn light brown, then remove outer layer with help of knife, and pound them in hot condition. 5. Fry the seeds in Castor oil, repeat above method.

Fatal dose: 1.8-3 g.

Fatal period: 5 minute-4 hours.

Symptoms: 1. Feeling of bitter taste is followed by a choking sensation in the throat. 2. Restlessness, spasm in throat, redness on mouth, increase of reflex action of muscles. 3. fibrillation of muscles. 4. The poison acts directly on the reflex centres of the spinal cord and spasm in muscles of different parts of body. 5. Clonic contraction at first but turns in tonic contraction. 6. Emprosthotonos or pleurosthotons or opisthotonos, at the time of spasm, the body bent forward or back or side. 7. Exophthalmia. 8. Pupils become dilated. 9. Patient can not open the mouth due to spasm of muscles of lower and upper jaw, lock jaw or trismus. 10. Cyanotic skin of mouth at the time of spasm. 11. Sometimes foaming from mouth or blood also. 12. Acute abdominal pain and dyspnea. 13. Risus sardonicus, characteristic appearance of face or a typical fixed smile. 14. Hyper-reflexia, spasm starts by lightly touching, sharp light or sound. 15. Apnea or asphyxia and death.

Treatment: Chloroform should be given by inhalation during the phase of relaxation to control convulsions. For spasms, short-acting barbiturates should be given immediately, the best being 0.3 to 0.6 g of pentobarbital sodium or sodium amytal intravenously. After controlling the spasms, the stomach is washed out with warm water containing potassium permanganate or animal charcoal or tannic acid or make vomit by emetic drug, as root powder of *Calotropis procera,* fruit powder of *Randia dumetorum* or injection of Apomorphine hydrochlor. Give cow milk 500 ml with 20 ml clarified butter or milk with white portion of egg, or decoction of *Terminalia chebula* 20 g. Gentle narcosis, and perfectly quite and dark surroundings are essential. Intravenous mephenesin 0.5 g to 1 g is recommended. Use oxygen inhalation or artificial respiration.

Note: For making powder of the seeds, after detoxification, pound or grind it immediately in wet or warm condition, in dry or cold condition, it is too much hard for pound or grind the seeds. Draw out the hilum of cotyledons, before pounding.

Clinical uses: Penile dysfunction: Seed powder of described plant, 50 mg, *'Lauha bhasma'* 125 mg, *Piper nigrum* 500 mg, with honey 10 g, two times a day, is useful. **Enuresis of children:** Seed powder of described plant, 25 mg, with decoction of bark of *Acacia nilotica* 20 g and honey 10 g, two times a day, is beneficial. **Constipation, asthma:** Seed powder of described plant, 50 mg, *Piper nigrum* 500 mg, with honey 10 g, two times a day, is useful. **Chorea:** Seed powder of described plant, 50 mg, *Zingiber officinale* 1 g, *Trachy spermumammi* 2 g, with clarified butter 10 g, two times a day, is beneficial. **Lumbego:** Seed powder of described plant, 50 mg, mix powder of *Zingiber officinale, Pluchea lanceolata, Trachy spermumammi, Asparagus racemosus, Withania somnifera, Argyreia nervosa,* 5 g, with water, two times a day, is beneficial. **Colic, indigestion, flatulence, chorea, depression, intoxication and remove habit of Opium and wine:** Mix powder of seeds of described plant, seeds of *Capsicum annum, 'Ras sindoora'* 125 mg, with honey 10 g, two times a day, is useful. **Penile dysfunction, anorthosis:** Mix powder of seeds of described plant, *Piper longum, Piper nigrum,* fruit of *Myristica fragrans,* 250 mg, in a capsule, with milk, before 1 hour of intercourse, is very beneficial. It is also very useful for middle aged men. **Osteo arthritis**: Seed powder of described plant, 100 mg, *'Lauha bhasma'* 125 mg, Gum of *Commiphora mukul* 1 g, with *'Maha raasnaadi kwatha'* 20 g, two times a day, is beneficial. **Scitica neuritis**: Seed powder of described plant 75 mg, *'Ropya maakhsika bhasma'* 250 mg, *'Abhraka bhasma'* 125 mg, with honey 20 g and clarified butter 10 g, two times a day, is beneficial.

Formulations: *Tinduka vati, Agnitundi vati, Maajun kuchalaa, Navajivan rasa, Laxmivilaasa rasa, Krimimudgar rasa, Kupiluhingvaadi vati.*

Recommended readings:

Bhutya, R.K. (2007), Vanaspati Aushadha Vigyana, Scientific Publishers (India), Jodhpur, PP. 117.

Brahmavarchas (2003), Ayurved Ka Pran Vanoshadhi Vigyan, Shanti Kunj, Haridwar, PP. 418.

Chunekar, K.C. (2004), Bhava Prakash Nighantu, Chaukhambha Bharti Academy, Varanasi, PP. 568.

Dhiman, A.K. (2006), Ayurvedic Drug Plants, Daya Publishing House, Delhi, PP. 216.

Khare, C.P. (2007), Indian Medicinal Plants, Springer (India) P.L. New Delhi, PP. 629.

Kirtikar, K.R. & Basu, B.D. (1998), Indian Medicinal Plants, L.M Basu, Allahabad, Vol. 2, PP. 1645.

Misra, B.L. (2005), Dravya Guna Hastamalaka, Publication scheme, Jaipur, PP. 444.

Nair, R.Vasudevan, (2007), Indian Medicinal Plants, Orient Longman P.L. Chennai, Vol. 5, PP. 202.

Pareek, G.N. (2005), Sudhanidhi, Vanoshadhi Ratnakar, Dhanvantari Karyalaya, Aligarh, Vol. 2, PP. 367.

Prajapati, N.D., Purohit, S.S., Sharma, A.K. & Tarun Kumar (2003), A Hand Book of Medicinal Plants, Agrobios India, Jodhpur, PP. 492.

Sharma, P.C., Yelne, MB. & Denis, T.J. (2000), Database on medicinal plants used in ayurveda, Central Council for research in Ayurveda and siddha, Vol. 5, PP. 139.

Sharma, P.V. (1981), Dravya gun vigyana, Chaukhambha Bharti Academy, Varanasi, Vol. 1, PP. 83.

Singh, R.S. (2002), Vanoshadhi Nirdeshika, Uttar Pradesh Hindi Sansthan, Lucknow, PP. 108.

Swami, K.N. (1985), Gavon Main Aushadh Ratna, Kalera Krishana Gopal, Kalera (Raj.), Vol. 1, PP. 147.

448. *Strychnos potatorum* Linn.

Family: Loganiaceae; Strychnaceae.

Name: English: Clearing Nut Tree, **Sanskrit:** *Karaka, Payahprashaadi, Chakhsusya,* **Hindi:** *Nirmali,* **Local:** *Nirmali.*

Botanical characteristics: Habit: A deciduous, glabrous tree, height about 12 m. **Stem:** With cracked and scaly black bark and irregularly fluted trunk. **Leaf:** 5-7.5 by 2.5-4.5 cm, simple, opposite, ovate or elliptic, sub-coriaceous, acute or sub-acuminate, glabrous and shining, nearly sessile, spuriously 3-or 5-nerved, the lateral nerves springing from the lower part of the midrib, not far from its base, base rounded or acute; petioles 2.5 mm long. **Flower:** White, fragrant, in short almost glabrous nearly sessile axillary cymes; peduncles 0.5 mm long; pedicles very short. **Fruit:** Berry, 1.7 cm diam., ovoid or globose, glabrous, black when ripe. **Seed:** One or two, yellow, circular, not much compressed, shining with short appressed silky hairs.

Flowering and fruiting period: March-April and November-December.

Habitat: Deciduous forests of West Bengal, central and south India, up to an altitude of 1200 m.

Parts used: Seed. **Dosage:** 1-3 g.

Collection period: December-January.

Ayurvedic properties: ***Ras:*** *madhur, tikta, kashaya,* ***Gun:*** *laghu, vishada,* ***Veerya:*** *sheeta* ***Vipaka:*** *madhur* ***Tridosha*** **Effect:** alleviates ***Vaata:*** ++, ***Kapha:*** ++.

Chemical constituents: The **leaves, seeds** and **trunk bark** contain diabolin (major alkaloid), mannogalactan and acetyldiabolin. The **seeds** also contain brucine, strychnine, novacine, icajine, oleanolic acid and its glucoside. The **leaves** and **bark** contain isomotiol, stigmasterol, campesterol and sitosterol. Diabolin exhibits hypotensive activity. Mannogalactan fron seeds reduces cholesterol and triglycerides.

Action and disease indications: The **seeds** are anti-diabetic, anti-dysenteric, emetic, cooling, demulcent, diuretic, digestive, anthelmintic, aphrodisiac, ophthalmic, appetizer, alexiteric, tonic, expectorant and water purifier, used for stammering, abscesses, gonorrhea, venereal sores, dysuria, polyuria, urolithiasis, heptomegaly, leucorrhea, flatulence, colic, bronchitis, chronic diarrhea, dysentery, strangury, diabetes, burning sensation, dipsia, conjunctivitis, scleritis, ulcers, epilepsy, hypercholesteremia and general debility.

Clinical uses: Chronic diarrhea: Seed powder of described plant, 2 g, with whey, two times a day, is beneficial. **Skin diseases:** Root powder of described plant, 3 g, with water, two times a day, is beneficial. **Abscess:** Local application of paste of seeds of described plant, with honey, is beneficial.

Formulations: *Shookavishaartihara lepa.*

Recommended readings:

Bhutya, R.K. (2007), Vanaspati Aushadha Vigyana, Scientific Publishers (India), Jodhpur, PP. 139.

Brahmavarchas (2003), Ayurved Ka Pran Vanoshadhi Vigyan, Shanti Kunj, Haridwar, PP. 418.

Chunekar, K.C. (2004), Bhava Prakash Nighantu, Chaukhambha Bharti Academy, Varanasi, PP. 584.

Khare, C.P. (2007), Indian Medicinal Plants, Springer (India) P.L. New Delhi, PP. 630.

Kirtikar, K.R. & Basu, B.D. (1998), Indian Medicinal Plants, L.M Basu, Allahabad, Vol. 2, PP. 1645.

Misra, B.L. (2005), Dravya Guna Hastamalaka, Publication scheme, Jaipur, PP. 444.

Nair, R.Vasudevan, (2007), Indian Medicinal Plants, Orient Longman P.L. Chennai, Vol. 5, PP. 207.

Prajapati, N.D., Purohit, S.S., Sharma, A.K. & Tarun Kumar (2003), A Hand Book of Medicinal Plants, Agrobios India, Jodhpur, PP. 492.

Sharma, P.V. (1981), Dravya gun vigyana, Chaukhambha Bharti Academy, Varanasi, Vol. 1, PP. 96.

Singh, R.S. (2002), Vanoshadhi Nirdeshika, Uttar Pradesh Hindi Sansthan, Lucknow, PP. 213.

449. *Styrax benzoin* Dry.

Family: Styraceae.

Other similar plants: *S. tonkinonsis.*

Name: English: True Gum Benzoin, Sumatra Benzoin, Gum Benjamin, **Sanskrit:** *Lohabaan,* **Hindi:** *Lobaan,* **Local:** *Lobaan.*

Botanical characteristics: Habit: A shrubby deciduous tree, height up to 9 m. **Leaf:** Pointed oval, pubescent beneath. **Flower:** White, fragrant, bell-shaped, axillary, pedicles densely white hairy, in clusters. **Fruit:** 8 mm diam., globose, densely white hairy. **Gum:** White or reddish-white, shiny, sticky tears, 3.125-10 mm by 20 mm-5 cm by 1 cm, fragrant.

Habitat: Native to South-east Asia and East-Indies, in tropical rainforests. The gum imported from Thailand, Java and Sumatra.

Parts used: Gum. **Dosage:** 0.5-1g.

Ayurvedic properties: ***Ras:*** *madhur, tikta,* ***Gun:*** *laghu, rukhsa, tikhsna,* ***Veerya:*** *ushna,* ***Vipaka:*** *madhur,* ***Tridosha*** **Effect:** alleviates ***Kapha:*** ++, ***Vaata:*** ++, aggrevates ***Pitta:*** ++.

Chemical constituents: The **gum** contains variable quantities of cinnamic, benzoic and sumaresinolic acid esters, free acids, benzaldehyde and vanillin.

Action and disease indications: The **gum** is strongly anti-septic, deodorant, anodyne, stimulant, astringent, anti-inflammatory and expectorant. It may be used externally for wounds and ulcers, also for stem inhalation for sore throats, head and chest colds, asthma and bronchitis, also in genito-urinary tract infections, stomatitis, vomiting and hiccough.

Clinical uses: Rheumatism, bell's palsy, skin diseases: Local application of paste of gum of described plant, with water is beneficial. **Chronic bronchitis, asthma, rhinitis:** Gum of described plant 1 g, with honey 10 g, two times a day, is useful.

Formulations: *Arka lobaan, Panchaguna taila, Jeevanrasaayan arka, Raghunatha vati, Siddhanira, Lupari.*

Recommended readings:

Bhutya, R.K. (2007), Vanaspati Aushadha Vigyana, Scientific Publishers (India), Jodhpur, PP. 199.

Chunekar, K.C. (2004), Bhava Prakash Nighantu, Chaukhambha Bharti Academy, Varanasi, PP. 214.

Khare, C.P. (2007), Indian Medicinal Plants, Springer (India) P.L. New Delhi, PP. 631.

Misra, B.L. (2005), Dravya Guna Hastamalaka, Publication scheme, Jaipur, PP. 434.

Prajapati, N.D., Purohit, S.S., Sharma, A.K. & Tarun Kumar (2003), A Hand Book of Medicinal Plants, Agrobios India, Jodhpur, PP. 493.

Sharma, P.V. (1981), Dravya gun vigyana, Chaukhambha Bharti Academy, Varanasi, Vol. 1, PP. 264.

Singh, R.S. (2002), Vanoshadhi Nirdeshika, Uttar Pradesh Hindi Sansthan, Lucknow, PP. 340.

450. *Swertia chirayita* (Roxb. ex Flem.) Karst.

Family: Gentianaceae.

Synonym: *S. chirata, S. tongluensis, Gentiana chirayita, G. chirata, Ophelia chirata.*

Name: English: Chiretta, **Sanskrit:** *Kiraatatikta, Kairaata, Katutikta, Kiraataka, Bhunimba, Raamsenaka, Anaaryatikta,* **Hindi:** *Chiraayataa,* **Local:** *Chiraayataa.*

Botanical characteristics: Habit: Erect, branched, annual herb, height 0.6-1.5 m. **Stem:** Robust, 1 m long and 6 mm diam., glabrous, yellowish brown to purplish, branching, cylindrical below and 4-angled upwards, terete expect near the top. **Leaf:** Opposite, cauline, ovate or broadly lanceolate, 10 by 3.8 cm, acute, entire, acuminate, glabrous, cordate at base, 3-7 nerved, subsessile. **Flower:** Small, numerous, greenish-yellow, tinged with purple, in profuse, leafly panicles. Two glands on corolla lobes. **Fruit:** Capsule, minute, ovoid or egg-shaped, 0.6 cm in diam., pointed, superior, bicarpellary, unilocular. **Seed:** Numerous, smooth, reticulated, 0.5 mm long, polyhedral.

Flowering and fruiting period: July-September and October-December.

Habitat: Temperate Himalayas, from Kashmir to Bhutan, between 1200-3000 m, and in Khassi hills.

Parts used: Whole plant. **Dosage:** 1-3 g.

Collection period: November-December.

Ayurvedic properties: ***Ras:*** *tikta,* ***Gun:*** *laghu, rukhsa,* ***Veerya:*** *sheeta,* ***Vipaka:*** *katu,* ***Tridosha*** **Effect:** alleviates ***Kapha:*** +++, ***Pitta:*** ++.

Chemical constituents: The **plant** contains oxygenated xanthone derivatives, including decussating, mangiferin, swerchirin, swertianin, isobellidifolin; iridoids including chiratin, alkaloids including gentianine, gentiocrucine, enicoflavine and glycosyl flavones. Anti-tubercular activity has been claimed in xanthones. Xanthone, swerchirin lowers blood sugar.

Action and disease indications: The **plant** is refrigerant, anti-inflammatory, hypoglycaemic, astringent, stomachic, anti-pyretic, sudorofic, anti-malarial, anthelmintic, anti-asthmatic, bechic, blood purifier, liver tonic and bitter tonic, used for all types of fevers, especially intermittent fevers, skin diseases, tuberculosis, inflammations, burning sensation, dipsia, cough, asthma, bronchitis, colic, dyspepsia and general debility.

Clinical uses: Impetigo contogiosa: Local application of paste of described plant, *'Maha sudarsan churna',* Borax powder, with water, is beneficial. **Epistaxis:** Cold infusion of described plant, *Santalum album,* with honey 10 g, two times a day, is useful. **Hyperacidity:** Cold infusion of described plant 2 g, pure leaves of *Cannabis sativa* 500 mg, with honey 10 g, is useful. **Indigestion, sprue, fever, helminthiasis:** Use *'Bhunimbaadi churna'* 5 g, with water, two times a day, is beneficial.

Formulations: *Mahaa sudarshana churna, Bhunimbaadi churna, Kiraataadi kwaatha, Kiraataadi taila, Chandraprabhaa vati, Chandanaasava, Sarvajwarahara lauha, Lodhraasava, Ushiraasava, Mustaadi kwaatha.*

Recommended readings:

Bhutya, R.K. (2007), Vanaspati Aushadha Vigyana, Scientific Publishers (India), Jodhpur, PP. 97.

Brahmavarchas (2003), Ayurved Ka Pran Vanoshadhi Vigyan, Shanti Kunj, Haridwar, PP. 420.

Chunekar, K.C. (2004), Bhava Prakash Nighantu, Chaukhambha Bharti Academy, Varanasi, PP. 73.

Dhiman, A.K. (2006), Ayurvedic Drug Plants, Daya Publishing House, Delhi, PP. 103.

Khare, C.P. (2007), Indian Medicinal Plants, Springer (India) P.L. New Delhi, PP. 632.

Kirtikar, K.R. & Basu, B.D. (1998), Indian Medicinal Plants, L.M Basu, Allahabad, Vol. 2, PP. 1664.

Misra, B.L. (2005), Dravya Guna Hastamalaka, Publication scheme, Jaipur, PP. 438.

Nair, R.Vasudevan, (2007), Indian Medicinal Plants, Orient Longman P.L. Chennai, Vol. 5, PP. 212.

Namjoshi, A.N. (2001), The Ayurvedic Pharmacopoeia of India, Government of India, Department of Indian Systems of Medicine & Homoeopathy, New Delhi, Part-1, Volume- 2, PP. 71 and 2-278.

Pareek, G.N. (2005), Sudhanidhi, Vanoshadhi Ratnakar, Dhanvantari Karyalaya, Aligarh, Vol. 2, PP. 349.

Prajapati, N.D., Purohit, S.S., Sharma, A.K. & Tarun Kumar (2003), A Hand Book of Medicinal Plants, Agrobios India, Jodhpur, PP. 493.

Sharma, P.C., Yelne, MB. & Denis, T.J. (2000), Database on medicinal plants used in ayurveda, Central Council for research in Ayurveda and siddha, Vol. 7, PP. 226.

Sharma, P.V. (1981), Dravya gun vigyana, Chaukhambha Bharti Academy, Varanasi, Vol. 1, PP. 691.

Singh, R.S. (2002), Vanoshadhi Nirdeshika, Uttar Pradesh Hindi Sansthan, Lucknow, PP. 151.

Swami, K.N. (1985), Gavon Main Aushadh Ratna, Kalera Krishana Gopal, Kalera (Raj.), Vol. 2, PP. 278.

451. *Symplocos racemosa* Roxb.

Family: Symplocaceae.

Synonym: *S. beddomei, S. candolleana.*

Other similar plants: *S. laurina* syn. *spicata, S. ramosissima, S. sumuntia.*

Name: English: Lodh Tree, Sapphire Berry, **Sanskrit:** *Lodhra, Tilva, Tirita, Shaavar, Gaalava,* **Hindi:** *Lodhra,* **Local:** *Lodha, Sawarlodha.*

Botanical characteristics: Habit: A small, glabrous, evergreen tree, height up to 6 m. **Stem:** 30-60 cm in girth, bark dark grey, rough, 1.25 cm thick, corky. **Leaf:** Simple, alternate, elliptic-oblong or elliptic-lanceolate, 9-18 by 3-5 cm, coriaceous, apex acute obtusely acuminate or obtuse, base acute cuneate, serrulate or obscurely crenate, rarely entire, glabrous and dark green above, pubescent beneath, glabrous or pilose midribs, lateral nerves indistinct, 5-9 pairs; petioles 7.5-18 mm long. **Flower:** White or fading yellow, 1-1.25 cm in diam., fragrant, nearly sessile, in simple axillary racemes 1.3-9 cm long, bracts ovate, tomentose; pedicles 1.3-5 mm long. **Fruit:** Drupes, oblong, 1-1.3 cm long, more or less distinctly ribbed, often slightly curved, purplish black when ripe, crowned with persistent calyx. **Seed:** 1-3 seeds in a fruit.

Flowering and fruiting period: May-June and September-October.

Habitat: Throughout North and eastern India, ascending in the Himalayas up to an altitude of 1400 m, extending Bengal, Assam and southwards to peninsular India.

Parts used: Bark. **Dosage:** 1-3 g.

Collection period: May-June.

Ayurvedic properties: ***Ras:*** *kashaaya,* ***Gun:*** *laghu, rukhsa,* ***Veerya:*** *sheeta,* ***Vipaka:*** *katu,* ***Tridosha*** **Effect:** alleviates ***Kapha:*** ++, ***Pitta:*** ++.

Chemical constituents: The **bark** contains colloturine, harman (loturine), loturidine, proanthocyanidine-3-monoglucofuranosides of 7-0-methyl-and 4'-0-methyl-leucopelargonidin, reducing sugars, oxalic acid and phytosterol.

Action and disease indications: The **bark** is astringent, refrigerant, alterant, expectorant, anti-inflammatory, depurative, febrifuge, haemostatic, constipating and suppurative and ophthalmic, used for leucorrhea, menorrhagia, vaginal ulcers, inflammations, liver disorders, cough, asthma, bronchitis, diarrhea, dysentery, epistaxis, skin diseases, fevers, haemorrhages, dropsy, arthritis, ulcers, tumours, ulemorrhagia, haemoptysis, dyspepsia, flatulence and gonorrhea.

Clinical uses: Diarrhea, dysentery: Powder of described plant 2 g, unripe fruit powder of *Aegle marmelos* 2 g, Stem bark of *Holarrhena antidysenterica* 2 g, pure fruit powder of *Strychnos nuxvomica* 25 mg **Or** powder of described plant 2 g, root of *Glycyrrhiza glabra* 1 g, fruit rind of *Punica grantum* 10 g, *Myrica nagi* 1g, with cold water, three times a day.

Formulations: *Lodhraasava, Lodhraadi kwaatha, Pushyaanuga churna, Vrihat gangaadhara churna, Laghu gangaadhara churna, Asthisandhaanakal lepa, Vajrakapaata rasa, Kutajaastaka churna.*

Recommended readings:

Bhutya, R.K. (2007), Vanaspati Aushadha Vigyana, Scientific Publishers (India), Jodhpur, PP. 198.

Brahmavarchas (2003), Ayurved Ka Pran Vanoshadhi Vigyan, Shanti Kunj, Haridwar, PP. 422.

Chunekar, K.C. (2004), Bhava Prakash Nighantu, Chaukhambha Bharti Academy, Varanasi, PP. 128.

Dhiman, A.K. (2006), Ayurvedic Drug Plants, Daya Publishing House, Delhi, PP. 237.

Khare, C.P. (2007), Indian Medicinal Plants, Springer (India) P.L. New Delhi, PP. 635.

Kirtikar, K.R. & Basu, B.D. (1998), Indian Medicinal Plants, L.M Basu, Allahabad, Vol. 2, PP. 1511.

Misra, B.L. (2005), Dravya Guna Hastamalaka, Publication scheme, Jaipur, PP. 433.

Nair, R.Vasudevan, (2007), Indian Medicinal Plants, Orient Longman P.L. Chennai, Vol. 5, PP. 215.

Namjoshi, A.N. (2001), The Ayurvedic Pharmacopoeia of India, Government of India, Department of Indian Systems of Medicine & Homoeopathy, New Delhi, Part-1, Volume- 2, PP. 82.

Pareek, G.N. (2005), Sudhanidhi, Vanoshadhi Ratnakar, Dhanvantari Karyalaya, Aligarh, Vol. 7, PP. 249.

Prajapati, N.D., Purohit, S.S., Sharma, A.K. & Tarun Kumar (2003), A Hand Book of Medicinal Plants, Agrobios India, Jodhpur, PP. 497.

Sharma, P.C., Yelne, MB. & Denis, T.J. (2000), Database on medicinal plants used in ayurveda, Central Council for research in Ayurveda and siddha, Vol. 5, PP. 164.

Sharma, P.V. (1981), Dravya gun vigyana, Chaukhambha Bharti Academy, Varanasi, Vol. 1, PP. 616.

Singh, R.S. (2002), Vanoshadhi Nirdeshika, Uttar Pradesh Hindi Sansthan, Lucknow, PP. 338.

452. *Syzygium aromaticum* (Linn.) Merr. & Perry

Family: Myrtaceae.

Synonym: *Eugenia aromatica, E. caryophyllata, Caryophyllus aromaticus.*

Name: English: Clove, **Sanskrit:** *Lavanga, Devakusuma, Shreeprasoonaka, Chandanapushpaka,* **Hindi:** *Lavanga,* **Local:** *Long.*

Botanical characteristics: Habit: A medium sized, evergreen, pyramidal or conical tree, height up to 12 m. **Stem:** With a single main stem bearing obliquely oriented branches and smooth grey bark and is gland dotted. **Leaf:** Simple, lanceolate, gland-dotted, fragrant, 2-4 in pairs, 7-13 by 2-4 cm. **Flower:** Flower buds 10-17.5 mm long, greenish to pink, lastly to crimson, clustered at the end of branches, highly aromatic, flowers are sessile, in terminal compound and trichichotomous cymes. **Fruit:** Drupes, fleshy, dark pink, globose, depressed, shining, 2.5 by 1.5 cm. **Seed:** Oblong, grooved on one side.

Flowering and fruiting period: January-February and April-May, may be vary.

Habitat: Cultivated in Tamilnadu and Kerala.

Parts used: Flower bud, oil.

Dosage: Flower bud 1-2 g, oil 1-2 drops.

Collection period: January-February.

Ayurvedic properties: ***Ras:*** *katu, tikta,* ***Gun:*** *laghu,* ***Veerya:*** *sheeta,* ***Vipaka:*** *katu,* ***Tridosha* Effect:** alleviates ***Kapha:*** +++, ***Pitta:*** ++.

Chemical constituents: The **flower buds** contain eugenin, triterpene acids, crategolic acid, polyoxygenated chromone C-glucoside, isobiflorin, biflorin and steroid glucosides afford anti-inflammatory and anti-septic properties. The **oil** contains eugenol, a major component, is anti-bacterial. Acetone extract of clove, eugenol and acetyleugenol possess cholagogue activity.

Action and disease indications: The **flower buds** are refrigerant, aromatic, digestive, carminative, stomachic, stimulant, anti-inflammatory, anti-spasmodic, anti-bacterial, rubefacient, aphrodisiac, appetizer, expectorant, emollient, anti-emetic, anthelmintic, sialogogue, rejuvenating, galacto-purifier, diuretic, febrifuge, ophthalmic and tonic and promotes white blood cells, used for dyspepsia, gastric irritation, anorexia, flatulence, colic, halitosis, odontalgia, ophthalmopathy, cough, asthma, bronchitis, burning sensation, skin diseases, helminthiasis, strangury, fevers, neuralgia, headache, agalactia, impurities of breast milk, lumbago, notalgia, dental carries, hyperacidity, vomiting, dipsia, hapatopathy, tuberculosis and general debility. The **oil** is rubefacient, local analgesic for hypersensitive dentlines and carious cavaties; internally as a carminative, anti-spasmodic, used for cough, asthma, bronchitis, catarrh, gastrohelcosis, flatulence, colic, skin diseases, dyspepsia, vomiting and cephalgia.

Clinical uses: Rhinitis, headache: Local application of paste of flower buds of described plant, in water, is beneficial. **Dentalgia, dental carries:** Local application of oil of flower buds of described plant is beneficial. **Dispesis:** Cold infusion of flower buds of described plant 2 g, with honey 10 g, two times a day, is useful. **Vomiting of pregnancy period:** Flower bud powder of described plant 1 g, with honey 10 g, two times a day, is useful. **Flatulence:** Soda bicarb 500 mg, with cold infusion of described plant 2 g, two times a day, is beneficial. **Hiccough:** Put 500 mg, black salt at the end of tongue, with cold infusion of flower buds of described plant 2 g and filtered water of black ash of bark of *Ficus religiosa,* by one hour, is very beneficial. Do not use cold water or cold exposure by one hour of this medication. **Whooping cough, bronchitis, nausea, halitosis:** Sucking of the roasted flower buds of described plant 1 g, three times a day, is useful. **Arthritis, sciatica, lumbago, neuritis, penile dysfunction, skin diseases:** Local massage of oil of flower buds of described plant and oil of *Brassica campestris,* in ratio of 1:10, is beneficial. **Intestinal colic, flatulence:** Oil of flower buds of described plant 2 drops, sugar 10 g, with warm water, two times a day, is beneficial. **Bronchitis:** (1) Mix powder of flower buds of described plant, *Piper longum, Piper nigrum, Pistacia integerrima,* sugar candy powder, 4 g, with honey 10 g and juice of fresh tuber of *Zingiber officinale,* 5 ml. two or three times a day, is useful. (2) Decoction of mix powder of flower buds of described plant, *Elettaria cardamomum, Cinamomum verum, Justisia adhatoda, Zingiber officinale, Inula racemosa, Hyssopus officinalis, Pistacia vera* 10 g, with extract of *Acacia catechu* 500 mg, two times a day, is beneficial. **Asthma, bronchitis:** Sucking of tablets of mix powder of flower buds of described plant, flowers of *Calotropis procera,* black salt, 500 mg, three times a day, is useful. **Abdominal pain:** Mix powder of flower buds of described plant, *Trachy spermum-ammi, Trigonella foenum-graecum, Cuminum cyminum,* common salt, 6 g, with lukewarm water, two times a day, is beneficial. **Diarrhea:** Mix powder of flower buds of described plant, fruits of *Myristica fragrans,* seeds of *Holarrhena antidysentrica,* extract of *Cinamomum camphora,* 3 g, with water, two times a day, is beneficial. **Anorexia, indigestion:** Mix powder of flower buds of described plant, *Zingiber officinale, Anacyclus pyrenthrum, Piper nigrum, Piper longum, Trachy spermum-ammi, Apium graveolens,* fried gum of *Ferula narthex, Cinamomum verum,* roasted seeds of *Cuminum cyminum,* rock salt, sugar, 5 g, with water, three times a day, is useful. **Ozostomina:** Mix powder of flower buds of described plant, *Elettaria cardamomum, Sassurea costus, Cinamomum camphora, Acorus calamus, Mesua ferrea,* with honey 10 g, two times a day, is useful. **Premature ejaculation:** Mix powder of flower buds of described plant, fruits and mace of *Myristica fragrans, Anacyclus pyrenthrum,* extract of *Tinospora cordifolia,* 4-4 parts, *Crosus sativus* 1 part, *Cinamomum camphora* 1 part, dose 500 mg, with milk, two times a day, is beneficial. **Spermatorrhea:** Mix powder of flower buds of described plant, *Acorus calamus, Anacyclus pyrenthrum, Zingiber officinale, fruits of Myristica fragrans, Santalum album,* 3 g, with water, two times a day, is beneficial. **Nocturnal emission:** Flower buds of described plant 1 g, *Withania somnifera* 3 g, with water, two times a day, is beneficial.

Formulations: *Lavangaadi vati, Lavangaadi churna, Dasansansakaar churna, Aswagand-haadi churna, Kumaaryaasava, Jeerakaarista, Saubhaagyasunthi, Avipattikara churna, Vrihat Chandrodayamakaradhwaja.*

Recommended readings:

Acharya, B.K. (2008), Ayurveda Jadi-buti Rahasya, Patanjali Yogapitha, Haridwar, PP. 272.

Bhutya, R.K. (2007), Vanaspati Aushadha Vigyana, Scientific Publishers (India), Jodhpur, PP. 196.

Brahmavarchas (2003), Ayurved Ka Pran Vanoshadhi Vigyan, Shanti Kunj, Haridwar, PP. 424.

Chunekar, K.C. (2004), Bhava Prakash Nighantu, Chaukhambha Bharti Academy, Varanasi, PP. 219.

Dhiman, A.K. (2006), Ayurvedic Drug Plants, Daya Publishing House, Delhi, PP. 235.

Khare, C.P. (2007), Indian Medicinal Plants, Springer (India) P.L. New Delhi, PP. 636.

Misra, B.L. (2005), Dravya Guna Hastamalaka, Publication scheme, Jaipur, PP. 381.

Nair, R.Vasudevan, (2007), Indian Medicinal Plants, Orient Longman P.L. Chennai, Vol. 5, PP. 221.

Namjoshi, A.N. (2001), The Ayurvedic Pharmacopoeia of India, Government of India, Department of Indian Systems of Medicine & Homoeopathy, New Delhi, Part-1, Volume- 2, PP. 80.

Pareek, G.N. (2005), Sudhanidhi, Vanoshadhi Ratnakar, Dhanvantari Karyalaya, Aligarh, Vol. 7, PP. 226.

Prajapati, N.D., Purohit, S.S., Sharma, A.K. & Tarun Kumar (2003), A Hand Book of Medicinal Plants, Agrobios India, Jodhpur, PP. 497.

Sharma, P.C., Yelne, MB. & Denis, T.J. (2000), Database on medicinal plants used in ayurveda, Central Council for research in Ayurveda and siddha, Vol. 4, PP. 358.

Sharma, P.V. (1981), Dravya gun vigyana, Chaukhambha Bharti Academy, Varanasi, Vol. 1, PP. 246.

Singh, R.S. (2002), Vanoshadhi Nirdeshika, Uttar Pradesh Hindi Sansthan, Lucknow, PP. 333.

Swami, K.N. (1985), Gavon Main Aushadh Ratna, Kalera Krishana Gopal, Kalera (Raj.), Vol. 3, PP. 268.

453. *Syzygium cumini* (Linn.) Sklles.

Family: Myrtaceae.

Synonym: *Eugenia jambulana.*

Variety: *Eugenia rubikunda* (small var.), *E.operculata- Kak jambu, E. jambos-Gulab jamun, E.heyneana.*

Name: English: Jamul tree, Jambolan, Black plum, Java plum, **Sanskrit:** *Phulendra, Nandi, Raaj jambu, Maahaphala, Surbhi patra, Jambu,* **Hindi:** *Jaamuna,* **Local:** *Jaamuna.*

Ayurvedic groups: Charak: *mutra sangrahaniya, poorisha sangrahaniya, chardi nigrahana,* **Sushruta:** *nyagrodhaadi gana, pancha pallava.*

Botanical characteristics: Habit: 15-30 m in height, up to 3 m in diam. **Stem:** Bark light grey, having dark patches, smooth, cylindrical, branched, solid. **Leaf:** Opposite, simple, elliptic-ovate, entire, acute, glabrous, variable in shape, distinct intra-marginal nerve, and gland dotted, shiny, about 2.5 cm broad and 7.5-15 cm long, petiole 2.5 cm long, special smell in crushed leaves. **Flower:** Greenish-white, clustered, fragrant, complete. **Fruit:** Drupe, oblong or ovoid-oblong, 1.25-3.5 cm long, green when unripe, dark purple when ripe, with pinkish juicy pulp, edible, one seeded. **Seed:** Hard, 1-2 cm long.

Flowering and fruiting period: May- June and July- August.

Habitat: Throughout India, in forests up to 1800 m, usually along river banks and moist localities, also cultivated.

Parts used: Fruit pulp, seed, bark, leaves.

Dosage: Seed powder 3-6 g, root, leaves 5-10 g, fruit 10-50 g.

Collection period: July- August.

Ayurvedic properties: ***Ras:*** *kashaya, madhur, amla,* ***Gun:*** *laghu, rukhsa,* ***Veerya:*** *sheet,* ***Vipaka:*** *katu,* ***Tridosha*** **Effect:** alleviates ***Kapha:*** ++, ***Pitta:*** +, aggravates ***Vaata:*** ++++.

Chemical constituents: The **Stem bark** contains friedelan-3-alpha-ol, kaempferol, quercetin, beta-sitosterol and its glycosides, kaempferol-3-o-glucoside, gallic acid, friedelin, betulinic acid, eugenin, epi-friedelanol, 10-12% tannins alsoalso presented. The **leaves** contain aliphatic alcohols, sitosterols, betulinic acid and crategolic (maslinic) acid. The **flowers** contain triteprnic acid, oleanolic acid and crategolic acids. The oleanolic acid is a strong protector against adriamycin- indused lipid peroxidation in liver and heart microsomes. The **fruits** contain anthocyanins and cirtic, malic and gallic acids. Gallic and tannins account for astringency of the fruit. Malic acid is the major acid (0.59%) of the weight of fruit; a small quantity of oxalic acid is also present. Glucose and fructose are principle sugars in the ripe fruit. The **seeds** contain tannins (19%), ellagic acid, gallic acid (1-2%), beta-sitosterol, 0.05% essential oil. Myricyl alcohol is present in the unsaponifiable matter. **Plant** phenol, including methylxanthoxylin and 2,6-dihydroxy-4-methoxy-acetophene have been isolated from the plant and also from the **seeds.**

Action and disease indications: The **bark** is astringent, sweet, sour, acrid, refrigerant, carminative, diuretic, anthelmintic, digestive, febrifuge, constipating, stomachic and anti-bacterial. Useful to cure leucorrhoea, diabetes, stomatalgia, fever, gastropathy, strangury and skin diseases. The **leaves** are anti-bacterial and useful to teeth and gums. The **tender leaves** are used for vomiting. The **fruits** and **seeds** are sweet, acrid, sour, tonic and cooling and are used in diabetes, diarrhea pharyngitis, spleen diseases, urethrorrhea, ring worm, fatigue, dipsesis, asthma, bronchitis, constipation, loss of appetite and polyuria.

Indication: There is no role of seed powder for diabetes mellitus by oral use, but in diabetes inspidus, it shuld be use. For diabetes mellitus, intra muscular injection of the aqua's extract of the seed, should be given.

Clinical uses: Diabetes, Hyperglycemia, chlolesterolemia: Mix powder of seeds of the described plant, leaves powder of *Aegle marmelos,* leaves of *Azadiracta indica, Curcuma longa, Tinospora cordifolia, Gymnema sylvestre, Mormodica charantia,* leaves of *Ficus recemosa,* fruit of *Termenalia chebula, Termenalia belliarica,* and *Phylanthus emblica,* 6 g, 3 times a day, with water. **Diarrhea, menorrhagia:** Leave juice of the plant, 10 ml, with honey 10 g, 2 times a day. **Gingivitis:** Gargles of decoction of stem bark of the plant, 20 g, 3 times a day, is beneficial. **Acne vulgaris**: Local application of Seed paste of the described plant, is very beneficial. **Vomiting, nausea**: Tender Leaves juice of the described plant 10 ml, with honey 5 g, 3-4 times a day. **Diabetes, diarrhea, loss of appetite, indigestion:** Vinegar of the plant 5-10 ml, 2 times a day, with water. **Diarrhea** of children: Fresh juice of leaves of plant 5 ml, two times a day, is beneficial. **Polyuria:** Decoction of stem barks of the plant, *Acacia nilotica* and *Acacia catechu* 20 g, with powder of *Symplocos racemosa* 2 g, with honey 10 g, 2 times a day. **To nullify the effect of intoxication of Opium:** Leaves juice of the described plant 10 ml, 1 hourly, 3-4 times a day. **To nullify the effect of intoxication of** *Strychnos nux-vomica*: Seed powder of the described plant 5-10 g, 3-4 times a day, with water. **Stomatitis:** Gargles of decoction of leaves of described plant 20 g, 2-3 times a day. **Burning sensation of palm and sole:** Local application of seed powder of the described plant and *Lens culinaris,* with water, is beneficial. **Spermaturia:** Seed powder of the described plant, *'Triphala churna'*, with water, 2 times a day. **Renal calculi:** Seed powder of the described plant 5 g, with whey, 2 times a day. **Menorrhagia:** Seed powder of the described plant and *Nelumbo nucifera,* 3 g, 2 times a day, with cow milk. **Diarrhea, dysentery:** Seed powder of the described plant and Mango 3 g, 3 times a day, with water. **Loss of appetite:** Fruit juice of plant 25 ml, juice of fresh rhizome of *Zingiber officinale,* 5 ml, powder of dry rhizome of *Zingiber officinale* 500 mg, Rock salt 500 mg, powder of *Piper nigrum* 500 mg, 2 times a day, before 1 hour of meal, is very beneficial.

Contra indication: 1. Do not use fruits empty stomach and with milk or tea. Use with common salt and Black pepper.

Formulations: *Chandanadi churna, Baalaatis-aarhar yoga, Siddhapayah, Jaamun ka sirkaa, Vrihat lavangaadhya churna, Panchapallava yoga, Jaambaavadhya taila.*

Recommended readings:

Acharya, B.K. (2008), Ayurveda Jadi-buti Rahasya, Patanjali Yogapitha, Haridwar, PP. 238.

Bhutya, R.K. (2007), Vanaspati Aushadha Vigyana, Scientific Publishers (India), Jodhpur, PP. 107.

Brahmavarchas (2003), Ayurved Ka Pran Vanoshadhi Vigyan, Shanti Kunj, Haridwar, PP. 425.

Chunekar, K.C. (2004), Bhava Prakash Nighantu, Chaukhambha Bharti Academy, Varanasi, PP. 570.

Dhiman, A.K. (2006), Ayurvedic Drug Plants, Daya Publishing House, Delhi, PP. 163.

Khare, C.P. (2007), Indian Medicinal Plants, Springer (India) P.L. New Delhi, PP. 637.

Kirtikar, K.R. & Basu, B.D. (1998), Indian Medicinal Plants, L.M Basu, Allahabad, Vol. 2, PP. 1052.

Misra, B.L. (2005), Dravya Guna Hastamalaka, Publication scheme, Jaipur, PP. 383.

Nair, R.Vasudevan, (2007), Indian Medicinal Plants, Orient Longman P.L. Chennai, Vol. 5, PP. 225.

Namjoshi, A.N. (2001), The Ayurvedic Pharmacopoeia of India, Government of India, Department of Indian Systems of Medicine & Homoeopathy, New Delhi, Part-1, Volume- 1, PP. 54.

Pareek, G.N. (2005), Sudhanidhi, Vanoshadhi Ratnakar, Dhanvantari Karyalaya, Aligarh, Vol. 10, PP. 181.

Prajapati, N.D., Purohit, S.S., Sharma, A.K. & Tarun Kumar (2003), A Hand Book of Medicinal Plants, Agrobios India, Jodhpur, PP. 497.

Sharma, P.C., Yelne, MB. & Denis, T.J. (2000), Database on medicinal plants used in ayurveda, Central Council for research in Ayurveda and siddha, Vol. 3, PP. 314.

Sharma, P.V. (1981), Dravya gun vigyana, Chaukhambha Bharti Academy, Varanasi, Vol. 1, PP. 659.

Singh, R.S. (2002), Vanoshadhi Nirdeshika, Uttar Pradesh Hindi Sansthan, Lucknow, PP. 163.

Swami, K.N. (1985), Gavon Main Aushadh Ratna, Kalera Krishana Gopal, Kalera (Raj.), Vol. 1, PP. 198.

454. *Tagetes erecta* Linn.

Family: Compositae; Asteraceae.

Other similar plants: *T. minuta,* syn. *glandulifera, T. patula.*

Name: English: Big Marigold, African Marigold, **Sanskrit:** *Zhandu,* **Hindi:** *Gendaa,* **Local:** *Gendaa, Hajaraa.*

Botanical characteristics: Habit: A hardy annual pubescent herb, height about 60 cm. **Stem:** Gland-punctate, erect, angular, stem and branches reddish-purple, branched. **Leaf:** Very strong scented, alternate, pubescent, pinnately divided, segments lanceolate-serrate, shape like leaves of *Cannabis sativa.* **Flower:** Vary in shape, colour and size, lemon-yellow or light sulphur-yellow or deep orange, 5-10 cm. Rays sometimes rather 2-lipped and in one of the garden forms they are quilled. **Seed:** Long, ovate, black.

Flowering and fruiting period: November-December and January-February.

Habitat: Throughout India, cultivated in gardens.

Parts used: Leaves. **Dosage:** Juice 10-20 ml.

Collection period: January-February.

Ayurvedic properties: ***Ras:*** *katu, kashaaya,* ***Gun:*** *laghu, rukhsa,* ***Veerya:*** *sheeta,* ***Vipaka:*** *katu,* ***Tridosha*** **Effect:** alleviates ***Kapha:*** ++, ***Pitta:*** +.

Chemical constituents: The **flowers** contain lutein esters of dipalmitate, dimyristate and mono-myristate, hydroxyflavones, quercetagetin and tagetiin. The plant yield an **essential oil** containing limonene, ocimene, linalyl acetate, linalool, tagetone and *n*-nonyl aldehyde as major components. The aqueous extract of flowers showed activity against Gram-positive bacteria.

Action and disease indications: The **flower** are pungent, bitter, acrid, astringent, alterative, carminative, stomachic, used for fevers, epileptic fits, otorrhea, inflammations, scabies, belching, liver disorders and bleeding piles. The **leaves** are styptic, emmenogogue, diuretic, vermifuge, used for piles, renal disorders, boils and carbuncles, muscular pain, earache, ophthalmia.

Clinical uses: bleeding piles: Juice of leaves of described plant 10 ml, juice of roots of *Musa paradisiaca* 20 ml, or medicated clarified butter, made by sauce of flowers of described plant, 10 ml, with milk, two times a day, is beneficial. **Epistaxis:** Nasal drops of juice of leaves of described plant, 4-4 drops, is useful. **Otalgia:** Warm juice of leaves of described plant, 4-4 drops, two times a day, is beneficial. **Dysuria, prolepse of rectum:** Leaves juice of described plant, 20 ml, with sugar candy powder 10 g, two times a day, is beneficial. **Ringworm:** Local application of paste of leaves of described plant is beneficial. **Dentalgia:** Gargles of leaves juice of described plant, three times a day, is useful. **Satyriasis:** Seed powder of described plant, 2 g, with water, two times a day, is beneficial.

Recommended readings:

Acharya, B.K. (2008), Ayurveda Jadi-buti Rahasya, Patanjali Yogapitha, Haridwar, PP. 199.

Chunekar, K.C. (2004), Bhava Prakash Nighantu, Chaukhambha Bharti Academy, Varanasi, PP. 822.

Khare, C.P. (2007), Indian Medicinal Plants, Springer (India) P.L. New Delhi, PP. 642.

Kirtikar, K.R. & Basu, B.D. (1998), Indian Medicinal Plants, L.M Basu, Allahabad, Vol. 2, PP. 1385.

Pareek, G.N. (2005), Sudhanidhi, Vanoshadhi Ratnakar, Dhanvantari Karyalaya, Aligarh, Vol. 10, PP. 64.

Sharma, P.V. (1981), Dravya gun vigyana, Chaukhambha Bharti Academy, Varanasi, Vol. 1, PP. 790.

455. *Tamarindus indica* Linn.

Family: Caesalpiniaceae.

Synonym: *T.occidentalis, T.officinalis.*

Name: English: Tamarind tree, **Sanskrit:** *Amalica, Chukrika, Amali, Churkam, Chinchaa, Danthashathaa, Tintidikaa, Shuktaa,* **Hindi:** *Imali,* **Local:** *Imali, Aamali.*

Botanical characteristics: Habit: Large to very large tree, evergreen, much branched, height up to 30 m. **Stem:** Bark dark grey having longitudinal fissure and deep cracks, cylindrical, branched, solid, rough, upper portion greenish-brown, in old age stem become hollow. **Leaf:** Up to 15 cm long, leaflets 10-20 pairs, 8-30 mm long and 5-8 mm broad, sub-sessile, alternate, compound, unipinnate and peripinnate, petiolate, entire, obtuse and glabrous. **Flower:** Yellow, striped with red in lax, few flowered racemes at the end of branchelets, complete. **Fruit:** Legume, brownish ash coloured, slightly curved, sub compressed, with a shallow oblong pit on each side of the flat faces, fruits are 7.5-20 cm long, 2-3 cm broad and 0.6 cm thick, pendulous on tree, unripe pods are sour, ripe pods are sour, sweet and fragrant. 3-12 seeded. **Seed:** Enclosed by a tough leathery membrane and pulpy mesocsrp, testa shining, hard, colour brownish-black, 1.5 cm across, compressed, inner portion white in two portion.

Flowering and fruiting period: May-June and February-March.

Habitat: Throughout India, plains and sub-Himalayan tracts, particularly in south.

Parts used: Fruit pulp, seed, root.

Dosage: Seeds 5-10 g, fruit pulp 5-20 g, roots 2-5 g.

Collection period: March- April.

Ayurvedic properties: ***Ras:*** *amla, madhur,* ***Gun:*** *rukhsa, guru,* ***Veerya:*** *ushna,* ***Vipaka:*** *katu,* ***Tridosha*** **Effect:** alleviates ***Kapha:*** ++,***Vaata:*** ++.

Chemical constituents: The **leaves** and **fruits** contain tartaric acid and malic acid. The **leaves** contain flavone c- glycosides- orintin, vitexin, iso-orientin and iso-vitexin. The **fruit pulp** yielded amino acids- phenylalanine and leucine. The **kernel** contains polysaccharides composed of d- glucose, d-xylose, d-glactose and arabinose. The fruit pulp contains amino acids- serine, beta-alanine, praline, pipecolinic acid, phenylalanine and leucine, also tamaridienal has fungicidal and bactericidal activity.

Action and disease indications: The **seeds** are cooling, stringent, aphrodisiac, stomachic, tonic and constipating. They are beneficial to cure leucorrhoea, menorrhagia, stomachalgia, diarrhea, dysentery, dipsia, burning sensation, hematuria, giddiness, inflammations, chronic ulcers, abscess, bleeding piles, vaginopathy, metroptosis, diabetes and general debility. The **fruits** are sour, sweet, refrigerant, digestive, carminative, laxative, antiseptic, anti scorbutic and febrifuge. Useful to cure bilious vomiting, arthritis, rheumatoid arthritis, *Datura innoxia* poisoning, alcoholic intoxication, dipsia, scabies, pharyngitis, pharyngodynia, stomatitis, constipation, hemorrhoids and gastropathy. The **leaves** and **unripe fruits** are sour, astringent, thermogenic, anthelmintic, anodyne, antifungal, anti-inflammatory, diuretic, febrifuge, and are useful to cure swelling, fever, gastropathy, helminthiasis, wounds, ulcers, jaundice, scabies, ring worm and boils. The **root bark** is astringent, constipating, emmenogogue and tonic. Useful for diarrhea, asthma, amenorrhea, gingivitis and ulcers. A bitter principle, tamarindienal, isolated from the fruit pulp, showed anti fungal and anti bacterial activity against

Aspergillus niger, Candida bicans, Basillus subtilis, stophylococus aureus, E.coli and *Pseudomonas aeruginosa.*

Clinical uses: Pains, rheumatoid arthritis, Osteo arthritis, indigestion, loss of appetite, sprue, diarrhoea, dysentery, for decrease '*Aam*' in the body: Fruit pulp of *Tamarindus indica,* 15-20 g, soak it in 200 ml water for 30 minuts, then rub it and filter it. Add 25 g, raw sugar, fried gum of *Ferula narthex* 1 g, powder of fried seeds of *Cuminum cyminum* 5 g, Black salt 2 g, powder of *Piper nigrum* 2 g. Take it before or with meal. Use it daily for 3 days, then after alternately for 1 week, and then twice a week. It gives quick relief and can be take without any fear. **Excess and contaminated urination, menorrhagia, leukorrhoea, spermaturia, premature ejaculation:** Seed powder of the described plant 5 g, 2 times a day, with milk, for 2-3 weeks. **Menorrhagia:** Black ash of stem bark 2 g, 2 times a day, with water. **Stomatitis:** Chewing of Leaves of the described plant 10 g, or gargles of decoction of leaves 20 g, is very useful. **Pain of piles:** Flowers of plant 5 g, curd 50 g, juice of *Punica grantum* 100ml, warm it and add *Coriandrum satium* 2.5 g, *Zingiber officinale* 1 g. Take it 2 times a day. **Abdominal pain:** White ash of root bark of plant 3 g, 4 times a day, with lukewarm water. **Diarrhea with vomiting:** Use '*Chinchabhallataka vati*' 250 mg, 3 times a day. **Restlessness of pregnancy:** Use '*Gulkanda*' made by flowers of described plant 10 g, 3 times a day. **Prolaps rectum:** Seed powder of the described plant 5 g, with curd 50 g, 2 times a day.

Formulations: *Chinchaabhallaatak vati, Chinchaa khand, Rambaan rasa, Shankha vati, Mahaa jwaraankus rasa, Amlika satva, Mahaa shankha vati, Amlikasatvaadi churna.*

Recommended readings:

Acharya, B.K. (2008), Ayurveda Jadi-buti Rahasya, Patanjali Yogapitha, Haridwar, PP. 232.

Bhutya, R.K. (2007), Vanaspati Aushadha Vigyana, Scientific Publishers (India), Jodhpur, PP. 29.

Brahmavarchas (2003), Ayurved Ka Pran Vanoshadhi Vigyan, Shanti Kunj, Haridwar, PP. 428.

Chunekar, K.C. (2004), Bhava Prakash Nighantu, Chaukhambha Bharti Academy, Varanasi, PP. 598.

Dhiman, A.K. (2006), Ayurvedic Drug Plants, Daya Publishing House, Delhi, PP. 31.

Khare, C.P. (2007), Indian Medicinal Plants, Springer (India) P.L. New Delhi, PP. 643.

Kirtikar, K.R. & Basu, B.D. (1998), Indian Medicinal Plants, L.M Basu, Allahabad, Vol. 2, PP. 887.

Misra, B.L. (2005), Dravya Guna Hastamalaka, Publication scheme, Jaipur, PP. 280.

Nair, R.Vasudevan, (2007), Indian Medicinal Plants, Orient Longman P.L. Chennai, Vol. 5235, PP. .

Pareek, G.N. (2005), Sudhanidhi, Vanoshadhi Ratnakar, Dhanvantari Karyalaya, Aligarh, Vol. 9, PP. 90.

Prajapati, N.D., Purohit, S.S., Sharma, A.K. & Tarun Kumar (2003), A Hand Book of Medicinal Plants, Agrobios India, Jodhpur, PP. 502.

Sharma, P.C., Yelne, MB. & Denis, T.J. (2000), Database on medicinal plants used in ayurveda, Central Council for research in Ayurveda and siddha, Vol. 5, PP. 29.

Sharma, P.V. (1981), Dravya gun vigyana, Chaukhambha Bharti Academy, Varanasi, Vol. 2, PP. 353.

Singh, R.S. (2002), Vanoshadhi Nirdeshika, Uttar Pradesh Hindi Sansthan, Lucknow, PP. 40.

Swami, K.N. (1985), Gavon Main Aushadh Ratna, Kalera Krishana Gopal, Kalera (Raj.), Vol. 1, PP. 76.

456. *Taraxacum officinale* Weber ex Wiggers.

Family: Compositae; Asteraceae.

Name: English: Common Dandelion, **Sanskrit:** *Lutaari, Payaswini,* **Hindi:** *Dugdhafeni,* **Local:** *Dudhal, Kanfoola.*

Botanical characteristics: Habit: A perennial herb, height 30-60 cm, and abundant milky juice in all parts. **Root:** Thick tap root, 15 cm long, 1.25-2.5 cm diam., cylindrical, tapering to end, yellowish-brown, brownish-black on dry. **Leaf:** Sessile, radical, glabrous, variable in shape, 5-20 cm long, narrowly oblong, irregularly pinnatifid, lobes linear or triangular, acute, toothed, pointing downwards, or rarely oblanceolate and nearly entire. **Flower:** Yellow, in ligulate heads 0.8-5 cm diam., glabrous, solitary on a hollow leafless stalk 5-20 cm long. Inner involucral bracts linear, erect, nearly equal, margins often white, tips usually thickened or hooked; outer bracts short, ovate, erect, or recurved; receptacle flat, naked. **Fruit:** Achenes, glabrous, flattened, ribbed minutely, spiny on the upper half, narrowed to the base, crowned with white pappus hairs.

Habitat: Temperate Himalayas, Khasi Hills, Mishmi Hills, Gujarat and in hills of South India, at 300-5400 m height.

Parts used: Root. **Dosage:** 1-3 g.

Ayurvedic properties: ***Ras:*** *tikta, katu,* ***Gun:*** *laghu, rukhsa, tikhsna,* ***Veerya:*** *ushna,* ***Vipaka:*** *katu,* ***Tridosha*** **Effect:** alleviates ***Kapha:*** ++, ***Pitta:*** +.

Chemical constituents: The **leaves and roots** contain sesquiterpene lactones; triterpenes and sterols-beta-sitosterols, beta-sitosterol-glucoside, taraxasterol. *psi*-taratexol and taraxol; flavonoids, epigenin-7-0-glucosides and luteolin-7-0-glucosides, mucilages and inulin.The amaroids are cholagogic and secretolytic. The vitamin A content is higher than in carrots. Most of diuretics cause loss of potassium, but dandelion leaves contain high levels of potassium.

Action and disease indications: The **roots** are diuretic, tonic, laxative, anti-rheumatic, aperient, thermogenic, digestive, stomachic, anthelmintic, liver tonic, chologogue, pancreatic and bile duct stimulant, stimulant, to portal circulation, choleretic, urinary anti-septic, detoxicant, promotes elimination of plasma cholesterol, used for infective hepatitis, rheumatism, dyspepsia, anorexia, diuresis, verminosis, constipation, inflammations, hypochondria, biliary calculi and general debility.

Clinical uses: Jaundice, enlargement of liver: Root powder of described plant, 3 g, with water, two times a day, is beneficial.

Recommended readings:

Bhutya, R.K. (2007), Vanaspati Aushadha Vigyana, Scientific Publishers (India), Jodhpur, PP. 125.

Chunekar, K.C. (2004), Bhava Prakash Nighantu, Chaukhambha Bharti Academy, Varanasi, PP. 828.

Khare, C.P. (2007), Indian Medicinal Plants, Springer (India) P.L. New Delhi, PP. 646.

Kirtikar, K.R. & Basu, B.D. (1998), Indian Medicinal Plants, L.M Basu, Allahabad, Vol. 2, PP. 1436.

Misra, B.L. (2005), Dravya Guna Hastamalaka, Publication scheme, Jaipur, PP. 301.

Nair, R.Vasudevan, (2007), Indian Medicinal Plants, Orient Longman P.L. Chennai, Vol. 5, PP. 243.

Prajapati, N.D., Purohit, S.S., Sharma, A.K. & Tarun Kumar (2003), A Hand Book of Medicinal Plants, Agrobios India, Jodhpur, PP. 503.

Sharma, P.V. (1981), Dravya gun vigyana, Chaukhambha Bharti Academy, Varanasi, Vol. 1, PP. 546.

Singh, R.S. (2002), Vanoshadhi Nirdeshika, Uttar Pradesh Hindi Sansthan, Lucknow, PP. 195.

457. *Tecomela undulata* (G. Don) Seem.

Family: Bignoniaceae.

Synonym: *Tecoma undulata, Bignonia undulata.*

Other similar plants: *Amoora rohituka* (Maliaceae)-found in Uttar Pradesh, Bihar, Bengal, Assam.

Name: English: Rohida Tree, **Sanskrit:** *Rohitaka, Rohi, Daadimapushpaka,* **Hindi:** *Rohitaka,* **Local:** *Rohidaa.*

Botanical characteristics: Habit: A small deciduous tree, height 8 m. **Stem:** With drooping branches and stellately grey-tomentose innovations, otherwise glabrous. **Leaf:** Simple 5-12.5 by 1-3.2 cm, narrowly oblong or oblong-lanceolate, obtuse, entire with undulate margins, petioles 2.5 cm long. **Flower:** Orange-yellow, large, 3.75-6.25 cm long, inodorous, bisexual, showy, in few flowered corymbose racemes terminating in short lateral branches, pedicels 6-13 mm long. **Fruit:** Capsules, 20 by 1 cm, slightly curved, linear-oblong, acute, smooth; valves thin. **Seed:** 2.5 by 1 cm, discoid and winged, wing absent at its base.

Flowering and fruiting period: February-April and June-July.

Habitat: North-west and Western India, and in the outer Himalayas, up to an altitude of 1200 m, Gujarat, Rajasthan, Punjab and Uttar Pradesh.

Parts used: Bark. **Dosage:** 5-10 g.

Collection period: December-January.

Ayurvedic properties: ***Ras:*** *katu, tikta, kashaya,* ***Gun:*** *laghu, rukhsa,* ***Veerya:*** *sheeta,* ***Vipaka:*** *katu,* ***Tridosha*** **Effect:** alleviates ***Kapha:*** ++, ***Pitta:*** +.

Chemical constituents: The **bark** contains tecomin (veratryl beta-D-glucoside), alkanols, beta-sitosterol, chromone glycosides-undulatoside A and B, and iridoid glucosides-tecomelloside and tecoside, a quinonoid-lapachol, veratric acid and dehydrotectol.

Action and disease indications: The **bark** is relaxant, cardio tonic, choleretic, used for leucorrhea, anorexia, indigestion, liver and spleen enlargement and other diseases, leucoderma, syphilis, ophthalmia and skin diseases. Heart wood is **toxic** due to lapachol.

Clinical uses: Excess and turbid micturition, leucorrhea, obesity, anorexia, enlargement of liver and spleen, jaundice, piles, helminthiasis: Decoction of bark of described plant, 10 g, with honey 10 g, two times a day, is useful.

Formulations: *Rohitakaarista, Rohitaka ghrita, Rohitaka lauha, Plihaashardoola rasa, Rohitakaadi vati, Mahaa mrityunjaya lauha.*

Recommended readings:

Bhutya, R.K. (2007), Vanaspati Aushadha Vigyana, Scientific Publishers (India), Jodhpur, PP. 194.

Chunekar, K.C. (2004), Bhava Prakash Nighantu, Chaukhambha Bharti Academy, Varanasi, PP. 527.

Dhiman, A.K. (2006), Ayurvedic Drug Plants, Daya Publishing House, Delhi, PP. 320.

Khare, C.P. (2007), Indian Medicinal Plants, Springer (India) P.L. New Delhi, PP. 649.

Kirtikar, K.R. & Basu, B.D. (1998), Indian Medicinal Plants, L.M Basu, Allahabad, Vol. 2, PP. 1841.

Misra, B.L. (2005), Dravya Guna Hastamalaka, Publication scheme, Jaipur, PP. 408.

Sharma, P.C., Yelne, MB. & Denis, T.J. (2000), Database on medicinal plants used in ayurveda, Central Council for research in Ayurveda and siddha, Vol. 6, PP. 321.

Sharma, P.V. (1981), Dravya gun vigyana, Chaukhambha Bharti Academy, Varanasi, Vol. 1, PP. 552.

Singh, R.S. (2002), Vanoshadhi Nirdeshika, Uttar Pradesh Hindi Sansthan, Lucknow, PP. 331.

458. *Tectona grandis* Linn. f.

Family: Verbenaceae.

Ayurvedic Groups: Sushruta: *Saalasaaraadi gana.*

Name: English: Teak Tree, **Sanskrit:** *Bhumisahaa, Dwaaradaaru, Varadaaru, Kharachhada,* **Hindi:** *Saagawan,* **Local:** *Saagawaan, Saagon.*

Botanical characteristics: Habit: A large to very large deciduous tree, height 25-35 m. **Stem:** Bark light brown or grey, having shallow longitudinal furrows, fluted and buttressed base and characteristically channeled branchlets. **Leaf:** Simple. Opposite, 30-60 by 15-30 cm, broadly elliptic or obovate, acute or acuminate, coriaceous, rough above but usually glabrous, the lower surface clothed with dense stellate grey or tawny tomentose, possessing minute glandular dots, entire, base usually cuneate, main nerves 8-10 pairs. **Flower:** White, numerous, small, sweet scented, in large erect terminal branched tomentose cymose panicles 0.3-0.9 m long, shortly pedicellate. **Fruit:** Drupes, 1.3 cm diam., hard, bony, irregularly globose, enveloped by light brown bladder-like calyx, somewhat 4-lobed. **Seed:** Usually 1-3, or 4, ovate, marble white, 4-8 mm long.

Flowering and fruiting period: July-August and November-December.

Habitat: Throughout India, Western peninsula, central India and Bihar, in deciduous forests, up to 1000 m.

Parts used: Heartwood, bark, flower, seed, seed oil, leaves.

Dosage: Heartwood, bark 3-6 g, flowers 10-20 g, seed, seed oil, leaves- for external use.

Collection period: December-January.

Ayurvedic properties: ***Ras:*** *kashaaya,* ***Gun:*** *laghu, rukhsa,* ***Veerya:*** *sheeta,* ***Vipaka:*** *katu,* ***Tridosha*** **Effect:** alleviates ***Kapha:*** *++,* ***Pitta:*** ++.

Chemical constituents: The **wood** contains anthraquinones, naphthalene compounds and triterpenic and hemi-terpenic compounds. The **leaves** contain tectoleafquinone. The **bark** contains 7.14% tannins. The **seed oil** contains linoleic acid (53%), along with lauric, myristic, palmitic, stearic, oleic, linolenic and arachidic acids. The **kernel** contains 44.5% of a fatty oil.

Action and disease indications: The **bark** is cooling, depurative, constipating, anthelmintic, used for burning sensation, bronchitis, hyperacidity, dysentery, verminosis, diabetes, skin diseases. The **flowers** are refrigerant, depurative, diuretic, anti-inflammatory, used for inflammations, burning sensation, dipsia, skin diseases, strangury and diabetes. The **leaves** are refrigerant, haemostatic, anti-inflammatory, depurative and vulnerary, used for inflammations, skin diseases, pruritis, stomatitis, indolent ulcers, haemorrhages and haemoptysis. The **seeds** are diuretic, emollient, and demulcent, used for strangury, skin diseases and pruritis. The **wood** is cooling, anti-inflammatory, anodyne, vermifuse, ophthalmic, expectorant, depurative and laxative, used for neuralgia, headache, arthritis, inflammations, dyspepsia, flatulence, cough, skin diseases, menorrhagia, leucorrhea, abortion, leucoderma, hyperacidity, dipsia, burning sensation, piles and dysentery. The **oil** is trichogenous, used for eczema and ringworm.

Clinical uses: Headache: Local application of paste of heartwood or bark of described plant is beneficial. **Indigestion, burning sensation of stomach:** Heartwood powder of described plant, 6 g, with water, two times a day, is beneficial. **Anuria, dysuria:** Cold infusion of flowers of described plant 15 g, with honey 10 g, two times a day, and local application of paste of flowers of described plant on lower part of abdomen, is beneficial. **Alopecia:** Local application of oil heartwood of described plant, is beneficial. **Hyperacidity, dysentery, helminthiasis:** Decoction of stem bark of described plant, 15 g, with honey 10 g, two times a day, is useful. **Excess and turbid micturition:** Vegetable of flowers of described plant, 50 g, two times a day, or decoction of root bark of described plant, 15 g, with honey 10 g, two times a day, is useful.

Recommended readings:

Bhutya, R.K. (2007), Vanaspati Aushadha Vigyana, Scientific Publishers (India), Jodhpur, PP. 226.

Brahmavarchas (2003), Ayurved Ka Pran Vanoshadhi Vigyan, Shanti Kunj, Haridwar, PP. 433.

Chunekar, K.C. (2004), Bhava Prakash Nighantu, Chaukhambha Bharti Academy, Varanasi, PP. 549.

Khare, C.P. (2007), Indian Medicinal Plants, Springer (India) P.L. New Delhi, PP. 649.

Kirtikar, K.R. & Basu, B.D. (1998), Indian Medicinal Plants, L.M Basu, Allahabad, Vol. 3, PP. 1924.

Misra, B.L. (2005), Dravya Guna Hastamalaka, Publication scheme, Jaipur, PP. 394.

Nair, R.Vasudevan, (2007), Indian Medicinal Plants, Orient Longman P.L. Chennai, Vol. 5, PP. 245.

Namjoshi, A.N. (2001), The Ayurvedic Pharmacopoeia of India, Government of India, Department of Indian Systems of Medicine & Homoeopathy, New Delhi, Part-1, Volume- 3, PP. 174.

Prajapati, N.D., Purohit, S.S., Sharma, A.K. & Tarun Kumar (2003), A Hand Book of Medicinal Plants, Agrobios India, Jodhpur, PP. 505.

Sharma, P.V. (1981), Dravya gun vigyana, Chaukhambha Bharti Academy, Varanasi, Vol. 1, PP. 791.

459. *Tephrosia purpurea* (L) Pers.

Family: Papilionaceae; Fabaceae.

Synonym: *T.hamiltonii.*

Other similar plants: *T.spinosa, T.uniflora* species *petrosa.*

Name: English: Purple Tephrosia, Wild Indigo, **Sanskrit:** *Sharapunkhaa, Plihashatru, Neelivrikhsaakriti,* **Hindi:** *Sharpunkhaa,* **Local:** *Sarphonkaa.*

Botanical characteristics: Habit: A perennial herb or undershrub, 0.5-1 m high. **Root:** 8-15 cm long, 0.5-1 cm in diam., cylindrical, outer surface pale yellowish-white. **Stem:** Woody, 0.5-1.5 cm thick, cylindrical, sub-erect, much spreading branched, glabrous or sparsely pilose. **Leaf:** Imparipinnate, 5-10 cm long, petioles 6-12 mm long, stipules linear-subulate, nerved, erect or sometimes reflexed, leaflets 11-21, narrow, oblanceolate, obtuse or retuse, mucronate, 2-2.8 by 0.8-1.2 cm, glabrous above, clothed with fine appressed silky hairs beneath, base cuneate, nerves close, ascending, slender, conspicuous on both surfaces; petiolules of lateral leaflets 1.5-2.5 mm, those of the terminal 3-4.5 mm. Leaf breaks in lanceolate shape. **Flower:** Bright rosy-purple or violate, 6.25-8 mm long, in leaf opposed lax racemes 7.5-12.5 cm long, the lower flowers of the racemes fascicled; pedicels slender; bracts subulate. **Fruit:** Pods, 3-4.5 cm long, slightly curved, linear, mucronateat first thiny hairy, finally glabrascent. **Seed:** 5-10, grey and smooth.

Flowering and fruiting period: August-September and November-December.

Habitat: Throughout India, on waste lands and along roadsides, up to an altitude of 1850 m in Himalayas,

Parts used: Root, whole plant, alkaline.

Dosage: Root, whole plant 3-6 g, Juice 10-20 ml, alkaline 0.5-1g.

Collection period: December-January.

Ayurvedic properties: ***Ras:*** *tikta, kashaaya,* ***Gun:*** *laghu, rukhsa, tikhsna,* ***Veerya:*** *ushna,* ***Vipaka:*** *katu,* ***Tridosha*** **Effect:** alleviates ***Kapha:*** ***++,*** ***Vaata:*** ***+.***

Chemical constituents: The **leaves** contain rutin, rotenoids (0.65-0.8% on dry basis), a triterpenoid, lupeol and beta-sitopsterol. The **seeds** contain rotenoid, a diketone-pongamol; a dimethylchromene flavanone, isolonchocarpin; furanoflavones karanjin and kanjone; a flavanone purpurin; sitosterol and a flavonoid, lanceolarin. The **plant** contains beta-sitosterol, lupeol, rutin, delphinidin chloride, cyaniding chloride, (-)isolonchocarpin, lanceolatin A & B, ongamol, karangin, kangone, 5,7-dimethoxy-8-flavonone, 2-methoxy-3,9-dihydroxycoumestone, flevichapparins B & C, methyl karanjic acid and purpurin, flavonoids-tephrosin A & B, (+)tephrosone. The **roots** contain tephrocin, deguelin, isotephrocin, rotenone, maxima sunstance A with 3,4,6,7-tetra-methoxyiso-flovone, maxima isoflavone B & C, lanceolatin A & B, ten-8-subsituted flavonoids, butenoids, butenolides, apollinine, semiglabrin, semiglabrinol, tephroglabrin, O-methyl pongamol, tepurindiolpurpurenone, beta-hydroxychalcone, beta-methoxychalcone, (+)purpurin, dehydroisoderricin, (-)maackiain, (-) solonchocarpin. Powdered aerial parts prevented elevation of SGPT, SGOT and serum bilirubin levels. The plant extract led to marked lowering of blood glucose level.

Action and disease indications: The **leaves** are useful in dyspepsia, pectoral diseases, piles, syphilis, gonorrhea, and bruises. The **seeds** are useful in skin diseases and boils. The **plant** is thermogenic, anthelmintic, diuretic, digestive, laxative, uterine tonic, depurative, styptic, anti-inflammatory, deobstruent, alexiteric, alterant and anti-pyretic, used for dyspepsia, colic, flatulence, piles, cough, asthma, bronchitis, inflammations, anemia, skin diseases, scrofula, elephantiasis, pimples, hepato-spleenomegaly, verminosis, strangury, dysmenorrhea, amenorrhea, chronic fever, boils, odontalgia and gingivitis.

Clinical uses: Liver and spleen enlargement: Root powder of described plant 6 g, *Terminalia*

chebula 3 g, with distillate of *Solanum nigrum* 20 ml, two times a day, is beneficial. **Flatulence:** Alkali of described plant 500 mg, *Terminalia chebula* 2 g, clarified butter 10 g, with warm water, two times a day, is beneficial. **Piles:** Root powder of described plant, 5 g, with whey, two times a day, is beneficial. **Bleeding diasthesis:** Root powder of described plant, 5 g, with rice water, two times a day, is beneficial. **Colic:** Root powder of described plant, 5 g, *Piper nigrum* 500 mg, lukewarm water, two times a day, is beneficial. **Scabies, pruritis:** Local application of paste of seeds of described plant is beneficial. **Gingivitis, dentalgia:** Gargles of root powder of described plant, two times a day, is beneficial.

Formulations: *Sarapunkhaa khsaara, Raktashodhakaarista, Mahaa mrityunjaya lauha, Yakritaplihodara lauha.*

Recommended readings:

Acharya, B.K. (2008), Ayurveda Jadi-buti Rahasya, Patanjali Yogapitha, Haridwar, PP. 368.

Bhutya, R.K. (2007), Vanaspati Aushadha Vigyana, Scientific Publishers (India), Jodhpur, PP. 223.

Brahmavarchas (2003), Ayurved Ka Pran Vanoshadhi Vigyan, Shanti Kunj, Haridwar, PP. 434.

Chunekar, K.C. (2004), Bhava Prakash Nighantu, Chaukhambha Bharti Academy, Varanasi, PP. 408.

Dhiman, A.K. (2006), Ayurvedic Drug Plants, Daya Publishing House, Delhi, PP. 353.

Khare, C.P. (2007), Indian Medicinal Plants, Springer (India) P.L. New Delhi, PP. 650.

Kirtikar, K.R. & Basu, B.D. (1998), Indian Medicinal Plants, L.M Basu, Allahabad, Vol. 1, PP. 724.

Misra, B.L. (2005), Dravya Guna Hastamalaka, Publication scheme, Jaipur, PP. 272.

Nair, R.Vasudevan, (2007), Indian Medicinal Plants, Orient Longman P.L. Chennai, Vol. 5, PP. 249.

Prajapati, N.D., Purohit, S.S., Sharma, A.K. & Tarun Kumar (2003), A Hand Book of Medicinal Plants, Agrobios India, Jodhpur, PP. 506.

Sharma, P.C., Yelne, MB. & Denis, T.J. (2000), Database on medicinal plants used in ayurveda, Central Council for research in Ayurveda and siddha, Vol. 6, PP. 358.

Sharma, P.V. (1981), Dravya gun vigyana, Chaukhambha Bharti Academy, Varanasi, Vol. 1, PP. 554.

Singh, R.S. (2002), Vanoshadhi Nirdeshika, Uttar Pradesh Hindi Sansthan, Lucknow, PP. 359.

460. *Teramnus libialis* Spreng.

Family: Papilionaceae; Fabaceae.

Ayurvedic Groups: Charak: *Jivaniya, Shukrajanaka, Madhuraskandha,* **Sushruta:** *Kakolyaadi, Vidarigandhaadi gana,*

Name: Sanskrit: *Maashaparni, Suryaparni, Kaamboji, Hayapuchhikaa, Paandulomashaparni, Krishnavrintaa, Mahaasahaa,* **Hindi:** *Maashaparni,* **Local:** *Van Urada.*

Botanical characteristics: Habit: A widely spreading twining herb. **Stem:** Slender, more or less appressedly hairy. **Leaf:** 3-foliate; 1.2-3.8 cm; stipules 3 mm long, ovate-lanceolate, acute, deciduous. Leaflets membranous or sub-coriaceous, 3.5-6.3 by1.5-2.5 cm, the terminal largest, ovate-oblong or oblong-lanceolate, sub-acute, apiculate, glabrous above, appressedly hairy beneath, base rounded or acute, stiples subulate, 1.5-2.5 mm long, ovate-lanceolate, deciduous. **Flower:** Reddish-purple or white, bisexual, in axillary few flowered lax racemes 5-15 cm long, solitary or fascicled, along a slender, more or less hairy rachis; pedicles 4 mm long; bracts 2 mm long, linear-lanceolate; brectioles 1.5 mm long, subulate. **Fruit:** Pods, 3.8-5 cm by 2.5 mm, narrowly linear, straight or slightly incurved, hairy when young, nearly glabrous when mature, with a short stout beak bent upwards so as to form nearly a right angle with the pod. **Seed:** 8-12, oblong, truncate or slightly rounded at the ends, smooth, dark brown when fresh, black when dry.

Flowering and fruiting period: August-September and November-December.

Habitat: Throughout the greater parts of India, especially Punjab eastwards to West Bengal, extending southwards into Peninsular India.

Parts used: Whole plant, root. **Dosage:** 5-10 g.

Collection period: December-January.

Ayurvedic properties: ***Ras:*** *tikta, madhur,* ***Gun:*** *laghu, rukhsa,* ***Veerya:*** *sheeta,* ***Vipaka:*** *madhur* ***Tridosha*** **Effect:** alleviates ***Vaata:*** **+++,** ***Pitta:*** **+++,** aggrevates ***Kapha:*** **++.**

Chemical constituents: The **Stem** and **aerial parts** contain flavonol glycoside, vitexin, bergenin, daidzin, 3-0-methyl-D-chiro-inositol. The **seeds** contain fradixin, amino acids, lycine, leucine, isolucine, arginine, valine, histidine, unsaturated fatty acids, minerals-potassium, magnesium, calcium, phosphorus, free phenols, tannins, L-DOPA, hydrogen cyanide, phytic acid; and proteins.

Action and disease indications: The **plant** is refrigerant, aphrodisiac, stomachic, nervine tonic, anti-pyretic, rejuvenating, seminiferous, and galactagogue and tonic, prescribed for seminal weakness, Penile dysfunction, inflammations, biliousness, gout, fevers, bronchitis, dipsia, burning sensation, paralysis, rheumatism, diseases of nerves system, haemoptysis, catarrh, tuberculosis and general debility.

Clinical uses: Leucorrhea: Local application of medicated oil, made with described plant, is beneficial. **Penile dysfunction, general debility:** Decoction of described plant, 10 g, with honey 10 g, two times a day, is useful.

Formulations: *Chyavanpraasha, Dashamoola kwaatha, Dashamoolarista, Brahmarasaayana, Balaa taila, Agurvaadi taila, Amritapraasha ghrita, Vrihat aswagandhaa ghrita, Vrihat chhaagalaadhya ghrita, Vidaaryaadi ghrita.*

Recommended readings:

Bhutya, R.K. (2007), Vanaspati Aushadha Vigyana, Scientific Publishers (India), Jodhpur, PP. 179.

Brahmavarchas (2003), Ayurved Ka Pran Vanoshadhi Vigyan, Shanti Kunj, Haridwar, PP. 436.

Chunekar, K.C. (2004), Bhava Prakash Nighantu, Chaukhambha Bharti Academy, Varanasi, PP. 297.

Khare, C.P. (2007), Indian Medicinal Plants, Springer (India) P.L. New Delhi, PP. 651.

Kirtikar, K.R. & Basu, B.D. (1998), Indian Medicinal Plants, L.M Basu, Allahabad, Vol. 1, PP. 774.

Namjoshi, A.N. (2001), The Ayurvedic Pharmacopoeia of India, Government of India, Department of Indian Systems of Medicine & Homoeopathy, New Delhi, Part-1, Volume- 3, PP. 118.

Sharma, P.C., Yelne, MB. & Denis, T.J. (2000), Database on medicinal plants used in ayurveda, Central Council for research in Ayurveda and siddha, Vol. 8, PP. 261.

Sharma, P.V. (1981), Dravya gun vigyana, Chaukhambha Bharti Academy, Varanasi, Vol. 1, PP. 747.

Singh, R.S. (2002), Vanoshadhi Nirdeshika, Uttar Pradesh Hindi Sansthan, Lucknow, PP. 305.

461. *Terminalia arjuna* (Roxb.) W. & A.

Family: Combretaceae.

Other similar plants: *Terminalia tomentosa.*

Ayurvedic Groups: Charak: *Kashaaya skandha, Udardaprashamana,* **Sushruta:** *Nyagrodhaadi, Saalasaaraadi gana.*

Name: English: Arjun Terminalia, **Sanskrit:** *Kakubha, Arjuna, Nadisarja, Indradru, Veeravrikhsa, Veera, Dhavala,* **Hindi:** *Arjun,* **Local:** *Kohada, Kohadiyaa.*

Botanical characteristics: Habit: A large evergreen tree, height, 18-25 m. **Stem:** With buttressed trunk and horizontally spreading branches, bark smooth, whitish outside and flesh coloured inside, flaking off in large flat pieces. **Leaf:** Simple, sub-opposite, 10-15 by 5-7 cm, oblong or elliptic-oblong, obtuse or subacute, coriaceous, pale dull green above, pale brown beneath, often unequal sided, nerves arculate, 10-15 pairs, reticulate, pellucid; petioles 6-10 mm long, with 1 or usually 2 prominent glands at the top immediately below the leaves. Shape like leaves of *Psidium guajava.* **Flower:** White, sessile, in terminal panicles of spikes with linear bracteoles. **Fruit:** Drupes, 2.5-5 cm long, ovoid or obovoid-oblong, fibrous-woody, glabrous, dark-brown, with 5-7, hard projecting wings or angles, striated with numerous curved veins. Shape like the fruit of *Averrhoa carambola.*

Flowering and fruiting period: April-May and September-November.

Habitat: Throughout the greater parts of India, in the sub-Himalayan tracts, along banks of rivers, streams, ravines and dry water-courses.

Parts used: Stem bark. **Dosage:** 3-6 g.

Collection period: November-December.

Ayurvedic properties: ***Ras:*** *kashaaya,* ***Gun:*** *laghu, rukhsa,* ***Veerya:*** *sheeta,* ***Vipaka:*** *katu,* ***Tridosha*** **Effect:** alleviates ***Kapha:*** +++, ***Pitta:*** ++.

Chemical constituents: The **bark** contains arachidic, stearate, ceracidin, hentriacontane, myristyl oleate, mannitol, betasitosterol, friedelin. The **bark extract** contains acids-arjunolic and terminic acids; glycosides-Arjunetin, arjunosides 1-4; and strong anti-oxydants-flavones, tannins, oligomeric proanthocyanidins. Oral administration of bark powder (400 mg/kg body waight) for 10 days produced significant increase in circulating histamine, a little increase in 5-HT, catecholamines and HDL cholesterol, and decrease in total lipids, triglycerides and toralcholesterol.

Action and disease indications: The **bark** is refrigerant, aphrodisiac, csrdio-tonic, cardio-protective, styptic, demulcent, anti-dysenteric, urinary astringent, expectorant, alexiteric, lithontriptic, and tonic, prescribed for angina, poor coronary circulation, herpes, leucoderma, obesity, excessive and turbid micturation, fractures, chronic fevers, epistaxis, ulcers, urethorrhea, leucorrhea, diabetes, anemia, hyperhydrosis, fatigue, cough, asthma, bronchitis, tumours, otalgia, dysentery, inflammations, internal and external haemorrhages, cirrhosis of liver and Hypertension.

Clinical uses: Cardiac debility, tachycardia, hypotension, epistaxis, chronic fever, osteoporosis: *'Khsira paka'* of stem bark of described plant, 10 g, *Elettaria cardamomum* 1 g, two times a day, is beneficial. **Diarrhea with bleeding:** Stem bark of described plant, 6 g, seed powder of *Holarrhena antidysentrica* 2 g, with milk of she goat, two times a day, is beneficial. **Bone fracture:** Local application of paste of bark of described plant is beneficial. Bark of described plant 4 g, sugar candy powder 10 g, with clarified butter 10 g, two times a day, is beneficial. **Wounds, ulcers:** Washing with decoction of bark of described plant, is beneficial. **Spermatorrhea, menorrhagia, metrorrhagia, leucorrhea:** Decoction of stem bark powder of described plant 10 g, *Santalum album* 1 g, with honey 10 g, two times a day, is useful. **Stomatitis:** Gargles of decoction of stem bark powder of described plant 10 g, with oil of *Sesamum orientale* 10 ml. two times a day, is beneficial. **Chlosma, acne vulgaris:** Local application of paste of bark of described plant, *Rubia cordifolia, Justisia adhatoda* and honey is beneficial. **Palpitation:** Mix powder of described plant, root powder of *Sida cordifolia, Tribulus terrestris, Nardostachys jatamansi, Withania somnifera,* 6 g, with milk, two times a day, is beneficial. **Obesity:** Stem bark powder of described plant 5 g, with decoction of roots of *Premna corymbosa* 6 g, two times a day, is beneficial. **Chronic fever:** Stem bark powder of described plant 5 g, juice of *Tinospora cordifolia* 20 ml, with honey 10 g, two times a day, is beneficial. **Excess and turbid micturition:** Mix powder of described plant, *Santalum album, Hygrophila auriculata,* 4-4 parts, *Curcuma longa* 1 part, dose 5 g, with milk, two times a day, is beneficial.

Formulations: *Arjunaarista, Arjun ghrita, Kakubhaadi churna, Arjunsiddha dugdha, Shankar vati, Lakhsaa guggulu, Dhaatakyaadi taila, Devadaarvyaadhyarista.*

Recommended readings:

Acharya, B.K. (2008), Ayurveda Jadi-buti Rahasya, Patanjali Yogapitha, Haridwar, PP. 87.

Bhutya, R.K. (2007), Vanaspati Aushadha Vigyana, Scientific Publishers (India), Jodhpur, PP. 20.

Brahmavarchas (2003), Ayurved Ka Pran Vanoshadhi Vigyan, Shanti Kunj, Haridwar, PP. 437.

Chunekar, K.C. (2004), Bhava Prakash Nighantu, Chaukhambha Bharti Academy, Varanasi, PP. 523.

Dhiman, A.K. (2006), Ayurvedic Drug Plants, Daya Publishing House, Delhi, PP. 41.

Khare, C.P. (2007), Indian Medicinal Plants, Springer (India) P.L. New Delhi, PP. 651.

Kirtikar, K.R. & Basu, B.D. (1998), Indian Medicinal Plants, L.M Basu, Allahabad, Vol. 2, PP. 1023.

Misra, B.L. (2005), Dravya Guna Hastamalaka, Publication scheme, Jaipur, PP. 398.

Nair, R.Vasudevan, (2007), Indian Medicinal Plants, Orient Longman P.L. Chennai, Vol. 5, PP. 253.

Namjoshi, A.N. (2001), The Ayurvedic Pharmacopoeia of India, Government of India, Department of Indian Systems of Medicine & Homoeopathy, New Delhi, Part-1, Volume- 1, PP. 17.

Pareek, G.N. (2005), Sudhanidhi, Vanoshadhi Ratnakar, Dhanvantari Karyalaya, Aligarh, Vol. 1, PP. 88.

Prajapati, N.D., Purohit, S.S., Sharma, A.K. & Tarun Kumar (2003), A Hand Book of Medicinal Plants, Agrobios India, Jodhpur, PP. 506.

Sharma, P.C., Yelne, MB. & Denis, T.J. (2000), Database on medicinal plants used in ayurveda, Central Council for research in Ayurveda and siddha, Vol. 3, PP. 57.

Sharma, P.V. (1981), Dravya gun vigyana, Chaukhambha Bharti Academy, Varanasi, Vol. 1, PP. 195.

Singh, R.S. (2002), Vanoshadhi Nirdeshika, Uttar Pradesh Hindi Sansthan, Lucknow, PP. 26.

Swami, K.N. (1985), Gavon Main Aushadh Ratna, Kalera Krishana Gopal, Kalera (Raj.), Vol. 1, PP. 45.

462. *Terminalia bellirica* Roxb.

Family: Combretaceae.

Name: English: Belleric Myrobalan, Bastard Myrobalan, **Sanskrit:** *Vibhitaka, Akhsa, Karshaphala, Kalidruma, Bhutavaasa, Kaliyugaalaya,* **Hindi:** *Baheara,* **Local:** *Baheraa.*

Botanical characteristics: Habit: A large deciduous buttressed tree, height 20-30 m. **Stem:** With 2.5-5 cm thick, brownish grey bark having shallow longitudinal fissures. **Leaf:** Simple, alternate, crowded about the extremities of the branches, coriaceous, 10-20 by 7-15 cm, broadly elliptic or elliptic-obovate, rounded or rarely sub-acute or shortly acuminate, both surfaces puberulous when young, glabrous and reticulate when old, margins entire, pellucid, base narrowed; main nerves 6-8 pairs, spreading, prominent on both surfaces; petioles 2.5-10 cm long, with glands at apex. **Flower:** Pale greenish yellow, with an offensive odour, in axillary slender spikes, longer than the petioles, but shorter than the leaves. **Fruit:** Drupes, ovoid, grey, 12-25 mm diam., suddenly narrowed into a very short stalk, velvety, obscurely 5-angled when dried. **Seed:** One seed in a fruit, thick walled, hard.

Flowering and fruiting period: March-May and December-February.

Habitat: Throughout India, in deciduous forests, up to an elevation of 900 m.

Parts used: Fruit pulp. **Dosage:** 3-6 g.

Collection period: February-March.

Ayurvedic properties: ***Ras:*** *kashaya,* ***Gun:*** *laghu, rukhsa,* ***Veerya:*** *ushna,* ***Vipaka:*** *madhur,*

Tridosha* Effect:** alleviates ***Kapha: +++, ***Pitta:*** ++.

Chemical constituents: The **fruits** contain beta-sitostrol, gallic and ellagic acids, ethyl gallate, galloyl glucose, chebulagic acid and a cardiac glycoside, bellaricanin. The fleshy fruit pulp contains 21.4% tannin, both condensed and hydrolysable.

Action and disease indications: The **fruits** are anti-pyretic, thermogenic, anodyne, anti-inflammatory, styptic, narcotic, digestive, anthelmintic, aperient, ophthalmic, expectorant, anti-emetic and rejuvenating, prescribed for diarrhea, dyspepsia, biliousness, cough, asthma, bronchitis and upper respiratory tract infections, tropical pulmonary eosinophilia and allergic eruptions, emesis, worm infestation, insomnia, dropsy, flatulence, dipsia, vomiting, haemorrhages, ophthalmopathy, strangury, cephalgia, skin diseases, fevers, ulcers and general debility. The **oil** obtained from seeds is trichogenous and used for dyspepsia, skin diseases, leucoderma and greyness of hairs.

Clinical uses: Penile dysfunction: Seed powder of described plant, 2 g, with milk, two times a day, is beneficial. **Alopecia, canities, skin diseases, leucoderma:** Local application of seed oil of described plant is beneficial. **Asthma, bronchitis, rhinitis, disphonia:** Sucking of roasted fruit powder of described plant, three times a day, is useful. **Navel displacement:** Decoction of fruit powder of described plant 6 g, with honey 10 g, 4 times a day, by 1-1 hour, is useful. **Leucoderma:** Local application of paste of black ash of king cobra snake and oil of described plant is beneficial. **Bronchitis:** Decoction of mix powder of fruits of described plant, *Syzygium aromaticum, Piper longum,* rind of fruit of *Punica grantum,* bark of *Acacia catechu, Glycyrrhiza glabra, Vitis vinifera,* 10 g, with honey 10 g, two times a day, is useful. (2) Sucking of tablets of 1 g, of mix powder of fruits of described plant and raw sugar, in ratio of 1:2, three times a day, is useful. **Disphonia:** Mix powder of fruits of described plant, *Phylanthus emblica, Piper nigrum, Tinospora cordifolia,* 10 g, with honey 10 g, two times a day, is useful. **Leucoderma:** Seed powder of *Psoralea corylifolia* 1.5 g, with decoction of fruits of described plant and 10 g, root bark of *Ficus hispida* 10 g, added raw sugar 15 g, two times a day, is beneficial. **Ptyalism:** Sucking of fruit powder of described plant and sugar, 10 g, two times a day, is beneficial.

Formulations: *Triphalaa churna, Triphalaa ghrita, Talisaadi churna, Lavangaadi vati, Phalatrikaadi kwaatha.*

Recommended readings:

Acharya, B.K. (2008), Ayurveda Jadi-buti Rahasya, Patanjali Yogapitha, Haridwar, PP. 118.

Bhutya, R.K. (2007), Vanaspati Aushadha Vigyana, Scientific Publishers (India), Jodhpur, PP. 160.

Brahmavarchas (2003), Ayurved Ka Pran Vanoshadhi Vigyan, Shanti Kunj, Haridwar, PP. 439.

Chunekar, K.C. (2004), Bhava Prakash Nighantu, Chaukhambha Bharti Academy, Varanasi, PP. 9.

Dhiman, A.K. (2006), Ayurvedic Drug Plants, Daya Publishing House, Delhi, PP. 63.

Khare, C.P. (2007), Indian Medicinal Plants, Springer (India) P.L. New Delhi, PP. 652.

Kirtikar, K.R. & Basu, B.D. (1998), Indian Medicinal Plants, L.M Basu, Allahabad, Vol. 2, PP. 1017.

Misra, B.L. (2005), Dravya Guna Hastamalaka, Publication scheme, Jaipur, PP. 397.

Nair, R.Vasudevan, (2007), Indian Medicinal Plants, Orient Longman P.L. Chennai, Vol. 5, PP. 258.

Namjoshi, A.N. (2001), The Ayurvedic Pharmacopoeia of India, Government of India, Department of Indian Systems of Medicine & Homoeopathy, New Delhi, Part-1, Volume- 2, PP. 26.

Pareek, G.N. (2005), Sudhanidhi, Vanoshadhi Ratnakar, Dhanvantari Karyalaya, Aligarh, Vol. 6, PP. 168.

Prajapati, N.D., Purohit, S.S., Sharma, A.K. & Tarun Kumar (2003), A Hand Book of Medicinal Plants, Agrobios India, Jodhpur, PP. 507.

Sharma, P.V. (1981), Dravya gun vigyana, Chaukhambha Bharti Academy, Varanasi, Vol. 1, PP. 239.

Singh, R.S. (2002), Vanoshadhi Nirdeshika, Uttar Pradesh Hindi Sansthan, Lucknow, PP. 267.

Swami, K.N. (1985), Gavon Main Aushadh Ratna, Kalera Krishana Gopal, Kalera (Raj.), Vol. 3, PP. 79.

463. *Terminalia chebula* Retz.

Family: Combretaceae.

Ayurvedic Groups: Charak: *Prajaasthan, Jwaraghan, Kushtaghan, Kaasaghan, Arshoghan,* **Sushruta:** *Triphalaa, Aamalakyaadi, Parushakaadi gana.*

Name: English: Chebulic Myrobalan, Black Myrobalan, **Sanskrit:** *Abhayaa, Pathyaa, Kaayasthaa, Shivaa, Vayasthaa, Shreyasi, Haritaki, Amritaa, Haimavati, Avyathaa,* **Hindi:** *Harad,* **Local:** *Harad, Harre.*

Botanical characteristics: Habit: A moderate sized to large deciduous tree, height 25-30 m. **Stem:** With a cylindrical bole, rounded crown and spreading branches, bark dark brown, young branchelets leafbuds, young leaves are covered with soft, shining, rust or silvery hairs. **Leaf:** 7-20 by 4-8 cm, alternate or sub-opposite, glabrous or nearly so when mature, not clustered, distant, ovate or elliptic-oblong, acute, rounded or cordate at base, penninerved, secondary nerves 6-8 pairs, arching, prominent; petioles 2-5 cm long, pubescent, usually with 2 glands near the top. **Flower:** Yellowish-white, hermaphrodite, 4 mm across, sessile, with an offensive smell, in terminal simple spikes or short penicles. **Fruit:** Drupes, 2-4 cm long, ellipsoidal, obovoid or ovoid, glabrous, shining, more or less 5-ribbed, yellow to orange-brown, sometimes tinged with red or black, pendulous. **Seed:** Hard, pale yellow, bony, very thick, obscurely angled.

Flowering and fruiting period: April-June and January-March.

Habitat: Throughout the greater parts of India, in deciduous forests, up to 1500 m in outer Himalaya, also in Assam, West Bengal, Bihar, Kokan, Tamilnadu and Western Ghats.

Parts used: Mature and Immature; Fruit. **Dosage:** 3-6 g.

Collection period: February-April.

Ayurvedic properties: ***Ras:*** *kashaya, madhur, amla, katu, tikta,* ***Gun:*** *laghu, rukhsa,* ***Veerya:*** *ushna,* ***Vipaka:*** *madhur,* ***Tridosha*** **Effect:** alleviates ***Kapha:*** ++++, ***Vaata:*** ++, ***Pitta:*** +.

Chemical constituents: The **fruits** contain shikimic, gallic, triacontanoic and palmitic acids, beta-sitosterol, daucosterol, triethyl ester og chebulic acid and ethyl ester of gallic acid; a new ellagitannin, terchebulin, along with punicalagin and teaflavin A have been isolated from the fruits. A new triterpene, chebupentol and arjungenin, terminoic acid and arjunilic acid were also isolated from fruit. Anti-oxidant constituents of the plant, phloroglucinol and pyrogallol have been isolated along with ferulic, vanillic, *p*-coumaric and caffeic acids. Ether extract showed higher anti-oxidant activity than BHA and BHT, acid esters present in phenolic fraction of extract, were found most effective.

Action and disease indications: The **mature fruits** are thermogenic, anodyne, anti-inflammatory, diuretic, vulnerary, alterant, carminative, digestive, anthelmintic, cardio-tonic, aphrodisiac, depurative, febrifuge, antiseptic, stomachic, laxative, anti-bilious, alterative and tonic, prescribed for flatulence, constipation, diarrhea, dysentery, cyst, indigestion, vomiting, wounds, ulcers, inflammations, anorexia, helminthiasis, piles, jaundice, pharyngodynia, hiccough, renal and vesical calculi, cephalgia, epilepsy, ophthalmopathy, skin diseases, leprosy, intermittent fever, cardiac-diseases, stomatitis, neuropathy, enlarged liver and spleen, cough, bronchial asthma, bronchitis, general debility, and for the metabolic harmony. The immature fruits are deobstruent, Purgative and Anti-inflammatory, used for centipation and jaundice.

Clinical uses: Constipation: Unripe fruit powder of described plant, 3-6 g, with warm water, at morning or night, is beneficial. Or fruit powder of described plant, 3 g, *Foeniculum vulgare* 3 g, with *'Gulkanda'* 20 g, is beneficial. **For deobstruction:** Soak and dry the unripe fruits of described plant by seven times in cow urine, dry them and fry in castor oil and make fine powder, dose 1-2 g, with lukewarm water, two times a day, is beneficial. **Stomatitis, sore throat:** Gargles by decoction of ripe fruits of described plant, two times a day, is beneficial. **Sprue:** Boil and dry the ripe fruits of described plant, make fine powder, 3 g, with water, two times a day, is beneficial. **Inflammation, pains:** Local application of paste of fruit of described plant is beneficial. **Wounds, ulcers:** Washing with decoction of ripe fruits of described plant is beneficial. **Anorexia:** Sucking of fruits of described plant, 6 g, two times a day, is beneficial. **Asthma, bronchitis, colic, hydrocele, inguinal hernia:** Black ash of unripe fruit powder of described plant, 10 parts, extract of urine of cow, 2 parts, *Zingiber officinale* 10 parts, rock salt and *Syzygium aromaticum* 1-1 part, dose 1-2 g, with warm water, two times a day, is beneficial. **Headache, pain of eyeballs, vertigo:** Decoction of mix powder of fruits of described plant, *Phylanthus emblica, Terminalia belliarica, Swertia chirata, Curcuma longa,* bark of *Azadirachta indica, Tinospora cordifolia,* 10 g, with honey 10 g, two times a day, is useful. **Piles:** Fried (in castor oil) unripe fruits of described plant, 3 g, with whey at morning and with milk at night, is beneficial. **Bronchitis:** Mix powder of fruits of described plant and fruits of *Terminalia belliarica,* 3 g, with honey 10 g, two times a day, is useful. **Hiccough:** Ripe fruit powder of described plant, 3 g, with warm water, two times a day, is beneficial. **Epistaxis:** Fruits of described plant 2 g, *Piper longum* 500 mg, with leaves juice of *Justisia adhatoda,* 10 ml, and honey 10 g, two times a day, is beneficial. **Alcoholism:** Decoction of fruits of described plant, 10 g, *Hyoscyamus niger* 1 g, with milk, two times a day, is beneficial. **Hyperacidity:** Fruit powder of described plant 3 g, *Vitis vinifera* 10 g, with water, two times a day, is beneficial. **Vomiting:** Fruit powder of described plant, 2 g, with honey 10 g, two times a day, is useful. **Obesity:** Fruit powder of described plant, 4 g, with water, after meal, two times a day, is beneficial. **Chronic rheumatism:** Mix powder of fruits of described plant 6 parts, rock salt 1 part, Nitrate of potash 1 part, *Apium graveolens* 1.5 part, *Zingiber officinale* 2.5 parts, dose 2.5 g, with water, two times a day, is very beneficial. Use it for 6 months. **Indigestion:** Fruit powder of described plant, 3 g, raw sugar 1o g, *Zingiber officinale* 1 g, with water, is beneficial. **Urticaria:** Mix powder of fruit powder of described plant, *Phylanthus emblica, Terminalia belliarica, Rubia cordifolia,* 6 g, with honey 10 g, four times a day, is useful. **Colic:** Mix powder of fruits of described plant 4 parts, *Trachy spermum-ammi* 3 parts, sodium nitrate 2 parts, rock salt 1 part, 4 g, with water, two times a day, is beneficial. **Liver and spleen enlargement, ascitis:** Decoction of fruits of described plant, *Zingiber officinale, Cedrus deodara, Boerhavia diffusa, Tinospora cordifolia,* 10 g, with gum of *Commiphora mukul* 1 g and urine of cow 6 ml, two times a day, is beneficial. **Disarthria:** Mix powder of fruit powder of described plant, *Zingiber officinale, Acorus calamus, Glycyrrhiza glabra, Sassurea costus, Piper longum, Cuminum cyminum, Trachy spermumammi,* rock salt, 4 g, with clarified butter 10 g, two times a day, is beneficial. **Bleeding piles:** Mix powder of fruits of described plant, seeds of *Holarrhena antidysentrica, Mesua ferrea, Phylanthus emblica,* 3 g, with whey, two times a day, is beneficial. **Obesity:** Mix powder of fruits of described plant, *Tinospora cordifolia, Cyperus scarissus,* 5 g, with honey 10 g, two times a day, is useful. **Vertigo:** Tablets of 1-1 g, of mix powder of fruits of described plant, *Zingiber officinale, Asparagus racemosus,* raw sugar, 2 tablets, two times a day, is beneficial. **Hyperacidity:** Mix powder of fruits of described plant, *Piper longum, Vitis vinifera, Coriandrum sativum,* sugar candy powder 10 g, with honey 10 g, two times a day, is useful. **Chronic constipation:** Mixture of yellow leaves of described plant 2.5 parts, leaves of *Cassia senna* 2.5 parts, seeds of *Prunus amyadalus* 2 parts, *'Gulkand'* 2.5 parts, seedless fruits of *Vitis vinifera* 4 parts, *Ficus carica* 1 part, Zizyphus sativa 1 part, dose 12 g, with warm milk, at night, is very beneficial. **Diabetes mellitus:** Mix powder of ripe fruits of described plant, leaves and seeds of *Syzygium cumini, Gymnema sylvestris,* soak and dry this powder with juice of *Momordica charanita,* by seven times and make tablets of 1 g, dose 1 tablet, two times a day, is beneficial.

Formulations: *Abhayaarista, Chitrakaharitaki, Braahmarasaayana, Agaatsyaharitaki, Pathyaadi kwaatha, Pathyaadi vati, Dantiharitaki, Vyaghriharitaki, Abhayaa modaka, Haritakileha, Abhayaadi guggulu.*

Recommended readings:

Acharya, B.K. (2008), Ayurveda Jadi-buti Rahasya, Patanjali Yogapitha, Haridwar, PP. 228.

Bhutya, R.K. (2007), Vanaspati Aushadha Vigyana, Scientific Publishers (India), Jodhpur, PP. 236.

Brahmavarchas (2003), Ayurved Ka Pran Vanoshadhi Vigyan, Shanti Kunj, Haridwar, PP. 440.

Chunekar, K.C. (2004), Bhava Prakash Nighantu, Chaukhambha Bharti Academy, Varanasi, PP. 7.

Dhiman, A.K. (2006), Ayurvedic Drug Plants, Daya Publishing House, Delhi, PP. 149.

Khare, C.P. (2007), Indian Medicinal Plants, Springer (India) P.L. New Delhi, PP. 653.

Kirtikar, K.R. & Basu, B.D. (1998), Indian Medicinal Plants, L.M Basu, Allahabad, Vol. 2, PP. 1020.

Misra, B.L. (2005), Dravya Guna Hastamalaka, Publication scheme, Jaipur, PP. 395.

Nair, R.Vasudevan, (2007), Indian Medicinal Plants, Orient Longman P.L. Chennai, Vol. 5, PP. 263.

Namjoshi, A.N. (2001), The Ayurvedic Pharmacopoeia of India, Government of India, Department of Indian Systems of Medicine & Homoeopathy, New Delhi, Part-1, Volume- 2, PP. 47.

Pareek, G.N. (2005), Sudhanidhi, Vanoshadhi Ratnakar, Dhanvantari Karyalaya, Aligarh, Vol. 8, PP. 303.

Prajapati, N.D., Purohit, S.S., Sharma, A.K. & Tarun Kumar (2003), A Hand Book of Medicinal Plants, Agrobios India, Jodhpur, PP. 508.

Sharma, P.C., Yelne, MB. & Denis, T.J. (2000), Database on medicinal plants used in ayurveda, Central Council for research in Ayurveda and siddha, Vol. 3, PP. 282.

Sharma, P.V. (1981), Dravya gun vigyana, Chaukhambha Bharti Academy, Varanasi, Vol. 1, PP. 753.

Singh, R.S. (2002), Vanoshadhi Nirdeshika, Uttar Pradesh Hindi Sansthan, Lucknow, PP. 399.

Swami, K.N. (1985), Gavon Main Aushadh Ratna, Kalera Krishana Gopal, Kalera (Raj.), Vol. 3, PP. 384.

464. *Terminalia tomentosa* W. & A.

Family: Combretaceae.

Other similar plants: *T. crenulata, T. alata.*

Ayurvedic Groups: Sushruta: *Saalsaaraadi gana.*

Name: English: Laurel, **Sanskrit:** *Ajakarna,* **Hindi:** *Asana,* **Local:** *Asana, Sarj, Saaj, Saandar.*

Botanical characteristics: Habit: A medium to large tree, height 15-30 m. **Stem:** With clear bole and grayish black bark having longitudinal fissures and transverse cracks, exfoliating in irregular flakes. **Leaf:** Simple, leathery18 by 8 cm, elliptic-oblong or linear oblong, obtuse or even emarginate or slightly acute at apex, rounded or cordate at base, undersurface villous, nerves many, prominently parallel, two large glands on the midrib. Panicles of spikes dense, villous; bracteoles linear. **Flower:** in villous panicles. **Fruit:** Large, glabrous, usually 5 cm diam., with 5 equal wings.

Flowering and fruiting period: April-June and January-March.

Habitat: Throughout India, sub-Himalayan tracts of North-west provinces, in semi-evergreen and mixed deciduous forests, especially in humid regions.

Parts used: Bark. **Dosage:** 3-6 g.

Collection period: February-April.

Ayurvedic properties: ***Ras:*** *kashaya,* ***Gun:*** *laghu, rukhsa,* ***Veerya:*** *sheeta,* ***Vipaka:*** *katu,* ***Tridosha*** **Effect:** alleviates ***Kapha:*** *++,* ***Pitta:*** *+.*

Chemical constituents: The **bark** contains tannin 18.7%, beta-sitosterol, arjunic and arjunolic acids, arjunetin, betulinic and ellagic acids. Hydrolysis of gum gaveoligo-saccharides, disaccharides and monosaccharides.

Action and disease indications: The **bark** is cooling, diuretic, styptic, cardio-tonic, constipating, vulnerary, expectorant, anthelmintic and uterine tonic, used for cardiac diseases, wounds, ulcers, strangury, haemorrhages, haemoptysis, diarrhea, dysentery, cough, asthma, bronchitis, verminosis, leucorrhea, gonorrhea, skin diseases, erysipelas and burning sensation.

Clinical uses: Cardiac debility, tachycardia: *'Khsir paka'* of bark of described plant, 6 g, two times a day, is beneficial.

Formulations: *Trikantaka taila, Trikantaka ghrita, Mahaa khadira ghrita.*

Recommended readings:

Bhutya, R.K. (2007), Vanaspati Aushadha Vigyana, Scientific Publishers (India), Jodhpur, PP. 24.

Brahmavarchas (2003), Ayurved Ka Pran Vanoshadhi Vigyan, Shanti Kunj, Haridwar, PP. 442.

Khare, C.P. (2007), Indian Medicinal Plants, Springer (India) P.L. New Delhi, PP. 655.

Kirtikar, K.R. & Basu, B.D. (1998), Indian Medicinal Plants, L.M Basu, Allahabad, Vol. 2, PP. 1028.

Misra, B.L. (2005), Dravya Guna Hastamalaka, Publication scheme, Jaipur, PP. 399.

Nair, R.Vasudevan, (2007), Indian Medicinal Plants, Orient Longman P.L. Chennai, Vol. 5, PP. 275.

Prajapati, N.D., Purohit, S.S., Sharma, A.K. & Tarun Kumar (2003), A Hand Book of Medicinal Plants, Agrobios India, Jodhpur, PP. 508.

Sharma, P.V. (1981), Dravya gun vigyana, Chaukhambha Bharti Academy, Varanasi, Vol. 1, PP. 682.

465. *Thespesia populnea* Soland. ex Correa.

Family: Malvaceae.

Synonym: *Hibiscus populneus.*

Name: English: Portia Tree, Tulip Tree, Umbrella Tree, False Rosewood, **Sanskrit:** *Paarisha, Palasha, Kamandala, Gardabhanda, Kandaraala, Kapitana, Suparswaka,* **Hindi:** *Paaras Pipal,* **Local:** *Gajadandasahor.*

Botanical characteristics: Habit: A medium to large sized, evergreen, quick growing tree, height up to 18 m. **Stem:** With greyish brown, fissured bark, 1.25 m in girth. **Leaf:** Simple, alternate, 7.5-15 by 5.5-12.5 cm, broadly ovate, cordate, acuminate, entire, smooth, finely reticulately veined, with 5-7 prominent nerves, with peltate scales on one or both surfaces; petioles 5-10 cm long; stipules subulate, deciduous; pedicles 5-7.5 cm long, axillary, shorter or longer than the petioles. **Flower:** Yellow with purple base, slowly changing to purple on withering, bell-shaped, 5-7.5 cm diam. **Fruit:** Capsules, 2.5 cm diam., globose or oblong, brown, covered with minute peltate scales, pubescent, 4-seeded, with much yellow latex, surrounded at the base by the persistent calyx. **Seed:** One cm long, ovoid, channeled along the back, pubescent.

Flowering and fruiting period: June-August and November-December.

Habitat: Mainly along coastal regions throughout India, largely grown as a roadside tree in tropical regions.

Parts used: Bark, fruit.

Dosage: Bark 3-6 g, fruit for external use.

Collection period: November-December.

Ayurvedic properties: ***Ras:*** *kashaya,* ***Gun:*** *laghu, snigdha,* ***Veerya:*** *sheeta* ***Vipaka:*** *katu, madhur* ***Tridosha*** **Effect:** alleviates ***Pitta:*** *+,* ***Vaata:*** *+,* aggravates ***Kapha:*** *+.*

Chemical constituents: The flowers contains populnetin, herbacetin, populneol, quercetin and its glycosides, kaempferol, and its glycosides, rutin, gossypol, beta-sitosterol and its glycosides, nonacosane, lupenone, myricyl alcohol, lupeol and gossypetin. The fruits contain thespesin (0.4%) and herbacetin. The gossypol has a high dextro-rotation, exhibits anti-fertility, anti-tumour, anti-amoebic and anti-HIV activities. Lupenone, lupeol and alkanes show activity against both Gram-positive and Gram-negetive bacteria.

Action and disease indications: The **bark** is cooling, depurative, anti-inflammatory, vulnerary, haemostatic, alterant, anti-diarrheal, anti-bacterial and seminiferous, used for skin diseases, psoriasis, scabies, piles, chronic dysentery, burning sensation, leucorrhea, ulcers, epistaxis, gonorrhea, haemorrhages, haemoptysis, inflammations, wounds, diarrhea, cholera, diabetes, ascitis, warts, dipsia, cough, asthma, bronchitis and catarrh.

Clinical uses: Skin diseases, scabies, ringworm: Local application of paste of black ash of fruit of described plant, with whey, is beneficial. Decoction of bark of described plant 6 g, with honey 10 g, two times a day, is also useful. **Excess and turbid micturition, leucorrhea, diarrhea:** Bark of described plant 3 g, with water, two times a day, is beneficial. **Burning sensation:** *'Khsir paka'* of bark of described plant, 5 g, is beneficial. **Obesity:** Decoction of bark of described plant, root bark of *Premna corymbosa* 6 g, with honey 10 g, two times a day, is useful.

Recommended readings:

Bhutya, R.K. (2007), Vanaspati Aushadha Vigyana, Scientific Publishers (India), Jodhpur, PP. 149.

Chunekar, K.C. (2004), Bhava Prakash Nighantu, Chaukhambha Bharti Academy, Varanasi, PP. 515.

Khare, C.P. (2007), Indian Medicinal Plants, Springer (India) P.L. New Delhi, PP. 659.

Kirtikar, K.R. & Basu, B.D. (1998), Indian Medicinal Plants, L.M Basu, Allahabad, Vol. 1, PP. 340.

Misra, B.L. (2005), Dravya Guna Hastamalaka, Publication scheme, Jaipur, PP. 308.

Nair, R.Vasudevan, (2007), Indian Medicinal Plants, Orient Longman P.L. Chennai, Vol. 5, PP. 281.

Pareek, G.N. (2005), Sudhanidhi, Vanoshadhi Ratnakar, Dhanvantari Karyalaya, Aligarh, Vol. 6, PP. 56.

Prajapati, N.D., Purohit, S.S., Sharma, A.K. & Tarun Kumar (2003), A Hand Book of Medicinal Plants, Agrobios India, Jodhpur, PP. 511.

Sharma, P.V. (1981), Dravya gun vigyana, Chaukhambha Bharti Academy, Varanasi, Vol. 1, PP. 680.

466. *Thevetia peruviana* (Pers.) K. Schum.

Family: Apocynaceae.

Synonym: *T. neriifolia.*

Name: English: Indian oleander, Yellow oleander, **Sanskrit:** *Karveera, Aswamaaraka, Divyapushpa, Haripriya, Aswaghna, Shatakumbha, Aswantaka, Hayamaaraka,* **Hindi:** *Kaner,* **Local:** *Kaner.*

Ayurvedic groups: Charaka: *tiktaskandha, kusthaghna,* **Sushruta:** *lakhsaadi, shirovirechan, upvisha.*

Botanical characteristics : Habit: Evergreen, large, glabrous shrub, 4.5-6 m high, 15 cm diam. with milky latex. **Stem:** Scaled with scars of fallen leaves, herbaceous, aerial, erect, cylindrical, branched, smooth and green. **Leaf:** 7.5-15 cm long, 0.5-1.5 cm wide, crowded, alternate, linear-lanceolate, entire, acute, glabrous, shining above, narrowed to both ends, milky latex present. **Flower:** Yellow, 5 cm across, complete, pentamerous, little fragrant. **Fruit:** Drupe, broadly obovate in longitudinal section 3.5 cm long, green when unripe, brown when ripe. **Seed:** 4 or fewer in a fruit by suppression, light brown, specific triangular.

Flowering and fruiting period: July-August and September-October.

Habitat: Cultivated as hedge plant in the plains, throughout India, up to 6500 m.

Parts used: Root and root bark.

Dosage: 30-125 mg, tincture (5:1) 10-15 drops.

Collection period: October-November.

Ayurvedic properties: ***Ras:*** *katu, tikta,* ***Gun:*** *laghu, rukhsa,* ***Veerya:*** *ushna,* ***Vipaka:*** *katu,* ***Tridosha*** **Effect:** alleviates ***Kapha:*** ++, ***Vaata:*** +.

Chemical constituents: Root bark contains peruvodide, thevetin, neriifolin, cerberin, cerebroside, 2-oacetyl ceberodide, peruvonside acid, thevetoxin, a phytosterolin, abaudin, kokilfin.

Action and disease indications: Root and **root bark** are diuretic, anti inflammatory, bitter tonic, cathartic, febrifuge, useful to cure intermittent fevers, malaria, heart diseases, arrhythmia, ulcer, leprosy, skin diseases, worms, pruritis, all type of inflammations, snake bite, alopecia, paralysis, impotency and canitis.

Contra indication: All parts of plant, especially latex is poisonous. Latex has burning property. Seeds are most poisonous. Overdose produce severe diarrhea, vomiting and excess sweating.

So beware to over dose. Do not use empty stomach and do not mix with other medicines.

Antidote: Oil and cheese and oil. For other symptoms, treat symptomatically. For stimulation of heart, use good quality of wine.

Clinical uses: Snake bite: Root bark of plant 100 mg, 2 times a day, with water. **Intermittent fever:** Root bark of plant 70 mg, before fever, with water. **Pruritis and scaled skin diseases, alopecia:** Local use of medicated oil, prepared by root bark of the plant. **Paralysis:** Local use of medicated oil, prepared by root bark of the plant, seeds of *Abrus precatorius*, leaves of *Datura stramonium*, as a massage oil. **Impotancy:** Local use of medicated oil, prepared by root bark of the described plant, *Myristica fragrans, Papaver somniferum, Elettaria cardamomum,* root bark of *Bombex ceiba,* and Mustard oil, in ratio of 1:1:1:2:4:8, and use as massage oil. **Canitis:** Local application of root powder of the described plant, with milk.

Formulations: *Kaashisaadi taila, Laghuavishagarbha taila, Kaam ratnaakaraarka, Karveer nasya, Gunjadhya taila, Karviraadhya taila.*

Recommended readings:

Acharya, B.K. (2008), Ayurveda Jadi-buti Rahasya, Patanjali Yogapitha, Haridwar, PP. 249.

Bhutya, R.K. (2007), Vanaspati Aushadha Vigyana, Scientific Publishers (India), Jodhpur, PP. 47.

Brahmavarchas (2003), Ayurved Ka Pran Vanoshadhi Vigyan, Shanti Kunj, Haridwar, PP. 443.

Chunekar, K.C. (2004), Bhava Prakash Nighantu, Chaukhambha Bharti Academy, Varanasi, PP. 314.

Khare, C.P. (2007), Indian Medicinal Plants, Springer (India) P.L. New Delhi, PP. 659.

Kirtikar, K.R. & Basu, B.D. (1998), Indian Medicinal Plants, L.M Basu, Allahabad, Vol. 2, PP. 1554.

Nair, R.Vasudevan, (2007), Indian Medicinal Plants, Orient Longman P.L. Chennai, Vol. 5, PP.

Pareek, G.N. (2005), Sudhanidhi, Vanoshadhi Ratnakar, Dhanvantari Karyalaya, Aligarh, Vol. 9, PP. 163.

Prajapati, N.D., Purohit, S.S., Sharma, A.K. & Tarun Kumar (2003), A Hand Book of Medicinal Plants, Agrobios India, Jodhpur, PP. 511.

Sharma, P.C., Yelne, MB. & Denis, T.J. (2000), Database on medicinal plants used in ayurveda, Central Council for research in Ayurveda and siddha, Vol. 2, PP. 313.

Sharma, P.V. (1981), Dravya gun vigyana, Chaukhambha Bharti Academy, Varanasi, Vol. 1, PP. 211.

Singh, R.S. (2002), Vanoshadhi Nirdeshika, Uttar Pradesh Hindi Sansthan, Lucknow, PP. 69.

Swami, K.N. (1985), Gavon Main Aushadh Ratna, Kalera Krishana Gopal, Kalera (Raj.), Vol. 2, PP. 148.

467. *Thuja orientalis* Linn.

Family: Cupressaceae.

Synonym: *Biota orientalis.*

Name: English: Oriental Arbor-Vitae. **Sanskrit:** *Mayurpankhi,* **Hindi:** *Mayurpankhi,* **Local:** *Morpankhi.*

Botanical characteristics: Habit: A coniferous, evergreen, monoecious large tree, height up to 25 m, but often densely branched shrub. **Stem:** 1 m in diam., branchlets 2-ranked, in a vertical plane. **Leaf:** Scalelike, less than 3 mm long, glandular, grooved. **Flower:** Male cones at the terminal of branches of the last year, 2-2.5 mm long, with 10 scales. Female cones larger, erect, the 3-9 pairs of scales fleshy when young, becoming woody strongly hooked at apex, 15-20 mm long. **Seed:** Wingless.

Flowering and fruiting period: Almost throughout year.

Habitat: Mountain thickets India, planted all over India in gardens.

Parts used: Whole plant. **Dosage:** 3-6 g.

Collection period: March-April.

Ayurvedic properties: ***Ras:*** *tikta, katu,* ***Gun:*** *laghu, rukhsa,* ***Veerya:*** *ushna,* ***Vipaka:*** *katu,* ***Tridosha*** **Effect:** alleviates ***Kapha:*** **+.**

Chemical constituents: The **plant** contains terpenoids, pinusolide, pinusolidic acid, cedrol, totarol, essential oil, flavonoids-quercetin, myricetin, hinokiflavone, amentoflavone and thugic acid.

Action and disease indications: The **plant** is expectorant, anti-inflammatory, anti-tussive, anti-bacterial, anti-fungal, haemostatic, lever tonic and tonic, used for platelets aggregation, asthma, bronchitis, inflammations, haemoptysis, dysentery, menorrhagia, epistaxis, fevers, palpitation, constipation, hyperhydrosis and general debility.

Clinical uses: Epistaxis, Dysentery, haematuria, menorrhagia, metrorrhagia, fever, bronchitis, arthritis: Decoction of described plant, 5 g, with honey 10 g, two times a day, is useful. **Vomiting:** Black ash of branches of described plant, 250 mg, with honey 10 g, two times a day, is useful. **Palpitation:** Fruit powder of described plant, 3 g, with honey 10 g, two times a day, is useful.

Recommended readings:

Bhutya, R.K. (2007), Vanaspati Aushadha Vigyana, Scientific Publishers (India), Jodhpur, PP. 187.

Brahmavarchas (2003), Ayurved Ka Pran Vanoshadhi Vigyan, Shanti Kunj, Haridwar, PP. 444.

Khare, C.P. (2007), Indian Medicinal Plants, Springer (India) P.L. New Delhi, PP. 660.

Prajapati, N.D., Purohit, S.S., Sharma, A.K. & Tarun Kumar (2003), A Hand Book of Medicinal Plants, Agrobios India, Jodhpur, PP. 512.

468. *Tinospora cordifolia* (Willd.) Miers ex Hook. & Thoms.

Family: Menispermaceae.

Other similar plants: *T. crispa-* syn. *rumphii, T.malabarica*-syn. *sinensis, tomentosa-* large var.-leaves size 20 by 25 cm.

Ayurvedic Groups: Charak: *Vayahasthapana, Daahaprashamana, Trishanaanigrahana, Stanyashodhana, Vriddhighna,* **Sushruta:** *Guduchyaadi, Patolaadi, Aaragvadhaadi, Kakolyaadi gana, Vallipanchamoola.*

Name: Sanskrit: *Guduchi, Amrita, Madhuparni, Amritavallari, Chhinna, Chinnaruhaa, Vatsaadani, Jivanti, Somaa, Jivanti, Somavalli, Chakralaxanikaa, Dheeraa, Rasaayani, Mandali, Vayasthaa.* **Hindi:** *Giloya,* **Local:** *Giloya, Neem Giloya.*

Botanical characteristics: Habit: A large, extensively spreading, glabrous, perennial, deciduous climber. **Stem:** Succulent, corky, grooved, branches sending down slender pendulous fleshy roots, terete, striate, bark papery, warty tubercled, pale, shining or glaucous, surface skin is longitudinally fissured. On removal of the surface skin the dark greenish, mucilaginous stem is seen. **Leaf:** Simple, alternate, membranous, broadly ovate, roundish or subdeltoid-cordate, with a broad sinus and large basal lobes, obtuse or more or less cuspidate, entire, glabrous, 7-9 nerved, 5-10 or 12-10 cm; petioles 2.5-7 cm long. **Flower:** Small, yellow or greenish-yellow, appearing when the plant is leafless, arising from nodes on the old wood, in axillary or terminal racemes or recemose panicles, male flowers clustered, female flowers usually solitary. **Fruit:** Drupes, ovoid or sub-globose, glossy, green when unripe and red when ripe, pea-sized. **Seed:** White, bean-shaped, warty.

Flowering and fruiting period: May-June and November-December.

Habitat: Throughout tropical India, up to an altitude of 900 m.

Parts used: Stem, extract starch.

Dosage: Stem powder 3-6 g, juice 10-20 ml, for decoction 20-30 g, extract 0.5-1.5 g. Starch 0.5-1 g.

Collection period: April-May.

Ayurvedic properties: ***Ras:*** *tikta, kashaaya,* ***Gun:*** *laghu, snigdha,* ***Veerya:*** *ushna,* ***Vipaka:*** *madhur,* ***Tridosha*** **Effect:** alleviates ***Pitta:*** +++. ***Vaata:*** +++, ***Kapha:*** +.

Chemical constituents: The **Stem** contains alkaloidal constituents, including berberine; bitter principle, includingcolumbin, chasmanthin, palmarin, tinosporon, tinosporic acid and tinosporol. Its aqueous extract has a high phagocytic index. Oral administration of of alcoholic extract of the root resulted in a significant reduction in blood and urine glucose and in lipids in serum and tissues. A significant reduction in levels of SGOT, SGPT, ALP and bilirubin were observed. A new hypoglycaemic agent was isolated from the plant; it was found to be 1,2-substituted pyrrolidine. The starch from roots and stem, used in chronic diarrhea, dysentery, contains a polysaccharide having 1-4 glucan with occasional branching points.

Action and disease indications: The **stem** is thermogenic, anodyne, alterant, anthelmintic, anti-periodic, anti-spasmodic, digestive, anti-rheumatic, anti-inflammatory, anti-pyretic, anti-emetic, carminative, appetizer, stomachic, constipating, cardio-tonic, febrifuge, depurative, hematinic, diuretic, expectorant, hypoglycemic, hepatoprotective, aphrodisiac, rejuvenating, galacto-purifier and bitter tonic, prescribed for chronic fevers, skin diseases, burning sensation, hyperdipsia, helminthiasis, gout, dyspepsia, flatulence, abdominal pain, intermittent fevers, inflammations, vomiting, cardiac debility, erysipelas, rheumatism, anemia, cough, asthma, bronchitis, jaundice, seminal weakness, uropathy, spleenomegaly, hepatomegaly and general debility.

Clinical uses: Skin diseases: Decoction of described plant 6 g, bark of *Azadirachta indica* 5 g, *Curcuma longa* 1 g, bark of *Acacia catechu* 5 g, fruits of *Phylanthus emblica* 3 g, added gum of *Commiphora mukul* 1 g, two times a day, is beneficial. **Gout:** Medicated oil, made by described plant, 10 ml, with milk, two times a day, is beneficial. **Neuritis, pains:** Decoction of mix powder of described plant, roots of *Ricinus communis, Zingiber officinale, Cedrus deodara, Terminalia chebula, Pluchea lanceolata,* 10 g, with honey 10 g, two times a day, is useful. **Amblyopia:** Decoction of mix powder of described plant, *Terminalia belliarica, Terminalia chebula, Phylanthus emblica,* 10 g, added *Piper longum* 500 mg, with honey 10 g, two times a day, is useful. **Burning sensation of sole:** Local application of paste of described plant, seeds of *Ricinus communis,* with curd, is beneficial. **Excess and turbid micturition, Diabetes inspidus:** Decoction of mix powder of described plant, *Phylanthus emblica* , *Curcuma longa,* 10 g, with honey 10 g, two times a day, is useful. **Rheumatism:** Juice of branches of described plant 20 ml, *Zingiber officinale* 1 g, with honey 10 g, two times a day, is useful. **Fevers, enlarment of spleen, anorexia:** *Piper longum* 500 mg, honey 10 g, with decoction of described plant 10 g, two times a day, **or** decoction of mix powder of described plant 10 g, *Coriandrum sativum* 3 g, bark of *Azadirachta indica* 5 g, *Pterocarpus santalinus* 2 g, with honey 10 g, two times a day, is useful. **For rejuvenating, skin diseases, syphilis, gout, chronic rheumatism, general debility after fevers:** Cold infusion of described plant 20 g, *Hemidesmus indicus* 10 g, with honey 10 g, two times a day, is useful. **Excess and turbid micturition, gonorrhea:** Powder of described plant 10 g, *Bergenia ciliata* 2 g, with honey 10 g, or milk, two times a day, is useful. **Jaundice, indigestion, colic, cholecystitis:** Juice of described plant 25 ml, with honey 10 g, two times a day, or paste of leaves of described plant 50 g, with whey, is useful. **Galactia:** Decoction of described plant 50 g, with honey 10 g, two times a day, is useful. **For rejuvenating:** Juice 50 ml or powder 10 g, of described plant, with honey 10 g or raw sugar 25 g, two times a day, is useful. **Spleen enlargement, cystitis, amebic dysentery, diarrhea with bleeding, hyperacidity, spermacresia, urinary tract infection, fever:** Extract of described plant 500 mg, with honey 10 g, two times a day, is useful. **Fevers:** Decoction of mix powder of described plant, *Fumaria indica, Cyperus scarissus, Zingiber officinale* 500 mg, *Swertia chirata* 3 g, with honey 10 g, two times a day, is useful. **Hyperacidity:** Extract of described plant 500 mg, with decoction of *Achyranthus aspera* 10 g, two times a day, is beneficial. **Headache:** Extract of described plant 500 mg, *'Mukta pisti'* 125 mg, with sweets of concentrated milk at morning, and extract of described plant 500 mg, with honey 10 g, at noon and night, is useful. **Angina pectoris, neuralgia:** *Piper nigrum* 500 mg, with decoction of described plant 10 g, two times a day, is beneficial. **Urticaria:** Decoction of mix powder of described plant, *Curcuma longa,* inner bark of *Azadirachta indica, Alhagi pseudalhagi,* 6 g, with honey 10 g, two times a day, is useful. **Acne vulgaris, chloasma:** Local application of juice of described plant and lemon juice, is beneficial.

Formulations: *Guduchyaadi kwaatha, Chyavanpraasha, Amritaa satva, Guduchi taila, Guduchi lauha, Guduchyaadi churna, Amrita-arista, Amritaa guggulu, Dashamoolarista, Sarwajwarahara lauha, Kaishore guggulu, Pathyaadi kwaatha, Sanjivani vati, Panchanimba churna, Vrihan marichyaadi taila.*

Recommended readings:

Acharya, B.K. (2008), Ayurveda Jadi-buti Rahasya, Patanjali Yogapitha, Haridwar, PP. 201.

Bhutya, R.K. (2007), Vanaspati Aushadha Vigyana, Scientific Publishers (India), Jodhpur, PP. 15.

Brahmavarchas (2003), Ayurved Ka Pran Vanoshadhi Vigyan, Shanti Kunj, Haridwar, PP. 445.

Chunekar, K.C. (2004), Bhava Prakash Nighantu, Chaukhambha Bharti Academy, Varanasi, PP. 270.

Dhiman, A.K. (2006), Ayurvedic Drug Plants, Daya Publishing House, Delhi, PP. 144.

Khare, C.P. (2007), Indian Medicinal Plants, Springer (India) P.L. New Delhi, PP. 662.

Kirtikar, K.R. & Basu, B.D. (1998), Indian Medicinal Plants, L.M Basu, Allahabad, Vol. 1, PP. 77.

Misra, B.L. (2005), Dravya Guna Hastamalaka, Publication scheme, Jaipur, PP. 410.

Nair, R.Vasudevan, (2007), Indian Medicinal Plants, Orient Longman P.L. Chennai, Vol. 5, PP. 283.

Namjoshi, A.N. (2001), The Ayurvedic Pharmacopoeia of India, Government of India, Department of Indian Systems of Medicine & Homoeopathy, New Delhi, Part-1, Volume- 2, PP. 41 and 1-171.

Pareek, G.N. (2005), Sudhanidhi, Vanoshadhi Ratnakar, Dhanvantari Karyalaya, Aligarh, Vol. 3, PP. 222.

Prajapati, N.D., Purohit, S.S., Sharma, A.K. & Tarun Kumar (2003), A Hand Book of Medicinal Plants, Agrobios India, Jodhpur, PP. 515.

Sharma, P.C., Yelne, MB. & Denis, T.J. (2000), Database on medicinal plants used in ayurveda, Central Council for research in Ayurveda and siddha, Vol. 3, PP. 256.

Sharma, P.V. (1981), Dravya gun vigyana, Chaukhambha Bharti Academy, Varanasi, Vol. 1, PP. 761.

Singh, R.S. (2002), Vanoshadhi Nirdeshika, Uttar Pradesh Hindi Sansthan, Lucknow, PP. 131.

Swami, K.N. (1985), Gavon Main Aushadh Ratna, Kalera Krishana Gopal, Kalera (Raj.), Vol. 1, PP. 171.

469. ***Trachyspermum ammi*** (Linn) Sprague.

Family: Umbelliferae; Apiaceae.

Synonym: *T.copticum, Carum copticum.*

Ayurvedic Groups: Charak: *Sheetaprashamana,* **Bhavaprakash:** *Chaturbeeja.*

Name: English: Ammi, Lovage, Carum, Ajowan, **Sanskrit:** *Yavaanikaa, Ugragandhaa,*

Brahmadarbhaa, Ajamodikaa, Dipyakaa, Dipyaa, Yavasaahvyaa, **Hindi:** *Ajawaayan,* **Local:** *Ajavaan, Ajun.*

Botanical characteristics: Habit: A erect annual herb, 30-90 cm high. **Stem:** Much branched, slender, striate, glabrous or minutely pubescent. **Leaf:** Rather distant, 2-3 pinnate, ultimate segments 1.3-2.5 cm, slender. Linear or filiform, shape like leaves of *Foeniculum vulgare or* Fennel; bracts usually numerous, linear, sometimes divided; bracteoles 3-5, small, linear. **Flower:** Pure white, Small, polygamous, in terminal or lateral peduncles 1.25-3.75 cm long, compound umbles. Rays of umbles pubescent, 5-8 or 12, unequal. **Fruit:** Cremocarps, 2-3 mm long, ovoid, muricate, sub-hispid, aromatic, greyish-brown, carples dorsally compressed, ridges distint; vittae solitary, small. **Seed:** One seed in a fruit.

Flowering and fruiting period: February-March and April-May.

Habitat: Cultivated almost throughout India, particularly in Uttar Pradesh, Madhya Pradesh, Gujarat, Rajasthan, Bihar, West Bengal, Maharastra and Andhra Pradesh.

Parts used: Fruit, distillate, extract.

Dosage: Fruit 3-6 g, distillate 5-20 ml, extract 30-125 mg.

Collection period: April-May.

Ayurvedic properties: ***Ras:*** *katu, tikta,* ***Gun:*** *laghu, tikhsna, rukhsa,* ***Veerya:*** *ushna,* ***Vipaka:*** *katu,* ***Tridosha*** **Effect:** alleviates ***Kapha:*** **+++,** ***Vaata:*** **++,** aggrevates ***Pitta:*** ++.

Chemical constituents: The **fruits** contain protein 17.1, fat 21.8, carbohydrates 24.6, and mineral matter 7.9%, also contain sugars, tannins, flavone and sterol. The **seeds** contain a phonolic glucoside, 2-methyl-3-glucosyloxy-5-isopropyl phenol. The principle constituents of the **seed oil** are phenols, mainly thymol 35-60% and some carvacrol. Thymol is a powerful anti-septic and anti-fungal, used as deodorant mouth wash, toothpastes and gargles.

Action and disease indications: The **fruits** are carminative, anti-spasmodic, anti-cholerin, anti-diarrhoeal, bechic, stimulant, used for constipation, colic, helminthiasis, tympanitis, diarrhea, atonic dyspepsia, cholera, flatulence, indigestion, spleenomegaly, sore throat, and bronchitis. The **Oil** used as an expectorant, in emphysema, bronchial and other respiratory diseases, used externally for rheumatism.

Clinical uses: Colic, flatulence: Mix powder of described plant, rock salt, sea salt, nitrate of potash, roasted gum of *Ferula narthex, Phylanthus emblica,* 0.5-1.5 g, with water, two times a day, is beneficial. **Helminthiasis:** Juice of leaves of described plant 10-20 ml, two times a day, **or** Mix powder of seeds of described plant and *Butea monosperma,* 4 g, raw sugar 15 g, with warm water, two times a day, is beneficial. **Chronic constipation:** Seed powder of described plant 2 g, with warm water, at night, is beneficial. **Urticaria:** Seed powder of described plant 2 g, raw sugar 10 g, two times a day, is beneficial. **Diabetes inspidus:** Raw sugar 10 g, seeds of described plant 2 g, *Brassica juncea* 1 g, with water, two times a day, is beneficial. **Acne vulgaris, chloasma:** Local application of paste of seeds of described plant, with curd, is beneficial. **Rheumatism:** Seed powder of described plant 2 g, with decoction of mix powder of *Zingiber officinale* and *Plumbego zeylanica,* 2.5 g, two times a day, is beneficial. **Amenorrhea, dysmenorrhea:** Mix powder of seeds of described plant 3 g, *Zingiber officinale* 1 g, two times a day, is beneficial. **Or** Seed powder of described plant 2.5 g, seeds of *Trigonella foenum-graecum* 2 g, with warm water, is beneficial. **Penile dysfunction:** Soak and dry the seeds of described plant, with juice of white onion, by three times, dose 3 g, clarified butter 10 g, sugar candy powder 10 g, two times a day, is beneficial. **Enuresis of children:** Seed powder of described plant 500 mg, at night, is beneficial.

Formulations: *Yavaanyarka, Yavaanikaa churna, Yavaanishaadava churna, Nimbaadi churna, Narayan churna, Vaiswaanara churna, Sudarshan churna, Agnimukha churna, Chaangeri ghrita, Phala ghrita, Nripativallabha rasa, Manmathaabhra rasa, Amrita bhallaataka, Devdaarvyaadhyarista, Lauhaasava, Saarivaadhyaasava, Yogaraaja guggulu.*

Recommended readings:

Acharya, B.K. (2008), Ayurveda Jadi-buti Rahasya, Patanjali Yogapitha, Haridwar, PP. 30.

Bhutya, R.K. (2007), Vanaspati Aushadha Vigyana, Scientific Publishers (India), Jodhpur, PP. 6.

Brahmavarchas (2003), Ayurved Ka Pran Vanoshadhi Vigyan, Shanti Kunj, Haridwar, PP. 119.

Chunekar, K.C. (2004), Bhava Prakash Nighantu, Chaukhambha Bharti Academy, Varanasi, PP. 25.

Dhiman, A.K. (2006), Ayurvedic Drug Plants, Daya Publishing House, Delhi, PP. 410.

Khare, C.P. (2007), Indian Medicinal Plants, Springer (India) P.L. New Delhi, PP. 665.

Kirtikar, K.R. & Basu, B.D. (1998), Indian Medicinal Plants, L.M Basu, Allahabad, Vol. 2, PP. 1204.

Misra, B.L. (2005), Dravya Guna Hastamalaka, Publication scheme, Jaipur, PP.

Namjoshi, A.N. (2001), The Ayurvedic Pharmacopoeia of India, Government of India, Department of Indian Systems of Medicine & Homoeopathy, New Delhi, Part-1, Volume- 2, PP. 129.

Pareek, G.N. (2005), Sudhanidhi, Vanoshadhi Ratnakar, Dhanvantari Karyalaya, Aligarh, Vol. 7, PP. 139.

Prajapati, N.D., Purohit, S.S., Sharma, A.K. & Tarun Kumar (2003), A Hand Book of Medicinal Plants, Agrobios India, Jodhpur, PP. 518.

Sharma, P.C., Yelne, MB. & Denis, T.J. (2000), Database on medicinal plants used in ayurveda, Central Council for research in Ayurveda and siddha, Vol. 7, PP. 496.

Sharma, P.V. (1981), Dravya gun vigyana, Chaukhambha Bharti Academy, Varanasi, Vol. 1, PP. 494.

Singh, R.S. (2002), Vanoshadhi Nirdeshika, Uttar Pradesh Hindi Sansthan, Lucknow, PP. 11.

Swami, K.N. (1985), Gavon Main Aushadh Ratna, Kalera Krishana Gopal, Kalera (Raj.), Vol. 1, PP. 5.

470. *Trapa natans* Linn

Family: Trapaceae.

Synonym: *T. bispinosa, T. quadrispinosa.*

Name: English: Water Chestnut, **Sanskrit:** *Shrangaataka, Jalaphala, Trikonphala,* **Hindi:** *Sigharaa,* **Local:** *Singharaa.*

Botanical characteristics: Habit: An attractive aquatic variable, floating annual herb. **Stem:** Flexuose, ascending, and green photosynthetic submerged roots. **Leaf:** Simple, alternate, crowded at the upper parts of stems in rosettes; 3.8-5 by 3.8-5.7 cm, rhomboid, apex triangular, irregularly inciso-serrate in the upper part, dark green above, glabrous and shining, reddish-purple and densely pubescent beneath; petioles terete, at first short, but ultimately reaching as much as 12.5 cm in length, the upper part hairy, the lower glabrous, dilated near the apex into a large fusiform spongy float; stipules linear-lanceolate, acute, membranous, caduceus. **Flower:** White, few, axillary, solitary, tubular, opening above the surface of water in the afternoon; pedicles short, stout, hairy, incurved during flowering, afterwards bending down beneath the water in which fruits ripens. **Fruit:** Nut, obovoid, bony, 4-angular, with a short conical beak in the centre at the apex and a spreading, flattened, very sharp spinous horn on either side, 2-2.5 cm long and broad, green to dark maroon-blackish, indehiscent, one seeded. **Seed:** White or pinkish, starchy.

Flowering and fruiting period: July-August and October-November.

Habitat: Extensively cultivated almost throughout India, Particularly in Uttar Pradesh, Madhya Pradesh, Bihar, Orissa and Southern India, occurring in lakes, tanks and ponds.

Parts used: Seed, leaves (in *Gangadhar churna*).

Dosage: 5-10 g.

Collection period: October-November.

Ayurvedic properties: ***Ras:*** *madhur, kashaaya,* ***Gun:*** *guru, rukhsa,* ***Veerya:*** *sheeta,* ***Vipaka:*** *madhur,* ***Tridosha*** **Effect:** alleviates ***Pitta:*** +++, aggrevates ***Vaata:*** +, ***Kapha:*** +.

Chemical constituents: The **seeds** are rich in proteins and minerals, also contain phosphorus 45, 48; sulphur 122.81, 130.16; calcium 60,20; magnesium 200, 160; sodium 100, 80; and potassium 1800, 1760 mg/100 g; iron 145.16, 129.02 and manganese 18.93,11.36 ppm, respectively, also contain amylopectin, amylase, carbohydrates, beta-amylase, phospholase, fat, nicotinic acid, riboflavin, thiamin, vitamin A and C. The starch, isolated from flour, consists of 15% amylase and 85% amylopectin.

Action and disease indications: The **seeds** are astringent, cooling, constipating, hemostatic, aphrodisiac, semeniferous, anti-pyretic, appetizer and tonic, used for bleeding disorders, threatened abortion, dysuria, polyuria, oedema, burning sensation, dipsia, dyspepsia, hemorrhages, hemoptysis, diarrhea, dysentery, strangury, intermittent fevers, fatigue, inflammations, seminal weakness, premature ejaculation, fractures, erysipelas, lumbago, urethrorrhea, pharyngitis, bronchitis and general debility.

Clinical uses: Diarrhea, dysentery, leucorrhea: Seed powder of described plant, 5 g, with water, two times a day, is beneficial. **Burning sensation:** Local application of paste of seeds and leaves of described plant is beneficial. **Spermacresia, fluidity of semen, general debility, abortion, somasthenia:** mix powder of seeds of described plant, *Eurale ferox* and seeds of *Nelumbo nusifera* 6 g, with milk, two times a day, is beneficial.

Formulations: *Chinchaabeejaadi yoga, Rajendraavaleha, Grahanikapaat rasa- dwitiya, Chandanaadi taila, Saubhaagya sunthi, Vrisya ghrita, Amritaprasha ghrita, Jeevaniya ghrita, Mahaa maayur ghrita, Gandha taila, Elaadi taila.*

Recommended readings:

Bhutya, R.K. (2007), Vanaspati Aushadha Vigyana, Scientific Publishers (India), Jodhpur, PP. 220.

Brahmavarchas (2003), Ayurved Ka Pran Vanoshadhi Vigyan, Shanti Kunj, Haridwar, PP. 447.

Chunekar, K.C. (2004), Bhava Prakash Nighantu, Chaukhambha Bharti Academy, Varanasi, PP. 578.

Khare, C.P. (2007), Indian Medicinal Plants, Springer (India) P.L. New Delhi, PP. 667.

Kirtikar, K.R. & Basu, B.D. (1998), Indian Medicinal Plants, L.M Basu, Allahabad, Vol. 2, PP. 1090.

Misra, B.L. (2005), Dravya Guna Hastamalaka, Publication scheme, Jaipur, PP. 473.

Nair, R.Vasudevan, (2007), Indian Medicinal Plants, Orient Longman P.L. Chennai, Vol. 5, PP. 308.

Prajapati, N.D., Purohit, S.S., Sharma, A.K. & Tarun Kumar (2003), A Hand Book of Medicinal Plants, Agrobios India, Jodhpur, PP. 519.

Sharma, P.C., Yelne, M.B. & Denis, T.J. (2000), Database on medicinal plants used in ayurveda, Central Council for research in Ayurveda and siddha, Vol. 7, PP. 445.

Sharma, P.V. (1981), Dravya gun vigyana, Chaukhambha Bharti Academy, Varanasi, Vol. 1, PP. 588.

Singh, R.S. (2002), Vanoshadhi Nirdeshika, Uttar Pradesh Hindi Sansthan, Lucknow, PP. 373.

471. *Tribulus terrestris* Linn.

Family: Zygophyllaceae.

Ayurvedic Groups: Charak: *Mutravirechaniya, Shothahara, Krimighna, Anuvaasanopaga,* **Sushruta:** *Vidaarigandhaadi, Veertarvaadi, Laghupanchamoola, Kantakapanchamoola, Vaataasmaribhedana gana.*

Name: English: Land-Caltrops, Puncture Vine, **Sanskrit:** *Gokhsuruka, Gokhsura, Swaadukantaka, Gokantaka, Vanashrangaata, Palankashaa, Swadamstraa, Ikhsugandhikaa,* **Hindi:** *Gokharu-Chotaa,* **Local:** *Chotaa Gokharu.*

Botanical characteristics: Habit: An annual or biennial prostrate herb, 90 cm in length. **Root:** 10-12.5 cm long, grey, fibrous, 7-18 cm long, 0.3-0.7 cm diam., cylindrical, tough, woody. **Stem:** With many slender, spreading branches, stem and branches pilose; young parts silky-villous. **Leaf:** Abruptly simple, pinnate, opposite, one of the each pair usually smaller than the other; stipules lanceolate, hairy; leaflets 3-6 pairs, almost sessile, 6-12 mm long, oblong, rounded or oblique at the base, mucronate at the apex, villous with appressed hairs beneath and more or less so on the upper surface. Shape like the leaves of Gram. **Flower:** Bright yellow, 1-1.5 cm across, pseudo-axillary or leaf-opposed, solitary, peduncles1.2-2 cm long, slender, hairy. **Fruit:** Schizocarp, globose, 5-angled or winged spinous tuberculate woody, separating into five cocci, each coccus having two long, stiff, sharp, divaricate spines towards the distal half and two shorter ones nearer the base. **Seed:** One or more in each coccus, with transverse partitions between them.

Flowering and fruiting period: July-August and September-October.

Habitat: Throughout India, up to an altitude of 5400 m, common in dry and hotter parts, particularly in Rajasthan, Gujarat and Southern India, as a weed along roadsides and waste places.

Parts used: Root, fruit.

Dosage: Root 3-6 g, fruit 3-6 g.

Collection period: October November.

Ayurvedic properties: ***Ras:*** *madhur,* ***Gun:*** *guru, snigdha,* ***Veerya:*** *sheeta,* ***Vipaka:*** *madhur,* ***Tridosha*** **Effect:** alleviates ***Vaata:*** ***+++,*** ***Pitta:*** ++.

Chemical constituents: The **plant** contains saponins, which on hydrolysis yield sapogenins-diosgenin, gitogenin, chlorogenin, ruscogenin, 25 D-spirosta-3,5-diene, among others. Flavonoids-rutin, quercetin, kaempferol-3-glucoside and rutiniside and tribuloside have been isolated from the **fruits** and **leaves**. The **seeds** contain carboline alkaloids-harmane and harmine. Harmol is also reported from the **herb.**

Action and disease indications: The **roots** and **fruits** are refrigerant, diuretic (more than furosemide), proerectile aphrodisiac, emollient, demulcent, anabolic, spasmolytic, muscle relaxant, hypotensive, hypoglycaemic, hypolipidaemic, appetizer, digestive, anthelmintic, expectorant, anti-inflammatory, anodyne, alterant, laxative, cardio-tonic, styptic, lithontriptic and tonic, prescribed for dysuria, strangury, renal and vesical calculi, anorexia, dyspepsia, helminthiasis, cough, asthma, bronchitis, inflammations, angina pectoris, coronary heart diseases, hemoptysis, spermatorrhea, seminal weakness, sexual inadequacy, anemia, scabies, pruritis-ani, ophthalmia, ulocace and general debility.

Clinical uses: Renal and vesical calculus: (1) Fruit and roots powder of described plant 6 g, with honey 10 g and milk of she goat, two times a day, for seven days, is very useful. (2) Mix powder of root powder of described plant, leaves of *Ricinus communis, Zingiber officinale,* bark of *Crataeva magna,* 10 g, two times a day, is beneficial. (3) Mix powder of roots of described plant, root bark of *Ricinus communis, Solanum surattense, Solanum ferox, Hygrophila auriculata,* 10 g, with curd, two times a day, for seven days, is beneficial. **Strangury:** *'Khsira paka'* of fruit powder of described plant 5 g, two times a day, is beneficial. **Dysurea, cystitis, nephritis:** decoction of root powder of described plant 6 g, with nitrate of potash 500 mg, Bitumen 1 g, two times a day, is beneficial. **Sterlity, azoospermia:** (1) Mix powder of roots of described plant and seeds of *Sesamum orientale* 20 g, with honey 10 g and milk of she goat, two times a day, is useful. (2) Fruit powder of described plant, seeds of *Mucana pruriens,* 6 g, with milk, two times a day, is beneficial. **Insufficiency of urine:** Nitrate of potash 500 mg, with decoction of described plant 6 g, two times a day, is beneficial. **Hematuria:** *'Khsira paka'* of fruit powder of described plant 5 g, with sugar candy powder 10 g, two times a day, is beneficial. **Leucorrhea:** Fruit powder of described plant 5 g, *Hygrophila auriculata* 3 g, with milk, two times a day, is beneficial. **Spermatorrhea, nocturnal emission:** (1) Mix seeds powder of described plant, *Hygrophila auriculata, Trapa natans, Lactuca serriola,* 5 g, with milk, two times a day, is beneficial. (2) Mix powder of fruits of described plant, seeds of *Blepheris edulis, Salvia plebeiat, Asparagus racemosus,* 6 g, with milk of she goat, two times a day, is beneficial. (3) Fruit powder of described plant, *Phylanthus emblica, Tinospora cordifolia,* with clarified butter 10 g, two times a day, is beneficial. **Prostatitis:** Decoction of roots of described plant, *Boerhavia diffusa,* 10 g, with honey 10 g, two times a day, is useful.

Formulations: *Gokhsuraadi kwaatha, Gokhsuraadi guggulu, Dashamoola kwaatha, Chyavanapraasha, Brahmarasaayana, Abhayaarista, Dashamoolarista, Dashamoola taila, Trikantakaadi kwaatha, Draakhsaai churna, Pugakhanda, Rasnaasaptaka kwaatha, Garbhachintaamani rasa, Ashmarihara kashaaya, Gokhsuraadi modaka.*

Recommended readings:

Acharya, B.K. (2008), Ayurveda Jadi-buti Rahasya, Patanjali Yogapitha, Haridwar, PP. 205.

Bhutya, R.K. (2007), Vanaspati Aushadha Vigyana, Scientific Publishers (India), Jodhpur, PP. 87.

Brahmavarchas (2003), Ayurved Ka Pran Vanoshadhi Vigyan, Shanti Kunj, Haridwar, PP. 448.

Chunekar, K.C. (2004), Bhava Prakash Nighantu, Chaukhambha Bharti Academy, Varanasi, PP. 292.

Dhiman, A.K. (2006), Ayurvedic Drug Plants, Daya Publishing House, Delhi, PP. 141.

Khare, C.P. (2007), Indian Medicinal Plants, Springer (India) P.L. New Delhi, PP. 669.

Kirtikar, K.R. & Basu, B.D. (1998), Indian Medicinal Plants, L.M Basu, Allahabad, Vol. 1, PP. 420.

Misra, B.L. (2005), Dravya Guna Hastamalaka, Publication scheme, Jaipur, PP. 440.

Nair, R.Vasudevan, (2007), Indian Medicinal Plants, Orient Longman P.L. Chennai, Vol. 5, PP. 311.

Namjoshi, A.N. (2001), The Ayurvedic Pharmacopoeia of India, Government of India, Department of Indian Systems of Medicine & Homoeopathy, New Delhi, Part-1, Volume- 2, PP. 38.

Pareek, G.N. (2005), Sudhanidhi, Vanoshadhi Ratnakar, Dhanvantari Karyalaya, Aligarh, Vol. 3, PP. 275.

Prajapati, N.D., Purohit, S.S., Sharma, A.K. & Tarun Kumar (2003), A Hand Book of Medicinal Plants, Agrobios India, Jodhpur, PP. 520.

Sharma, P.C., Yelne, MB. & Denis, T.J. (2000), Database on medicinal plants used in ayurveda, Central Council for research in Ayurveda and siddha, Vol. 3, PP. 229.

Sharma, P.V. (1981), Dravya gun vigyana, Chaukhambha Bharti Academy, Varanasi, Vol. 1, PP. 632.

Singh, R.S. (2002), Vanoshadhi Nirdeshika, Uttar Pradesh Hindi Sansthan, Lucknow, PP. 138.

Swami, K.N. (1985), Gavon Main Aushadh Ratna, Kalera Krishana Gopal, Kalera (Raj.), Vol. 2, PP. 254.

472. *Tricodesma indicum* R. Br.

Family: Boraginaceae.

Name: Sanskrit: *Adhahpushpi, Adhomukhaa, Gandhapushpikaa, Andhaka,* **Hindi:** *Adhahpushpi,* **Local:** *Andhahuli.*

Botanical characteristics: Habit: An annual, erect, much branched very hispid herb, height 15-45 cm. **Stem:** Erect, hispid, herbaceous. **Leaf:** Simple, opposite, very variable in shape, 3.8-10 by 0.6-5 cm, sessile, ovate or oblong, or lanceolate-oblong, obtuse or sub-acute, clothed above with stiff hairs, arising from white circular tubercles, less harshly hairy and more or less densely villous beneath, cordate or hirsute at the base. **Flower:** Pale violate-blue, 2.5 cm in diam., changing pink or white on drooping axillary stalks, sometimes in terminal few-flowered cymes; pedicles 6-13 mm long, slender, nodding, hispid, cones of anthers large and very pointed, clothed on the back with dense white hairs. **Fruit:** Nutlets, pyramidal, 4-ribbed, 5 mm long, ovoid, smooth and polished on the back, rugose on the inner face, bluish white or nearly white when fully ripe, leaving 5 deep ovate pits on the membranous axis when falling.

Flowering and fruiting period: September-October and November-January.

Habitat: Throughout the greater parts of India, on roadsides and stony dry wastelands, up to an altitude of 1500 m.

Parts used: Root, whole plant.

Dosage: Root 5-10 g, plant juice 10-20 ml.

Collection period: January-February.

Ayurvedic properties: ***Ras:*** *tikta, katu,* ***Gun:*** *laghu, rukhsa,* ***Veerya:*** *ushna,* ***Vipaka:*** *katu,* ***Tridosha*** **Effect:** alleviates ***Kapha: ++, Vaata: +.***

Chemical constituents: The **seeds** contain linoleic, linolenic, oleic, palmitic and srearic acids. The **leaves** contain hexacosane, ethylex-acosanoate, 21,24-hexacosadienoic acid ethyl ester.

Action and disease indications: The **plant** is diuretic, emollient, thermogenic, alexiteric, anodyne, carminative, constipating, ophthalmic, febrifuge, depurative, anti-inflammatory, anti-dysenteric, sudorofic and pectoral, used for ulcers, inflammations, joints pains, dyspepsia, diarrhea, dysentery, strangury, skin diseases, ophthalmopathy, dysmenorrhea, amenorrhea, sore and fevers.

Clinical uses: Abscess: Poultice of root powder of described plant is beneficial. **Arthralgia, burning sensation, skin diseases:** Local application of paste of roots of described plant, with water is beneficial. **Dysuria:** Root powder of described plant 5 g, with milk of coconut, two times a day, is beneficial.

Formulations: *Shadabindu taila.*

Recommended readings:

Bhutya, R.K. (2007), Vanaspati Aushadha Vigyana, Scientific Publishers (India), Jodhpur, PP. 9.

Chunekar, K.C. (2004), Bhava Prakash Nighantu, Chaukhambha Bharti Academy, Varanasi, PP. 810.

Khare, C.P. (2007), Indian Medicinal Plants, Springer (India) P.L. New Delhi, PP. 670.

Kirtikar, K.R. & Basu, B.D. (1998), Indian Medicinal Plants, L.M Basu, Allahabad, Vol. 2, PP. 1692.

Misra, B.L. (2005), Dravya Guna Hastamalaka, Publication scheme, Jaipur, PP. 489.

Nair, R.Vasudevan, (2007), Indian Medicinal Plants, Orient Longman P.L. Chennai, Vol. 5, PP. 316.

Prajapati, N.D., Purohit, S.S., Sharma, A.K. & Tarun Kumar (2003), A Hand Book of Medicinal Plants, Agrobios India, Jodhpur, PP. 520.

Sharma, P.V. (1981), Dravya gun vigyana, Chaukhambha Bharti Academy, Varanasi, Vol. 1, PP. 231.

Swami, K.N. (1985), Gavon Main Aushadh Ratna, Kalera Krishana Gopal, Kalera (Raj.), Vol. 2, PP. 63.

473. *Tricholepsis glaberrima* DC.

Family: Compositae; Asteraceae.

Name: Sanskrit: *Brahamdandi, Ajadandi,* **Hindi:** *Brahmadandi,* **Local:** *Ajadandi.*

Botanical characteristics: Habit: An annual, erect, quite glabrous herb, 30-120 cm high. **Stem:** Erect, slender, branches angled and ribbed. **Leaf:** Sessile, 2.5-6.3 cm by 3-6 mm, linear-oblong or lanceolate, acute, entire, spinous-toothed or spinous-serrate, punctate, midrib and nerves very prominent beneath. **Flower:** Heads 6-8 mm long, ovoid, glabrous, corollas 1.25-1.4 cm long, purple; involucral bracts linear-lanceolate, aristate-acuminate, ciliolate, sub-erect or slightly recurved. **Fruit:** Achenes, oblong, faintly ribbed.

Flowering and fruiting period: August-September and October-November.

Habitat: Rajasthan, Mount Abu, Madhya Pradesh and Peninsular India.

Parts used: Whole plant. **Dosage:** 5-10 g.

Collection period: October-November.

Ayurvedic properties: ***Ras:*** *tikta,* ***Gun:*** *laghu, snigdha,* ***Veerya:*** *ushna,* ***Vipaka:*** *katu,* ***Tridosha*** **Effect:** alleviates ***Kapha: +, Vaata: +.***

Chemical constituents: The **plants** contain betulinspinasterol, stigmasterol, stigma-7-enol and a triterpenoid-cycloart-23-en-3-beta, 25-diol.

Action and disease indications: The **plant** is anti-septic, nervine tonic, aphrodisiac, bechic, used for leucoderma, seminal weakness, urinary tract infections, skin diseases, penile dysfunction, insanity, burning sensation, helminthiasis, cough, asthma and bronchitis.

Clinical uses: Penile dysfunction: Mix powder of described plant, *Zingiber officinale, Asparagus racemosus, Sphyeranthus indicus, Cannabis sativa, Eclipta alba, cinnamomum cassia,* 6 g, with milk, two times a day, is beneficial.

Recommended readings:

Bhutya, R.K. (2007), Vanaspati Aushadha Vigyana, Scientific Publishers (India), Jodhpur, PP. 160.

Chunekar, K.C. (2004), Bhava Prakash Nighantu, Chaukhambha Bharti Academy, Varanasi, PP. 831.

Khare, C.P. (2007), Indian Medicinal Plants, Springer (India) P.L. New Delhi, PP. 671.

Kirtikar, K.R. & Basu, B.D. (1998), Indian Medicinal Plants, L.M Basu, Allahabad, Vol. 2, PP. 1425.

Swami, K.N. (1985), Gavon Main Aushadh Ratna, Kalera Krishana Gopal, Kalera (Raj.), Vol. 3, PP. 431.

474. *Tricosanthes bracteata* (Lam.) Viogt.

Family: Cucurbitaceae.

Synonym: *T. palmata, T. lepiniana, Involucraria lepiniana.*

Name: Sanskrit: *Vishalaa, Mahaakaalaa, Mahendravaaruni,* **Hindi:** *Bari Indrayan,* **Local:** *Mahaakaar, Mahaakaal, Laal Indrayan, Kondal.*

Botanical characteristics: Habit: A large branched woody tendril climber, climbing often to a height of 9 m. **Stem:** Robust, woody below, branched, grooved, the older light grey, with scabrous spots, the younger smooth, green, tendril 2, commonly cleft into 3. **Leaf:** 6.3-12.5 cm long and about as broad as long, shape variable, usually palmately 3-5 lobed, dark green above, paler beneath, with dark coloured circular glands scattered along the lower side, glabrous, often scabrous with small scales above and on the nerves beneath, base cordate; lobes usually ovate-oblong, acute, more or less dentate or serrate; petioles 2.5-7.5 cm long, striate, puberulous or at length glabrous. **Flower:** Unisexual, white, 6.25-7.5 cm diam., male flowers in axillary 5-10 flowered racemes 15-23 cm long; pedicles thick, erect, very short; bracts 2.5 cm long or more, broadly ovate, pale green, many-nerved, fringed, dotted with dark green glandular spots. Female flowers axillary, solitary; peduncles less than 2.5 cm long. **Fruit:** Berry, fleshy, indehiscent, 3.8-5 cm diam., globose, red when ripe, streaked with 10 orange streaks; pericarp thick. **Seed:** Numerous, 1-1.3 cm long, ellipsoid, smooth, slightly attenulated at the base, not margined.

Flowering and fruiting period: February-March and April-May.

Habitat: Throughout India, in moist places, up to an altitude of 2500 m.

Parts used: Fruit, root.

Dosage: Fruit 125-250 mg, root 1-3 g.

Collection period: May-June.

Ayurvedic properties: ***Ras:*** *tikta,* ***Gun:*** *laghu, rukhsa, tikhsna,* ***Veerya:*** *ushna,* ***Vipaka:*** *katu,* ***Tridosha* Effect:** alleviates ***Kapha:* ++, *Pitta:* +.**

Chemical constituents: The **roots** contain tetrahydroxypentacyclic triterpenoid, trichotetrol. The **leaves** contain cyclotrichosantol and cycloeucalenol.

Action and disease indications: The **fruits** are cathartic, anti-asthmatic, anti-inflammatory, used for hemicrania, inflammations, rheumatic affections, weakness of limbs, dental diseases, asthma, ophthalmia, epilepsy and leprosy. The **roots** are thermogenic, carminative, emetic, abortifacient, purgative, used for hemicrania, carbuncles and gonorrhea.

Clinical uses: Inflammation, mastitis, boils: Local application of paste of roots of described plant, is beneficial. **Pneumonia:** Decoction of root bark of the described plant, 3 g, with honey 10 g, two times a day, is useful.

Formulations: *Naaraayan churna, Vishaalaadi vati, Vishaalaavaleha, Abhayaarista, Updansahara kwaatha.*

Recommended readings:

Chunekar, K.C. (2004), Bhava Prakash Nighantu, Chaukhambha Bharti Academy, Varanasi, PP. 405.

Khare, C.P. (2007), Indian Medicinal Plants, Springer (India) P.L. New Delhi, PP. 671.

Kirtikar, K.R. & Basu, B.D. (1998), Indian Medicinal Plants, L.M Basu, Allahabad, Vol. 2, PP. 1107.

Nair, R.Vasudevan, (2007), Indian Medicinal Plants, Orient Longman P.L. Chennai, Vol. 5, PP. 328.

Prajapati, N.D., Purohit, S.S., Sharma, A.K. & Tarun Kumar (2003), A Hand Book of Medicinal Plants, Agrobios India, Jodhpur, PP. 522.

Sharma, P.V. (1981), Dravya gun vigyana, Chaukhambha Bharti Academy, Varanasi, Vol. 1, PP. 405.

475. *Tricosanthes cucumerina* Linn.

Family: Cucurbitaceae.

Synonym: *T.lobata.*

Other similar plants: *T.dioica.*

Name: English: Bitter Snakegourd. **Sanskrit:** *Amritphala, Vana-patola, Tikta-patola,* **Hindi:** *Tikta Patol,* **Local:** *Aankhaphor.*

Botanical characteristics: Habit: An annual, slender, monocious, tendril climber. **Stem:** 3.6-4.5 m long, slender, furrowed, slightly hairy or sub-glabrous, leafy, tendrils 2-3 fid. **Leaf:** Simple, 5-12.5 cm long, usually a little broader than long, orbicular-reniform or broadly ovate, distsntly denticulate, more or less deeply 5 (rarely 3-7) lobed, the lobes broad, acute, glabrous or nearly so above, more or less pubescent, or, when old sometimes scrabidbense deeply cordate, the sinus often sub-rectangular; petioles 2.5-7.5 cm long, striate, pubescent. **Flower:** White, unisexual, male flowers in axillary racemes, with sometimes a solitary male flower from the same axil as the racemes; peduncles of the racemes 5-15 cm long, slender, striate, bearing 8-15 flowers near the apex; pedicles puberlous, 8-20 mm long, bracts 0. Female flowers axillary, solitary, or occasionally a female flower in the same axil as the male peduncle; peduncles of the female flower 3-16 mm long. **Fruit:** Berries, indehiscent, 2.5-7.5 cm long, ovoid, fusiform, tapering at both ends and with a long sharp beak, green and striped with white when immature, scarlet red when ripe; pericarp thin. **Seed:** Semi-ellipsoid, compressed, rugulose, surrounded with red pulp.

469. *Trachyspermum ammi*-Ajawayan

470. *Trapa natans*-Singhara

471. *Tribulus terrestris*-Golharu chota

472. *Trichodesma indicum*-Adhahpushpi

473. *Tricholepsis glaberrima* - Brahmadandi

474. *Trichosanthes cucurmerina* -Tikta Patol

475. *Trichosanthes dioica* - Patol

476. *Trichosanthus bracteata* -Indrayan bari

477. *Trigonella foenum-gracum*- Methi

478. *Triticum aestivum* - Gehun

479. *Tylophora indica*-Arkapatri

480. *Typha elephentiana*-Eraka

481.*Uraria picta*-Prisnaparni

484. *Vateria indica* - Sarja

483. *Valeriana jatamansi*-Tagar

485.

486. *Vetiveria zizaniodes*-Khasa

487. *Viola odorata*-Banafsa

488. *Vitex negundo*-Nirgundi

489. *Vitis vinifera*-Drakhsa

490. *Wedelia calandulacea*-Kesharaj

493. *Xanthium strumarium*-Aadhaashishi

491. *Withania somnifera*-Aswagandha

492. *Woodfordia fruticosa*-Dhataki

494. *Zanthoxylum acanthapodium* - Tumburu

495. *Zee mays*-Makkaa

496. *Zinziber officinale* - Shunthi

497. *Zingiber zerumbet*-Karpoorhaldi

498. *Zizyphus jujoba*-Ber baraa

499. *Zizyphus nummularia*-Ber chota

500. *Zizyphus sativa*-Unnaaba

Flowering and fruiting period: July-August and September-October.

Habitat: Throughout India, in scrub-jungals and waste places.

Parts used: Seed, whole plant.

Dosage: Seed 125-375 mg, plant 5-10 g.

Collection period: September-October.

Ayurvedic properties: ***Ras:*** *tikta, katu,* ***Gun:*** *laghu, rukhsa,* ***Veerya:*** *ushna,* ***Vipaka:*** *katu, madhur,* ***Tridosha*** **Effect:** alleviates ***Kapha:*** +++, ***Pitta:*** ++.

Chemical constituents: The **leaves** contain luteolin-7-glucoside, kaempferol, 3,7-dirhmnoside and 3-glucoside-7-rhmnoside, cucurbitacin B and E, oleanolic acid, beta-sitosterol and its D-glucoside. The **root tuber** contains glycoproteins and beta-trichosanthin. The **fruit** contains cucurbitacin B. The **seed oil** contains punicic acid; oleic, linoleic, eleostearic, palmitic, stearic and arachidic acids.

Action and disease indications: The **plant** is thermogenic, emollient, depurative, alexiteric, anthelmintic, appetizer, laxative, carminative, digestive, cholagogue, stomachic, anodyne, expectorant, cardio-tonic, suppurative, anti-inflammatory, vulnerary, hepato-protective, antipyretic and tonic, used for skin diseases, leucoderma, pruritis, anorexia, dyspepsia, flatulence, colic, dipsia, hyperacidity, hepatopathy, jaundice, helminthiasis, piles, headache, cough, asthma, bronchitis, cardiac debility, wounds, ulcers, inflammations, intermittent fever, alopecia, boils and general debility.

Clinical uses: Fever: Decoction of leaves of described plant 4 g *Coriandrum sativum* 3 g, with honey 10 g, two times a day, is useful. **Skin diseases:** Leaves powder of described plant 5 g, *Tinospora cordifolia* 10 g, with water, two times a day, is beneficial. Local application of juice of leaves of described plant, is also beneficial. **Penile dysfunction:** Seed powder of described plant 250 mg, with milk, two times a day, is beneficial.

Formulations: *Panchatikta ghrita.*

Recommended readings:

Bhutya, R.K. (2007), Vanaspati Aushadha Vigyana, Scientific Publishers (India), Jodhpur, PP. 115.

Chunekar, K.C. (2004), Bhava Prakash Nighantu, Chaukhambha Bharti Academy, Varanasi, PP. 687.

Khare, C.P. (2007), Indian Medicinal Plants, Springer (India) P.L. New Delhi, PP. 672.

Kirtikar, K.R. & Basu, B.D. (1998), Indian Medicinal Plants, L.M Basu, Allahabad, Vol. 2, PP. 1112.

Nair, R.Vasudevan, (2007), Indian Medicinal Plants, Orient Longman P.L. Chennai, Vol. 5, PP. 320.

Prajapati, N.D., Purohit, S.S., Sharma, A.K. & Tarun Kumar (2003), A Hand Book of Medicinal Plants, Agrobios India, Jodhpur, PP. 521.

Singh, R.S. (2002), Vanoshadhi Nirdeshika, Uttar Pradesh Hindi Sansthan, Lucknow, PP. 227.

Swami, K.N. (1985), Gavon Main Aushadh Ratna, Kalera Krishana Gopal, Kalera (Raj.), Vol. 1, PP. 73.

476. *Trichosanthus dioica* Roxb.

Family: Cucurbitaceae.

Ayurvedic Groups: Charak: *Triptighna, Trisnaa nigrahana,* **Sushruta:** *Patolaadi, Aaragvadh-aadi gana.*

Name: English: Patol, Pointed Gourd, **Sanskrit:** *Patol, Kulaka, Raajiphala, Karkashachhadaa, Karkashaa, Bijagarbhaa,* **Hindi:** *Patol,* **Local:** *Parwal.*

Botanical characteristics: Habit: An extensive climbing perennial dioecious herb. **Stem:** Slender, angled, hispid, more or less scabrous and wooly; tendrils 2-4 fid. **Leaf:** 7.5 by 5 cm, ovate-oblong, cordate, acute, sinute-dentate, not lobed, rigid, rough on both surfaces; petioles 2 cm long. **Flower:** Dioecious, white, male peduncle paired, both one flowered; female flower solitary. **Fruit:** 5-10 cm, oblong, or nearly spherical, acute, smooth, striped, whitish green when unripe and red when ripe. **Seed:** Half-ellipsoid, compressed, corrugated on the margin.

Flowering and fruiting period: August-September and October-November.

Habitat: Warmer regions of India, particularly in Uttar Pradesh, Bihar, West Bengal and Assam.

Parts used: Whole plant.

Dosage: 5-10 g, juice 10-20 ml.

Collection period: October-November.

Ayurvedic properties: ***Ras:*** *tikta,* ***Gun:*** *laghu, snigdha,* ***Veerya:*** *ushna,* ***Vipaka:*** *katu,* ***Tridosha*** **Effect:** alleviates ***Kapha:*** +++, ***Pitta:*** ++, ***Vaata:*** +.

Chemical constituents: The **fruits** contain free amino acids, nicotinic acid, riboflavin, vitamin C, thiamine, 5-hydroxytryptamine. The **plant** and **roots** contain cucurbita-5, 24-dienol, colocynthin, trichosanthin, hentriacontane. The **seeds** contain fatty acids-elaeostearic, linoleic oleic and saturated acids. The whole **fruit** and **pulp** produced significant hypocholesterolaemic, hypotriglyceridaemic, and hyper phospholipidaemic effects.

Action and disease indications: The **leaves** are chologogue, aperient, tonic, febrifuge, expectorant, alterative, used for liver and spleen enlargement, piles, fistula in ano, fever, leprosy, haemorrhages, erysipelas, alopecia, inflammations and wounds. The **roots** are drastic purgative, used for jaundice, anasarca and ascitis. The **fruit** is cooling, laxative, febrifuge, anti-bilious, chologogue, aperient, used for diarrhea, acid gastritis, obesity, oedema, fever and spermatorrhea.

Clinical uses: Alopecia: massage of leaves juice of described plant, is beneficial. **Skin diseases:** Leaves powder of described plant 5 g, *Tinospora cordifolia,* with water, two times a day, is beneficial. Local application of juice of fruit of described plant, is also beneficial. **Fever, malaria:** Decoction of described plant 5 g, *Acorus calamus* 1 g, *Swertia chirata* 5 g, with honey 10 g, two times a day, is useful. **Allergy, urticaria:** Decoction of mix powder of described plant, *Picrorhiza kurroa, Rubia cordifolia, Acorus calamus, Curcuma longa, 'Triphalaa',* bark of *Azadirachta indica,* 10 g, with honey 10 g, two times a day, is useful. **Typhoid fever:** Decoction of mix powder of described plant, *Hemidesmus indicus, Cyperus scarissus, Picrorhiza kurroa, Cissampelos pariera,* 10 g, with honey 10 g, two times a day, is useful. **Chronic fever:** Decoction of mix powder of described plant, *Cassia fistula, Picrorhiza kurroa, 'Triphalaa', Operculina turpenthum,* 10 g, with honey 10 g and nitrate of potash 500 mg, two times a day, is useful. **Excess and turbid micturition:** Decoction of mix powder of described plant, bark of *Azadirachta indica, Phylanthus emblica, Tinospora cordifolia,* two times a day, is beneficial. **Epistaxis:** Decoction of mix powder of described plant, *Santalum album, Pterocarpus santalinus, Nelumbo nusifera,* leaves of *Jasminum grandiflorum,* bark of *Azadirachta indica,* with honey 10 g and sugar candy powder 10 g, two times a day, is useful.

Formulations: *Patolaadi kwaatha, Patolaadi churna, Panchatikta ghrita guggulu.*

Recommended readings:

Bhutya, R.K. (2007), Vanaspati Aushadha Vigyana, Scientific Publishers (India), Jodhpur, PP. 142.

Brahmavarchas (2003), Ayurved Ka Pran Vanoshadhi Vigyan, Shanti Kunj, Haridwar, PP. 450.

Chunekar, K.C. (2004), Bhava Prakash Nighantu, Chaukhambha Bharti Academy, Varanasi, PP. 686.

Dhiman, A.K. (2006), Ayurvedic Drug Plants, Daya Publishing House, Delhi, PP. 299.

Khare, C.P. (2007), Indian Medicinal Plants, Springer (India) P.L. New Delhi, PP. 672.

Kirtikar, K.R. & Basu, B.D. (1998), Indian Medicinal Plants, L.M Basu, Allahabad, Vol. 2, PP. 1110.

Misra, B.L. (2005), Dravya Guna Hastamalaka, Publication scheme, Jaipur, PP. 334.

Pareek, G.N. (2005), Sudhanidhi, Vanoshadhi Ratnakar, Dhanvantari Karyalaya, Aligarh, Vol. 5, PP. 218.

Prajapati, N.D., Purohit, S.S., Sharma, A.K. & Tarun Kumar (2003), A Hand Book of Medicinal Plants, Agrobios India, Jodhpur, PP. 512.

Sharma, P.C., Yelne, MB. & Denis, T.J. (2000), Database on medicinal plants used in ayurveda, Central Council for research in Ayurveda and siddha, Vol. 5, PP. 269.

Sharma, P.V. (1981), Dravya gun vigyana, Chaukhambha Bharti Academy, Varanasi, Vol. 1, PP. 697.

Singh, R.S. (2002), Vanoshadhi Nirdeshika, Uttar Pradesh Hindi Sansthan, Lucknow, PP. 227.

Swami, K.N. (1985), Gavon Main Aushadh Ratna, Kalera Krishana Gopal, Kalera (Raj.), Vol. 1, PP. 258.

477. *Trigonella foenum-graecum* Linn.

Family: Papilionaceae, Fabaceae.

Variety: *T. carniculata* (*Kasuri methi*)

Similar plant: *Melilotus parviflora* (*Van methi*)

Name: English: Fenugreek, Greek heys, **Sanskrit:** *Methicaa, Peetbeejaa, Deepani, Gandhaphalaa, Bahubeeja, Kairavi, Vastikaa, Shelu, Bahupatrikaa, Municchadaa, Methini, Gandhaphalaa, Chandrika, Jyoti,* **Hindi:** *Methi,* **Local:** *Methi.*

Ayurvedic groups: Bhavaprakasha: *Chaturbeeja.*

Botanical characteristics: Habit: An aromatic, erect, annual, hairy, herb, height 30-60 cm. **Root:** Nodular, branched, tap root. **Stem:** Herbaceous, aerial, erect, cylindrical, green, branched, glabrous. **Leaf:** Cauline and ramal, alternate, stipulate, petiolate, compound, tripinnate, serrete, unicostate reticulate, 3-foliate, leaflets toothed, 1.75-2.5 cm long, obovate, rounded, trunicate, emerginate, glabrous. **Flower:** White or yellowish-white, axillary, bracteate, pedicillate, hermaphrodite, pentamerous, complete, zygomorphic. **Fruit:** Legume or pods, 5-12 cm long, with long persistent beak, straight or slightly covered, flatted, 10-20 seeded. **Seed:** yellow or greenish-brown, along with a deep groove, across one corner, rhomboidal, flat, 2-5 mm long and 2-3 mm wide.

Flowering and fruiting period: January-February and March-April.

Habitat: Wild in Kashmir, Punjab and upper Gangetic plains, also widely cultivated in many parts of India.

Parts used: Seeds, leaves

Dosage: Seeds 3-5 g, fresh leaves 50-100 g.

Collection period: March- April.

Ayurvedic properties: ***Ras:*** *katu,* ***Gun:*** *laghu, snigdha,* ***Veerya:*** *ushna,* ***Vipaka:*** *katu,* ***Tridosha*** **Effect:** alleviates ***Vaata:*** +++, ***Kapha:*** ++.

Chemical constituents: Seeds contains alkaloids, including trigonelline, gentianine and carpaine; saponins, based mainly on the sapogenins, diosgenin and its isomer yamogenin and trigogenin; flavonoids, including vitexin and its glycosides and esters and luteolin; a volatile oil in small quantities. The mucilage (25-30%) is mostly a galactomannan. A C-steroidal sapogenin peptide ester, fenugreekine, exhibited hypoglycaemic activity. About 80% of the total content of free amino acids in the **seeds** is present as 4-hydroxisoleucine, which directly stimulates insulin. Saponin rich extract reduce blood level of the cholesterol. The fibrous fraction of seeds also causes a reduction in blood lipids. Extract containing trigonellin and trigonellic acid may be used as a hair growth stimulant.

Action and disease indications: Seeds are aromatic, mucilaginous, carminative, anti-inflammatory, tonic, thermogenic, secrolytic, emollient, hyperemic, mild anti-septic, demulcent, hypoglycaemic, reduce blood level of cholesterol and lipids, hair growth stimulant, anti-bacterial, stimulated the lever microsomal cytochrome, uterine stimulant, increase bile secretion, galactogogue, anaphrodisiac. They are good for fever, vomiting, anorexia, cough, bronchitis, colonitis, diabetes mellitus, hypercholesterolaemia, alopecia, flatulence, dysmenorrhea, amenorrhea, inflammations. Aqueous extract is demulcent, promotes heeling of gastric ulcers. Poultice is good for boils, abscess, and ulcers. **Leaves** are cooling, refrigerant, anti-inflammatory, laxative and aperients. Good for burning sensation, constipation, swelling and burns.

Clinical uses: Anuria, dysuria, leucorrhea: Seeds powder of the described plant 3 g, raw sugar 10 g, with water, 3 times a day. **Polyurea:** Leaves juice of plant 20-50 ml, along the heart wood extract of *Acacia catechu* 1g, and sugar cube powder 10 g, 2-3 times a day. **Sun stroke, burning sensation, inflammations:** Cold sponging by juice of leaves is very beneficial. **Diarrhea, dysentery:** Seed powder (fried in butter) 3 g, with cold water, 3 times a day. **Indigestion, loss of appetite, rheumatism, leanness, pains:** Seed powder 3-5 g, with water, 2 times a day. **Diabetes mellitus:** Seed powder of plant 3 g, seed powder of *Azadiracta indica* 3 g, with water, 2 times a day. **Agalactia, hypogalactia:** Seed powder 3-5 g, with *'Lapasi'* a sweet dish of wheat, is very beneficial.

Formulations: *Siddh methikaa, Sunthyaadi paak, Vrinshodhak lep, Mustakaarista, Mritasanjeevani suraa, Chaturbeej churna, Mopharvaa, Shivaa modaka, Methi modak.*

Recommended readings:

Bhutya, R.K. (2007), Vanaspati Aushadha Vigyana, Scientific Publishers (India), Jodhpur, PP. 185.

Brahmavarchas (2003), Ayurved Ka Pran Vanoshadhi Vigyan, Shanti Kunj, Haridwar, PP. 452.

Chunekar, K.C. (2004), Bhava Prakash Nighantu, Chaukhambha Bharti Academy, Varanasi, PP. 37.

Dhiman, A.K. (2006), Ayurvedic Drug Plants, Daya Publishing House, Delhi, PP. 262.

Khare, C.P. (2007), Indian Medicinal Plants, Springer (India) P.L. New Delhi, PP. 674.

Kirtikar, K.R. & Basu, B.D. (1998), Indian Medicinal Plants, L.M Basu, Allahabad, Vol. 1, PP. 700.

Misra, B.L. (2005), Dravya Guna Hastamalaka, Publication scheme, Jaipur, PP. 269.

Nair, R.Vasudevan, (2007), Indian Medicinal Plants, Orient Longman P.L. Chennai, Vol. 5, PP. 331.

Namjoshi, A.N. (2001), The Ayurvedic Pharmacopoeia of India, Government of India, Department of Indian Systems of Medicine & Homoeopathy, New Delhi, Part-1, Volume- 1, PP. 107.

Prajapati, N.D., Purohit, S.S., Sharma, A.K. & Tarun Kumar (2003), A Hand Book of Medicinal Plants, Agrobios India, Jodhpur, PP. 523.

Sharma, P.C., Yelne, MB. & Denis, T.J. (2000), Database on medicinal plants used in ayurveda, Central Council for research in Ayurveda and siddha, Vol. 4, PP. 404.

Sharma, P.V. (1981), Dravya gun vigyana, Chaukhambha Bharti Academy, Varanasi, Vol. 1, PP. 823.

Singh, R.S. (2002), Vanoshadhi Nirdeshika, Uttar Pradesh Hindi Sansthan, Lucknow, PP. 317.

Swami, K.N. (1985), Gavon Main Aushadh Ratna, Kalera Krishana Gopal, Kalera (Raj.), Vol. 3, PP. 223.

478. *Triticum aestivum* Linn.

Family: Gramineae; Poaceae.

Synonym: *T. sativum, T. vulgare.*

Name: English: Wheat, **Sanskrit:** *Godhooma, Madhuli, Nandimukha, Suman, Gomaka, Gomiki, Gopik,* **Hindi:** *Gehun,* **Local:** *Gehun.*

Botanical characteristics: Habit: Tufted annual grass, 60-150 cm in height. **Stem:** Herbaceous, erect, cylindrical, branched, hollow, smooth, green, branching is on the basal region of the stem. **Leaf:** Alternate, sessile, entire, acute, very long and narrow with ligule and auricles. **Flower:** Sessile, complete, spike or 2-ranked compressed spikelets. **Fruit:** Cariopsis. **Seed:** Whitish grey, 4-10 mm long, ovate or oblong, more or less swollen, blunt at both ends, with longitudinal furrow in front.

Flowering and fruiting period: January-February and March-April.

Habitat: Widely cultivated in India. Mostly in Punjab, Rajasthan, Uttar Pradesh, Bihar, Andhra Pradesh, mainly up to 4000 m.

Parts used: Seeds, small plant.

Dosage: 100-200 g, plant juice 10-20 ml.

Collection period: March-April.

Ayurvedic properties: ***Ras:*** *madhur,* ***Gun:*** *guru, snigdha,* ***Veerya:*** *sheet,* ***Vipaka:*** *madhur,* ***Tridosha*** **Effect:** alleviates ***Vaata:*** **++**, ***Pitta:*** +, aggregats ***Kapha:*** **++.**

Chemical constituents: Wheat germ oil is rich in tocopherol (Vit.E) contain, total tocopherols 1897mcg/g, alpha-tocopherol 67%. The presence of ergosterol (proVit.D) has also been reported. **Bran oil** contains tocopherols, but major part of them (68%) is in epsilon form; alpha-tocopherol forms only 11% of the total. **Seeds** contain P-aminobenzoic acid, biotin, carotene, choline, folic acid, inositol, nicotinic acid, pentothenic acid, riboflavin, thiamine, alpha-tocopherol, beta-tocoferol, alpha-beta-tocotrienols etc. Mainly starch 63-71, sugar 2-3, protein 8-15, fiber 2-2.5, fat 1.5-2, ash 1.5-2% present. In minerals calcium 41, magnesium 138, phosphorus 306, iron 4-9, sodium 17.1, potassium 284, copper 0.49, sulphur 128, chlorine 4 mg per 100g.

Action and disease indications: Grains are refrigerant, emollient, laxative, appetizer, rejuvenating, vulnerary, demulcent, aphrodisiac, tonic, vitalizer, anti aging and promotes physical strength, semen quantity and complexion, useful to cure fractures, ulcers, anorexia, flatulence, boils, pruritis, skin diseases, constipation, menorrhagia and general debility.

Clinical uses: Constipation: Use wheat flour with bran. **Cancer:** Juice of fresh small plants 10 ml, leaves juice of *Ocimum santum* 5 ml, Juice of *Tinospora cordifolia* 20 ml, with urine of cow 10 ml, at morning only. **Bronchitis, asthma:** Decoction of bran of described plant 10 g, common salt 1 g, two times a day, is beneficial. **Renal and vesical calculus:** Mix half-grinded seeds powder of described plant, *Cicer arietinum, Macrotyloma uniflorum,* 25 g, two times a day, is beneficial. **Diabetes mellitus, hypertension, hyperlipemia:** Use flour of wheat, barley and green gram, in ratio of 10:4:1, for making *'Chapati'*. **Spermatorrhea, fluidity of semen, burning sensation:** Soak the seeds of described plant 100 g, in water, at night, at morning, grind them with water, add honey 20 g, take this medication at morning, it is very beneficial. **Bone fractures:** Bark of *Terminalia chebula* 5 g, *Curcuma longa* 2 g, with *'Halwaa'* of flour of wheat, is beneficial. **Rhinitis, headache:** Decoction of bran of wheat 10 g, *Piper nigrum* 500 mg, added *Prunus amyadalus* 10 g, with honey 10 g, two times a day, is useful.

Formulations: *Sukhaprasavakari yoga, Godhoom pindi, Prasutaamrita, Sitasaagar yoga.*

Recommended readings:

Bhutya, R.K. (2007), Vanaspati Aushadha Vigyana, Scientific Publishers (India), Jodhpur, PP. 89.

Chunekar, K.C. (2004), Bhava Prakash Nighantu, Chaukhambha Bharti Academy, Varanasi, PP. 642.

Khare, C.P. (2007), Indian Medicinal Plants, Springer (India) P.L. New Delhi, PP. 676.

Kirtikar, K.R. & Basu, B.D. (1998), Indian Medicinal Plants, L.M Basu, Allahabad, Vol. 4, PP. 2700.

Nair, R.Vasudevan, (2007), Indian Medicinal Plants, Orient Longman P.L. Chennai, Vol. 5, PP. 335.

Pareek, G.N. (2005), Sudhanidhi, Vanoshadhi Ratnakar, Dhanvantari Karyalaya, Aligarh, Vol. 10, PP. 67.

Prajapati, N.D., Purohit, S.S., Sharma, A.K. & Tarun Kumar (2003), A Hand Book of Medicinal Plants, Agrobios India, Jodhpur, PP. 524.

Sharma, P.V. (1981), Dravya gun vigyana, Chaukhambha Bharti Academy, Varanasi, Vol. 2, PP. 152.

479. *Tylophora indica* (Burm. f.) Merrill.

Family: Asclepiadaceae.

Synonym: *T. asthamatica.*

Name: English: Emetic Swallow Wort, Indian or Country Ipecacuanha. **Sanskrit:** *Shaastaa, Antamoolaa, Mulini, Arkaparni,* **Hindi:** *Arkapatri,* **Local:** *Antamoola, Jangali Pikavan.*

Botanical characteristics: Habit: A slender, much branched, tough, lactiferous, perennial climber. **Root:** Many, fleshy, knotty, long. **Stem:** Elongated, glabrous or pubescent. **Leaf:** Simple, opposite, 5-10 by 2.5-5.7 cm, somewhat fleshy, ovate or elliptic-oblong, acute or acuminate, often apiculate, glabrous, more or less pubescent beneath, base usually cordate; petioles 6-13 mm long. **Flower:** Greenish-yellow outside, purplish within, in umbellate cymes, pedicles filiform with a number of filiform hairy bracts at their base. **Fruit:** Folicles, 7.5-10 cm long, fusiform, divaricate, glabrous, tapering to a fine point at the apex, scarcely tapering to the base. **Seed:** Ovate, 8 mm long, with coma 2-2.5 cm long.

Flowering and fruiting period: July-August and September-October.

Habitat: Throughout India, particularly in Assam, West Bengal, Orissa and peninsular India, up to an altitude of 815 m in hilly parts, in hedges and open forests.

Parts used: Root, leaves. **Dosage:** 250-500 mg.

Collection period: November-December.

Ayurvedic properties: ***Ras:*** *madhur, katu,* ***Gun:*** *laghu, rukhsa,* ***Veerya:*** *ushna,* ***Vipaka:*** *katu,* ***Tridosha*** **Effect:** alleviates ***Kapha:*** ++, ***Vaata:*** +.

Chemical constituents: The **leaves** contain tylophorinidine, *d*-septicine, *d*-iso-tylocrebrine; triterpenoids alpha and beta-amyrin; beta-sitosterol, stigmasterol and campesterol; phenylalanine; and quercetin. The **roots** contain alkaloids tylophorinidine and gamma-fagarine. The **whole plant** contain alkaloids including tylophorine, desmythyltylophorine, tylophorinine, desmythyltylophorinine, a flavonoid kaempferol, and certl alcohol.

Action and disease indications: The **roots** and **leaves** are aromatic, emetic, expectorant, purgative, vulnerary, diaphoretic, stomachic and anti-viral, used for bronchial asthma, allergic rhinitis, bronchitis, whooping cough, dysentery, diarrhea, hydrophobia, piles, gout, wounds, ulcers, dyspepsia, flatulence, cancerous tumours and murine leucaemia.

Clinical uses: Gout: Local application of paste of root of described plant is beneficial. **Asthma, bronchitis, whooping cough:** Powder of described plant, 250-500 mg, *Acorus calamus* 250 mg, *Glycyrrhiza glabra* 1 g, with honey 10 g, two times a day, is useful. **Diarrhea, dysentery:** Powder of described plant, 500 mg, with water, two times a day, is beneficial.

Recommended readings:

Bhutya, R.K. (2007), Vanaspati Aushadha Vigyana, Scientific Publishers (India), Jodhpur, PP. 20.

Brahmavarchas (2003), Ayurved Ka Pran Vanoshadhi Vigyan, Shanti Kunj, Haridwar, PP. 454.

Chunekar, K.C. (2004), Bhava Prakash Nighantu, Chaukhambha Bharti Academy, Varanasi, PP. 81.

Dhiman, A.K. (2006), Ayurvedic Drug Plants, Daya Publishing House, Delhi, PP. 36.

Khare, C.P. (2007), Indian Medicinal Plants, Springer (India) P.L. New Delhi, PP. 679.

Kirtikar, K.R. & Basu, B.D. (1998), Indian Medicinal Plants, L.M Basu, Allahabad, Vol. 2, PP. 1631.

Nair, R.Vasudevan, (2007), Indian Medicinal Plants, Orient Longman P.L. Chennai, Vol. 5, PP. 339.

480. *Typha elephantina* Roxb.

Family: Typhaceae.

Other similar plants: *T.australis* syn. *angustata, T.laxmanni.*

Name: English: Elephant Grass, Bulrush, Indian Reed-Mace. **Sanskrit:** *Erakaa, Gundramulaa, Shivi, Gundraa, Shari,* **Hindi:** *Erakaa,* **Local:** *Eryaa, Pateraa.*

Botanical characteristics: Habit: A gigantic gregarious marsh herb, height 1.8-3.6 m, grows in groups. **Leaf:** Erect, grass like equitant leaves, 1.2-1.8 m by 1.8-3.8 cm, somewhat convex dorsally and concave ventrally, becoming narrower keeled and trigonous towards the sheath. **Flower:** Flowering stem embraced at the base by the leaf-sheaths, straight, glossy, spongy withen the top forming the rhachis of the female and male spikes. Lower female spike 15-25 cm long by 7.5-25 mm diam., finally brown, a deciduous foliaceous spathe embraces the whole inflorescence when young. Male spike 5-7.5 cm above the female 20-30 cm long, pale coloured with a basal spathe and 2-3 smaller upper ones, all deciduous, anthers 1-5, 2.5 mm long. Bracts between the flowers very numerous, filiform 2-3-cleft. Female flowers with lanceolate stigma.

Flowering and fruiting period: November-December and January-February.

Habitat: North-West India to Assam and southwards, in stagnant, fresh and brackish water.

Parts used: Whole plant, flower. **Dosage:** 3-6 g.

Collection period: February-March.

Ayurvedic properties: ***Ras:*** *tikta, kashaaya,* ***Gun:*** *laghu, rukhsa,* ***Veerya:*** *sheeta,* ***Vipaka:*** *katu,* ***Tridosha*** **Effect:** alleviates ***Pitta:*** ++. *Kapha:* +, aggravates ***Vaata:*** +.

Chemical constituents: The **plant** contains isorhmnetin, pentacosane and plant sterols.

Action and disease indications: The **rhizome** is astringent and diuretic, used for dysentery. The **pollen** are lithontriptic, styptic, and seminiferous, used for internal and external bleeding; uterine bleeding, haematuria, epistaxis, burning sensation, ophthamia and lithiasis.

Clinical uses: Wounds: Make bandage with flower powder of described plant is beneficial. **Burning sensation:** Local application of paste of described plant, with water, is beneficial.

Formulations: *Agurvaadi taila.*

Recommended readings:

Bhutya, R.K. (2007), Vanaspati Aushadha Vigyana, Scientific Publishers (India), Jodhpur, PP. 37.

Chunekar, K.C. (2004), Bhava Prakash Nighantu, Chaukhambha Bharti Academy, Varanasi, PP. 381.

Khare, C.P. (2007), Indian Medicinal Plants, Springer (India) P.L. New Delhi, PP. 680.

Kirtikar, K.R. & Basu, B.D. (1998), Indian Medicinal Plants, L.M Basu, Allahabad, Vol. 4, PP. 2595.

481. *Uraria picta* Desv.

Family: Papilionaceae; Fabaceae.

Synonym: *Hedysarum pictum.*

Other similar plants: *U.lagopoides-* bigger var.

Ayurvedic Groups: Charak: *Angamarda prashamana, Sandhaaniya, Shothahara, Madhuraskandha,* **Sushruta:** *Vidaarigandhaadi, haridraadi, Laghu panchamoola, Dashamoola.*

Name: Sanskrit: *Prishnaparni, Prathakaparni, Chitraparni, Ahiparni, Singhapuchhi, Kalashi, Dhaavani, Guhaa,* **Hindi:** *Prisnaparni,* **Local:** *Pithavan.*

Botanical characteristics: Habit: A suffriticose sparingly branched perennial herb or undershrub, height 0.9-1.8 m. **Root:** Tape root, 15-30 cm long, woody, pale yellow. **Stem:** Erect, stout, reaching 1.2 cm diam., at the base, finely downy with hooked hairs. **Leaf:** Imparipinnate, 20-30 cm long; petioles 3.8-6.3 cm long, striate, downy; stipules 1.2 cm long, triangular, long acuminate, striate; leaflets 5-7 (rarely 9), 6-20 by 1-2 cm, linear-oblong, rigidly sub-coriaceous, acute, base rounded, blotched with white, glabrous above; stipels subulate, 4.5 mm long; lower leaves generally 1-3 foliolate, sub-orbicular or oblong. **Flower:** Pink or purple, in close fascicles along the rhachis of spicate cylindric racemes 15-30 cm by 1.6-2 cm, rhachis and pedicles downy with hooked hairs; pedicles 6-10 mm long; bracts large, scarious, striate, strongly ciliate. **Fruit:** Pods, glabrous, pale-lead coloured; jointes 3-6, smooth, polished. **Seed:** Ovate, 3 by 2 mm, 1-12, light brown, reniform.

Flowering and fruiting period: July-September and October-December.

Habitat: Throughout India, including Sub-Himalayan tracts from Kashmir to Assam, up to an altitude of 1800 m, in dry grasslands, waste places and open deciduous forests.

Parts used: Root, whole plant. **Dosage:** 5-15 g.

Collection period: November-December.

Ayurvedic properties: ***Ras:*** *madhur, tikta,* ***Gun:*** *laghu, snigdha,* ***Veerya:*** *ushna,* ***Vipaka:*** *madhur,* ***Tridosha*** **Effect:** alleviates ***Vaata:*** +++,***Pitta:*** ++, ***Kapha:*** +.

Chemical constituents: The **plant** contains amino acids, and fatty acids.

Action and disease indications: The **plant** is used for alcoholism, insanity, psycosis, cough, asthma, bronchitis, dyspnoia, gout, bleeding piles, bloody dysentery and acute diarrhea, The plant has fracture healing properties due to earlyaccumulation of phosphorus and more deposition of calcium. The **leaves** are antiseptic, used for urinary discharge and genitor-urinary infections. The **roots** are aphrodisiac, astringent, appetizer, union promoter, anti-inflammatory, anodyne, prescribed for cough, chills, burning sensation, dipsia, bleeding piles, asthma, inflammations and fevers.

Clinical uses: Bleeding piles, alcoholism: Decoction of described plant 10 g, roots of *Sida cordifolia,* 5 g, with honey 10 g, two times a day, is useful. **Bone fractures:** Root powder of described plant 10 g, with meat soup, for 21 days, is beneficial. **Spermacresia, dysuria, gout, inflammation, diarrhea with bleeding:** Decoction of described plant 10 g, with honey 10 g, two times a day, is useful. **Leucorrhea:** Decoction of mix powder of described plant, *Tinospora cordifolia, Solanum surattense, Solanum ferox, Sida cordifolia,* root bark of *Ricinus communis, Desmodium gangaticum,* 15 g, with honey 10 g, two times a day, is useful. **To nullify toxin of *Aconitum ferox,* bleeding piles:** Leaves juice of described plant 50 ml, with sugar candy powder 10 g, two times a day, is beneficial. **Dipsesis, asthma, bronchitis:** Decoction of mix powder of described plant, *Cyperus scarissus, Vitis vinifera,* 15 g, with honey 10 g, two times a day, is useful.

Formulations: *Dashamoolarista, Chyavanapraasha, Dashamoola kwaatha, Bhunimbaadi kwaath, Dashamoola taila, Madhyam naaraayana taila, Mushakaadhya taila, Dashamoola haritaki, Vyaaghri taila, Vayuchaayaasurendra taila.*

Recommended readings:

Acharya, B.K. (2008), Ayurveda Jadi-buti Rahasya, Patanjali Yogapitha, Haridwar, PP. 350.

Bhutya, R.K. (2007), Vanaspati Aushadha Vigyana, Scientific Publishers (India), Jodhpur, PP. 147.

Brahmavarchas (2003), Ayurved Ka Pran Vanoshadhi Vigyan, Shanti Kunj, Haridwar, PP. 455.

Chunekar, K.C. (2004), Bhava Prakash Nighantu, Chaukhambha Bharti Academy, Varanasi, PP. 286.

Dhiman, A.K. (2006), Ayurvedic Drug Plants, Daya Publishing House, Delhi, PP. 304.

Khare, C.P. (2007), Indian Medicinal Plants, Springer (India) P.L. New Delhi, PP. 684.

Kirtikar, K.R. & Basu, B.D. (1998), Indian Medicinal Plants, L.M Basu, Allahabad, Vol. 1, PP. 749.

Misra, B.L. (2005), Dravya Guna Hastamalaka, Publication scheme, Jaipur, PP. 269.

Pareek, G.N. (2005), Sudhanidhi, Vanoshadhi Ratnakar, Dhanvantari Karyalaya, Aligarh, Vol. 6, PP. 98.

Prajapati, N.D., Purohit, S.S., Sharma, A.K. & Tarun Kumar (2003), A Hand Book of Medicinal Plants, Agrobios India, Jodhpur, PP. 528.

Sharma, P.C., Yelne, MB. & Denis, T.J. (2000), Database on medicinal plants used in ayurveda, Central Council for research in Ayurveda and siddha, Vol. 6, PP. 314.

Sharma, P.V. (1981), Dravya gun vigyana, Chaukhambha Bharti Academy, Varanasi, Vol. 1, PP. 822.

482. *Urginea indica* (Roxb.) Kunth.

Family: Liliaceae.

Synonym: *Drimia indica.*

Other similar plants: *U. maritima* - in mediterEranean region, *U. coramandeliana* syn. *wightiana* - in Coramandel coast and Andhra Pradesh, *Scilla indica*- in Madhya Pradesh, *S.hohemackery*- in Punjab.

Name: English: Indian Siquill, Sea Onion. **Sanskrit:** *Van Palandu, Kolkanda, Vajrakanda,* **Hindi:** *Jangali Pyaaj,* **Local:** *Koli Kaandaa.*

Botanical characteristics: Habit: An annual herb, height 30-45 cm. **Bulb:** Pale, 5-10 cm long, ovoid, thick, tunicate, very bitter. **Leaf:** Radical, appearing after the flowers, 15-45 by 1.3-2.5 cm, nearly flat, sub-bifarious, linear, acute. **Flower:** Scape erect, 30-45 cm long by 4-6 mm diam., at the base, flowers greenish-white or dingy-brown, very distant, in slender laxly flowered racemes 15-30 cm long; bracts minute, soon falling; pedicles 2.5-3.8 cm long, slender, spreading or decurved; perianth canpanulate; segments 10 by 2.5-3 mm oblong-oblanceolate, obtuse. **Fruit:** Capsule, ellipsoid, tapering at both ends, 1.3-2 cm long, the cells 6-9 seeded. **Seed:** Elliptic, 6 by 3 mm, flattened, black.

Flowering and fruiting period: March-May and May-July.

Habitat: Abundantly throughout India, mostly in Western Himalaya, Bihar, Konkan and Coramandel coast.

Parts used: Bulb. **Dosage:** 120-200 mg.

Collection period: November-December.

Ayurvedic properties: ***Ras:*** *tikta, katu,* ***Gun:*** *laghu, tikhsna,* ***Veerya:*** *ushna,* ***Vipaka:*** *katu,* ***Tridosha*** **Effect:** alleviates ***Vaata:*** **++,** ***Kapha:*** **+.**

Chemical constituents: The **bulbs** contain cardiac glycosides, scillarens A nad B, hentriacontanol, octacosanoic acid and 6-desacetoxyscillirosidin. The **bulb, leaves** and **root** contain stigmasterol, sitosterol, and campesterol.

Action and disease indications: The **bulbs** are pungent, thermogenic, expectorant, anti-spasmodic, diuretic, emetic, cardiac tonic, anthelmintic, alexiteric, used for skin diseases, dry respiratory conditions, whooping cough, bronchial asthma, heart diseases, paralysis, bronchitis, dropsy, rheumatism, renal and vesical calculi, headache, dandruff and seborrhea.

Clinical uses: Attack of asthma: Tuber of described plant 125 mg, opium 25 mg, rock salt 250 mg, with lukewarm water, repeat after 2 hours, as required. **Corn, warts, calcaneodynia:** Local application of warm poultice of tuber of described plant is beneficial. **Dropsy, ascitis:** Alcoholic extract of tuber of described plant 10-15 drops, with honey 10 g, two times a day, or tuber of described plant 125 mg, with *'Punarnavaastaka kwatha'* 15 g, two times a day, is beneficial. **Cough, asthma, bronchitis of children:** Use syrup of tuber of described plant, 5-15 drops, two times a day, is beneficial. **Skin diseases, furunculosis, acne vulgaris, sinus:** Local application of paste of tuber of described plant is beneficial. Tuber of described plant 125 mg, with distillate of *Sphyeranthus indicus* 20 ml, two times a day, is beneficial. **Chronic bronchitis:** Tuber of described plant 125 mg, root bark of *Calotropis procera* 125 mg, with honey 10 g, two times a day, is beneficial. **Helminthiasis:** Tuber of described plant 125 mg, seeds of *Butea monosperma* 500 mg, *Terminalia chebula* 2 g, two times a day, is beneficial.

Contraindication: Do not use in acute respiratory tract diseases, acute diseases of kidney and irritation of alimentary canal.

Formulations: *Madhushukta kolakanda.*

Recommended readings:

Bhutya, R.K. (2007), Vanaspati Aushadha Vigyana, Scientific Publishers (India), Jodhpur, PP. 100.

Brahmavarchas (2003), Ayurved Ka Pran Vanoshadhi Vigyan, Shanti Kunj, Haridwar, PP. 456.

Chunekar, K.C. (2004), Bhava Prakash Nighantu, Chaukhambha Bharti Academy, Varanasi, PP. 136.

Dhiman, A.K. (2006), Ayurvedic Drug Plants, Daya Publishing House, Delhi, PP. 68.

Khare, C.P. (2007), Indian Medicinal Plants, Springer (India) P.L. New Delhi, PP. 685.

Kirtikar, K.R. & Basu, B.D. (1998), Indian Medicinal Plants, L.M Basu, Allahabad, Vol. 4, PP. 2518.

Misra, B.L. (2005), Dravya Guna Hastamalaka, Publication scheme, Jaipur, PP. 325.

Pareek, G.N. (2005), Sudhanidhi, Vanoshadhi Ratnakar, Dhanvantari Karyalaya, Aligarh, Vol. 5, PP. 281.

Prajapati, N.D., Purohit, S.S., Sharma, A.K. & Tarun Kumar (2003), A Hand Book of Medicinal Plants, Agrobios India, Jodhpur, PP. 519.

Sharma, P.V. (1981), Dravya gun vigyana, Chaukhambha Bharti Academy, Varanasi, Vol. 1, PP. 206.

Singh, R.S. (2002), Vanoshadhi Nirdeshika, Uttar Pradesh Hindi Sansthan, Lucknow, PP. 89.

Swami, K.N. (1985), Gavon Main Aushadh Ratna, Kalera Krishana Gopal, Kalera (Raj.), Vol. 2, PP. 289.

483. *Valeriana jatamansi* Jones.

Family: Valerianaceae.

Synonym: *V. wallichii.*

Other similar plants: *V. dubia* syn. *officinalis, V. hardwickii, V. leschenaultii, V. officinalis, V. pyrolaefolia.*

Ayurvedic Groups: Charak: *Sheetaprashamana, Tiktaskandha,* **Sushruta:** *Elaadi gana.*

Name: English: Indian Valerian, **Sanskrit:** *Nat, Vakra, Kutila, Nahusha, Kaalaanusaaryaka,* **Hindi:** *Tagar,* **Local:** *Tagar.*

Botanical characteristics: Habit: A tufted, hairy, perennial, aromatic herb, height up to 50 cm. **Rootstock:** Thick, horizontal, with 6-10 cm, long fibrous roots knotted by uneven circular ridges. **Stem:** Several, 15-45 cm long, usually tufted. **Leaf:** Basal radical leaves are cordate-ovate, 2.5-8 cm, toothed or sinuate, long stalked, while cauline leaves are few, small, entire or lobulate. **Flower:** White, or tinged with pink and occur in flat toped corymbose clusters on erect, nearly leafless penducles. Flowers are unisexual; male and female flowers appear on different plants. Corolla is funnel shaped with five lobes. **Fruit:** Oblong, compressed, hairy or glabrous, crowned with a persistent pappus-like calyx.

Flowering and fruiting period: March-April and May-June.

Habitat: Frequent in temperate Himalaya, from Kashmir to Bhutan, and Khassi Hills. It grows naturally at altitude of 1800-3000 m in North-western Himalaya and 1200-1800 m in Assam and North-east India.

Parts used: Rhizome. **Dosage:** 1-3 g.

Collection period: May-June.

Ayurvedic properties: ***Ras:*** *tikta, kashaaya, madhur,* ***Gun:*** *laghu, snigdha,* ***Veerya:*** *ushna,* ***Vipaka:*** *katu,* ***Tridosha*** **Effect:** alleviates ***Kapha:*** **+++,** ***Vaata:*** +, ***Pitta:*** +.

Chemical constituents: The **rhizomes** and **roots** contain cyclopentapyrans, acacetin-7-0-rutinosides, valtrate, didrovaltrate, linarin, *iso*-valerinate, valepottriates and an iridoid ester glycoside, valesosidatum. Cyclopentapyrans exhibits sedstive, tranquilizing and bacteriocidal properties. The **essential oil** from **roots** contains calerene, beta-bargamotene, valeranone, *ar*-curcumene, maalioxide and maalitol.

Action and disease indications: The **rhizomes and roots** are thermogenic, alexiteric, emollient, anodyne, vulnerary, hyptonic, carminative, digestive, stomachic, laxative, trichogenous, expectorant, emmenogogue, aphrodisiac, febrifuge, ophthalmic, stimulant, hypotensive, sedative, anti-pyretic, diuretic, hepatic and nervine tonic, used for epilepsy, hysteria, hypochondriasis, nervous unrest, convulsions, dyspepsia, flatulence, colic, ascitis, constipation, jaundice, cardiac debility, dry cough, asthma, bronchitis, arthralgia, wounds, ulcers, strangury, dysmenorrhea, amenorrhea, seminal weakness, penile dysfunction, chronic and intermittent fevers, eye diseases, canitis, spleenomegaly, gleet, pharyngitis, general debility and skin diseases.

Clinical uses: Whooping cough, bronchial asthma, constipation, rheumatism, arthalgia: Cold infusion of described plant, 3 g, with honey 10 g, two times a day, is useful. **Palpitation, unconsciousness:** Oil of roots of described plant 2-5 g, with cold infusion of *Cinamomum verum* 2 g, two times a day, is beneficial. **Diabetes mellitus, polyuria caused by nervous irritability:** Opium 5 mg, with cold infusion of described plant 3 g, two times a day, is beneficial.

Formulations: *Nataadi taila, Nataadi leha, Tagaraadi kwaatha, Dashaanga lepa, Mahaa sudarshan churna, Phala ghrita, Jatiphaladhya churna, Dhaanvantara taila, Manjisthaadi taila, Madhvaasava, Pippalyaasava, Devdaarvyadhyarista, Karpuradhyarka, Agurvaadhya taila, Khsaaraagada, Nilikaadhya taila, Balaa taila.*

Recommended readings:

Acharya, B.K. (2008), Ayurveda Jadi-buti Rahasya, Patanjali Yogapitha, Haridwar, PP. 397.

Bhutya, R.K. (2007), Vanaspati Aushadha Vigyana, Scientific Publishers (India), Jodhpur, PP. 112.

Chunekar, K.C. (2004), Bhava Prakash Nighantu, Chaukhambha Bharti Academy, Varanasi, PP. 200.

Dhiman, A.K. (2006), Ayurvedic Drug Plants, Daya Publishing House, Delhi, PP. 370.

Khare, C.P. (2007), Indian Medicinal Plants, Springer (India) P.L. New Delhi, PP. 694.

Kirtikar, K.R. & Basu, B.D. (1998), Indian Medicinal Plants, L.M Basu, Allahabad, Vol. 2, PP. 1322.

Misra, B.L. (2005), Dravya Guna Hastamalaka, Publication scheme, Jaipur, PP. 449.

Nair, R.Vasudevan, (2007), Indian Medicinal Plants, Orient Longman P.L. Chennai, Vol. 5, PP. 345.

Namjoshi, A.N. (2001), The Ayurvedic Pharmacopoeia of India, Government of India, Department of Indian Systems of Medicine & Homoeopathy, New Delhi, Part-1, Volume- 2, PP. 109.

Pareek, G.N. (2005), Sudhanidhi, Vanoshadhi Ratnakar, Dhanvantari Karyalaya, Aligarh, Vol. 10, PP. 234.

Prajapati, N.D., Purohit, S.S., Sharma, A.K. & Tarun Kumar (2003), A Hand Book of Medicinal Plants, Agrobios India, Jodhpur, PP. 531.

Sharma, P.C., Yelne, MB. & Denis, T.J. (2000), Database on medicinal plants used in ayurveda, Central Council for research in Ayurveda and siddha, Vol. 8, PP. 445.

Sharma, P.V. (1981), Dravya gun vigyana, Chaukhambha Bharti Academy, Varanasi, Vol. 1, PP. 64.

Singh, R.S. (2002), Vanoshadhi Nirdeshika, Uttar Pradesh Hindi Sansthan, Lucknow, PP. 375.

Swami, K.N. (1985), Gavon Main Aushadh Ratna, Kalera Krishana Gopal, Kalera (Raj.), Vol. 2, PP. 348.

484. *Vateria indica* Linn.

Family: Dipterocarpaceae.

Synonym: *V. malabarica.*

Ayurvedic Groups: Charak: *Kashaya skandha.*

Name: English: White damar, Indian copal tree, Malabar tallow tree, Piney varnish tree, **Sanskrit:** *Sarjaka, Ajakarna, Shaal, Marichapatraka,* **Hindi:** *Sarja,* Resin- *Chandras, Safed daamar,* **Local:** *Sarjaka.*

Botanical characteristics: Habit: A large, very handsome, evergreen tree, 20-30 m in height. **Stem:** With thick, grey bark often blotched with green and white. **Leaf:** Simple, alternate, 12.5-20 by 5-10 cm, elliptic-oblong or ovate, shortly pointed or obtuse, cordate or rounded at the base, glabrous, thick and coriaceous with 12-15 pairs of lateral nerves, very prominent beneath, petioles 2.5 cm long, stout. **Flower:** White, fragrant, 6 mm diam., remote, in large drooping, terminal panicles 15-20 mm long, bracts ovate, acute, caduceus; pedicels 6-12 cm long. **Fruit:** Capsule, 6.3 by 3.8 cm, oblong, ovoid, obtuse, rough, pale brown, fleshy, 3-valved, each valve one-seeded. **Seed:** Reddish-white or cream-coloured. **Resin** becomes yellowish white or reddish white on solidifying.

Flowering and fruiting period: February-March and May-June.

Habitat: Chiefly in evergreen forests of South-Western India, from North Kanara to Travakore and Coorga, up to an altitude of 1400 m, also along the streams.

Parts used: Bark, resinous exudate, oil.

Dosage: Bark 3-6 g, resinous exudate 1-2 g, oil for external use.

Collection period: April-May.

Ayurvedic properties: ***Ras:*** *katu, tikta, kashaaya,* ***Gun:*** *laghu, rukhsa,* ***Veerya:*** *ushna,* ***Vipaka:*** *katu,* ***Tridosha*** **Effect:** alleviates ***Kapha:*** ***++.*** ***Pitta:*** *+.*

Chemical constituents: The **Resin** contains several triterpene hydrocarbons, ketones, alcohols and acids, and small amounts of sesquiterpenes. **Essential oil** contains phenolic constituents and azulenes. It shows marked antibacterial activity against Gram-positive and Gram-negetive micro-organism. **Bark** contains polyphenols- *dl-epi*-catechin, levorotatory isomers of fisetinidol, fzelecgin; and bergenin.

Action and disease indications: Resin is bitter, astringent, alexeteric, bechic, carminative, expectorant, detergent, antibacterial, antidiarrhoeal, emmenogogue and tonic. Used for chronic bronchitis, tubercular glands, piles, skin diseases, ringworm, scrofula ulcers, wounds, boils, amenorrhoea, dysmenorrhea, diarrhea, gonorrhea, syphilis, hemicrenia and urinary discharges. **Bark** is thermogenic, alexeteric, depurative, expectorant, antidysentaric, vulnerary and tonic. Used for cough, asthma, skin diseases, wounds, ulcers, otorrhoea, anaemia, dysentery and urethrorrhea. **Oil** is antirheumetic, antibacterial and is useful for neuralgia and rheumatism.

Clinical uses: Rheumetism, neuralgia: Gum-resin of described plant 2 g, with honey water, 3 times a day.

Recommended readings:

Bhutya, R.K. (2007), Vanaspati Aushadha Vigyana, Scientific Publishers (India), Jodhpur, PP. 224.

Chunekar, K.C. (2004), Bhava Prakash Nighantu, Chaukhambha Bharti Academy, Varanasi, PP. 521.

Khare, C.P. (2007), Indian Medicinal Plants, Springer (India) P.L. New Delhi, PP. 696.

Kirtikar, K.R. & Basu, B.D. (1998), Indian Medicinal Plants, L.M Basu, Allahabad, Vol. 1, PP. 292.

Nair, R. Vasudevan, (2007), Indian Medicinal Plants, Orient Longman P.L. Chennai, Vol. 5, PP. 349.

Prajapati, N.D., Purohit, S.S., Sharma, A.K. & Tarun Kumar (2003), A Hand Book of Medicinal Plants, Agrobios India, Jodhpur, PP. 533.

Sharma, P.V. (1981), Dravya gun vigyana, Chaukhambha Bharti Academy, Varanasi, Vol. 1, PP. 674.

485. *Vernonia cinerea* Lees.

Family: Compositae; Asteraceae.

Synonym: *V. albicans.*

Name: English: Ash coloured Fleabane, Purple Fleabane, **Sanskrit:** *Sahadevi, Khsetrabalaa,* **Hindi:** *Sahadevi,* **Local:** *Sahadei.*

Botanical characteristics: Habit: An annual, erect or somewhat decumbent herb, 15-75 cm in height. **Stem:** Stiff, cylindric, striate, more or less pubescent, slightly branched. **Leaf:** Simple, alternate, variable in shape, broadly-elliptic or lanceolate, obtuse or acute, shortly mucronate, irregularly toothed or shallowly crenate-serrate, 2.5-5 by 2-3.8 cm. The upper leaves the smallest, petioles 6-13 cm long. **Flower:** Many, pinkish-violet, in small heads, 6 mm diam., about 20 flowered, in lax divaricated terminal corymbose, involucral bracts oblong, lanceolate, acuminate, awned, silky on the back. **Fruit:** Achene, 1.25 mm long, oblong, slightly narrowed at the base, clothed with appressed white hairs. **Seed** Shape like *Vernonia anthelmintica* but small in size.

Flowering and fruiting period: August-September and November-December.

Habitat: Throughout India, common as a weed on roadsides and open waste places, ascending up to an altitude of 1800 m in Himalaya and Khasi hills. Abundant in crops of Maize, Millet and Sugarcane.

Parts used: Root, seed, whole plant.

Dosage: Whole plant juice 10-20 ml, powder 5-10 g, seed 0.5-1 g, root 1-3 g.

Collection period: November-December.

Ayurvedic properties: ***Ras:*** *tikta,* ***Gun:*** *laghu, rukhsa,* ***Veerya:*** *ushna,* ***Vipaka:*** *katu,* ***Tridosha*** **Effect:** alleviates ***Vaata:* +++, *Kapha:* ++.**

Chemical constituents: The **whole parts** contain luteolin-7-mono-beta-D-glucopyranoside, triterpene compounds-beta-amyrin acetate, lupeol acetate, beta-amirin and lupeol; sterols-beta-sitosterol, stigmasterol and alpha-apinasterol; phenolic resin andpotassium chloride. The **seeds** contain archidic, behenic, linoleic, myristic, oleic and oxygenated oleic, palmitic and stearic acids.

Action and disease indications: Plant is thermogenic, anthelmintic, febrifuge, diaphoretic, styptic, blood purifier, depurative, diuretic, anodyne, lithontriptic, anti-inflammatory, sudorofic, stomachic, alexetric, antibacterial, antifungal, antiviral and antiperiodic. Used for leucorrhea, dysuria, anuria, spasm of bladder, strangury, asthma, herpes, eczema, ringworm, elephantiasis, pityriasis versicolor, blisters, boils, veginal discharges, psychoneurosis. The plant possesses anticancerous activities and used for cancerous malformation. The **seeds** are anthelmintic, antiflatulant, antispasmodic, used in dysuria, roundworm, threadworm, cough, flatulence, leucoderma, psoriasis and skin diseases.

Clinical uses: Fever: Decoction 10 g, or juice 10 ml, of described plant, two times a day, is beneficial. **Piles, burning sensation of urine, spasm:** Juice of described plant 10 ml, with honey 10 g, two times a day, is beneficial. **Inflammation:** Local application of paste of described plant, is beneficial.

Formulations: *Chandanaadi arka, Maleria vati, Chandrakalaa rasa, Mahaa chandrakalaa rasa.*

Recommended readings:

Bhutya, R.K. (2007), Vanaspati Aushadha Vigyana, Scientific Publishers (India), Jodhpur, PP. 226.

Brahmavarchas (2003), Ayurved Ka Pran Vanoshadhi Vigyan, Shanti Kunj, Haridwar, PP. 460.

Chunekar, K.C. (2004), Bhava Prakash Nighantu, Chaukhambha Bharti Academy, Varanasi, PP. 369.

Khare, C.P. (2007), Indian Medicinal Plants, Springer (India) P.L. New Delhi, PP. 699.

Kirtikar, K.R. & Basu, B.D. (1998), Indian Medicinal Plants, L.M Basu, Allahabad, Vol. 2, PP. 1322.

Misra, B.L. (2005), Dravya Guna Hastamalaka, Publication scheme, Jaipur, PP. 296.

Nair, R.Vasudevan, (2007), Indian Medicinal Plants, Orient Longman P.L. Chennai, Vol. 5, PP. 358.

Namjoshi, A.N. (2001), The Ayurvedic Pharmacopoeia of India, Government of India, Department of Indian Systems of Medicine & Homoeopathy, New Delhi, Part-1, Volume- 3, PP. 169.

Prajapati, N.D., Purohit, S.S., Sharma, A.K. & Tarun Kumar (2003), A Hand Book of Medicinal Plants, Agrobios India, Jodhpur, PP. 536.

Sharma, P.C., Yelne, MB. & Denis, T.J. (2000), Database on medicinal plants used in ayurveda, Central Council for research in Ayurveda and siddha, Vol. 5, PP. 286.

Sharma, P.V. (1981), Dravya gun vigyana, Chaukhambha Bharti Academy, Varanasi, Vol. 1, PP. 690.

Singh, R.S. (2002), Vanoshadhi Nirdeshika, Uttar Pradesh Hindi Sansthan, Lucknow, PP. 367.

486. *Vetiveria zizaniodes* (Linn.) Nash.

Family: Gramineae; Poaceae.

Synonym: *Andropogon muricatus, A.squarrosus.*

Ayurvedic Groups: Charak: *Varnya, Stanyajanana, Chardinigrahana, Dahaprashamana, Tikta skandha,* **Sushruta:** *Pittaprashamana, Saarivaadi gana.*

Name: English: Vetiver, Khas, **Sanskrit:** *Viran, Veerataru, Veer, Bahumoolaka, Usheera, Sugasndhimoola, Naladaa, Laamajjaka, Sevyaa, Samagandhakaa, Jalavaasa,* **Hindi:** *Khas,* **Local:** *Khas.*

Botanical characteristics: Habit: A densely tufted perennial grass, up to 2 m high. **Stem:** With aromatic, fibrous roots and rhizomes. **Leaf:** Narrow, linear or linear-lanceolate, 30-90 by 4-10 mm wide, erect, acute, glabrous, margins ciliate, sheaths compressed, sharply keeled and fan-like, imbricate, very smooth, firm, ligules reduced to a scarious rim, pale green, midrib slender, lateral nerves close, 6 or more on each side, rather stout slightly prominent. **Flower:** Panicles up to 30 cm long, spikes 5-7.5 cm long, sessile spikelets grey, green or purplish, linear-lanceolate, glabrous, 4-6 cm long, lower glumes spinulose; pedicelled spikelets smaller, 2-flowered. **Fruit:** Oblong. **Seed:** Grains, slightly oblique at the apex.

Flowering and fruiting period: July-August and October-November.

Habitat: Throughout the warmer parts of India, in the plains, found in moist and shaded places and along the ravines, cultivated chiefly in Rajasthan, Uttar Pradesh, Punjab, West Coast and lower hills up to 1200 m.

Parts used: Fibrous root.

Dosage: 3-6 g, distillate 25-50 ml.

Collection period: May-June.

Ayurvedic properties: ***Ras:*** *tikta, madhur,* ***Gun:*** *laghu, rukhsa,* ***Veerya:*** *sheeta,* ***Vipaka:*** *katu,* ***Tridosha*** **Effect:** alleviates ***Pitta:*** +++, ***Kapha:*** ++.

Chemical constituents: The **Roots** contain an essential oil 1.1-1.7%, the Khas **oil** containslarge amounts of khusilal, other sesquiterpenes include khusol, khusimol, khusitone, cadinene and laevojuneol.

Action and disease indications: The **roots** are refrigerant, febrifuge, diaphoretic, depurative, digestive, carminative, constipating, haematinic, haemostatic, diuretic, expectorant, stimulant, stomachic, antispasmodic, emmenogogue, astringent, blood purifier and tonic, used for fevers, colic, flatulence, vomiting, spermatorrhea, strangury, hyperdipsia, burning sensation, ulcers, skin diseases, nausea, dyspepsia, cough, asthma, hiccough, lumbago, gout, halitosis, cephalgia, hysteria, insomnia, hyperhidrosis, amentia, cardiac debility, dysmenorrhea, amenorrhea, helminthiasis, eryseplas, emaciation and general debility.

Clinical uses: Nausea, vomiting: Cold infusion of described plant 6 g, *Coriandrum sativum* 3 g, with honey 10 g, two times a day, is useful. **Diarrhea:** Oil of described plant 2 drops, with sugar candy powder 10 g, two times a day, is beneficial. **Hyperhydrosis:** Mix distillate of described plant 50 ml, with water of bath, two times a day, is beneficial. **Headache:** Smoking of powder of described plant 5 g, gum of *Styrax benzoin* 1 g, two times a day, is beneficial.

Formulations: *Chandan balaalaakhsaadi taila, Ushiradi kwaatha, Ushiraadi churna, Ushiraasava, Sarvajwarhara lauha, Shadangapaaniya, Yogaraaja guggulu, Madhurajwarantaka kwaatha, Ushiraadhya taila, Angamardaprashamana kashaaya churna, Stanyajanana kashaaya churna.*

Recommended readings:

Bhutya, R.K. (2007), Vanaspati Aushadha Vigyana, Scientific Publishers (India), Jodhpur, PP. 34.

Chunekar, K.C. (2004), Bhava Prakash Nighantu, Chaukhambha Bharti Academy, Varanasi, PP. 239.

Dhiman, A.K. (2006), Ayurvedic Drug Plants, Daya Publishing House, Delhi, PP. 393.

Khare, C.P. (2007), Indian Medicinal Plants, Springer (India) P.L. New Delhi, PP. 701.

Kirtikar, K.R. & Basu, B.D. (1998), Indian Medicinal Plants, L.M Basu, Allahabad, Vol. 4, PP. 2671.

Nair, R.Vasudevan, (2007), Indian Medicinal Plants, Orient Longman P.L. Chennai, Vol. 5, PP. 361.

Prajapati, N.D., Purohit, S.S., Sharma, A.K. & Tarun Kumar (2003), A Hand Book of Medicinal Plants, Agrobios India, Jodhpur, PP. 537.

Sharma, P.C., Yelne, MB. & Denis, T.J. (2000), Database on medicinal plants used in ayurveda, Central Council for research in Ayurveda and siddha, Vol. 1, PP. .

Sharma, P.V. (1981), Dravya gun vigyana, Chaukhambha Bharti Academy, Varanasi, Vol. 1, PP. 114.

Singh, R.S. (2002), Vanoshadhi Nirdeshika, Uttar Pradesh Hindi Sansthan, Lucknow, PP. 120.

487. *Viola odorata* Linn.

Family: Violaceae.

Other similar plants: *V.biflora, V.cinerea, V. patrinii, V.pilosa, V.sylvestris, V.tricolor.*

Name: English: Sweet Violet, **Sanskrit:** *Kaam pushapa, Sukhsamapatra, Neelapatra,* **Hindi:** *Banafshaa,* **Local:** *Banafshaa.*

Botanical characteristics: Habit: A small perinnial glabrous or pubescent creeping herb. **Stem:** Stock short, but sometimes branched, knotted with the remains of the old leaf-stalks and stipules. **Leaf:** Radical tufts, 1.25-2.5 cm diam., broadly cordate, rounded at the top, and crenate, shape like *Centella asiatica,* downy or shortly hairy, with rather long stalks. Stipules narrow-lanceolate or linear, and entire. **Flower:** Penducles as long as the leaf-stalks, with a pair of small bracts about half way up. Flowers Nodding, of the bluish purple or white or yellow or pink, more or less scented. **Roots:** dry, thready, fibrous pale yellow knotty, slender as thick as a quill. **Fruit:** Very small scented like Musk.

Flowering and fruiting period: July-August and October-November.

Habitat: Found in Kashmir and the temperate western Himalayas, at 1524-2400 m height.

Parts used: Flower, whole plant.

Dosage: Flower 3-6 g, distillate 20-30 ml, whole plant powder 1.5-2.5 g.

Collection period: September-October.

Ayurvedic properties: ***Ras:*** *katu, tikta,* ***Gun:*** *laghu, snigdha,* ***Veerya:*** *ushna,* ***Vipaka:*** *katu,* ***Tridosha*** **Effect:** alleviates ***Vaata:*** ***++,*** ***Pitta:*** ***++.***

Chemical constituents: The **Flower** contains rutoside, anthocyanin, violanin chloride, which on hydrolysis yield glucose, delfinidin, rhamnose, *p*-coumaric acid and high content of tocopherol. Dried **flowers** contain anthocyanin 4, total flavonoids 1.1, rutoside 0.4, mucilage 18, and ash 8.5%. The **leaves** contain friedelin and beta-sitosterol. The essential **oil** from the plant contain methyl salisylate and a *di*-C-glycoside, violanthin.

Action and disease indications: Plant is expectorant diuretic, anti-pyretic, diaphoretic, aperient, carminative, thermogenic, antiperiodic, used for cough, bronchitis, asthma, respiratory tract congestion, bleeding piles, constipation, fever, headache, skin diseases, malarial fevers, hoarseness of voice, hemorrhages, dysentery and pyrexia.

Clinical uses: Bleeding diasthesis: Decoction of described plant 6 g, with *'Drakhsaasava'* 20 ml, two times a day, is beneficial. **Dysentery:** Distillate of described plant, 30 ml, two times a day, is beneficial. **Acute rhinitis:** Decoction of described plant 3 g, *Piper nigrum* 500 mg, leaves powder of *Ocimum sanctum* 500 mg, two times a day, is beneficial. **Fever, bronchitis:** Decoction of mix powder of described plant 3 g, *Foeniculum vulgare* 5 g, *Zingiber officinale* 1 g, leaves of *Cassia senna* 3 g, with raw sugar 15 g, two times a day, is beneficial.

Formulations: *Banafsaadi kwaatha, Chandanaadi arka, Gojihvaadi kwaatha, Drakhsaadfi kwaatha.*

Recommended readings:

Bhutya, R.K. (2007), Vanaspati Aushadha Vigyana, Scientific Publishers (India), Jodhpur, PP. 158.

Brahmavarchas (2003), Ayurved Ka Pran Vanoshadhi Vigyan, Shanti Kunj, Haridwar, PP. 462.

Chunekar, K.C. (2004), Bhava Prakash Nighantu, Chaukhambha Bharti Academy, Varanasi, PP. 830.

Dhiman, A.K. (2006), Ayurvedic Drug Plants, Daya Publishing House, Delhi, PP. 66.

Khare, C.P. (2007), Indian Medicinal Plants, Springer (India) P.L. New Delhi, PP. 706.

Kirtikar, K.R. & Basu, B.D. (1998), Indian Medicinal Plants, L.M Basu, Allahabad, Vol. 1, PP. 207.

Misra, B.L. (2005), Dravya Guna Hastamalaka, Publication scheme, Jaipur, PP. 462.

Prajapati, N.D., Purohit, S.S., Sharma, A.K. & Tarun Kumar (2003), A Hand Book of Medicinal Plants, Agrobios India, Jodhpur, PP. 540.

Sharma, P.V. (1981), Dravya gun vigyana, Chaukhambha Bharti Academy, Varanasi, Vol. 1, PP. 268.

Singh, R.S. (2002), Vanoshadhi Nirdeshika, Uttar Pradesh Hindi Sansthan, Lucknow, PP. 259.

Swami, K.N. (1985), Gavon Main Aushadh Ratna, Kalera Krishana Gopal, Kalera (Raj.), Vol. 3, PP. 72.

488. *Vitex negundo* Linn.

Family: Verbenaceae.

Other similar plants: *V.trifolia-Sinduvar-Nirgundi-* white var.

Ayurvedic Groups: Charak: *Vishaghna, Krimighna,* **Sushruta:** *Surasaadi gana*

Name: English: Five-leaved Chaste-Tree, **Sanskrit:** *Nirgundi, Shefaali, Suvahaa,* **Hindi:** *Nirgundi,* **Local:** *Negar, Negadyo, Samhalu, Meundi.*

Botanical characteristics: Habit: An aromatic large shrub or small slender tree, up to 4.5 m in height. **Stem:** Bark thin, grey, branchlets quandrangular, whitish with a fine tomentum. **Leaf:** Opposite, exstipulate, long petioled and digitately 3-5 foliate, leaflets lanceolate or elliptic-lanceolate, unequal, the terminal leaflet 5-10 by 1.6-3.2 cm, the lateral leaflets smaller with a very short petiolule, leadlets entire or coarsely crenate-serrate, acute to acuminate, nearly glabrous above, tomentose beneath, all leaves with petiolules, the middle one longer. Specific smell in crushed leaves. **Flower:** Bluish- purple, crowed in short cymes, forming erect, narrow, tapering, terminal or axillary panicles up to 30 cm long. **Fruit:** Drupe, sub globose or ovoid or obovoid, 2-6 mm across, 4-seeded, with accrescent calyx, black when ripe. **Seed:** Obovate or oblong, in bony endocarp.

Flowering and fruiting period: July-August and October-November.

Habitat: Throughout India in the warmer zones; ascending to 1500 m in outer Himalaya, common in waste lands, on roadsides, banks of streams or in moist places near deciduous forests.

Parts used: leaves, seed, root.

Dosage: Leaves juice 10-20 ml, leaves powder 2-5 g, seed 3-6 g, root 3-6 g.

Collection period: September-October.

Ayurvedic properties: ***Ras:*** *tikta, kashaaya, katu,* ***Gun:*** *laghu, rukhsa,* ***Veerya:*** *ushna,* ***Vipaka:*** *katu,* ***Tridosha*** **Effect:** alleviates ***Vaata:*** ***+++,*** ***Kapha:*** *+++.*

Chemical constituents: The **leaves** contain iridoid glycosides, isomeric flavanones and flavonoids, casticin and the glucosides, luteolin-7-glucoside and alpha-D-glucoside of a tetrahydroxy mono-methoxyflavone. Flavone vitexicarpin (1), exhibited broad cyto-toxicity in human cancer cell line panel. Two pentacyclic triterpenoids, betulinic acid and ursolic acid, along with an aliphatic alcohol, *n*-hentriacontanol, beta-sitosterol and *p*-hydroxybenzoic acid has been isolated from leaves. The **roots** contain hentriacontane, beta-sitosterol and its aetat stigmasterol. The **seeds** contain *p*-hydroxybenzoic acid, 5-oxyisophthalic acid, glucose and the triterpen, vitextriterpene. Several anti-inflammatory triterpenoids and flavonoids have also been isolated from the seeds.

Action and disease indications: The **plant** is thermogenic, anthelmintic, digestive, carminative, expectorant, stomachic, anodyne, anti-inflammatory, antiseptic, antipyretic, cephalic, alterant, diuretic, emmenogogue, depurative, rejuvenating, good for eyes, memory and hairs, ophthalmic, vulnerary and tonic. **leaves** are anti-inflammatory, analgesic, used in foetid discharges and worms from ulcers, cephalgia, sprains, orchitis, otorrhoea, gout, spleenohepatomegaly and inflammations. **Flowers** are astringent, febrifuge, antidiarrheal, prescribed in liver disorders, diarrhoea, fever, haemorrhage and cardiac disorders. The **oil** applied to sinus, scrofulous sores. The **seeds** are rejuvenatig tonic for reta-rding old age and for retaining and promoting virility, and prescribed in spermatorrhea, and for promoting spermatogenesis.

Clinical uses: Cough, fever, pneumonia: Leaves juice of described plant 10 ml, *Piper longum* 1 g, with honey 10 g, two times a day, is useful. **Rhinitis, laryngitis:** Leaves powder of described plant 5 g, *Piper longum* 1 g, *Acorus calamus* 250 mg, with honey 10 g, two times a day, is useful. **Rheumatism:** Seed powder of *Trachy spermum-ammi* 1 g, with juice of described plant 10 ml, *Ocimum sanctum* 5 ml, *Eclipta alba* 10 ml, honey 10 g, two times a day, is useful. **Sciatic neuritis, paralysis, bell's palsy, lock jaw:** Decoction of leaves of described plant 10 g, leaves of *Nyctanthes arbortristis* 10 g, with clarified butter 10 g and raw sugar 20 g, two times a day, is very beneficial. Fomentation by stem or warm decoction of above plants, after massage of oil of *Brassica campestris* or *Sesamum orientale*, is beneficial. **Burning sensation of sole, headache, acne vulgaris:** Local application of paste of leaves of described plant is beneficial. **Stomatitis:** Gargles with leaves juice of described plant 100 ml, with honey 10 g, two times a day, is useful. **Hypogalactia:** Seed powder of described plant 4 g, with milk, two times a day, is beneficial. **Hiccough:** Decoction of seeds of described plant, 5 g, *Piper longum* 1 g, added gum of *Ferula narthex* 125 mg, as required, is beneficial. **For fair complexion:** Root powder of described plant 3 g, with clarified butter 10 g, two times a day, is beneficial.

Formulations: *Mahaa vishagarbha taila, Laghu vishagarbha taila, Jai mangal rasa, Mahaa vaatavidhavansana rasa, Laxmi naaraayana rasa, Drakhsaasava, Nirgundi taila, Nirgundi ghrita, Trivikrama rasa, Pusparaajaprasaarani taila.*

Recommended readings:

Acharya, B.K. (2008), Ayurveda Jadi-buti Rahasya, Patanjali Yogapitha, Haridwar, PP. 321.

Bhutya, R.K. (2007), Vanaspati Aushadha Vigyana, Scientific Publishers (India), Jodhpur, PP. 139.

Brahmavarchas (2003), Ayurved Ka Pran Vanoshadhi Vigyan, Shanti Kunj, Haridwar, PP. 464.

Chunekar, K.C. (2004), Bhava Prakash Nighantu, Chaukhambha Bharti Academy, Varanasi, PP. 345.

Dhiman, A.K. (2006), Ayurvedic Drug Plants, Daya Publishing House, Delhi, PP. 278.

Khare, C.P. (2007), Indian Medicinal Plants, Springer (India) P.L. New Delhi, PP. 710.

Kirtikar, K.R. & Basu, B.D. (1998), Indian Medicinal Plants, L.M Basu, Allahabad, Vol. 3, PP. 1937.

Misra, B.L. (2005), Dravya Guna Hastamalaka, Publication scheme, Jaipur, PP. 393.

Nair, R.Vasudevan, (2007), Indian Medicinal Plants, Orient Longman P.L. Chennai, Vol. 5, PP. 387.

Namjoshi, A.N. (2001), The Ayurvedic Pharmacopoeia of India, Government of India, Department of Indian Systems of Medicine & Homoeopathy, New Delhi, Part-1, Volume- 3, PP. 142.

Pareek, G.N. (2005), Sudhanidhi, Vanoshadhi Ratnakar, Dhanvantari Karyalaya, Aligarh, Vol. 5, PP. 205.

Prajapati, N.D., Purohit, S.S., Sharma, A.K. & Tarun Kumar (2003), A Hand Book of Medicinal Plants, Agrobios India, Jodhpur, PP. 543.

Sharma, P.C., Yelne, MB. & Denis, T.J. (2000), Database on medicinal plants used in ayurveda, Central Council for research in Ayurveda and siddha, Vol. 3, PP. 450.

Sharma, P.V. (1981), Dravya gun vigyana, Chaukhambha Bharti Academy, Varanasi, Vol. 1, PP. 66.

Singh, R.S. (2002), Vanoshadhi Nirdeshika, Uttar Pradesh Hindi Sansthan, Lucknow, PP. 212.

Swami, K.N. (1985), Gavon Main Aushadh Ratna, Kalera Krishana Gopal, Kalera (Raj.), Vol. 2, PP. 405.

489. *Vitis vinifera* Linn.

Family: Vitaceae.

Ayurvedic Groups: Charak: *Snehopaga, Virechanopaga, Kaasahara, Jwarahara,* **Sushruta:** *Kaakolyaadi, Parushakaadi gana.*

Name: English: Wine Grape, European Grape, **Sanskrit:** *Draakhsaa, Mridvikaa, Gostani, Swaaduphalaa, Madhurasaa, Haarahuraa,* **Hindi:** *Drakhsaa, Angoor,* **Local:** *Daakh, Angoor, Munakkaa.*

Botanical characteristics: Habit: A large perinnial, deciduous tendril climber. **Stem:** Tendrils leaf-opposed, often bifid. **Leaf:** 7.5-15 cm long, orbicular-cordate, more or less deeply 3-5 lobed, margin irregularly and coarsely toothed, glabrous or nearly so above, clothed beneath with deciduous grey tomentum, thin, membranous; petiole 3.8-7.5 cm long. **Flower:** Small, greenish or white, leaf-opposed, penicled cymes. **Fruit:** Berry, globose, ovoid or oblong, varying in size, bluish black, purplish or greenish pale. **Seed:** 2-4, pear-shaped, oblong-obovoid, brown, with a discoidal tubercle on the back from which a ridge runs over the top and down the ventral face.

Flowering and fruiting period: April-May and June-July.

Habitat: Cultivated in Jammu-Kashmir, Himachal Pradesh, Rajasthan, Uttar Pradesh, Punjab, Hariyana, Maharastra, Karnataka, Ahdhra Pradesh and Tamilnadu.

Parts used: Fruit.

Dosage: Dried mature fruits 20-50 g, fresh fruit juice 50-100 ml.

Collection period: June-July.

Ayurvedic properties: ***Ras:*** *madhur,* ***Gun:*** *guru, snigdha, mridu,* ***Veerya:*** *sheeta,* ***Vipaka:*** *madhur,* ***Tridosha*** **Effect:** alleviates ***Vaata:*** **+++,** ***Pitta:*** ++.

Chemical constituents: The **fruits** contain 3-monoglucosides of delphinidin, cyaniding, petunidin, peonidin, malvidin, acetil and coumaryl glycosides, biflavonoids, tartaric acid, malic acid, tanic acid, dehydroascorbic acid, cholesterol, beta-sitosterol, ergosterol, glucose, fructose, galactose, mannose, arabinose, rhamnose and amino acids like alanine, arginine and praline. Also pectin, tannin, flavone glycosides, vitamins A, B1, B2, C and minerals; anthocyanins in red leaves and red grapes. Anthocyanins reduce capillary permeability. Red leaves are astringent and anti-inflammatory; an infusion is used for diarrhea, heavy menstrual bleeding and uterine haemorrhage; also in the treatment of varicose veins and piles.

Action and disease indications: The dried mature **fruits** are refrigerant, laxative, emollient, cardio-tonic, intellect-promoting, haematinic, haemostatic, diuretic, aphrodisiac, rejuvenating, nervine tonic, febrifuge, depurative, antispasmodic, digestive, stomachic, suppurative, expectorant and tonic, used for anaemia, Jaundice, seminal weakness, Penile dysfunction, dyspepsia, constipation, haemorrhagic diseases, gout, cough, dyspnoea, alcoholism, burning sensation, dipsia, amentia, cardiac debility, haemoptysis, strangury, emaciation, fever, skin diseases, colic, flatulence, cough, bronchitis, asthma, opthalmopathy, pharyngopathy and general debility. The **leaves** are astringent, anodyne, diuretic and depurative, and are useful in cephalgia, strangury, scabies, skin diseases, syphilis, piles, spleenomegaly and vomiting.

Clinical uses: Dryness of mouth, anorexia: Roasted dry and seedless fruits of described plant 25-50 g, with rock salt 500 mg and *Piper nigrum* 500 mg, two times a day is beneficial. **Hemicrania:** Cold infusion of fruits of described plant 25 g, *Coriandrum sativum* 3 g, with honey 10 g, two times a day, is useful. **Hyperacidity:** Cold infusion of fruits of described plant 25 g, *Foeniculum vulgare* 15 g, two times a day, is beneficial. **Dry bronchitis:** Mix powder of fruits of described plant, *Phylanthus emblica, Phoenix* *dactylifera, Piper longum, Piper nigrum,* 5 g, with honey 10 g, or clarified butter 10 g, sugar candy powder 5 g, two times a day, is beneficial. **Somasthenia, general debility, anaemia:** Fruits of described plant 25-50 g, or *'Drakhsaavaleha'* 20 g, two times a day, is beneficial. **Anaemia:** Soak fruits of described plant 50 g and fruits of *Ficus carica* 15 g, in vinegar of *Syzygium cumini* 10 ml and water 20 ml, at night, at morning masticate fruits and take water, this medication is very useful.

Formulations: *Drakhsaavaleha, Elaadigutikaa, Drakhsaasava, Drakhsaadhya ghrita, Gojihvaadi kwaatha, Vrihat aswagandhaa ghrita, Aswagandhaa taila, Draakhsaadi churna.*

Recommended readings:

Acharya, B.K. (2008), Ayurveda Jadi-buti Rahasya, Patanjali Yogapitha, Haridwar, PP. 71.

Bhutya, R.K. (2007), Vanaspati Aushadha Vigyana, Scientific Publishers (India), Jodhpur, PP. 125.

Brahmavarchas (2003), Ayurved Ka Pran Vanoshadhi Vigyan, Shanti Kunj, Haridwar, PP. 466.

Chunekar, K.C. (2004), Bhava Prakash Nighantu, Chaukhambha Bharti Academy, Varanasi, PP. 585.

Dhiman, A.K. (2006), Ayurvedic Drug Plants, Daya Publishing House, Delhi, PP. 123.

Khare, C.P. (2007), Indian Medicinal Plants, Springer (India) P.L. New Delhi, PP. 711.

Kirtikar, K.R. & Basu, B.D. (1998), Indian Medicinal Plants, L.M Basu, Allahabad, Vol. 1, PP. 607.

Misra, B.L. (2005), Dravya Guna Hastamalaka, Publication scheme, Jaipur, PP. 416.

Nair, R.Vasudevan, (2007), Indian Medicinal Plants, Orient Longman P.L. Chennai, Vol. 5, PP. 396.

Namjoshi, A.N. (2001), The Ayurvedic Pharmacopoeia of India, Government of India, Department of Indian Systems of Medicine & Homoeopathy, New Delhi, Part-1, Volume- 3, PP. 45.

Pareek, G.N. (2005), Sudhanidhi, Vanoshadhi Ratnakar, Dhanvantari Karyalaya, Aligarh, Vol. 4, PP. 324.

Prajapati, N.D., Purohit, S.S., Sharma, A.K. & Tarun Kumar (2003), A Hand Book of Medicinal Plants, Agrobios India, Jodhpur, PP. 544.

Sharma, P.C., Yelne, MB. & Denis, T.J. (2000), Database on medicinal plants used in ayurveda, Central Council for research in Ayurveda and siddha, Vol. 5, PP. 43.

Sharma, P.V. (1981), Dravya gun vigyana, Chaukhambha Bharti Academy, Varanasi, Vol. 1, PP. 133.

Singh, R.S. (2002), Vanoshadhi Nirdeshika, Uttar Pradesh Hindi Sansthan, Lucknow, PP. 308.

Swami, K.N. (1985), Gavon Main Aushadh Ratna, Kalera Krishana Gopal, Kalera (Raj.), Vol. 3, PP. 200.

490. *Wedelia calendulacea* Lees. Non-Rich.

Family: Compositae; Asteraceae.

Synonym: *W. chinensis.*

Name: Sanskrit: *Kesharanjan,* **Hindi:** *Kesharaaj,* **Local:** *Kesharaaj, Peela Bhaangaraa.*

Botanical characteristics: Habit: A procumbent, perennial herb, height 0.3-0.9 m. **Stem:** Procumbent at the base and rooting at the lower nodes, terete, more or less appressedly hairy. **Leaf:** Opposite, simple, subsessile, 2.5-7.5 by 1-2.8 cm, lanceolate-oblong, entire or irregularly crenate-serrete, scabrous with short white hairs or at length more or less glabrate, base tapering. **Flower:** Yellow in tetragonous rayed axillary or terminal heads. Heads 2-3.2 cm diam., solitary; pendunscles 2.5-15 cm long, erect, slender, slightly thickned beneath the heads. **Fruit:** Achenes, truncate, compressed or tubercled, without pappus or with a ring of round scales.

Flowering and fruiting period: September-October and December-January.

Habitat: Throughout India, mostly in Bengal, Assam, Konkan and Tamilnadu, in wet places and coastal areas.

Parts used: Whole plant.

Dosage: Powder 3-5 g, juice 5-10 ml.

Collection period: December-January.

Ayurvedic properties: ***Ras:*** *katu, tikta,* ***Gun:*** *laghu, rukhsa,* ***Veerya:*** *ushna,* ***Vipaka:*** *katu,* ***Tridosha*** **Effect:** alleviates ***Kapha:*** ***++,*** ***Vaata:*** ***++.***

Chemical constituents: The expressed juice of the **plant** contains an oil soluble black dye11.2; tannin 220; saponin 500 and phytosterol 3.75 mg/100 g. Also contain isoflavonoids, bisdesmosidic oleanolic acid saponins have been isolated from the fresh leaves. Significant heptoprotective activity has been found in the prosaponin; and in coumestans, wedelolactone and demethyl wedelo-lactone, isolatedfrom the menthanol extract of the herb.

Action and disease indications: The **plant** is thermogenic, bechic, deobstruent, anti-inflammatory, vulnerary, ophthalmic, cardio-tonic, anthelmintic, sudorofic, diuretic, aphrodisiac, febrifuge and trichogenous, used for inflammations, otalgia, wounds, ulcers, cephalalgia, nyctalopia, dysopia, hepatosplenomegaly, Jaundice, piles, asthma, bronchitis, colic, dyspepsia, helminthiasis, strangury, anaemia, seminal weakness, fever, baldness and greyness of hairs.

Plant has very significant activity on viral hepatitis.

Clinical uses: Chronic skin diseases, pruritis, canities, alopecia: Local application of medicated oil, made by paste of described plant, is beneficial. **Bronchitis of children:** Plant juice of described plant 5 ml, with honey 10 g, two times a day, is useful. **Penile dysfunction:** Seed powder of described plant 3 g, with milk, two times a day, is beneficial. **Wounds:** Local application of juice of described plant, is beneficial.

Formulations: *Nalini taila, Vrihat vishamajwa-raantaka lauha.*

Recommended readings:

Bhutya, R.K. (2007), Vanaspati Aushadha Vigyana, Scientific Publishers (India), Jodhpur, PP. 75.

Chunekar, K.C. (2004), Bhava Prakash Nighantu, Chaukhambha Bharti Academy, Varanasi, PP. 429.

Khare, C.P. (2007), Indian Medicinal Plants, Springer (India) P.L. New Delhi, PP. 716.

Kirtikar, K.R. & Basu, B.D. (1998), Indian Medicinal Plants, L.M Basu, Allahabad, Vol. 2, PP. 1364.

Nair, R.Vasudevan, (2007), Indian Medicinal Plants, Orient Longman P.L. Chennai, Vol. 5, PP. 404.

Prajapati, N.D., Purohit, S.S., Sharma, A.K. & Tarun Kumar (2003), A Hand Book of Medicinal Plants, Agrobios India, Jodhpur, PP. 545.

Sharma, P.V. (1981), Dravya gun vigyana, Chaukhambha Bharti Academy, Varanasi, Vol. 1, PP. 123.

Singh, R.S. (2002), Vanoshadhi Nirdeshika, Uttar Pradesh Hindi Sansthan, Lucknow, PP. 383.

491. *Withania somnifera* (L.) Dunal.

Family: Solanaceae.

Variety: 1. *W. aswagandgha-Nagori asgandha*-cultivated var. 2. *W. coagulans* - found in Punjab, Gujarat, Simla and Kumaun, known as *Desi asgandha, Panner, Paneer-band.*

Name: English: Winter cherry, **Sanskrit:** *Varahkarni, Varadaa, Baladaa, Vajigandhaa, Hayagandhaa, Turangaa, Vajikari, Aswaga-ndha,* **Hindi:** *Aswagandhaa, Puneera,* **Local:** *Asgandhaa, Asanga.*

Ayurvedic groups: Charaka: *Balya, vrinhaniya, madhuraskandha.*

Botanical characteristics: Habit: An erect much branches perennial undershrub, 0.5-2 m high, usually clothed with minutely stellate tomen-tum. **Root:** Cylindrical, branched tap root, gradually tapering down with a brownish-white surface and pure white inside when broken, 30-45 cm long and 2.5-3.75 cm diam., smell of fresh broken root is just like horse urine. Taste is bitter. **Stem:** Herbaceous, lower portion woody, aerial, erect, cylindrical, solid, green and covered with wooly hairs. **Leaf:** Alternate, 5-15 cm by 2.5-6 cm, ovate, entire, acute, glabrous. **Flower:** Complete, inconspicuous, greenish-yellow or lurid yellow, bell-shaped. **Fruit:** Berry, globose, orange coloured when matured, enclosed in a 6-angled persistent calyx and about 6 mm across. **Seed:** Numerous, discoid, 2-2.3 mm across, smooth flat, yellow, reniform.

Flowering and fruiting period: July-August and January-February.

Habitat: Throughout India, up to 1700 m, drier and sub-tropical parts of India, in waste places, also cultivated, mostly in Rajasthan, Punjab, Gujarat, Maharastra.

Parts used: Root, leaves.

Dosage: Roots 3-5 g, alkaloid 1-2 g, leaves 1-3 g.

Collection period: March-April.

Ayurvedic properties: ***Ras:*** *tikta, katu, madhur,* ***Gun:*** *laghu, snigdha,* ***Veerya:*** *ushna,* ***Vipaka:*** *madhur,* ***Tridosha*** **Effect:** alleviates ***Vaata:*** +++, ***Kapha:*** ++.

Chemical constituents: Root contains several alkaloids including withanin, withananine, withaninine, pseudo withanine, somnine, somniferin, somniferinine. The free amino acids are present in the root including aspartic acid, glycine, tyrosine, alanine, proline, tryptophan, glutamic acid and cystine. The root extract contains an ingredient which has GABA mimetic activity. The **leaves** contains 12 withanoides, including withaferin A, steroidal lactones of withanolide series have been isolated.

Action and disease indications: The tuberous **roots** are thermogenic, anti-ageing, anti oxida-nt, somniferous, stimulant, aphrodisiac, diuretic, tonic, anti-inflammatory, sedative, hyptonic, anti convalescent and nervine tonic, useful to cure sexual debility, nervous breakdown, swel-ling, tumours, scrofula, rheumatism, anxiety neurosis. They induced a marked impairment in libido, sexual performance, sexual vigor and penile dysfunction. Also useful in leucoderma, constipation, insomnia, tissue-building, lack of strength, low quality and quantity of semen, leucorrhoea, backache, rickets, coma, vertigo, hypertension, hypotension, asthma, bronchitis, it promotes quantity of flesh in the body, reduce degeneration process of body cell and produce new cells of nervous system. Also useful to cure osteoporosis, osteodynia, algimers and chorea. It acts same as by mouth or by anus as medicated enema. **Leaves** are anti-inflammatory, anti tumour, anti-arthritic, heptoprotective, anti bacterial, and are useful to cure painful swelling, fevers, opthmitis, carbuncles, ulcers, rheumo and osteo arthritis. Withaferin-A, a major contain of **leaves,** is a major component of biologically active steroids, as effective as hydrocortisone dose, effective anti-bactirial, anti-tumour, anti-arthritic and significantly protective against heptotoxicity. **Fruits** and **seeds** are diuretic and diaphoretic.

Contra indication: Do not give wild variety by mouth, it is sedative, nervine depressant, diaphoretic and diuretic. It is useful for external use for pain and swelling as medicated oil etc.

Clinical uses: It is recommended that *Withania somnifera* is good for oral use, and *Withania aswagandha* is good for external use. **Agalactia, hypogalactia:** Mix root powder of *Withania somnifera* 3 g, *Pueraria tuberosa* 2 g, *Glycyrrhiza glabra* 1 g, boil with milk take 2 times a day. **For spermatogenesis, premature ejaculation:** Root powder of the described plant 3 g, *Argeria nervosa* 2 g, with milk, 2 times a day. **Dyspnea of old age:** Alkaline of plant 500 mg, with honey 10 g, and clarified butter 5g, 3 times a day. **Insomnia, Tuberculosis:** Root powder of the described plant 3 g, clarified butter 10 g, Sugar cube powder 10 g, *Piper longum* 1 g, 2 times a day. **Rheumatism**: Root powder of the described plant 3 g, *Zingiber officinale* 1 g, with milk, 2 times a day. Use local application of leaves paste of the described plant. **Sterility**: Fried root powder of the described plant in clarified butter, 4 g, boil in milk 250 g, and add clarified butter 10 g, Sugar cube powder 10 g, 2 times a day, for 7 days, after 3 days of menstrual period. **Oligospermia, promoting semen quantity, for restoration:** Root powder of the described plant 4 g, boil with milk 250 ml, add clarified butter 10 g, Sugar cube powder 10 g, honey 10 g, powder of *Piper longum* 1 g, 2 times a day, for 3 weeks. **For anti ageing:** Root powder of the described plant 3 g, *Tinospora cordifolia* 6 g, white extract of *Tinospora cordifolia* 1 g, with clarified butter 10 g, honey 15 g, at morning. **Pains, neuralgia, rheumatism, migraine, headache, lumbago, fluttering:** Use *'Aswagandha ghrita'* with milk 250 ml, 2 times a day. **Hemicrenia:** Root powder of the described plant 2 g, with Sugar cube powder 10 g, with milk 250 ml, at morning before sun rise and bed time. Local application of fresh root paste is also useful. **Swelling, tumours:** Local application of leaves paste, of the described plant, made in cow urine. **Stiffness of joint:** Fresh root paste of plant, seed powder of the *Brassica campestris* and worm cast clay, at ratio of 2:1:10, make fine paste with honey. Apply thick coat on effected area, also give *'Aswagandhadi guggulu* 1 g, 3 times a day, for oral use. **Hypertension, insomnia, epilepsy:** Root powder of *Withania somnifera, Asparagus racemosus, Baccopa monerii, Convolvulus pluricaulis, Centella asiatica, Cyperus rotundus, Tribulus terrestris, Tinospora cordifolia, Glycyrrhiza glabra Nardostachys jatamansi, Hemidesmus inducus,* each two parts, *Canabis sativa* (Boiled and fried in some *'Ghee'*) one part, Sugar cube powder 10 parts. Dose 6 g, 2 times a day, with water. It is very safe and effective medicine. If blood pressure level cross above 150/110 mm hg, add *Rauvolfia serpentina* root powder one part. Check up level regularly. **Leanness of pregnancy:** Root powder of the described plant 2 g, with milk, 2 times a day. **Penile dysfunction:** Massage with medicated oil, made with root powder of plant, or paste of root powder of the described plant, 10 g, rock salt 1 g, butter 20 g, is beneficial. **Lumbago, backache of female, weakness after child birth:** Root powder of the described plant 3 g, clarified butter 10 g, Sugar cube powder 10 g, with decoction of *Zingiber officinale* 1 g, 2 times a day. **Cardiac pain:** Root powder of the described plant 2 g, with warm water as required. **Asthenopia:** Root powder of the described plant 2 g, *Phylanthus emblica* 2 g, *Glycyrrhiza glabra* 1 g, with warm water. **Intestinal worms:** Root powder of the described plant 2 g, *Tinospora cordifolia* 3 g, with honey 10 g, at night, use any purgative medicine with this drug. **Pain of heel:** Root powder of the described plant, *Trigonella foenum gracum, Pluchea lanceolata,* mix powder 5 g, with water, 2 times a day. **Lack of memory:** Root powder of the described plant, *Baccopa monerii,* 5 g, with honey 10 g, 2 times a day.

Formulations: *Aswagandhaarishta, Aswagandhaa ghrita, Aswagandhaadi churna, Aswagandhaa taila, Vrihatchaagalaadhya ghrita, Nagbalaa ghrita, Pramehamihir taila, Aswagandhaa rasaayana, Vrihat chhaagalaadhya ghrita.*

Recommended readings:

Acharya, B.K. (2008), Ayurveda Jadi-buti Rahasya, Patanjali Yogapitha, Haridwar, PP. 100.

Bhutya, R.K. (2007), Vanaspati Aushadha Vigyana, Scientific Publishers (India), Jodhpur, PP. 23.

Brahmavarchas (2003), Ayurved Ka Pran Vanoshadhi Vigyan, Shanti Kunj, Haridwar, PP. 468.

Chunekar, K.C. (2004), Bhava Prakash Nighantu, Chaukhambha Bharti Academy, Varanasi, PP. 393.

Dhiman, A.K. (2006), Ayurvedic Drug Plants, Daya Publishing House, Delhi, PP. 51.

Khare, C.P. (2007), Indian Medicinal Plants, Springer (India) P.L. New Delhi, PP. 717.

Kirtikar, K.R. & Basu, B.D. (1998), Indian Medicinal Plants, L.M Basu, Allahabad, Vol. 3, PP. 1774.

Misra, B.L. (2005), Dravya Guna Hastamalaka, Publication scheme, Jaipur, PP. 316.

Nair, R.Vasudevan, (2007), Indian Medicinal Plants, Orient Longman P.L. Chennai, Vol. 5, PP. 409.

Namjoshi, A.N. (2001), The Ayurvedic Pharmacopoeia of India, Government of India, Department of Indian Systems of Medicine & Homoeopathy, New Delhi, Part-1, Volume- 2, PP. 15.

Pareek, G.N. (2005), Sudhanidhi, Vanoshadhi Ratnakar, Dhanvantari Karyalaya, Aligarh, Vol. 1, PP. 215.

Prajapati, N.D., Purohit, S.S., Sharma, A.K. & Tarun Kumar (2003), A Hand Book of Medicinal Plants, Agrobios India, Jodhpur, PP. 546.

Sharma, P.C., Yelne, MB. & Denis, T.J. (2000), Database on medicinal plants used in ayurveda, Central Council for research in Ayurveda and siddha, Vol. 3, PP. 88.

Sharma, P.V. (1981), Dravya gun vigyana, Chaukhambha Bharti Academy, Varanasi, Vol. 1, PP. 763.

Singh, R.S. (2002), Vanoshadhi Nirdeshika, Uttar Pradesh Hindi Sansthan, Lucknow, PP. 30.

Swami, K.N. (1985), Gavon Main Aushadh Ratna, Kalera Krishana Gopal, Kalera (Raj.), Vol. 2, PP. 88.

492. *Woodfordia fruticosa* Kurz.

Family: Lythraceae.

Synonym: *W. floribunda.*

Ayurvedic Groups: Charak: *Purishasangrahaniya, Mutravirjaniya, sandhaaniya,* **Sushruta:** *Priyangwadi, Ambasthaadi gana.*

Name: English: Fire-flame Bush, Shiranjitea, **Sanskrit:** *Dhaataki, Dhaatupushpi, Taamrapushpi, Kunjaraa, Subhikhsaa, Bahupushpi, Vanhijwaalaa,* **Hindi:** *Dhaataki,* **Local:** *Dhaaya, Dhaawad.*

Botanical characteristics: Habit: A much branched, beautiful, deciduous, straggling leafy shrub, height 1-4 m, rarely up to 7 m. **Stem:** With many long arching branches and smooth, cinnamon- brown bark, peeling of in fibres; young shoots terete, often clothed with `fine white pubescence, young branches quandrangular. **Leaf:** 5-9 by 1.3-2.5 cm, opposite, sometimes in whorls of 3, entire, sessile, ovate-lanceolate, lanceolate or oblong-lanceolate, acute, base rounded or cordate, main nerves 6-12 pairs, softly pubescent above, hoary beneath with black, glandular dots on the undersurface. **Flower:** Numerous, 1.2 cm long, bright red, in dense 2-15 flowered, axillary, paniculate-cymose clusters. **Fruit:** Capsule, 1 cm long ellipsoid, membranous, usually splitting the calyx near the base, irregularly dehiscent. **Seed:** Brown, minute, numerous, smooth, ovate or oboviod. Plant becomes leafless at the time of flowering.

Flowering and fruiting period: January-April and May-June.

Habitat: Throughout India, more abundant in North India, ascending up to an altitude of 1700 m, common in deciduous forests.

Parts used: Flower. **Dosage:** 3-6 g.

Collection period: February-March.

Ayurvedic properties: ***Ras:*** *kashaaya,* ***Gun:*** *laghu, rukhsa,* ***Veerya:*** *sheeta* ***Vipaka:*** *katu,* ***Tridosha*** **Effect:** alleviates ***Kapha:*** *+++,* ***Pitta:*** +++.

Chemical constituents: The **Flowers** contain polyphenols – ellagic acid, polystachoside, myricetin-3-galactoside, anthocyanins-pelargonidin-3,5-diglucoside and cyaniding-3,5-diglucoside; octasanol, chrysophanol-8-O-beta-D-glucopyranoside and beta-sitosterol, hecogenin, mesoinositol and flavoneglycosides-quercetin-3-rhamnoside, naringenin-7-glucoside and kaempherol, also contain tannins-24.1% respectively. Dimeric hydrolyzble tannins-woodfordins A,B and C, and trimeric tannins woodfordin D and oenothein A and B, also a new tannin monomer, isoschimawalin, A and five oligomers-woodfordin E,F,G,H and I, have been isolated. Oenothein A and B exhibited remarkable host-mediated antitumour activity. Woodfordin C and D also showed antitumour activity. Woodfordin C showed inhibitory activitytoward DNA topoisomerase 2.

Action and disease indications: The **Flowers** are astringents, refrigerant, stimulant, depurative, styptic, uterine sedative, anthelmintic, constipating, antibacterial, vulnerary, alexeteric and febrifuge, used for diarrhea haemorrhages, ulcerations, eryseplas, haemmetemesis, dysentery, menorrhagia, leucorrhea, skin diseases, burning sensation, haemoptysis, foul ulcers, diabetes, bilious fever, verminosis and heptopathy. They are an important ingredient of alcohol-based formulations as *Aasava* and *Arista* for fermentation.

Clinical uses: Migraine: Local application of paste of leaves of described plant is beneficial. **Menorrhagia, metrorrhagia:** Flower powder of described plant 3g, *Mesua ferrea* 2 g, with rice water, two times a day, is beneficial. **Or** Mix powder of flowers of described plant, *Symplocos* *racemosa, Amomum subulatum, Cinamomum verum,* seeds of *Nelumbo nusifera,* bark of *Saraca asoca, Santalum album, Quercus infectoria,* sugar candy powder, 5 g, with honey 10 g, two times a day, is useful. **Bleeding piles:** Flower powder of described plant 3 g, with honey 10 g, two times a day, is useful. **Diarrhea, dysentery:** Flower powder of described plant 4 g, with whey or curd, two times a day, is beneficial. **Or** Decoction of mix powder of described plant, *Aegle marmelos, Symplocos racemosa, Pavonia odorata, Scindsapus officinalis,* 20 g, with honey 10 g, two times a day, is useful. **Diarrhea of habitual of opium:** Flower powder of described plant 3 g, with gum of *Shorea robusta* 4 g, with whey, two times a day, is beneficial. **Diarrhea of children:** Flower powder of described plant 2 g, *Aconitum heterophyllum* 250-500 mg, with honey 10 g, two times a day, is useful. **Burning sensation:** Local application of paste of flowers of described plant is beneficial. **Epistaxis:** Flower powder of described plant 3 g, with juice of *Cynodon dactylon* 10 ml, two times a day, is beneficial.

Formulations: *Dhaatakyaadi leha, Dhaatakyaadi churna, Dhaatakyaadi taila, Pushyaanuga churna, Vrihat gangaadhara churna, Vrihat shringaaraabhra rasa, Piyushavalli rasa, Laghu gangaadhara churna, Kutajaashtaka churna, Aravindaasava.*

Recommended readings:

Acharya, B.K. (2008), Ayurveda Jadi-buti Rahasya, Patanjali Yogapitha, Haridwar, PP. 169.

Bhutya, R.K. (2007), Vanaspati Aushadha Vigyana, Scientific Publishers (India), Jodhpur, PP. 131.

Brahmavarchas (2003), Ayurved Ka Pran Vanoshadhi Vigyan, Shanti Kunj, Haridwar, PP. 470.

Chunekar, K.C. (2004), Bhava Prakash Nighantu, Chaukhambha Bharti Academy, Varanasi, PP. 109.

Khare, C.P. (2007), Indian Medicinal Plants, Springer (India) P.L. New Delhi, PP. 719.

Kirtikar, K.R. & Basu, B.D. (1998), Indian Medicinal Plants, L.M Basu, Allahabad, Vol. 2, PP. 1074.

Misra, B.L. (2005), Dravya Guna Hastamalaka, Publication scheme, Jaipur, PP. 448.

Nair, R.Vasudevan, (2007), Indian Medicinal Plants, Orient Longman P.L. Chennai, Vol. 5, PP. 412.

Namjoshi, A.N. (2001), The Ayurvedic Pharmacopoeia of India, Government of India, Department of Indian Systems of Medicine & Homoeopathy, New Delhi, Part-1, Volume- 2, PP. 32.

Pareek, G.N. (2005), Sudhanidhi, Vanoshadhi Ratnakar, Dhanvantari Karyalaya, Aligarh, Vol. 5, PP. 102.

Prajapati, N.D., Purohit, S.S., Sharma, A.K. & Tarun Kumar (2003), A Hand Book of Medicinal Plants, Agrobios India, Jodhpur, PP. 547.

Sharma, P.C., Yelne, MB. & Denis, T.J. (2000), Database on medicinal plants used in ayurveda, Central Council for research in Ayurveda and siddha, Vol. 3, PP. 206.

Sharma, P.V. (1981), Dravya gun vigyana, Chaukhambha Bharti Academy, Varanasi, Vol. 1, PP. 472.

Singh, R.S. (2002), Vanoshadhi Nirdeshika, Uttar Pradesh Hindi Sansthan, Lucknow, PP. 204.

Swami, K.N. (1985), Gavon Main Aushadh Ratna, Kalera Krishana Gopal, Kalera (Raj.), Vol. 1, PP. 235.

493. *Xanthium strumarium* Linn.

Family: Compositae; Asteraceae.

Synonym: *X.indicum.*

Name: English: Cocklebur, Burweed, Ditch bur, Louse bur, **Sanskrit:** *Aartagal,* **Hindi:** *Aadhaashishi,* **Local:** *Aadhaashishi, Van-okaraa.*

Botanical characteristics: Habit: An erect tall coarse unarmed herb, height 1-2 m. **Stem:** Short, stout, slightly branched, rough with short hairs. **Leaf:** Numerous, alternate, 5-7.5 cm long and almost as broad as long, broadly trinagular-ovate or suborbicular, acute, often 3-lobed, rough with appressed hairs on both sides, irregularly toothed, somewhat cordate and shortly cuneate at the base, petioles 2.5-7.5cm long, hairy. **Flower:** Numerous, white or green in terminal and axillary racemes with both male and female flowers on the same plant; male heads upper most, globose, about 0.75 cm in diam. Female heads ovoid, 1.25 cm long with hooked bristles. **Fruit:** Achenes, 1.3 cm long, oblong-ovoid, thick, anclosed in the hardened, involucral bracts and clothed with strong hooked spines. **Seed:** Numerous.

Flowering and fruiting period: October-November and January-February.

Habitat: Throughout India, up to an altitude of 2500 m.

Parts used: Fruit, leaves, root. **Dosage:** 3-6 g.

Collection period: February-March.

Ayurvedic properties: ***Ras:*** *tikta,* ***Gun:*** *laghu, rukhsa,* ***Veerya:*** *ushna,* ***Vipaka:*** *katu,* ***Tridosha*** **Effect:** alleviates ***Kapha:*** ++.

Chemical constituents: The **leaves** contain sesquiterpene lactones-xanthinin, xanthumin, xanthanol, iso-xanthanol, isohexacosane, chlorobutanol, stearyl alcohol, beta-sitosterol and palmitic acid. Beta-sitosterol glucoside is anti-inflammatory, xanthumin is a central nervous system depressant. Alcoholic solution of xanthinin shows strong antibacterial activity against Gram-negative bacteria and fungi. The **Roots** contain *n*-heptacosanol, stigmasterol, 3,4,-dihydro oxycinnamic acid, beta-sitosterol and its D-glucoside, and campesterol.

Action and disease indications: The **leaves** are sialogogue, diuretic, anti-inflammatory, given internally in scrofula and herpes in powder form, also for leucoderma. The **root** is bitter tonic, useful in cancer and scrofula. Its extract is used pocally over ulcers, boils and abscesses. The **fruits** are diuretic, diaphoretic, sedative, cooling and demulcent and tonic, used for small-pox, and general debility.

Clinical uses: Chronic fever, chicken pox: Decoction of leaves of described plant 5 g, with honey 10 g, two times a day, is useful. **Scrofula, glands:** Local application of paste of fruit of described plant, with water, is beneficial.

Recommended readings:

Bhutya, R.K. (2007), Vanaspati Aushadha Vigyana, Scientific Publishers (India), Jodhpur, PP. 24.

Chunekar, K.C. (2004), Bhava Prakash Nighantu, Chaukhambha Bharti Academy, Varanasi, PP. 811.

Khare, C.P. (2007), Indian Medicinal Plants, Springer (India) P.L. New Delhi, PP. 723.

Kirtikar, K.R. & Basu, B.D. (1998), Indian Medicinal Plants, L.M Basu, Allahabad, Vol. 2, PP. 1355.

Prajapati, N.D., Purohit, S.S., Sharma, A.K. & Tarun Kumar (2003), A Hand Book of Medicinal Plants, Agrobios India, Jodhpur, PP. 548.

494. *Zanthoxylum armatum* DC.

Family: Rutaceae.

Synonym: *Z.alatum, Z.* var. *planispinum.*

Other similar plants: *Z.acanthopodium, Z.rhetsa, Z.oxyphyllum, Z.ovalifolium, Z.hamiltonianum.*

Ayurvedic Groups: Charak: *Tiktaskandha, Shirovirechana.*

Name: English: Toothache tree, Indian Prickly Ash, **Sanskrit:** *Tumburu, Saurabha, Saura, Vanaj, Saanuja, Andhaka,* **Hindi:** *Tumburu,* **Local:** *Nepali Dhaniyaa, Timur, Tejphala.*

Botanical characteristics: Habit: An evergreen or subdeciduous armed aromatic shrub or a small tree, 3-8 m high. **Stem:** 23 cm diam., with dense glabrous foliage and straight prickles 2 cm long on stems, blaze yellowish-brown rapidly darkening on exposure, furrowed, corky. Bark pungent as red Chilly. Wood is very strong. **Leaf:** Compound, imparipinnate, 10-23 cm long, 3-7 foliolet, rachis winged, often bearing straight pink prickles up to 15 mm long, leaflets 5-11, lanceolate, more or less serrete and each serrature with a pellucid gland, acute or acuminate, sessile, glabrous, dark glossy green above, pale beneath, the terminal 6-11 by 1.5-2.8 cm, the lateral smaller. **Flower:** Small, yellow or green, polygamous, in dense terminal or axillary panicles 2.5-7.5 cm long. **Fruit:** Of 1-3 carples, dehiscent, 4-5 mm across, sub-globose, reniform or ovoid, pale-red, tubercled, glabrous, scented. **Seed:** Solitary, black, globose, shining, 2.5 mm diam.

Flowering and fruiting period: March-May and August-October.

Habitat: Hot valleys of Sub-tropical Himalaya, from Jammu to Bhutan including Kumaon, Punjab up to 2100 m, also at Khasi hills, Eastern Ghats up to 1350 m.

Parts used: Bark, fruit.

Dosage: Fruit 1-2 g, bark for decoction 10-20 g.

Collection period: October-November.

Ayurvedic properties: ***Ras:*** *tikta, katu,* ***Gun:*** *laghu, rukhsa, vidaahi,* ***Veerya:*** *ushna,* ***Vipaka:*** *katu,* ***Tridosha*** **Effect:** alleviates ***Vaata:*** **++,** ***Kapha:*** ++.

Chemical constituents: The **essential oil** from dried **fruits** contains linalool (64.1%), linalylacetate, citral, geraniol methyl cinnamate, limonene and sabinene. The dried **bark** contains lignans-sesamin, fargesin, eudesmin; a lactonepulviatide; dictamine, 8-hydroxydictamine and gamma-fagarine; magnoflorine and xanthoplanine. The **seeds** contain flavonoids tambulin and tambulol.

Action and disease indications: The **bark** and **fruits** are aromatic, deodorant, stimulant, antiseptic, digestive, carminative, stomachic, diuretic, anthelmintic, liver tonic, constipation, sudorofic, depurative, febrifuge and tonic, prescribed for lose of appetite, indigestion, intestinal worms, skin diseases, colic, asthma, spleenomegaly, dysuria, cephalgia, odontalgia, ophthalmopathy, dyspepsia, flatulence, diarrhea, heptomegaly, strangury, fever, leucoderma, cough, paralysis, gout, convulsions, diabetes, wounds, ulcers, cardiac debility and general debility. The **essential oil of the fruit** is antibacterial, antifungal and deodorant, used in tooth powders.

Clinical uses: Headache: Local application of paste of bark of described plant is beneficial. **Asthma:** Smoking of fruit powder of described plant 3 g, is useful. **Headache, colic:** Mix powder of fruits of described plant 2 g, *Syzygium aromaticum* 1 g, rock salt 500 mg, black salt 500 mg, *Cuminum cyminum* 2 g, roasted gum of

Ferula narthex 125 mg, with lukewarm water, two times a day, is beneficial.

Formulations: *Tiktekhsavaadi taila, Tumbarvaadi churna, Panchatikta ghrita guggulu, Tejovatyaadi ghrita, Kanakakhsiri taila, Kaalak lepa, Tiktekshvakaadi taila.*

Recommended readings:

Bhutya, R.K. (2007), Vanaspati Aushadha Vigyana, Scientific Publishers (India), Jodhpur, PP. 119.

Chunekar, K.C. (2004), Bhava Prakash Nighantu, Chaukhambha Bharti Academy, Varanasi, PP. 56.

Dhiman, A.K. (2006), Ayurvedic Drug Plants, Daya Publishing House, Delhi, PP. 382.

Khare, C.P. (2007), Indian Medicinal Plants, Springer (India) P.L. New Delhi, PP. 729.

Kirtikar, K.R. & Basu, B.D. (1998), Indian Medicinal Plants, L.M Basu, Allahabad, Vol. 1, PP. 461.

Misra, B.L. (2005), Dravya Guna Hastamalaka, Publication scheme, Jaipur, PP. 360.

Nair, R.Vasudevan, (2007), Indian Medicinal Plants, Orient Longman P.L. Chennai, Vol. 5, PP. 423.

Namjoshi, A.N. (2001), The Ayurvedic Pharmacopoeia of India, Government of India, Department of Indian Systems of Medicine & Homoeopathy, New Delhi, Part-1, Volume- 1, PP. 160.

Pareek, G.N. (2005), Sudhanidhi, Vanoshadhi Ratnakar, Dhanvantari Karyalaya, Aligarh, Vol. 4, PP. 225.

Prajapati, N.D., Purohit, S.S., Sharma, A.K. & Tarun Kumar (2003), A Hand Book of Medicinal Plants, Agrobios India, Jodhpur, PP. 550.

Sharma, P.C., Yelne, MB. & Denis, T.J. (2000), Database on medicinal plants used in ayurveda, Central Council for research in Ayurveda and siddha, Vol. 7, PP. 486.

Sharma, P.V. (1981), Dravya gun vigyana, Chaukhambha Bharti Academy, Varanasi, Vol. 1, PP. 327.

Singh, R.S. (2002), Vanoshadhi Nirdeshika, Uttar Pradesh Hindi Sansthan, Lucknow, PP. 203.

495. *Zea mays* Linn.

Family: Gramineae; Poaceae.

Name: English: Maize, Corn, Indian Corn, **Sanskrit:** *Mahaa kaayaa,* **Hindi:** *Makkaa,* **Local:** *Makkaa.*

Botanical characteristics: Habit: A robust monoecious annual grass, height up to 6 m. **Stem:** Smooth, bearing adventitious fibrous roots from the lower nodes. **Leaf:** Large, with sheathing base, ciliate ligule and broadly lanceolate blade. **Flower:** Male spiklets in long spike-like racemes in large numbers forming large terminal panicles, female inflorescence in the axil of the leaves with the spikelets arranged on woody axis, styles silky very long, 2-fid at the tip, papillose upwards, protruding from the summit as a mass of threads, surround by the dried up glumes, valves and valvules. **Seed:** Grains large, sub-globose or dorsally flattened.

Flowering and fruiting period: September-October and October-November.

Habitat: Cultivated widely throughout India, mainly in Uttar Pradesh, Punjab, Madhya Pradesh, Bihar, Andhra Pradesh and Rajasthan.

Parts used: Seed, corn silk.

Dosage: Seed 50-100 g, corn silk 1-2 g.

Collection period: October-November.

Ayurvedic properties: ***Ras:*** *madhur,* ***Gun:*** *laghu, rukhsa,* ***Veerya:*** *sheeta,* ***Vipaka:*** *madhur,* ***Tridosha*** **Effect:** alleviates ***Kapha:*** *++,****Pitta:*** ++.

Chemical constituents: The **corn silk** contains saponins; alantoin;sterols, especially beta-sitosterol and stigmesterol; alkaloid hodenine; polyphenols; mucilage, potassium, vitamin C and K; cryptoxanthin, anthocyanins, plant acids, tannin. The glycoproteins, separated from corn silk, inhibited IgE antibody formation and enhanced IgG and IgM formation; they showed antiviral and anti-tumour activities. The **grains** contain starch, flucose, fructose, sucrose, raffinose, fatty compounds, vitamins E,C,K,B-carotene.

Action and disease indications: The **seed** are sweet, astringent, appetizer, roborant, resolvent, nutritious and diuretic, used for anorexia, emaciation, general debility, strangury, piles. The **styles** are diuretic, urinary demulcent, antilithic, used for renal and vesical calculi, cholelithiasis, cystitis, urethritis, prostatitis, irritation of urinary tract by phosphatic and uric acids, nephritis, retention, pus in urine, bed-wetting and uncontrollable bladder, coronary thrombosis, hypertension, hepatitis, rheumatism and diabetes mellitus. Black ash of the seeds bearing **cob** is expectorant, used for whooping cough, chronic bronchitis and asthma.

Clinical uses: Renal and vesical calculus, cholelithiasis: Black ash of corn silk 2 g, with water or *'Punarnavaastaka kwatha'* 15 g, two times a day, is beneficial. **Whooping cough, chronic bronchitis, asthma:** Black ash of base of grains of described plant, 1 g, with honey 10 g, three times a day, is useful. **Coronary thrombosis:** Decoction of corn silk of described plant 15 g, with honey 10 g, two times a day, is useful.

Formulations: *Asmarihar kwaatha.*

Recommended readings:

Bhutya, R.K. (2007), Vanaspati Aushadha Vigyana, Scientific Publishers (India), Jodhpur, PP. 170.

Khare, C.P. (2007), Indian Medicinal Plants, Springer (India) P.L. New Delhi, PP. 732.

Kirtikar, K.R. & Basu, B.D. (1998), Indian Medicinal Plants, L.M Basu, Allahabad, Vol. 4, PP. 2659.

Nair, R.Vasudevan, (2007), Indian Medicinal Plants, Orient Longman P.L. Chennai, Vol. 5, PP. 427.

Prajapati, N.D., Purohit, S.S., Sharma, A.K. & Tarun Kumar (2003), A Hand Book of Medicinal Plants, Agrobios India, Jodhpur, PP. 551.

Sharma, P.V. (1981), Dravya gun vigyana, Chaukhambha Bharti Academy, Varanasi, Vol. 2, PP. 168.

496. *Zingiber officinale* Rosc.

Family: Zingiberaceae.

Variety: There are three main types of Indian ginger, 1. Cochin ginger-light brown or yellowish-grey, 2. Calicut ginger- orange or reddish brown, 3. Kolkata ginger-grayish brown to grayish blue.

Ayurvedic Groups: Charak: *Triptighana, Arsh-oghna, Deepaniya, Shoolaprashamana, Trshn-aanigrahana,* **Sushruta:** *Trikatu, Pippalyaadi gana.*

Name: English: Ginger, **Sanskrit:** Fresh rhizome- *Aadraka, Aadrika, Shringibera, Shrngavera, Katubhadra,* Dried rhizome- *Shunthi, Viswaa, Viswabheshaja, Viswaa, Naagar, Usana, Mahoshadha,* **Hindi:** Fresh rhizome- *Adaraka,* Dried rhizome-*Shunthi,* **Local:** Fresh rhizome- *Adaraka, Aada,* Dried rhizome- *Sontha.*

Botanical characteristics: Habit: A slender, perennial rhizomatous herb, 0.6-1.2 m high. **Rhizome:** White to yellowish brown, irregularly branched, somewhat annulated and laterally flattened. The growing tips are covered over by a few scales. The surface of the rhizome is smooth and if broken a few fibrous elements of the vascular bundles project out from the cut ends. **Stem:** Erect leafy. **Leaf:** Sessile, linear-lanceolate, glabrous10-25 by 1.5-3 cm, narrowed to the base, acute or acuminate, sheath 10-15 cm long. **Flower:** Yellowish-green, with a small dark purple or purplish black lip, in redical, oblong, cylindric spikes 3.8-7.5 cm long and 2.5 cm diam, ensheathed in a few scarious, glabrous bracts. **Fruit:** Capsules, oblong. **Seed:** Many, endospermic, globose and arillate.

Flowering and fruiting period: July-August and October-November.

Habitat: Cultivated throughout India, mainly in Kerala, Andhra Pradesh, Uttar Pradesh, West Bengal and Maharastra, run wild in some places in the Western Ghats.

Parts used: Rhizome.

Dosage: Fresh rhizome 5-10 g, juice 5-10 ml, dry rhizome 0.25-1 g.

Collection period: October-November.

Ayurvedic properties:

Fresh rhizome: ***Ras:*** *katu,* ***Gun:*** *rukhsa, guru, tikhsna,* ***Veerya:*** *ushna,* ***Vipaka:*** *madhur* ***Tridosha*** **Effect:** alleviates ***Vaata: ++, Kapha: ++.***

Dry rhizome: ***Ras:*** *katu, madhur,* ***Gun:*** *laghu, snigdha,* ***Veerya:*** *ushna,* ***Vipaka:*** *madhur* ***Tridosha*** **Effect:** alleviates ***Kapha: +++, Vaata: ++.***

Chemical constituents: The **Rhizome** contains an **essential oil** (1-5%) containing monoterpenes, mainly geranial and neral; and sesquiterpenes, mainly beta-sesquiphellandrene, beta-bisabolene, ar-curcumene and alpha-zingiberene; pungent principles, consisting of gingerols, shogaols and related phenolic ketone devatives. Other constituents include diarylheptenones, diterpens, gingesulphonic acid and monoacyldigalactosyl glycerols. The **Rhizome** also contains aspartic acid, threonine, serine, glycine, cysteine, valine, isoleucine, leucine and arginine. Gingerol and shogaol suppress gastric contractions. Both fresh and dried rhizomes suppress gastric secretion and reduce vomiting. Also have sedative, anti-inflammatory, analgic, antipyretic, hypotensive and heptoprotective activities. 6-and 8-shagaols and gingerols have cardio-tonic effect. Anti-migraine effect is due to ginger's ability to decrease platelets aggregation.

Action and disease indications: The **Raw ginger** is thermogenic, carminative, digestive and laxative, prescribed in anorexia, dyspepsia, inflammations and pharyngopathy. **The dry ginger** is thermogenic, diaphoretic, circulatory stimulant, emollient, appetizer, laxative, stomachic, rubefacient, anodyne, aphrodisiac, hypocholesterolaemic, anti-spasmodic, anthelmintic, carminative and expectorant, increases bioavailability of prescription drugs. used for irritable bowel, migraine and cluster headache, asthma, cough, colic, dropsy, otalgia, cephalgia, diarrhea, flatulence, anorexia, dyspepsia, tympanitis, anaemia, rheumatism, dyspnoea, piles, urticaria, Jaundice, arthralgia, cardiac diseases, phryngopathy, cholera, nausea, vomiting, inflammations and elephantiasis.

Clinical uses: Flatulence, indigestion, vomiting: Soda bi carb 500 mg, with cold infusion of described plant 1 g, three times a day, is useful. **Indigestion:** Juice of fresh tuber of described plant 5 ml, lemon juice 5 ml, rock salt 500 mg, two times a day, is beneficial. **Constipation, dysentery due to indigestion:** Castor oil 20 ml, with decoction of described plant 1 g, at morning, is beneficial. **Dry cough:** Sucking of roasted piece of fresh tuber of described plant 2 g, with common salt 250 mg, as required, is beneficial. **Oseto-arthritis:** Cold infusion of described plant 1 g, with honey 10 g, at night, is useful. **Rheumatism, osteo-arthritis, arthralgia:** Root powder of described plant 1 g, *Withania somnifera* 3 g, with lukewarm water or milk, two times a day, is beneficial. **Headache, Neuralgia, dentalgia:** Local application of paste of described plant is beneficial. **Piles, indigestion, diarrhea, inflammation, jaundice, excess and turbid micturition:** Root powder of described plant 1 g, raw sugar 15 g, with lukewarm water, two times a day, is beneficial. **Chronic diarrhea:** Root powder of described plant 1 g, roasted seeds of *Cuminum cyminum* 1 g, rock salt 500 mg, with whey, after meal, two times a day, is beneficial. **Piles:** Root powder of described plant 1 g, raw sugar 20 g, with diluted wine 20 ml, two times a day, is beneficial. **Colic:** Root powder of described plant 2 g, soda bi carb 500 mg, fried gum of *Ferula narthex* 125 mg, with lukewarm water, two times a day, is beneficial. **Nausea, vomiting:** Juice of fresh tuber of described plant 5 ml, juice of *Mentha spicata* 5 ml, or *Allium cepa* 5 ml, three times a day, is useful. **Rhinitis, cough, bronchitis, low fever:** Syrup of roasted tuber powder of described plant 3 g, with raw sugar 20 g, two times a day, is beneficial. **Hiccough:** Snuff of powder of described plant 250 mg, as required. **Unconsciousness:** Snuff of root powder of described plant, *Zingiber officinale, Piper longum,* 500 mg, two times a day, is beneficial. **Urticaria:** Juice of fresh tuber of described plant 5 ml, with honey 10 g, two times a day, is useful. **Inflammation:** Rubbing the tuber powder of described plant is beneficial. **Hypothermia, depression:** Local application of paste of tuber of described plant, or massage of powder of described plant with oil, is beneficial. **Neuralgia, convulsions, calcaneo-dynea, inflammation:** First make massage with castor oil on affected part, dust the powder of described plant, then paint some oil on leaves of *Ricinus communis* or *Nicotiana tabacum* and warm them, then put them on affected part, put some cotton and tie bandage or cloth. Make this medication at night before sleeping and no cold exposure or cold water allowed to patient. This application gives very quick relief. **Hypera-cidity:** Juice of fresh tuber of described plant 5 ml, juice of *Phylanthus emblica* 5 ml, with sugar candy powder 10 g, or juice of *Punica grantum* 25 ml, two times a day, is beneficial. **Renal and vesical calculus:** Decoction of mix powder of described plant, bark of *Crataeva magna, Tribulus terrestris, Bergenia ciliate, solanum nigrum,* 10 g, with nitrate of potash 500 mg and raw sugar 15 g, two times a day, is beneficial. **Senile polyuria:** Juice of fresh tuber of described plant 10 ml, with sugar candy powder 10 g, two times a day, is beneficial. **Lumbago of women:** Root powder of described plant 1 g, seeds of *Trachy spermum-ammi* 2 g, root powder of *Piper longum* 500 mg, sugar candy powder 10 g, with milk, two times a day, is beneficial. **Gout:** Root powder of described plant 2 g, *Smilax china* 1 g, *Colchicum leutium* 500 mg, with *'Punarnavastak kwatha'* at morning, *'Manjisthadi kwatha'* at noon and *'Dashamoola kwatha,* 10 g, at evening, is beneficial. **Penile dysfunction:** (1) Root powder of described plant 2 g, juice of *Allium cepa* 5 ml, honey 10 g, clarified butter 10 g, two times a day, is beneficial. (2) Mix powder of root powder of described plant, fruits of *Myristica fragrans, Cinamomum verum, Piper cubeba,* 3 g with honey 10 g or milk, two times a day, is useful. **General debility, somasthenia:** Mix powder of root powder of described plant, *Argyreia nervosa,* roots of *Sida cordifolia, Anacyclus pyrenthrum, Cuminum cyminum, Terminalia chebula, Mesua ferrea,* 4 g, with milk, two times a day, is beneficial. **Allergic bronchitis:** Mix powder of root powder of described plant, *Clerodendron serratum, Piper longum, Ephedra gerardiana, Vitis vinifera, Curcuma zedoria,* 4 g, with oil of *Sesamum orientale* 10 ml, is beneficial. **Epilepsy:** Mix powder of root powder of described plant, *Coriandrum sativum, Cedrus deodara, Curcuma longa, Allium sativum, Tinospora cordifolia, Vitex negundo,* with honey 10 g, two times a day, is useful. **Liver and spleen enlargement:** Mix powder of root powder of described plant, nitrate of potash, soda bi carb, salt petre, Amonium chloride, borax, with lukewarm water, 30 minutes, after the meal, two times a day, is beneficial.

Formulations: *Panchaka churna, Samasharkar churna, Aadraka khanda, Shobhagyasunthi paaka, Trikatu churna, Panchakola churna, Eranda paaka, Abhayaarista, Saaraswataarista, Aswagandhaarista, Jwaraankusha rasa, Kanakaasava, Jeerakaadhyarista, Shothaari* *mandoora, Elaadi ghrita, Vaiswaanara churna, Shunthi suraa, Shunthi paanaka.*

Recommended readings:

Acharya, B.K. (2008), Ayurveda Jadi-buti Rahasya, Patanjali Yogapitha, Haridwar, PP. 374.

Bhutya, R.K. (2007), Vanaspati Aushadha Vigyana, Scientific Publishers (India), Jodhpur, PP. 217.

Brahmavarchas (2003), Ayurved Ka Pran Vanoshadhi Vigyan, Shanti Kunj, Haridwar, PP. 472.

Chunekar, K.C. (2004), Bhava Prakash Nighantu, Chaukhambha Bharti Academy, Varanasi, PP. 13.

Dhiman, A.K. (2006), Ayurvedic Drug Plants, Daya Publishing House, Delhi, PP. 362.

Khare, C.P. (2007), Indian Medicinal Plants, Springer (India) P.L. New Delhi, PP. 733.

Kirtikar, K.R. & Basu, B.D. (1998), Indian Medicinal Plants, L.M Basu, Allahabad, Vol. 4, PP. 2435.

Misra, B.L. (2005), Dravya Guna Hastamalaka, Publication scheme, Jaipur, PP. 337.

Nair, R.Vasudevan, (2007), Indian Medicinal Plants, Orient Longman P.L. Chennai, Vol. 5, PP. 431.

Namjoshi, A.N. (2001), The Ayurvedic Pharmacopoeia of India, Government of India, Department of Indian Systems of Medicine & Homoeopathy, New Delhi, Part-1, Volume- 1, PP. 12 and 2-103.

Pareek, G.N. (2005), Sudhanidhi, Vanoshadhi Ratnakar, Dhanvantari Karyalaya, Aligarh, Vol. 8, PP. 176.

Prajapati, N.D., Purohit, S.S., Sharma, A.K. & Tarun Kumar (2003), A Hand Book of Medicinal Plants, Agrobios India, Jodhpur, PP. 552.

Sharma, P.C., Yelne, MB. & Denis, T.J. (2000), Database on medicinal plants used in ayurveda, Central Council for research in Ayurveda and siddha, Vol. 5, PP. 315.

Sharma, P.V. (1981), Dravya gun vigyana, Chaukhambha Bharti Academy, Varanasi, Vol. 1, PP. 331.

Singh, R.S. (2002), Vanoshadhi Nirdeshika, Uttar Pradesh Hindi Sansthan, Lucknow, PP. 389.

Swami, K.N. (1985), Gavon Main Aushadh Ratna, Kalera Krishana Gopal, Kalera (Raj.), Vol. 1, PP. 14.

497. *Zingiber zerumbet* Rosc. Ex Sm.

Family: Zingiberaceae.

Synonym: *Z.spurium, Amomum spurium, A.sylvestre.*

Name: English: Zerumbet Ginger, **Sanskrit:** *Karpoori Haridraa, Mahaabhari vachaa,* **Hindi:** *Kapoor Haldi,* **Local:** *Mahabhari vachaa, Narkachura.*

Botanical characteristics: Habit: An erect annual herb, 0.9-2 m high, like sugarcane. **Rhizome:** Thick, yellowish, yellow inside, hard, biennial, with a strong aromatic ginger-like taste, but some bitterness, root fibres vermiform, **Stem:** Leafy, about 13 mm in diam., cylindric, glabrous, **Leaf:** Arising in two ranked from unbranched, fleshy, aerial stems, 20-30 by 5-7.5 cm, sessile, oblong-lanceolate or oblanceolate, acuminate, glabrous, base narrowed; like the leaf of *Lobelia nicotianaefolia,* ligule 1.3-2 cm long, truncate, membranous, **Flower:** Flowering stem 30-45 cm long, stout, usually flexuous, clothed with long appressed obtuse sheaths, flowers white to pale sulphur-yellow, born on a fleshy spike with each flower arising from under a green to reddish bract, the inflorescence many flowered, but usually only 1-3 flowers open at a time. **Fruit:** Capsule, small, ellipsoid, 2.5 cm long, **Seed:** 4 mm long, oblong, black.

Flowering and fruiting period: December to April and June-August.

Habitat: Throughout India, from Himalaya to Southwards, widely cultivated in the tropics, common in moist forests to over 500 m.

Parts used: Rhizome. **Dosage:** 1-3 g.

Collection period: April to June.

Ayurvedic properties: ***Ras:*** *katu, tikta,* ***Gun:*** *laghu, rukhsa,* ***Veerya:*** *ushna,* ***Vipaka:*** *madhur,* ***Tridosha*** **Effect:** alleviates ***Kapha:*** *++,* ***Vaata:*** *+.*

Chemical constituents: The **rhizome** contains flavonoid such as afzelin, flavonoid glycosides, essential oils, chlorgenic acid, ferullic acid and curcumin. Also alkaloids; camphene, camphor and monoterpenoids; gigerol, zingeberol, zingerone, sesquiterpenoids including zerumbone and zerumbone epoxide, oxalic acid, kaempferol derivatives, The **oil** contains about 13% monoterpens and several sesquiterpenes of which humulene and zerumbone are major constituents. The major constituents of monoterpenes is camphene. Zerumbone inhibits the growth of *Micrococcus pyogenes* var. *aures* and *Mycobacterium tuberculosis.*

Action and disease indications: The **Rhizomes** are thermogenic, stimulant, antibacterial, hypotensive, febrifuge, carminative, prescribed in cough, thrush, diabetes, dyspepsia, wounds, piles, flatulence, bronchitis, asthma, intestinal worms, skin diseases, colic, fever, peptic ulcers and mouth infections.

Clinical uses: Skin diseases: Local application of paste of tuber of described plant is beneficial. **Asthma, bronchitis:** Tuber powder of described plant 1 g, with honey 10 g, two times a day, is useful.

Recommended readings:

Bhutya, R.K. (2007), Vanaspati Aushadha Vigyana, Scientific Publishers (India), Jodhpur, PP. 54.

Chunekar, K.C. (2004), Bhava Prakash Nighantu, Chaukhambha Bharti Academy, Varanasi, PP. 47.

Khare, C.P. (2007), Indian Medicinal Plants, Springer (India) P.L. New Delhi, PP. 734.

Kirtikar, K.R. & Basu, B.D. (1998), Indian Medicinal Plants, L.M Basu, Allahabad, Vol. 4, PP. 2438.

Prajapati, N.D., Purohit, S.S., Sharma, A.K. & Tarun Kumar (2003), A Hand Book of Medicinal Plants, Agrobios India, Jodhpur, PP. 552.

498. *Ziziphus jujuba* (Lam.) Gaertn. non-Mill.

Family: Rhamnaceae.

Synonym: *Z.mauritiana, Rhamnus jujuba.*

Name: English: Indian Jujube, Common Jujube, **Sanskrit:** *Kol, Badara, Fenil, Kuval, Ghontaa,* **Hindi:** *Baraa Ber,* **Local:** *Baada Bor.*

Botanical characteristics: Habit: A large thorny branched deciduous shrub or small tree with dense spreading crown, 6 m in height and 0.6 m in girth. **Stem:** Bark rough grey or black, having irregular deep cracks and strong reddish hard wood, prickles on stem and branches, mostly in pairs, 2.5 cm long, one straight and the other curved, young branches more or less densely pubescent. The wood of branches is very elastic. **Leaf:** Alternate, 3-6.3 by 2.5-5 cm, oblong or ovate, usually serrulate or apex distinctly toothed, obtuse, base oblique and 3-nerved, nerves depressed on the glabrous shining upper surface, and densely clothed beneath with white or buff tomentum. Petioles 2.5-10 mm long. **Flower:** Bisexual, 3.8-5 mm diam., greenish-yellow, in axillary dense fascicles 1.2-1.9 cm long, or sessile or short penducled tomentose cymes. **Fruit:** Drupes, 1.2-2.5 cm diam., globose or ovoid, succulent, fleshy, smooth, turning from yellow to orange and finally red or brown, pulp enclosing a hard stone. **Seed:** 1-2 celled.

Flowering and fruiting period: September-October and December-January.

Habitat: Indigenous and naturalized throughout India, outer Himalaya, in dry deciduous forests, up to 1500 m elevation.

Parts used: Fruit, fruit pulp, devoid of seed, stem bark, leaves.

Dosage: Fruit 25-50 g, dried fruit pulp 3-6 g, devoid of seed 3-6 g, stem bark 5-10 g.

Collection period: January-February.

Ayurvedic properties: ***Ras:*** *madhur, kashaaya,* ***Gun:*** *laghu, snigdha,* ***Veerya:*** *sheeta,* ***Vipaka:*** *madhur,* ***Tridosha*** **Effect:** alleviates ***Vaata:*** **++**, aggravates ***Pitta:*** +, *Kapha:* +.

Chemical constituents: The **Leaves** contain protopine and berbeline; exhibits anticholinergic activity. The **fruits** contain cyclic AMP and cyclic GMP, Sisyphus saponins 1,2 and 3; jujuboside B and *p*-caumaroylates of alphitolic acid. The **seeds** contain saponins- jujubosides A and B; the saponin yield the sapogenin-jujubogenin. The **Bark** contains leucocyanidin, leucopelargocyanidin.

Action and disease indications: The **leaves** are cooling, astringent, anthelmintic, diaphoretic, antipyretic, good for washing hairs, used for stomatitis, burning sensation, wounds, ulorrhea, syphilitic ulcers, asthma, pyrexia, typhoid fever, diarrhea and obesity. The **fruits** are cooling, purgative, mucilaginous, expectorant, anodyne, pectoral, styptic, aphrodisiac, cardio-tonic, depurative, appetizer and tonic, used for burning sensation, hyperdipsia, consumption, urticaria, vomiting, flatulence, constipation, dyspepsia, nausea, skin diseases, pruritis, wounds, ulcers, hemorrhages, and general debility. The **bark** is astringent, constipating and tonic, used for diarrhea, dysentery, gingivitis and boils. The **seeds** are astringent, good for eyes, soporific and tonic, used for hiccough, dipsia, cough, asthma, wounds, burning sensation, diarrhea, vomiting, leucorrhea, insomnia and general debility.

Clinical uses: Bleeding diasthesis: Gum of described plant 6 g, with juice of fruit of *Benincasa hispida,* 50 ml, three times a day, is useful. **Boils, furunculosis:** Poultice of leaves of described plant is useful. **For conditioning of hairs:** Washing of hairs by mixture of decoction of leaves of described plant, fruits of *Phylanthus emblica, Acacia sinuta, Sapindus emarginatus,* 25 g, is beneficial.

Formulations: *Shelaadi kwaatha, Agurvaadi taila, Mahaa balaa taila, Hapushaadhya ghrita, Yavaanishaadava churna, Chandanaadhya taila, Balaa taila, Gojihvaadi kwaatha, Dadhikaa ghrita, Dhanvantara ghrita, Vrihat Maasha Taila.*

Recommended readings:

Bhutya, R.K. (2007), Vanaspati Aushadha Vigyana, Scientific Publishers (India), Jodhpur, PP. 165.

Brahmavarchas (2003), Ayurved Ka Pran Vanoshadhi Vigyan, Shanti Kunj, Haridwar, PP. 474.

Chunekar, K.C. (2004), Bhava Prakash Nighantu, Chaukhambha Bharti Academy, Varanasi, PP. 573.

Khare, C.P. (2007), Indian Medicinal Plants, Springer (India) P.L. New Delhi, PP. 735.

Kirtikar, K.R. & Basu, B.D. (1998), Indian Medicinal Plants, L.M Basu, Allahabad, Vol. 1, PP. 589.

Misra, B.L. (2005), Dravya Guna Hastamalaka, Publication scheme, Jaipur, PP. 441.

Nair, R.Vasudevan, (2007), Indian Medicinal Plants, Orient Longman P.L. Chennai, Vol. 5, PP. 439.

Namjoshi, A.N. (2001), The Ayurvedic Pharmacopoeia of India, Government of India, Department of Indian Systems of Medicine & Homoeopathy, New Delhi, Part-1, Volume- 3, PP. 94.

Sharma, P.C., Yelne, MB. & Denis, T.J. (2000), Database on medicinal plants used in ayurveda, Central Council for research in Ayurveda and siddha, Vol. 8, PP. 219.

Sharma, P.V. (1981), Dravya gun vigyana, Chaukhambha Bharti Academy, Varanasi, Vol. 1, PP. 572.

Swami, K.N. (1985), Gavon Main Aushadh Ratna, Kalera Krishana Gopal, Kalera (Raj.), Vol. 3, PP. 106.

499. *Ziziphus nummularia* (Burm. f.) Wight & Arn.

Family: Rhamnaceae.

Synonym: *Z.rotundifolia, Rhamnus nummularia.*

Name: English: Wild Jujube, **Sanskrit:** *Karkandhu, Badari, Ajapriyaa, Kuhaa, Koli, Vishamaa, Ubhayakantakaa,* **Hindi:** *Chota Ber,* **Local:** *Chota Ber.*

Botanical characteristics: Habit: A small spinous shrub, height 0.65-2 m. **Stem:** Branched from near the root; branches diverticate, slender, zigzag, bark light coloured. **Leaf:** 1.2-2 cm in size, orbicular or ovate, spinous-dentate, clothed beneath with a whitish or buff tomentum; less densely tomentose above; petioles 3-6 mm long, tomentose; stipular thorns usually in pairs, one straight, sharp and slender, nearly as long as leaf, the other short, hooked. **Flower:** Small, greenish-yellow, in axillary, sessile pubescent cymes, buds globose, pedicels short. **Fruit:** Drupes globose, 8 mm diam., glabrous, green when unripe, yellow and turning red when ripe, edible, containing a single stone. **Seed:** 1-2 celled.

Flowering and fruiting period: September-October and October-November.

Habitat: Dry and arid zones of India, mostly in Punjab, Rajasthan.

Parts used: Fruit, fruit pulp, devoid of seed, root and stem bark, leaves.

Dosage: Fruit 25-50 g, dried fruit pulp 3-6 g, devoid of seed 3-6 g, root and stem bark 5-10 g, leaves for external use.

Collection period: October-November.

Ayurvedic properties: ***Ras:*** *amla, kashaaya,* ***Gun:*** *laghu, rukhsa,* ***Veerya:*** *sheeta,* ***Vipaka:*** *katu,* ***Tridosha*** **Effect:** alleviates ***Vaata:*** *++,* ***Pitta:*** *++.*

Chemical constituents: The **leaves** contain ascorbic acid, The **root bark** contains 12% of tannin and cyclopeptide alkaloids- numularines A and B and C, mucronineD and amphibineH. The **stem bark** contains numularine M, R and S, besides frangufoline. Numularine R and S, showed antibacterial activity against Gram-negative and Gram-positive bacteria. The alkaloid fraction, obtained from the bark, showed significant analgesic activity.

Action and disease indications: The **Fruit** is cooling, astringent, appetizer, stomachic, used for bilious affections. The **leaves** are cooling, good for washing hairs, used for sore throat, bleeding gums, scabies and skin diseases. The **seeds** are good for eyes, seminal weakness, tonic, aphrodisiac, pains, used for asthma, bronchitis and burning sensation.

Clinical uses: Hiccough: Powder of devoid of seeds of described plant 6 g, with honey 10 g, as required. **Eczema, boils:** Local application of paste of leaves of described plant, is beneficial. **Diarrhea, dysentery, leucorrhea, epistaxis:** Root bark powder of described plant 6 g, with water, two times a day, is beneficial. **Disphonia:** Sucking of root bark of described plant, 5 g, is beneficial. **Leucorrhea:** Root bark powder of described plant 5 g, raw sugar 15 g, with water, two times a day, is beneficial. **Stomatitis:** Gargles by decoction of leaves of described plant, 20 g, two times a day, is beneficial.

Formulations: *Dashamooladhya taila, Mahaa drakhsaasava, Updansahara kwaatha.*

Recommended readings:

Bhutya, R.K. (2007), Vanaspati Aushadha Vigyana, Scientific Publishers (India), Jodhpur, PP. 164.

Chunekar, K.C. (2004), Bhava Prakash Nighantu, Chaukhambha Bharti Academy, Varanasi, PP. 573.

Khare, C.P. (2007), Indian Medicinal Plants, Springer (India) P.L. New Delhi, PP. 736.

Kirtikar, K.R. & Basu, B.D. (1998), Indian Medicinal Plants, L.M Basu, Allahabad, Vol. 1, PP. 592.

Swami, K.N. (1985), Gavon Main Aushadh Ratna, Kalera Krishana Gopal, Kalera (Raj.), Vol. 3, PP. 107.

500. *Ziziphus sativa* Gaertn.

Family: Rhamnaceae.

Synonym: *Z. vulgaris.*

Name: English: Chinese Tsao, **Sanskrit:** *Sauveera, Raajbadar,* **Hindi:** *Unnaaba,* **Local:** *Unnaaba.*

Botanical characteristics: Habit: A small deciduous tree, often shrubby, quite glabrous. **Stem:** Branches of young plants armed with very short spines, one straight, 2.5 cm long, the other much shorter, recurved, older trees usually unarmed. **Leaf:** 2.5-5 cm long, ovate-lanceolate, glabrous, crenate-serrete, oblique, 3-nerved; petioles 2.5-7.5 mm long. If leaves masticate in mouth, the tongue becomes taste senseless for 5-20 minutes. **Flower:** Greenish-white, few-flowered, axillary clusters, petal clawed. **Fruit:** Drupes, red, fleshy, pulp yellow, sweet, ellipsoid, 2 cm long. **Seed:** Tuberculate, long, hard, flat, brown.

Flowering and fruiting period: September-October and February-March.

Habitat: Found in Punjab, Himachal Pradesh, up to 1950 m, eastwards to West Bengal.

Parts used: Fruit. **Dosage:** 5-10 g.

Collection period: February-March.

Ayurvedic properties: ***Ras:*** *madhur,* ***Gun:*** *guru, snigdha,* ***Veerya:*** *sheeta,* ***Vipaka:*** *madhur,* ***Tridosha*** **Effect:** alleviates ***Vatta:*** **++,** aggravates ***Kapha:*** **+,** ***Pitta:*** **+.**

Chemical constituents: The **fruits** contain saponins of dammaran type, known as Sisyphus saponins; jujubosides, zizybeosides and zizyvy-osides, together with pentacyclic triterpenoids. Flavonoids include naringanin glycosides, vomifoloil and roseoside. Also contains mucilage and sugars. Fruits have antiallergic, sedative activity. The **seed** extract produces a transient fall in blood pressure.

Action and disease indications: The **fruits** are emollient, anti-tussive, anti-allergic, seminal weakness, burning sensation, excessive thirst, nourishing tonic, protects liver and prevents stress ulcer formation. The **seeds** used for dry cough and skin diseases.

Clinical uses: Vomiting, anorexia, dry cough: Fruit powder of described plant 10 g, sugar candy powder 10 g, with honey 10 g, two times a day, is useful. **Dry bronchitis:** Sucking of tablets of 500 mg, of mix powder of fruit powder of described plant, gum of *Gossipium religiosum,* flower petals of *Rosa centifolia,* sugar candy powder, dose 3-6 tablets, per day, is useful. **Disphonia:** Syrup of fruits of described plant, 10 ml, three times a day, is useful. **Rhinitis, constipation:** Decoction of fruits of described plant 10 g, fruits of *Cordia dichotoma* 6 g, *Zingiber officinale* 1 g, *Cichorium antybus* 3 g, *Viola odorata* 3 g, raw sugar 15 g, two times a day, is beneficial. **Diabetes inspidus:** Leaves powder of described plant 5 g, with water, two times a day, is beneficial.

Formulations: *Gojihvaadi kwaatha, Lauka sapista, Raktashodhakaarista, Raktashodhaka sarbata.*

Recommended readings

Bhutya, R.K. (2007), Vanaspati Aushadha Vigyana, Scientific Publishers (India), Jodhpur, PP. 32.

Chunekar, K.C. (2004), Bhava Prakash Nighantu, Chaukhambha Bharti Academy, Varanasi, PP. 572.

Khare, C.P. (2007), Indian Medicinal Plants, Springer (India) P.L. New Delhi, PP. 736.

Kirtikar, K.R. & Basu, B.D. (1998), Indian Medicinal Plants, L.M Basu, Allahabad, Vol. 1, PP. 593.

Misra, B.L. (2005), Dravya Guna Hastamalaka, Publication scheme, Jaipur, PP. 442.

Pareek, G.N. (2005), Sudhanidhi, Vanoshadhi Ratnakar, Dhanvantari Karyalaya, Aligarh, Vol. 9, PP. 113.

Singh, R.S. (2002), Vanoshadhi Nirdeshika, Uttar Pradesh Hindi Sansthan, Lucknow, PP. 50.

Swami, K.N. (1985), Gavon Main Aushadh Ratna, Kalera Krishana Gopal, Kalera (Raj.), Vol. 2, PP. 120.

Classification of Plants According to Action

Adrenergic:

Abies spectabilis - Talisapatra
Acorus calamus - Vacha
Cinamomum verum - Dalchini
Common Salt - *Lawana*
Compound drugs of Arsenic
Datura innoxia - Dhattura
Ferula foetida - Hingu
Piper nigrum - Kali Mircha
'Rasa manikya'
Strychnos nux-vomica - Tinduka

Analgesic:

Aconitum ferox - Vatsanabha
Acorus calamus - Vacha
Apium graveolens - Ajamoda
Datura innoxia - Dhattura
Moringa oleifera - Shobhanjana
'Panchakola'
Root of *Piper longum - Pippalamoola*
Shita prashamana gana
Shulaghna gana
Strychnos nux-vomica - Tinduka
Trachyspermum ammi - Ajawayana

Anaphrodiasiac:

Azadirachta indica – Neem
Coriandrun sativum - Dhanyaka
Diospyrus malabarica - Tendu
Papaver sommniferum – Afima
Syzygium cumini – Jamun
Alkaline of Medicinal Plants - *Khsara*
Old Gum of *Commifora mukul - Guggulu*
Carthanus tinctorius - Kusumbha
Macrotyloma uniflorum - Kulathi
Dolichos lablab – Sem
Terminalia belliarica - Bahera

Anthelmintic:

Aconitum heterophyllum - Atisha
Adiantum incisum - Mayurshikhai
Allium sativum - Rasona
Aloe barbadensis - Ghritakumari
Anthum graveolens - Soya
Areca catechu - Supari
Argemone maxicana - Satyanasi
Aristolochia bractiolata - Keetamari
Artimisia maritima – Kirmani-Ajavayana
Bambusa arundinacea - Vansa
Blumea lacera - Kukaronda
Catunaregan spinosa - Madanaphala
Centipeda orbicularis - Nakachhikani
Chenopodium album - Bathua
Cleome gynendra - Hulhula
Cucumis maculata - Kachara
Curcuma aromatica - Vana haridra
Curcuma longa - Haridra
Embelia ribes - Vidanga
Ferula foetida - Hingu
Fruit rind of *Punica grantum - Anara twaka*
Holarrhena antidysenterica - Kutaja
Justisia adhatoda - Vasa
Mallolotus Philipensis - Kampillaka
Malus pumila - Seba
Merremia gangetica - Mushakarni
Momordica charantia - Karela
Morus indica - Sahatoota
Mucana pruriens - Kavancha roma
Operculina turpenthum - Nishotha
Pinus roxburghii - Sarala
Pongamia pinnata - Karanja
Portulaca oleracea - Lona
Prosopis cineraria - Shami
Psoralea corylifolia - Bakuchi
Ruta graveolens - Sitaba
Seeds of *Butea Monosperma - Palasha beeja*
Swertia chiryata - Chirayata
Tectona grandis - Sagavan
Trachyspermum ammi - Ajavayana

Anti-allergic:

Abies spectabilis - Talishpatra
Acacia catechu - Khadira
Achyranthus aspera - Apamarga
Albizia lebbeck - Shirisha
Andrographis peniculata - -Kalamegha
Anthum graveolens - Ajamoda
Azadirachta indica - Nimba
Berberis aristata - Daruharidra
Boerhavia diffusa - Punarnava
Brassica campestris - Sarson
Buchanania lanzan - Chironji
Callicarpa macrophylla - Priyangu
Cassia fistula - Amalatasa
Cassia tora - Chakramarda
Cedrus deodara - Devadaru
Centella asiatica - Mandookaparni
Cinamomum camphora - Kapura
Cinamomum verum - Dalchini
Commifora mukul - Guggulu
Coriandrun sativum - Dhanyaka
Curcuma longa - Haridra
Cyperus scarissus - Nagarmotha
Datura innoxia - Dhattura
Eclipta prostrate - Bhringaraja
Elettaria cardamomum - Choti-Ilayachi
Fagonia indica - Dhamasa
Ferula foetida - Hingu
Foeniculum vulgare - Saunfa
Fumaria indica - Pittapapara
Hemidesmus indicus - Anantamoola
Holarrhena antidysenterica - Kutaja
Justisia adhatoda - Vasa
Lawsonia inermis - Mehandi
Melia azedarach - Bakayana
Mentha spicata - Pudina
Mesua ferrea - Nagakesara
Nelumbo nucifera - Kamal
Ocimum basilicum - Van Tulasi
Ocimum sanctum - Tulasi
Operculina turpenthum - Nishotha
Papaver sommniferum - Afima
Phyllanthus emblica - Aamalaki
Phyllanthus fraternus - Bhumyamalaki
Picrorhiza kurroa - Kutaki
Piper cubeba - Kankola
Piper nigrum - Kali Mircha

Pongamia pinnata - Karanja
Pterocarpus santalinus - Chandan-rakta
Rauvolfia serpentina - Sarpagandha
Ricinus cumonis - Eranda
Santalum album - Chandan-sweta
Saussurea lappa - Kushtha
Solunum ferox - Vrihati
Solunum surattense - Kantakari
Tinospora cordifolia - Amrita
Trachyspermum ammi - Ajavayana
Trichosanthus dioica - Patol
Vetiveria zizanoiodes - Ushira

Anti-anxiety:

Asparagus racemosus - Shatavari
Bacopa monnieri - Brahmi
Benincasa hispida - Kushamanda
Cannabis sativa - Bhanga
Centella asiatica - Mandukaparni
Cocus nucifera - Nariyal
Convolvulus pluricaulis - Shankhapushpi
Coriandrun sativum - Dhanyaka
Fagonia indica - Dhanvayasa
Foeniculum vulgare - Saunfa
Glycyrrhiza glabra - Madhuyashti
Gmelina arboria - Gambhari
Nardostachys jatamansi - Jatamansi
Papaver sommniferum - Afima
Rauvolfia serpentina - Sarpagandha
Rosa centifolia - Gulab
Saccharum officinale - Ikhsu
Scirpus grossus - Kasheruka
Valeriana jatamansi - Tagar
Vetiveria zizanoiodes - Ushira
Vigna mungo - Urada
Withania somnifera - Aswagandha

Anti-biotic:

Acorus calamus - Vacha
Argemone maxicana - Satyanasi
Azadirachta indica - Nimba
Berberis aristata - Daru Haridra
Cinamomum verum - Tejpata
Citrullus cololynthis - Indrayava
Commifora mukul - Guggula
Curcuma longa - Haridra
Justisia adhatoda - Vasa
Moringa oleifera - Shobhanjana
Picrorhiza kurroa - Kutaki
Pluchea lanceolata - Rasona
'Saptavinshati Guggula'
Saussurea lappa - Kustha
Tinospora cordifolia - Amrita
Trachyspermum ammi - Ajawayana
Tricosanthus dioica - Patola
Trijata

Anti-cholagogue:

Datura innoxia - Dhattura
Ephedra gerardiana - Suchi
Mimosa pudica - Lajjavanti
Papaver sommniferum - Afima
Plants containing Astringent Taste
Seeds of *Mongifera indica - Aama beeja majja*
Syzygium cumini - Jamun beeja majja

Anti-coagulant:

Aconitum heterophyllum - Ativisha
Acorus calamus - Vacha
Alkalines of plants - *Khsara*
Allium sativum - Rason
Azadirachta indica - Nimba
Berberis aristata - Daru Haridra
Borex
Calotropis procera - Arka
Common salt - *Lavana*
Compound drugs of Arsenic
Curcuma longa - Haridra
Cyperus scarissus - Nagarmotha
Dashamoola
Excrement of Pigeon - Kapot Vistha
Hemidesmus indicus - Anantamoola
Justisia adhatoda - Vasa
Picrorhiza kurroa - Kutaki
Pinus Roxburghii - Sarala
Piper Nigrum - Kali Mircha
Plumbago zeylanica - Chitraka
Trichisanthus dioica - Patola
Trifala
Trikatu
Urine of Cow

Anti-convulsant:

Allium sativum - Rasona
Alpina galangal-uniflorum - Kulinjana
Anacyclus pyrenthrum - Akarkara
Anthum graveolens - Ajamoda
Artimisia maritime - Kiramani Ajavayana
Asparagus racemosus - Satavari
Atrpa belladonna - Suchi
Bacopa monnieri - Brahmi
Celestrus paniculatus - Jyotismati
Commifora mukul - Guggulu
Cuminum cyminum - Jiraka-sweta
Curcuma zedoria - Kachura
Datura innoxia - Dhattura
Ephedra gerardiana - Soma
Ferula foetida - Hingu
Glycyrrhiza glabra - Madhyasthi
Hyoscyamus niger - Khurasani Ajavayana
Lepideum sativum- Chandrasoora
Nardostachys jatamansi - Jatamansi
Ocimum sanctum - Tulasi
Papaver sommniferum - Afima
Pluchea lanceolata - Rasna
Rauvolfia serpentina - Sarpagandha
Sisymbrium ireo - Khubakalan
Strychnos nux-vomica - Tinduka
Styrax benzoin - Lobana
Trachyspermum ammi - Ajavayana
Vetiveria zizanoiodes - Ushira
Vitis vinifera - Drakhsa

Anti-diarrheal:

Agele marmelos -Bilva
Alum - *Shubhra*
Fruit rind of *Punica grantum - Anara phala twaka*
Gum of *Bombax cieba - Mocharasa*
Holarrhena antidysenterica - Kutaja
Seeds of *Mongifera indica - Aama Beeja*
Seeds of *Phyllanthus emblica - Aamalaki Beeja*
Syzygium cumini - Jamuna

Anti-diuretic:

Acacia katechu - Khadira
Aegle marmelos - Bilva
Albizia lebbeck - Shirisha
Anogeisus latifolia - Dhava
Bauhinia racemosa - Ashamantaka
Calotropis procera - Arka
Ficus bangalensis - Vata
Ficus racemosa- Udumber
Ficus religiosa - Pipal

Ficus virens - Plakhsa
Grewia tillifolia - Dhanvana
Gum of *Bombax cieba- Mocharasa*
Momordica charantia - Karela
Semecarpus anacardium - Bhallataka
Syzygium cumini - Jamun
Trifala

Anti-emetic:

Boerhavia diffusa - Punarnava
Clay
Coriandrun sativum - Dhanyaka
Elettaria cardamomum - Elayachi-Choti
Ferula foetida - Hingu
Foeniculum vulgare - Saunfa
Fried seeds of *Oryza sativa - Chaval ka lava*
Garcinia penduculata - Amlaveta
Hedycium spicatum - Kapoorakachari
Hemidesmus indicus - Anantamoola
Hordeum vulgare - Jo
Leaves of *Mangifera indica - Aama Patra*
Leaves of *Syzygium cumini- Jamun patra*
Limonia acidissima - Kapittha
Mentha pipertia - Piparamenta
Mentha spicata - Pudina
Oxalis corniculata - Changeri
Papaver sommniferum - Afima
Pterocarpus santalinus - Chandana-rakta
Punica grantum - Anara
Rhus parviflora - Tintidika
Rosa centifolia - Gulab
Santalum album - Chandana-Sweta
Stem bark of *Ficus religiosa - Pipal twaka*
Syzygium aromaticum - Lavanga
Vetiveria zizanoiodes - Ushira
Vitis vinifera - Drakhsa
Zizyphus nummularia - Bera
Zizyphus sativa - Unnaba

Anti-emmenogogue:

Alkaline of *Musa paradisiaca - Kadali Khsara*
Amaranthus spinosus - Kanta Cholai
Androecium of *Nelumbo nusifera - Kamal kesar*
Anthocephalus chinensis - Kadamba
Boswellia serrata - Shallaki
Butea monosperma - Palasha
Clerodendrum serratum - Bharangi
Commifora myrrha - Bol
Glycyrrhiza glabra - Madhuyasti
Gmelina arboria - Gambhari
Musa paradisiaca - Kela
Myrica esculenta - Kayaphala
Orxylum indicum - Syonaka
Phyllanthus emblica - Aamalaki
Resin of *Ficus religiosa - Lakhsa*
Saraca asoca - Ashok
Seeds of *Mengifera indica - Aama beeja*
Seeds of *Syzygium cumini- Jamun beeja*
Shorea robusta - Shala
Symplocos racemosa - Lodhra

Anti-fungal:

Acacia catechu - Khadira
Alstonia scholaris - Saptaparna
Azadirachta indica - Nimba
Berberis aristata - Daru Haridra
Brassica campestris - Sarson
Brassica juncea - Rai
Caesalpinia bonduc - Kantaki Karanja
Cassia fistula - Amalatasa
Cassia tora - Chakramarda
Curcuma longa - Haridra
Embelia ribes - Vidanga
Hemidesmus indicus - Anantamoola
Holarrhena antidysenterica - Kutaja
Jasminum grandiflorum - Jati
Justisia adhatoda - Vasa
Mallolotus philipensis - Kampillaka
Ocimum sanctum - Tulasi
Phyllanthus fraternus - Bhumyamalaki
Pongamia pinnata - Karanja
Rubia cordifolia - Manjistha
Semecarpus anacardium - Bhallataka
Trachyspermum ammi - Ajavayana

Anti-galactogogue:

Acacia catechu - Khadira
Anthocephalus chinensis - Kadamba
Callicarpa macrophylla - Priyangu
Clerodendrum serratum - Bharangi
Fruit rind of *Punica grantum - Anara twaka*
Gum of *Bombax cieba - Mocharasa*
Hemidesmus indicus - Anantamoola
Mimosa pudica - Lajavanti
Seeds of *Phyllanthus emblica - Aamalaki beeja*
Seeds of *Mangifera indica - Aama beeja*
Seeds of *Syzygium cumini - Jamuna beeja*
Symplocos racemosa - Lodhra
Terminalia belliriaca- Bahera
Woodfordia fruticosa - Dhataki

Anti-histamine:

Azadirachta indica - Nimba
Buchanania lanzan - Chironji
Cassia fistula - Amalatasa
Clarified butter of cow - *Ghrita*
Cocus nucifera - Nariyal
Cuminum cyminum - Gerika
Curcuma longa - Haridra
Cyperus scarissus - Nagarmotha
Fagonia indica - Dhanvayasa
Fumaria indica - Pittapapara
Justisia adhatoda - Vasa
Luffa echinata - Devdali
Pavonia odorata - Netrabala
Piper nigrum - Kali Mircha
Ricinus cumonis - Eranda
Saccharum officinale - Ikhsu
Santalum album - Chandana
Solunum surattense - Kantakari
Terminalia arjuna - Arjuna
Tricosanthus dioica - Patola
Udardaprashamana mahakashaya
Vetiveria zizanoiodes - Ushira
Zingiber officinale – Shunthi

Anti-inflammatory:

Boerhavia diffusa - Punarnava
Commifora mukul - Guggula
Dashamola
Shothaghna gana
Solunum nigrum - Makoya
Tribulus terrestris - Gokhar
Trina panchamoola

Anti-oxidant:

Abutilon indicum - Atibala

Acorus calamus - *Vacha*
Aegle marmelos - *Bilva*
Albizia lebbeck- *Shirisha*
Allium sativum - *Rason*
Amorphophallus paeoniifolius - *Surana*
Anacyclus pyrenthrum - *Akarkara*
Anthum graveolens - *Soya*
Asparagus adscendens - *Safed-Mushali*
Asparagus racemosus - *Shatawari*
Azadirachta indica - *Nimbu*
Bacopa monnieri - *Brahmi*
Butea monosperma - *Palasha*
Celestrus paniculatus - *Jyotishmati*
Centella asiatica - *Mandookaparni*
Cinamomum verum - *Dalchini*
Cocus nucifera - *Nariyala*
Convolvulus pluricaulis - *Shankhapushpi*
Coriandrun sativum - *Dhanyaka*
Crocus sativus - *Kesara*
Cucurligo orchioides - *Kali-Mushali*
Dactylorhiza hatagirea - *Salama mishri*
Dalbergia sissoo- *Sisama*
Daucas carota - *Gajar*
Dioscorea bulbifera - *Varahikanda*
Elettaria cardamomum - *Choti-Ilayachi*
Eurale ferox - *Makhana*
Fagonia indica - *Dhanvayasa*
Ficus bengalensis - *Vata*
Ficus carica - *Anjira*
Ficus religiosa - *Pipala*
Foeniculum vulgare - *Saunfa*
Glycyrrhiza glabra - *Madhuyasti*
Grewia helicterifolia - *Nagabala*
Grewia subinequalis - *Phalasa*
Hemidesmus indicus - *Anantamoola*
Jivaniya gana
Mangifera indica - *Aama*
Nardostachys jatamansi – *Jatamansi*
Nelumbo nucifera - *Kamala*
Ocimum sanctum- *Tulasi*
Phoenix sylvestris - *Khajoora*
Phyllanthus emblica - *Aamalaki*
Piper longum - *Pippali*
Punica grantum - *Anara*
Saccharum officinale - *Ikhsu*
Santalum album - *Chandan-Sweta*
Sida cordifolia - *Bala*
Sida rhombifolia - *Mahabala*
Solunum nigrum - *Makoya*
Sphyeranthus indicus - *Gorakhamundi*
Strychnos nux-vomica - *Tinduka*
Tecomela undulata - *Rohitaka*
Tectona grandis - *Sagavana*
Terminalia chebula - *Haritaki*
Tinospora cordifolia - *Amrita*
Trapa natans - *Singhara*
Tribulus terrestris - *Gokharu*
Vigna mungo - *Urada*
Vitis vinifera - *Drakhsa*
Vrihaniya Mahakashaya
Withania somnifera - *Aswagandha*
Zingiber officinale - *Shunthi*

Anti-pyretic:

Aconitum ferox - *Vatsanabha*
Cedrus deodara - *Devadaru*
Curcuma longa - *Haridra*
Cyperus scarissus - *Nagarmotha*
Dashamoola
Grewia subinequalis - *Phalasha*
Hemidesmus indicus - *Anantamoola*
Justisia adhatoda - *Vasa*
Nardostachys jatamansi - *Jatamansi*
Ocimum sanctum - *Tulasi*
Panchakola
Rubia cordifolia - *Manjistha*
Salvadora persica - *Pilu*
Santalum album - *Chandana-sweta*
Swertia chiryata - *Chirayata*
Tinospora cordifolia - *Amrita*
Trichosanthes dioica - *Patha*
Trifala
Vetiveria zizanoiodes - *Ushira*
Vitis vinifera - *Drakhsa*
Zingiber officinale - *Shunthi*

Anti-rheumatic

Alhagi pseudalhagi - *Javasa*
Aloe barbadensis - *Ghritakumari*
Aquilaria malaccensis - *Agara*
Aristolochia indica - *Iswari*
Boerhavia diffusa - *Punarnava*
Calotropis procera,- *Arka*
Capparis decidua - *Karira*
Celestrus paniculatus - *Jyotishmati*
Citrullus colocynthis - *Indrayana*
Coculus hirsutus - *Patalagarudi*
Colchicum leutium - *Suranjana*
Cymbopogon martini - *Rohis trina*
Holarrhena antidysenterica - *Kutaja*
Iris insata - *Balvacha*
Lepidium sativum - *Chandrasoora*
Moringa oleifera - *Sobhanjana*
Myristica fragrans - *Jatiphala*
Oroxylum indicum - *Syonaka*
Plumbago zeylanica - *Chitraka*
Ricinus cumonis - *Eranda*
Salvadora persica - *Pilu*
Semecarpus anacardium - *Bhallataka*
Smilax china - *Chopachini*
Solunum surattense - *Kantakari*
Terminalia chebula - *Haritaki*
Tinospora cordifolia - *Amrita*
Trigonella foinum gracum - *Methi*
Valeriana jatamansi - *Tagara*
Vitex negundo - *Nirgundi*
Withania somnifera - *Aswagandha*
Zingiber officinale - *Shunthi*

Anti-septic:

Acacia catechu - *Khadira*
Acacia nilotica - *Babula*
Albizia lebbeck - *Shirisha*
Allium sativum - *Rason*
Apium graveolens - *Ajamoda*
argemone maxicana - *Satyanasi*
Azadirachta indica - *Nimba*
Bauhinia variegata - *Kachanara*
Berberis aristata - *Daruharidra*
Cassia tora - *Chakramarda*
Cedrus deodara - *Devadaru*
Chaturjata
Cinamomum camphora - *Kapoora*
Commifora mukul - *Guggulu*
Crocus sativus - *Kesar*
Curcuma longa - *Haridra*
Elettaria cardamomum - *Choti-Ilayachi*
Embelia ribes - *Vidanga*
Ferula foetida - *Hingu*
Ficus racemosa - *Udumbara*
Hemidesmus indicus - *Anantamoola*
Holarrhena antidysenterica - *Kutaja*
Hyoscyamus niger - *Khurasani Ajavayana*
Justisia adhatoda - *Vasa*

Melia azedarach - *Bakayana*
Mentha spicata - *Pudina*
Moringa oleifera - *Shobhanjana*
Piper cubeba - *Kankola*
Pistacia khinjuk - *Kakarasingi*
Pterocarpus santalinus - *Chandan-rakta*
Rubia cordifolia - *Manjistha*
Saussurea costus - *Kushtha*
Smilax china - *Chopachini*
Solunum surattense - *Kantakari*
Terminalia belliarica - *Bahera*
Trachyspermum ammi - *Ajavayana*
Trichosanthes dioica - *Patola*
Vitex negundo - *Nirgundi*

Anti-sialagogue:

Areca ctechu - *Supari*
Bauhinia veriegata - *Kanchanara*
Crotalaria verrucusa - *Shanapushpi*
Diospyrus malabarica - *Tendu*
Flowers of *Punica grantum* - *Anara Pushpa*
Fruit rind of *Punica grantum* - *Anara tvaka*
Fruits of *Acacia catechu* - *Khadira Phala*
Gum of *Bombax ceiba* - *Mocharasa*
Resin of *Ficus religiosa* - *Lakhsa*
Seeds of *Phyllanthus emblica* - *Aamalaki Beeja*
Seeds of *Tamarindus indica* - *Imali Beeja*
Stem bark of *Acacia catechu* - *Khadira Twaka*
Symplocos racemosa - *Lodhra*
Syzygium cumini - *Jamuna*
Terminalia belliarica - *Bahera*
Zingiber officinale - *Shunthi*

Anti-spasmodic:

Achyranthus aspera - *Apamarga*
Acorus calamus - *Vacha*
Alkaline of plants - *Khsara*
Apium graveolens - *Ajamoda*
Ferula foetida - *Hingu*
Glycyrrhiza glabra - *Madhuyasthi*
Gum of *Bombax ceiba* - *Mocharasa*
Hyoscyamus niger - *Khurasani Ajavayana*
Jivaniya gana
Panchakola
Piper longum - *Pippali*
Saccharum officinale - *Ikhsu*
Strychnos nux-vomica - *Tinduka*
Tephrosia purpuria - *Sharapunkha*
Trachyspermum ammi - *Ajavayana*

Anti-tussive:

Aquilaria malaccensis - *Agara*
Boerhavia diffusa - *Punarnava*
Cinamomum camphora - *Kapura*
Inula racemosa - *Pushkaramoola*
Ocimum sanctum - *Tulasi*
Phyllanthus emblica - *Aamalaki*
Phyllanthus fraternus - *Bhumyamalaki*
Piper longum - *Pippali*
Pistacia khinjuk - *Kakarasingi*
Solunum surattense - *Kantakari*
Terminalia chebula - *Haritaki*
Tinospora cordifolia - *Amrita*
Vitis vinifera - *Drakhsa*

Aphrodisiac:

Abelmoschus moschatus - *Latakastoori*
Abrus precatorius - *Gunja*
Acorus calamus - *Vacha*
Allium cepa - *Palandu*
Allium sativum- *Rason*
Ambergris - *Amber*
Anacyclus pyrenthrum - *Akarkara*
Blepheris edulis - *Utangana*
Celestrus paniculatus - *Jyotishmati*
Cinamomum verum - *Dalchini*
Crocus Sativus - *Kesara*
Echinops echinatus - *Untakatela*
Embelia ribes - *Vidanga*
Ferula foetida - *Hingu*
Fruits of *Myristica fragrans* - *Jayaphala*
Musk - *Kasturi*
Ocimum sanctum - *Tulasi*
Piper betel - *Nagarbel*
Piper longum - *Pippali*
Roots of *Mucana pruriens* - *Kavancha moola*
Seed carnel of *Myristica fragrans* - *Javitri*
Semecarpus anacardium - *Bhallataka*
Sida cordifolia - *Bala*
Strychnos nux-vomica - *Tinduka*
Syzygium aromaticum - *Lavanga*
Trachyspermum ammi - *Ajavayana*
Tricolepsis glaberrina - *Brahmadandi*
Tuber of *Aloe barbadensis* - *Ghrita kumari kanda*

Appetizer:

Apium graveolens - *Ajamoda*
Ferula foetida - *Hingu*
Piper longum - *Pippali*
Piper nigrum - *Kali Mircha*
Piper retrofectum - *Cavya*
Plumbago zeylanica - *Chitraka*
Roots of *Piper longum* - *Pippalimoola*
Semecarpus anacardium - *Bhallataka*
Zingiber officinale - *Santha*

Astringent:

Acacia catechu - *Khadira*
Alum - *Shubhra*
Areca catechu - *Supari*
Datura innoxia - *Dhattura*
Eupatorium triplinerve - *Ayapana*
Fruit rind of *Punica grantum* - *Anara twaka*
Gum of *Bombax ceiba* - *Mocharasa*
Gum resin of *Ficus religiosa* - *Lakhsa*
Holarrhena antidysenterica - *Kutaja*
Mimosa pudica - *Lajjavanti*
Papaver sommniferum - *Afima*
Quercus infectoria - *Majuphala*
Seeds of *Mangifera indica* - *Aama beeja*
Seeds of *Phyllanthus emblica* - *Aamalaki beeja*
Seeds of *Syzygium cumini* - *Jamuna beeja*
Seeds of *Tamarindus indica* - *Imali beeja*
Sympolocos racemosa - *Lodhra*
Terminalia arjuna - *Arjuna*

Biliary lithotriptic:

Abies spectabilis - *Talishapatra*
Alkaline of *Achyranthus aspera* - *Apamarga Khsara*
Alkaline of *Cocos nucifera* - *Narikela lavana*
Alkaline of *Hygrophila auriculata* - *Talmakhana Khsara*
Alkaline of *Picrorhiza kurroa* - *Kutaki khsara*

Alkaline of *Tephrosia purpuria - Sharapunkha khsara*
'Arka lavana'
Bauhinia veriegata - Kachanara
Berberis aristata - Daruharidra
Bergenia ciliata - Pashanabheda
Citrus medica - Bijora
Crataeva magna - Varuna
'Mayurpichha Bhasma'
Moringa oleifera - Shobhanjana
Oil of *Olea europaea - Jaitoona taila*
Piper cubeba - Kankola
Rubia cordifolia - Manjistha
Saccharum officinale – Ikhsu
Tribulus terrestris - Gokhsuru
Zea mays - Makka ke baal

Bronchodilator:

Abies spectabilis - Talishapatra
Acorus calamus - Vacha
Alpina galanga - Kulinjana
Celestrus paniculatus - Madhuyasthi
Chaturjata
Clerodendrum serratum - Bharangi
Curcuma longa - Haridra
Datura innoxia - Dhattura
Ephedra gerardiana - Soma
Inula racemosa - Pushkaramoola
Justisia adhatoda - Vasa
Ocimum sanctum - Tulasi
Piper betel- Nagarbel
Piper nigrum - Kali Mircha
Solunum surattense - Kantakari-laghu
Terminalia belliarica - Vibhitaka

Cardiac depressant:

Abrus precatorius - Gunja
Acorus calamus - Vatsanabha
Areca catechu - Supari
Balanites aegyptica - Hingota
Citrullus colosynthis - Indrayana
Diospyrus malaberica - Tendu
Drimia indica - Vana plalandu
Gloriosa superba - Kalihari
Rauvolfia serpentine - Sarpagandha
Seeds of *Syzygium cumini - Jamuna beeja majja*
Terminalia arjuna - Arjuna
Thevertia neriifolia - Kanera

Cardiac stimulant:

Acorus calamus - Vacha
Chaturjata
Cinamomum camphora - Kapoora
Crocos sativa - Kesara
Hridhya gana
Inula racemosa - Pushkaramoola
Musk - *Kasturi*
Ocimum sanctum - Tulsi
Piper betel - Nagarbel
Punica grantum - Anara
Syzygium aromaticum - Lavanga
Terminalia Arjuna - Arjuna

Cardiac tonic:

Artocarpus lacucha - Lakucha
Carissa carandas - Karonda
Citrus medica - Matulunga
Digitalis purpuria - Hritapatri
Drimia indica - Van Plandu
Eurale ferox - Makhana
Garcinia indica - Vrikhsamla
Garcinia penduculata - Amlavetasa
Glycyrrhiza glabra - Madhuyasti
Grewia subinequalis - Phalasa
Inula racemosa - Pushkaramoola
Mangifera indica - Aama
Phyllanthus emblica - Aamalaki
Punica grantum - Anara
Tamarindus indica - Imali
Terminalia arjuna - Arjuna
Tinospora cordifolia - Amrita
Zizyphus nummularia – Bera

Carminative:

Abelmoschus moschatus - Lata kasturi
Allium sativum - Rasona
Aloe barbadensis - Ghritakumari
Anacyclus pyrenthrum - Akarakara
Benincasa hispida - Kushamanda
Brassica juncea - Rai
Cassia fistula - Amalatasa
Citrullus lanatus - Tarbooja
Commifora mukul - Guggulu
Cuminum cyminum- Jiraka-sweta
Ferula foetida - Hingu
Garcinia penduculata - Amlaveta
Glycyrrhiza glabra - Madhuyashti
Mentha pipertia - Piparamenta
Mentha spicata - Pudina
Nardostachys jatamansi - Jatamansi
Oxalis corniculata - Changeri
Piper longum - Pippali
Piper nigrum - Kali Mircha
Piper retrofectum - Chavya
Plantego ovata - Isabagola
Plumbago zeylanica - Chitraka
Ricinus cumonis - Eranda
Rosa centifolia - Gulab
Trachyspermum ammi - Ajavayana
Valeriana jatamansi - Tagara
Vitis vinifera - Drakhsa

Catalyst:

Aconitum ferox - Vatsanabha
Acorus calamus - Vacha
Compound drugs of Gold
Honey
Kajjali
'Rasamanikya'
Rasa sindoora
'Samira pannaga rasa'
Semecarpus anacardium - Bhallataka
Strychnos nux-vomica - Tinduka
'Swarna samara pannaga rasa'

Cerebral stimulant:

Acorus calamus - Vacha
Allium sativum - Rason
Anacyclus pyrenthrum - Akarkara
Bacopa monnieri - Brahmi
Celestrus paniculatus - Jyotishmati
Cinamomum camphora - Kapura
Cinamomum verum - Dalchini
Curcuma longa - Haridra
Ferula foetida - Hingu
Lepideum sativum - Chandrasoora
'Mansyadi kwatha'
Mucana pruriens - Kavancha
Nardostachys jatamansi - Jatamansi
Ocimum sanctum - Tulsi
Piper longum - Pippali
Pistacia lentiscus - Rumi mastangi
Semecarpus anacardium - Bhallataka
'Tagaradi Kwatha'
Withania somnifera - Aswagandha
Zingiber officinale - Shunthi

Cholagogue:

Aegle marmelos - Bilva
Aloe barbadensis - Ghrita kumari

Ammonium chloride - *Navasadara*
'Arkalavana'
Berberis aristata - Daruharidra
Cichorium intybus - Kasani
Citrullus colocynthis - Indrayana
Croton tiglium - Jayaphala
Curcuma longa - Haridra
Echinops echinatus - Untakatela
Eclipta prostrata - Bhringaraja
Euphorbia neriifolia - Sehunda
Ficus hispida- Kakodumber
Holarrhena antidysenterica - Kutaja
Justisia adhatoda - Vasa
Lagenaria siceraria - Ikhsavaku
Leucas cephalotus - Dronapushpi
Luffa aegyptica - Dhamargava
Luffa echinata - Devdali
Nardostachys jatamansi - Jatamansi
Phyllanthus fraternus - Bhumyamalaki
Picrorhiza kurroa - Kutaki
Pluchea lanceolata - Rasna
Rheum australe - Revandachini
Ricinus cumonis - Eranda
Salix tetrasperma - Jalavetasa
Tinospora cordifolia - Amrita

Cholinergic:

Aconitum ferox - Vatsanabha
Areca catechu - Supari
Curd
Dahaprashamana gana
Plants having cold, astringent, dull, and viscid property
Rauvolfia serpentina - Sarpagandha

Demulcent:

Aegle marmelos - Bilva
Asparagus adscendens - Safed-Mushali
Asparagus racemosus - Shatavari
Azadirachta indica - Nimbu
Benincasa hispida - Kushamanda
Buchanania lanzan - Chironji
Callicarpa macrophylla - Priyangu
Cocos nucifera- Nariyal
Dacrtlorhiza hatagirea - Salama mishri
Desmodium gangeticum - Shalaparni
Elettaria cardamomum - Choti Ilayachi
Ficus carica - Anjira
Foeniculum vulgare - Saunfa
Fried seeds of *Oryza sativa - Laja*
Glycyrrhiza glabra - Madhuyasti
Gmelina arboria - Gambhari
Grewia helicterifolia- Nagabala
Grewia subinequalis - Phalasha
Grewia tanax - Gangerana
Gum of *Bambusa arundenasia - Vansalochana*
Jivaniya gana
Madhuca longifolia - Mahuva
Mangifera indica - Aama
Mucana pruriens - Kavancha
Phoenix sylvestris - Khajura
Phyllanthus emblica - Aamalaki
Plantego ovata - Isabgol
Powder of fried seeds of *Hordeum vulgare* and sugar - *Yavasattu*
Pueraria lobata - Mudgaparni
Pueraria tuberosa - Vidarikanda
Punica grantum - Anara
Rosa centifolia - Gulab
Scirpus grosus - Kasheruka
Sphyeranthus indicus - Gorakhamundi
Tamarindus indica - Imali
Tectona grandis - Sagavan
Teramnus labialis - Mashaparni
Trapa natans - Singhara
Tribulus terrestris - Gokharu
Uraria picta - Prishnaparni
Vetiveria zizanoiodes - Ushira
Vigna mungo - Urada
Vitis vinifera - Drakhsa
Withania somnifera - Aswagandha
Zizyphus nummularia - Ber

Deobstruent:

All Bitter Medicinal Plant
Cissampelos pariera - Patha
Compound Drugs of Arsenic
Curcuma longa - Haridra
Curcuma zedoria - Kachura
Holarrhena antidysenterica - Kutaja
Honey
Justisia adhatoda - Vasa
'Maha vata vidhwansana rasa'
Medication by nose - *Nasya Karma*
Tribulus terrestris - Gokhsuru Chota
Trikatu

Deodorant:

Acacia nilotica - Babula
Albizia lebbeck - Shirisha
Aquilaria malaccensis – Agara
Berberis aristata - Daruharidra
Brassica campestris - Sarson
Buchanania lanzan - Chironji
Cassia fistula - Amalatasa
Cicer arietinum - Chana
Cinamomum verum - Dalchini
Commifora mukul - Guggulu
Coriandrun sativum - Dhanyaka
Crocus sativus - Kesar
Curcuma longa - Haridra
Cyperus scarissus - Nagarmotha
Datura innoxia - Dhattura
Elettaria cardamomum - Choti-Ilayachi
Fegonia indica - Danvayasa
Ferula foetida - Hingu
Ficus racemosa- Udumbara
Flowers of *Butea monosperma - Palasha pushpa*
Foeniculum vulgare - Saunfa
Glycyrrhiza glabra - Madhuyasti
Hemidesmus indicus - Anantamoola
Holarrhena antidysenterica - Kutaja
Lawsonia inermis - Mehandi
Lens culinaris - Masura
Mentha spicata - Pudina
Mesua ferrea - Nagakesar
Nelumbo nucifera - Kamal
Ocimum basillicum - Van tulasi
Piper chaba - Kankola
Pterocarpus santalinus - Chandan-Rakta
Rosa centifolia - Gulab
Rubia cordifolia - Manjistha
Santalum album - Chandan-sweta
Saussarea lappa - Kustha
Strychnos nux-vomica - Tinduka
Symplocos racemosa - Lodhra
Syzygium aromaticum - Lavanga
Tecomela undulata - Rohitaka
Terminalia arjuna - Arjuna
Valeriana jatamansi - Tagara
Vernonia anthelmintica - Kalijiri
Vetiveria zizanoiodes - Ushira

Depurative:

Acacia catechu - Khadira

Alstonia scholaris - Saptaparna
Azadirachta indica - Nimba
Berberis aristata - Daruhaldi
Brassica campestris - Sarson
Caesalpinia bonduc - Kantaki Karanja
Cassia fistula - Amalatasa
Curcuma longa - Haridra
Cynodon dactylon - Durva
Cyperus scarissus - Nagarmotha
Embelia ribes - Vidanga
Glycyrrhiza glabra - Madhuyasti
Holarrhena antidysenterica - Kutaja
Jasminum grandiflorum - Jati
Nardostachys jatamansi - Jatamansi
Phyllanthus emblica - Aamalaki
Pterocarpus santalinus - Chandana-rakta
Rubia cordifolia - Manjistha
Semecarpus anacardium - Bhallataka
Terminalia chebula - Haritaki
Thevertia neriifolia - Kanera
Vetiveria zizanoiodes - Ushira

Diaphoretic:

Aconitum ferox - Vatsanabha
Aconitum heterophyllum - Ateesha
Alkaline of *Hordeum vulgare - Yava khsara*
Alstonia scholaris - Saptaparna
Ammonium chloride - *Nosadara*
Artemisia nilagirica - Damanaka
Boerhavia diffusa - Punarnava
Carthumus tinctoius - Kusumbha
Celestrus paniculatus - Jyotishmati
Cinamomum camphora - Kapura
Cinamomum verum - Dalachini
Cymbopogon martinii - Rohishtrina
Cyperus scarissus - Nagarmotha
Exercise
Foeniculum vulgare - Saunpha
Hemidesmus indicus - Anantamoola
Hordium vulgare - Jou
Hot water
Leucas cephalotus - Dronapushpi
Macrolytoma uniflorum - Kulathi
Nitrate of Potash - *Kalamishora*
Ocimum sanctum - Tulasi
Picrorhiza kurroa - Kutaki
'Praval Bhasma'
Root of *Calotropis procera - Arka moola*
Root of *Ricinus cumonis - Eranda moola*
Sesamum orientale - Til
Stem bark of *Moringa oleifera - Shobhanjana twaka*
'Shubhra Bhasma'
Sun light
Vigna mungo - Urada
Zingiber officinale - Shunthi
Zizyphus nummularia - Ber

Diuretic:

Achyranthus aspera - Apamarga
Aklaline - *Khsara*
Aloe barbadensis - Ghrita Kumari
Bergenia ciliata - Pashanbheda
Boerhavia diffusa - Punarnava
Butea monosperma - Palasha
Carum bulbocastanum - Jiraka-Krishna
Citrullus lanatus - Tarabooja
Cmmon Salt - *Lavana*
Cuminum cyminum - Jiraka-Sweta
Eclipta prostrate - Bhringaraja
Macrolyloma uniflorum - Kulathi
'Rabari'
Saccharum officinale - Ikhsu
Seeds of *Cucumis satvus - Khira Kakari ke Beeja*
Solunum nigrum - Makoya
Tephrosia purpuria - Sharapunkha
Tribulus terrestris - Gokhsuru
'Trifala'
Trina Panchamoola

Emetic:

Acorus calamus - Vacha
Anthocephalus chinensis - Kadamba
Barringtonia acutangula - Samudraphala
Bauhinia tomentosa - Kovidara
Calotropis procera - Arka
Catunaregan spinosa - Madanaphala
Convolvulus pluricaulis - Shanapushpi
Glycyrrhiza glabra - Madhuyashti
Lagenaria siceraria - Ikhsavaku
Luffa aegyptiaca - Dhamargava
Luffa cylendrica - Kritavedhan
Sapindua emarginatus - Aritha

Emmenogogue:

Abroma augusta - Ulatakambala
Bacopa monnieri - Brahmi
Bauhinia veriegata - Kachanar
Borax
Cinamomum verum - Dalchini
Cinchona officinais - Kunena
Cleviceps purpurea - Argata
Commifora mukul - Guggulu
Commifora myrrha- Bol
Compound drugs of Arsenic
Dashamoola
Extract of *Aloe barbadensis - Elava*
Ferula foetida - Hingu
Flowers of *Cannabis sativa - Ganja*
'Kasisa bhasma'
'Lauha bhasma'
Piper retrofectum - Chavya
Root of *Plumbago zeylanica - Chitraka moola*
Roots of *Gossipium herbacum - Kapasa moola*
Roots of *Piper longum - Pippali moola*
Seeds of *Daucus carota - Gajar beeja*
Styrax benzoin - Loban
Trachyspermum ammi - Ajavayana
Trigonella foinum gracum - Methi
Zingiber officinale - Shunthi

Emollient:

Clarified butter of cow - *Ghrita*
Desmodium gangeticum - Shalaparni
Glycyrrhiza glabra - Madhuyasti
Jivaniya Gana
Kandughna Mahakashya
Leptadenia reticulata - Jivanti
Manilkara hexandra - Khirani
Oil of *Sesamum orientale*
Pueraria tuberose – Vidarikanda
Ricinus cumonis - Eranda
Swedopaga mahakashaya
Tinospora cordifolia - Amrita
Twakaprasadakara mahakashaya
Vitis vinifera - Drakhsa
Vrihaniya Mahakashaya

Exhilarant:

Alcohols
Ashtavarga
Asparagus racemosus - Shatavari
Cannabis sativa - Bhanga

Foeniculum vulgare - Saunfa
Glycyrrhiza glabra - Madhuyasti
Jivaniya gana
Nardostachys jatamansi - Jatamansi
Phoenix sylvestris - Khajura
Vetiveria zizanoiodes - Ushira
Vitis vinifera - Drakhsa

Expectorant:

Acorus calamus - Vacha
Alkaline of *Hordeum vulgare - Yava khsara*
Alkalines - *Khsara*
Allium cepa - Palandu
Allium sativum- Rason
Bitumen - *Shilajeeta*
Calotropis procera - Arka
Cedrus deodara - Devdaru
Cinamomum camphora - Kapura
Commifora myrrha - Bol
Curcuma amada - Aamahaldi
Curcuma longa - Haridra
Ficus religiosa - Pipal
Glycyrrhiza glabra - Madhuyasti
Honey
Justisia adhatoda - Vasa
Myrica esculenta - Kayaphala
Ocimum sanctum - Tulasi
Pistacia khinjuk - Kakarasingi
Premna corymbosa - Agnimantha
Pure Sulphur
Salts - *Lavana*
Solunum ferox - Vrahati
Solunum nigrum - Kali Mircha
Solunum surattense - Kantakari
Strychnos nux-vomica - Tinduka
Styrex benzoin - Loban
Syzygium aromaticum - Lavanga
'Tamra bhasma'
Terminalia belliarica - Bahera
Viola odorata - Banaphsha
Vitex negundo - Nirgundi

(A) Stimulant expectorants-

'Abhraka bhasma'
Allium cepa - Palandu
Ammonium chloride - *Nosadara*
Aromatic plants
Cinamomum camphora - Kapura
Ferula foetida - Hingu
Justisia adhatoda - Vasa
Roots of *Ricinus cumonis - Eranda moola*
'Shringa bhasma'
Solunum surattense - Kantakari
Styrex benzoin - Loban

(B) Antispasmodic expectorants-

Alkaline of *Hordeum vulgare - Yava khsara*
Alkaline of *Justisia adhatoda - Vasa khsara*
Datura innoxia - Dhattura
Ephedra gerardiana - Soma
Nitrate of potash - *Kalamishora*
Punica grantum - Anaradana
Seeds of *Papaver sommniferum - Postadoda*

(C) Sedative expectorants-

Acorus calamus - Vacha
Glycyrrhiza glabra - Madhuyasti
Papaver sommniferum - Afima

Galactogogue:

Amaranthus spinosus - Kanta cholai
Arundo donex - Nala
Asparagus racemosus - Shatavari
Astavarga
Butea monosperma - Palasha
Celestrus paniculatus - Jyotishmati
Cuminum cyminum - Jiraka-sweta
Cyperus scarissus - Nagarmotha
Dashamoola
Eryngium cocruleum - Sakakula mishri
Euphorbia thymifolia - Dugdhika
Foeniculum vulgare - Saunfa
Glycyrrhiza glabra - Madhuyasti
Gossipium herbacum - Kapasa
Imperata cylindrical – Darbha
Jivaniya gana
Lepidium iberis - Todari
Lepidium sativum - Chandrasoora
Phoenix sylvestris - Khajura
Piper longum - Pippali
Pueraria tuberose - Vidarikanda
Saccharum spontaneum - Kasa
Scirpus grosus - Kasheruka
Trigonella foinum-gracum - Methi
Vitis vinifera - Drakhsa
Withania somnifera - Aswagandha
Zingiber officinale - Shunthi

Haematinic:

Ananas comosus - Annanasha
Boerhavia diffusa - Punarnava
Chenopodium album - Bathua
Citrullus lanatus - Tarbooja
Citrus medica - Bijora
Clarified butter of cow - *Ghrita*
Daucus carota - Gajara
Eclipta prostrata - Bhringaraja
Ferula foetida - Hingu
Ficus carica - Anjira
Glycyrrhiza glabra - Madhuyasti
Grewia subinequalis - Phalasa
Justisia adhatoda - Vasa (for platelets)
Malus pumila - Seba
Mesua ferrea- Nagakesara
Morus indica - Shahatoota
Oxalis corniculata - Changeri
Phoenix sylvestris - Khajura
Phyllanthus emblica - Aamalaki
Phyllanthus fraternus - Bhumyamalaki
Piper longum - Pippali
Punica grantum - Anara
Saccharum officinale - Ikhsu
Semecarpus anacardium - Bhallataka
Spinacea oleracea - Palaka
Spyeranthus indicus - Gorakhamundi
Tecomela undulata - Rohitaka
Terminalia belliarica - Arjuna
Tinospora cordifolia - Amrita
Trifala
Vitis vinifera - Drakhsa

Hypertensive:

Abelmoschus moschatus - Latakasturi
Allium sativum - Rason
Ambergris - *Ambara*
Anacyclus pyrenthrum - Akarkara
Asparagus racemosus - Shatavari
Bacopa monnieri - Brahami
Celestrus paniculatus - Jyotishmati
Cinamomum tamala - Tejapat
Cinamomum verum - Dalchini
Cinamomum camphora - Kapura
Coffea arebica - Kofi
Crosus sativus - Kesar
Datura innoxia - Dhattura
Daucus carota - Gajar

Ferula foetida - Hingu
Ficus carica - Anjira
Grewia helicterifolia - Nagabala
Hyoscyamus niger - Khurasani Ajavayana
Jivaniya gana
Mucana pruriens - Kavancha
Musk - *Kastoori*
Nicotiana tabacum - Tambaku
Ocimum sanctum - Tulasi
Phoenix sylvestris - Khajura
Piper betel - Nagarbel
Piper longum - Pippali
Piper retrofectum - Chaya
Punica grantum - Anara
Roots of *Piper longum - Pippalimoola*
Semecarpus anacardium - Bhallataka
Sida cordifolia - Bala
Strychnos nux-vomica - Tiduka
Syzygium aromaticum - Lavanga
Terminalia arjuna - Arjuna
Vigna mungo - Urada
Vitis vinifera - Drakhsa
Withania somnifera- Aswagandha

Hypolipidemic:

Acorus calamus - Vacha
Alkaline - *Khsara*
Berberis aristata - Daruharidra
Bergenia ciliata - Pashanabheda
Boerhavia diffusa - Punarnava
Brassica campestris - Sarson
Commifora mukul - Guggulu
Curcuma longa - Haridra
Curcuma zedoria - Kachura
Cyperus scarissus - Nagarmotha
Dashamoola
Eclipta prostrate - Bhringaraj
Embelia ribes - Vidanga
Inula racemosa - Pushkarmoola
Phyllanthus emblica - Aamalaki
Picrorhiza kurroa - Kutaki
Piper longum - Pippali
Piper nigrum - Kali Mirch
Plumbago zeylanica - Chitraka
Psoralea corylifolia - Bakuchi
Semecarpus anacardium - Bhallataka
Swertia chiryata - Chirayata
Terminalia chebula - Haritaki
Urine of Cow - *Gomutra*
Zingiber officinale - Shunthi

Hypotensive:

Aegle marmelos - Bilva
Allium sativum - Rason
Asparagus racemosus - Shatavari
Bacopa monnieri - Brahmi
Benincasa hispida - Kushmanda
Boerhavia diffusa - Punarnava
Cannabis sativa - Bhanga
Convolvulus pluricaulis - Shankhapushpi
Cyperus scarissus - Nagarmotha
Elaecarpus sphaericus - Rudrakhsa
Elettaria cardamomum - Ilayachi-choti
Fumaria indica - Pittapapara
Glycyrrhiza glabra - Madhuyasti
Hemidesmus indicus - Anantamoola
Nardostachys jatamansi - Jatamansi
Pavonia odorata - Sugandhabala
Rauvolfia serpentina - Sarpagandha
Rosa centifolia - Gulab
Rubia cordifolia - Manjistha
Santalum album - Chandana-sweta
Terminalia belliarica - Arjuna
Tinospora cordifolia - Amrita
Tribulus terrestris - Gokharu
Vetiveria zizanoiodes - Ushira
Withania somnifera - Aswagandha

Hypotonic:

Bacopa monnieri - Brahmi
Centella asiatica - Mandookaparni
Nardostachys jatamansi - Jatamansi
Papaver sommniferum - Afima
Rauvolfia serpentina - Sarpagandha
Roots of *Piper longum - Pipalamoola*
Withania somnifera - Aswagandha

Lactigenous:

Abutilon indicum - Atibala
Amorphophallus paeoniifolius - Surana
Asparagus adscendens - Safed-Mushali
Asparagus racemosus - Shatavari
Benincasa hispida - Kushamanda
Bombax cieba - Semal
Buchanania lanzan - Chironji
Cocus nucifera - Nariyal
Cucurligo orchioides - Kali-Mushali
Dactylorhiza hatagirea - Salama mishri
Desmodium gangeticum - Shalaparni
Eurale ferox - Makhana
Foeniculum vulgare - Saunfa
Fruits of *Gmelina arboria - Gambhari phala*
Glycyrrhiza glabra - Madhuyashti
Grewia subinequalis - Phalasa
Grewia tanax - Gangerana
Leptadenia reticulate - Jivanti
Madhuca longifolia - Mahuva
Mucana pruriens - Kavancha
Nelumbo nucifera - Kamal
Phoenix sylvestris - Khajura
Pueraria tuberosa - Vidarikanda
Saccharum officinale - Ikhsu
Scirpus grosus - Kasheruka
Seeds of *Tectona grendis - Sagavan beeja*
Sesamum orientale - Til
Sida cordifolia - Bala
Sphyeranthus indicus - Gorakhamundi
Tribulus terrestris - Gokharu
Vigna mungo - Urada
Vitis vinifera - Drakhsa
Withania somnifera - Aswagandga

Lithagogue:

Abies spectabilis - Talishapatra
Achyranthus aspera - Apamarga
Adiantum incisum - Mayurapankhi
Bauhinia veriegata - Kachanara
Berberis aristata - Daruharidra
Bergenia ciliata - Pashanabheda
Boerhavia diffusa - Punarnava
Citrus aurantifolia - Nimbu
Crataeva magna - Varuna
Hygrophila auriculata - Talmakhana
Moringa oleifera - Shobhanjan
Phyllanthus emblica - Aamalaki
Piper cubeba - Kankola
Tephrosia purpuria - Sharapunkha
Tribulus terrestris - Gokharu
Trinapanchamoola
Zea mays - Makka ke baal

Nervine stimulant:

Acorus calamus - Vacha
Anacyclus pyrenthrum - Akarakara

Bacopa monnieri - Brahmi
Convolvulus pluricaulis - Shankhapushpi
Hyoscyamus niger - Khurasani Ajawayana
'Mansyadi kwatha'
Nardostachys jatamansi - Jatamansi
Piper longum - Pippali
Valeriana jatamansi - Tagara
Withania somnifera - Aswagandha

Nervine tonic:

Acorus calamus - Vacha
Alcohals
Anacyclus pyrenthrum - Akarakara
Asparagus racemosus - Satawari
Bacopa monnieri - Brahmi
Bacopa monnieri - Mandookaparni
Celestrus paniculatus - Jyotishmati
Convolvulus pluricaulis - Shankhapushpi
Dactylorhiza hatagirea - Salamamishri
Glycyrrhiza glabra - Madhuyasthi
Jivaniya gana
Nardostachys jatamansi - Jatamansi
Pueraria tuberosa - Vidarikanda
Roots of *Sida cordifolia - Balamoola*
Semecarpus anacardium - Bhallataka
Sphyeranthus indicus - Gorakhamundi
Tinospora cordifolia - Amrita
Vitis vinifera - Drakhsa
Withania somnifera - Aswagandha
Zingiber officinale - Shunthi

Nutriet:

Abutilon indicum - Atibala
Asparagus racemosus - Shatavari
Astavarga
Balya gana
Celestrus paniculatus - Madhuyasti
Eurale ferox - Makhana
Grewia subinequalis - Phalasa
Jivaniya gana
Madhuca longifolia - Mahuva
Manilkara hexandra – Khirani
Musa paradisiaca - Kela
Phoenix sylvestris - Khajura
Punica grantum - Anara
Saccharum officinale - Ikhsu
Sida cordifolia - Bala
Sida rhombifolia - Mahabala
Tinospora cordifolia - Amrita
Trapa natans - Sinhara
Vitis vinifera - Drakhsa
Vrinhaniya gana
Withania somnifera - Aswagandha

Oxytocic:

Abroma augusta - Ulatakambala
Acacia nilotica - Babul
Aloe barbadensis - Ghritkumari
Areca catechu - Supari
Atropa belladonna - Suchi
Cleviceps purpuria - Argata
Dashamoola
Ficus racemosa - Udumber
Gloriosa superba - Kalihari
Mimosa pudica - Lajjavanti
Papaver sommniferum - Afima
Roots of *Zizyphus nummularia - Ber moola*
Saraca asoca - Ashoka
Zizyphus nummularia - Ber

Purgative:

Cassia fistula - Amalatasa
Cassia senna - Sanaya
Croton tiglium - Jayapala
Gmelina arboria - Gambhari
Grewia subinequalis - Phalasa
Phyllanthus emblica - Aamalaki
Picrorhiza kurroa - Kutaki
Ricinus communis - Eranda
Terminalia belliarica - Bahera
Terminalia chebula - Haritaki
Vitis vinifera - Drakhsa
Zizyphus jujuba - Ber-bara
Zizyphus nummularia - Ber-chota

Refrigerant:

Aegle marmelos - Bilva
Albizia lebbeck - Shirisha
Asparagus racemosus - Shatavari
Benincasa hispida - Kushamanda
Buchanania lanzan - Chironji
Butea monosperma - Palasha
Citrus aurantifolia - Nimbu
Cocos nucifera - Nariyal
Coriandrun sativum - Dhanyaka
Cynodon dactylon - Durva
Cyperus scarissus - Nagarmotha
Dactylorhiza hatagirea - Salam mishri
Elettaria cardamomum - Choti-Ilayachi
Eurale ferox - Makhana
Fagonia indica - Dhanvayasa
Foeniculum vulgare - Saunfa
Fumaria indica - Pittapapara
Glycyrrhiza glabra - Madhuyasti
Gmelina arboria - Gambhari
Grewia subinequalis - Phalasa
Lawsonia inermis - Mehandi
Leptadenia reticulata - Jivanti
Madhuca longifolia - Mahuva
Manilkara hexandra - Khirani
Nelumbo nucifera - Kamal
Pandnus fascicularis - Ketaki
Phoenix sylvestris - Khajura
Phyllanthus emblica - Aamalaki
Pterocarpus santalinus - Chandan-rakta
Punica grantum - Anar
Rosa centifolia - Gulab
Saccharum officinale - Ikhsu
Santalum album - Chandan-Sweta
Scirpus grosus - Kasheruka
Tribulus terrestris - Gokharu
Trinapanchamoola
Vetiveria zizanoiodes - Ushira
Vitis vinifera – Drakhsa

Sedative:

Glycyrrhiza glabra - Madhuyasti
Hemidesmus indicus - Anantamoola
Madhuca longifolia - Mahuva
Nardostachys jatamansi - Jatamansi
Papaver sommniferum - Ahifena
Prunella vulgaris - Ustakhaddusa
Rosa centifolia - Gulab
Santalum album - Chandana-sweta
Vetiveria zizanoiodes - Ushira
Zizyphus sativa - Unnaba

Semen-viscosity promoter:

Acacia nilotica - Babula
Albizia lebbeck - Shirisha
Anthocephalus chinensis - Kadamba
Azadirachta indica - Nimba
Bitumen - Shilajeeta
Bombax ceiba - Semala
Boswellia serrata - Shallaki

Buchanania lanzan - Chironji
Butea monosperma - Palasha
Cannabis sativa - Bhanga
Coriandrun sativum - Dhanyaka
Cuminum cyminum - Jiraka-Sweta
Euphorbia thymifolia - Dugdhika
Ficus racemosa - Udumber
Ficus virens - Plakhsa
Glycyrrhiza glabra - Madhuyasti
Justisia adhatoda - Vasa
Latex of *ficus bengalensis - Vata dhugdha*
Madhuca longifolia - Mahuva
Papaver sommniferum - Afima
Picrorhiza kurroa - Kutaki
Seeds of *Crotalaria pallida - Shana beeja*
Seeds of *Tamarindus indica - Imali beeja*
Seeds of *Tectona grandis - Sagavana beeja*
Solunum surattense - Kantakari
Spondias pinnata - Aamrataka
Symplocos racemosa - Lodhra
Syzygium cumini - Jamuna
Terminalia arjuna - Arjuna
Thespesia populnea - Parasa Pipala
Tricosanthes dioica - Patola
Unripe fruits of *Aegle marmelos - Bilva phala (apakva)*
Zingiber officinale - Shunthi
Zizyphus nummularia - Ber

Seminiferous:

Abutilon indicum - Atibala
Amorphophallus paeoniifolius - Surana
Anthum graveolens - Soya
Argyreia nervosa - Vidhayara
Asparagus adscendens - Safeda Musali
Asparagus racemosus - Shatavari
Benincasa hispida - Kushmanda
Clarified butter of cow - *Ghrita*
Cucurligo orchioides - Kali Musali
Dactylorhiza hatagirea - Salamamisri
Dioscorea bulbifera - Varahikanda
Eryngium cocruleum - Shakakul mishri
Eurale ferox - Makhana
Foeniculum vulgare - Saunfa
Glycyrrhiza glabra - Madhuyasti
Grewia helicterifolia - Nagabala
Hygrophila auriculata - Talmakhana
Leptadenia reticulata - Jivanti
Mangifera indica - Aama
Meat soup - *Mansa rasa*
Milk - *Dugdha*
Mucana pruriens - Kavancha
Phoenix sylvestris - Khajura
Pistacia lentiscus - Rumi Mastangi
Pueraria lobata - Mudgaparni
Pueraria tuberosa - Vidarikanda
Ripe fruits of *Aegle marmelos - Bilva phala (pakwa)*
Scirpus grosus - Kasheruka
Seeds of *Citrullus lanatus - Tarbooja beeja*
Seeds of *Cucumis sativus - Khira kakari beeja*
Seeds of *Manilkara hexandra - Khirani beeja*
Sida cordifolia - Bala
Sida rhombifolia - Mahabala
Sphyeranthus indicus - Gorakhamundi
Trapa natans - Singhara
Tribulus terrestris - Gokharu
Triticum aestivum - Gehun
Vigna mungo - Urada
Vitis vinifera - Drakhsa
Withania somnifera - Aswagandha

Sialagogue:

Abrus precatorius - Gunja
Achyranthus aspera - Akarkara
Acorus calamus - Vacha
Apium graveolens - Ajamoda
Celestrus paniculatus - Jyotishmati
Citrus aurantifolia - Nibu
Fresh tubers of *Zingiber officinale - Aadraka*
Myrica esculenta - Kayaphala
Piper betel - Nagarbel
Piper longum - Pippali
Piper nigrum - Kali Mircha
Piper retrofectum - Chavya
Plumbago zeylanica - Chitraka
Rhus parviflora - Tintidika
Roots of *Piper longum - Pippalimoola*
Salts - *Lavana*
Semecarpus anacardium - Bhallataka
Tamarindus indica - Imali
Trachyspermum ammi - Ajavayana

Styptic:

Acacia catechu - Khadira
Acacia nilotica - Babula
Albizia lebbeck - Shirisha
Allium cepa - Palandu
Anthum graveolens - Soya
Asparagus adscendens - Safed-Mushali
Benincasa hispida - Kushmanda
Berberis aristata - Daruharidra
Blepheris edulis - Utangana
Butea monosperma - Palasha
Callicarpa macrophylla - Priyangu
Cassia fistula - Amalatasa
Cocos nucifera - Nariyal
Cucurligo orchioides - Kali-Mushali
Curcuma longa - Haridra
Cynodon dactylon - Durva
Dactylorhiza hatagirea - Salam misri
Dalbergia sissoo - Sisama
Elettaria cardamomum - Choti Ilayachi
Eurale ferox - Makhana
Fagonia indica - Dhanvayasa
Ficus religiosa - Pipal
Foeniculum vulgare - Saunfa
Glycyrrhiza glabra - Madhuyasti
Gmelina arboria - Gambhari
Gum of *Bombax ceiba - Semala niryasa*
Gum-resin of *Ficus religiosa - Lakhsa*
Hemidesmus indicus - Anantamoola
Hygrophila auriculata - Talmakhana
Justisia adhatoda - Vasa
Mesua ferrea - Nagakesara
Mimosa pudica - Lajjavanti
Nelumbo nucifera - Kamal
Panchakhsiri vrikhsa
Pandanus fascicularis - Ketaki
Papaver sommniferum - Afima
Phyllanthus emblica - Aamalaki
Pterocarpus santalinus - Chandan-rakta
Punica grantum - Anara
Rauvolfia serpentina - Sarpagandha
Rosa centifolia - Gulab
Saccharum officinale - Ikhsu
Santalum album - Chandana-sweta
Saraca asoca - Ashoka

Symplocos racemosa - Lodhra
Tecomela undulata - Rohitaka
Tectona grandis - Sagavana
Terminalia arjuna - Arjuna
Terminalia chebula - Haritaki
Tinospora cordifolia - Amrita
Tribulus terrestris - Gokharu
Vetiveria zizanoiodes - Ushira
Vitis vinifera - Drakhsa
Woodfordia fruticosa - Dhataki

Thermogenic :

Abies spectabilis - Talisapatra
Acorus calamus - Vacha
Allium sativum - Rason
Apium graveolens - Ajamoda
Aquilaria malaccensis - Agara
Brassica juncea - Rajika
Celestrus paniculatus - Jyotishmati
Cinamomum camphora - Kapura
Cinamomum verum - Dalachini
Crocus sativa - Kesar
Embelia ribes - Vidanga
Ferula foetida - Hingu
Hyoscyamus niger - Khurasani Ajavayana
Linum usitatissimum - Alasi
Ocimum sanctum - Tulasi
Piper betel - Nagarbel
Piper cubeba - Kankola
Piper longum - Pippali
Piper nigrum - Kali-Mircha
Piper retrofectum - Chavya
Pluchea laceolata - Rasna
Plumbago zeylanica - Chitraka
Premna corymbosa - Agnimantha
Psoralea corylifolia - Bakuchi
Semecarpus anacardium - Bhallataka
Smilax china - Chopachini
Strychnos nux-vomica - Tinduka
Syzygium aromaticum - Lavanga
Trachyspermum ammi - Ajavayana
Vetiveria zizanoiodes – Tagar
Zingiber officinale - Shunthi

Tranquilizer:

Alcohols
Alhagi pseudalhagi - Yavasa
Asparagus racemosus - Shatavari
Benincasa hispida - Kushmanda
Canabis sativa - Bhanga
Celestrus paniculatus - Jyotishmati
Citrullus lanatus - Tarbooja
Crocus sativus - Kesar
Fagonia indica - Dhanvayasa
Grewia tanax - Gangerana
Jasminum grandiflorum - Jati
Pandanus fascicularis - Kevara
Papaver sommniferum - Afima
Phoenix sylvestris - Khajura
Punica grantum - Anara
Rosa centifolia - Gulab
Santalum album - Chandana-Sweta
Vetiveria zizanoiodes - Ushira
Vitis vinifera - Drakhsa
Withania somnifera - Aswagandha

Vasoconstrictor:

Areca catechu - Supari
Bacopa monnieri - Brahmi
Gum of *bombax ceiba - Mocharasa*
Nicotiana tabacum - Tambaku
Plants containing astringent taste
Seeds of *Phyllanthus emblica - Aamalaki Beeja Majja*
Seeds of *Syzygium cumini - Jamuna Beeja Majja*
Strychnos nux-vomica - Tinduka
Tannin Containing Plants
Terminalia arjuna - Arjuna

Vasodilator:

Aconitum ferox - Vatsanabha
Acorus calamus - Vacha
Chaturjata
Inula racemosa - Pushkaramoola
Nardostachys jatamansi - Jatamansi
Oil of *Brassica campestris - Sarsapa taila*
Oil of *Sesamum orientale - Til Taila*
Piper longum - Pippali
Punica grantum - Anar
Terminalia chebula - Haritaki
Trachyspermum ammi - Ajavayana
Vetiveria zizanoiodes - Tagara

Vitality promoter:

Buchanania lanzan - Chironji
Dactylorhiza hatagirea - Salampanja
Ficus carica - Anjeera
Jivaniya gana
Phoenix sylvestris - Kharjura
Phyllanthus emblica - Aamalaki
Piper longum - Pippali
Prunus amygdalus - Badam
Semecarpus anacardium - Bhallataka
Vitis vinifera - Drakhsa
Vrihaniya gana

Vulnerary:

Anogeisus latifolia - Dhava
Aquilaria malaccensis - Agara
Berberis aristata - Daruharidra
Bombax ceiba - Semal
Boswellia serrata - Shallaki
Buchanania lanzan - Chironji
Calotropis procera - Arka
Clarified butter of cow - *Ghrita*
Cleome gynendra - Hulhula
Clerodendrum serratum - Bharangi
Curcuma longa - Haridra
Elettaria cardamomum - Ilayachi
Glycyrrhiza glabra - Madhuyasti
Gum of *Ficus religiosa - Lakhsa*
Honey
Jasminum grandiflorum - Jati
Marsdenia tenacissima - Murva
Mimosa pudica - Lajjavanti
Oil of *Sesamum oriantale - Til taila*
Pancha khsiri Vrikhsa
Pistacia khinjuk - Kakarasingi
Prunus cerasoides - Padmakha
Pterocarpus santalinus - Chandan-rakta
Pueraria tuberosa - Vidarikanda
Roots of *Sida cordifolia - Bala moola*
Rubia cordifolia - Manjistha
Salix caprea - Vetasa
Symplocos racemosa - Lodhra
Terminalia arjuna - Arjun
Terminalia chebula - Haritaki
Thevertia neriifolia - Karvira
Tinospora cordifolia - Amrita
Unripe fruit of *Diospyrus malaberica - Tendu ke apakwa phala*
Valeriana jatamansi - Tagar
Vetiveria zizanoiodes - Ushira

Classification of Clinical Uses
According to Serial Number of Medicinal Plant

Index of Formulations

According to Serial Numbers of Plants

Families of Medicinal Plants

Acanthaceae:
Peristrophe bicaliculata-353.
Anacardiaceae:
Mangifera indica-296.
Pistacia intergerrima-373.
Pistacia lentiscus-374.
Rhus parviflora-404.
Semecarpus anacardium-427.
Spondias pinnata-444.
Annonaceae:
Polyalthia longifolia-380.
Apocynaceae:
Nerium indicum-323.
Rauvolfia serpentine-402.
Thevetia peruviana-466.
Araceae:
Pistia stratiotes-375.
Scindapsus officinalis-425.
Araliaceae:
Panax pseudoginseng-344.
Asclepiadaceae; Pariplocaceae:
Pergularia daemia-352.
Asclepiadaceae:
Marsdenia tenacissima-298.
Sarcostema brevistigma-422.
Tylophora indica-479.
Bignoniaceae:
Oroxylum indicum-338.
Stereospermum suaveolens-446.
Tecomela undulate-457.
Boraginaceae:
Tricodesma indicum-472.
Cactaceae:
Opuntia dellenii-336.
Caesalpiniaceae:
Saraca asoca-421.
Tamarindus indica-455.
Chenopodiaceae:
Spinacea oleracea-443.
Combretaceae:
Terminalia arjuna-461.
Terminalia bellirica-462.
Terminalia chebula-463.
Terminalia tomentosa-464.
Compositae; Asteraceae:
Matricaria chamomilla-301.
Pluchea lanceolata-378.
Saussurea costus-423.
Sphaeranthus indicus-441.
Spilanthes oleracea-442.
Tagetes erecta-454.
Taraxacum officinale-456.
Tricholepsis glaberrima-473.
Vernonia cinerea-485.
Wedelia calendulacea-490.
Xanthium strumarium-493.
Convolvulaceae:
Merremia gangetica-306,
Operculina turpethum-335.
Cruciferae; Brassicaceae:
Raphanus sativus-401.
Sisymbrium irio-434.
Cucurbitaceae:
Momordica charantia-312.
Momordica dioca-313.
Tricosanthes bracteata-474.
Tricosanthes cucumerina-475.
Trichosanthus dioica-476.
Cupressaceae:
Thuja orientalis-467.
Cyperacae:
Scirpus grossus-426.
Dipterocarpaceae:
Shorea robusta-431.
Vateria indica-484.
Euphorbiaceae:
Mallotus philipensis-293.
Phylanthus distichus-360.
Phylanthus emblica-361.
Phylanthus fraternus-362.
Ricinus communis-405.
Fagaceae:
Quercus infectoria-398.
Gentianaceae:
Swertia chirayita-450.
Gramineae; Poaceae:
Oryza sativa-339.
Saccharum bengalense-410.
Saccharum officinale-411.
Saccharum spontaneum-412.
Triticum aestivum-478.
Vetiveria zizaniodes-486.
Zea mays-495.
Guttiferae; Clusiaceae:
Mesua ferrea-307.
Ochrocarpus longifolus-328.
Hippocrateaceae; Celastraceae:
Salacia chinensis-413.
Labiatae; Lamiaceae:
Majorana hortensis-290.
Mentha piperata-304.
Mentha spicata-305.
Ocimum basilicum-329.
Ocimum canum-330.
Ocimum gratissimum-331.
Ocimum kilimandscharicum-332.
Ocimum sanctum-333.
Salvia plebeian-417.
Leguminosae, Fabaceae:
Pisum sativum-376.
Liliaceae:
Polygonatum cirrhifolium-381.
Polygonatum verticillatum-382.
Sansevieria roxburghiana-418.

List of Botanical Names Synonyms and Species
According to Serial Numbers of Plants

(Names printed in bold letters are presently in vogue, while those printed in light prints are synonyms and species)

Abbreviations

+	Mild in action
++	Moderate in action
+++	Good in action
++++	Very good in action
ACTH	Andrenocorticotrophic hormone
cm	Centimeter
CNS	Central nervous system
CVS	Cardiovascular system
ESR	Erythrocyte sedimentation rate
EtOH	Ethyl alcohol
g	Gram
GABA	Gamma aminobutyric acid
Hb	Haemoglobin
i.m.	Intramuscular
i.v.	Intravenous
IU	International units
LDL	Low density lipoproteins
mg	Milligram
ml	Milliliter, 20 drops of water, 1cc
mm	Millimetre
No.	Number
SGOT	Serum glutamic-oxaloacetic transaminase
SGPT	Serum glutamic-pyruvic transaminase
UTI	Urinary track infection

Index of English Words
(According to serial number of plant)

Glossary of Botanical Words
(Used in this book)

Acaulescent Stem less or very small stem

Accumbent Opposite

Achene A small indehiscent, one seeded fruit developing from a monocarpellary, superior ovary, and in which the seed coat is not fused with to the pericarp; e.g. *Mirabilis.*

Acicular Needle-shaped leaf i.e., long, narrow and cylindrical; e.g. Pine, Onion.

Actinomorphic Applied to a flower in witch the parts of each whorl are similar in shape; the flower can be divided into two equal halves along more then one median longitudinal plane; e.g. Dianthus, ipomoea.

Acumen An apex drawn into a tail

Acuminate [caudate] A leaf apex drawn out into a long slender tail; e.g. *Ficus religiosa.*

Acute Sharp apex, ending in a point forming an acute angle; e.g. China rose.

Acyclic Arranged in spirals and not in whorls; e.g. *Ranunculus.*

Adherent Two dissimilar parts united or fused

Adhesion Union of dissimilar parts

Adnate Two lateral stipules that grow adhering to the petiole up to a certain height thus making it some what winged; e.g. rose.

Adventitious root Roots that grow from any part of the body other than the radical.

Aerial Which remains above ground in air.

Aestivation The arrangement of perianth parts in bud condition

Aggregate fruit Fruit developed from a flower having a number of free carpels, all of which ripen together, and are more or less coherent at maturity.

Album White coloured

Alpine Existing in or connected with high mountains.

Alternate or spiral A single leaf arising at each node; e.g. Ipomoea.

Amphisarca a fleshy fruit with a woody pericarp developing from a syncarpous, superior, many seeded ovary. The edible portion is the placenta and the inner pulpy layers of pericarp; e.g. *Aegle marmelos.*

Amplexicaul A sessile leaf whose basal lobes completely enclose the stem; e.g. sonchus.

Androecium The third or male whorl of flower; made of stamens.

Androgyno phore An axis bearing both stamens and carpels above the point of perianth attachment

Androgynous Bearing both sramens and carpels or male and female flowers

Androphore An axis bearing the stamens

Angular A stem, which shows many lateral angles in a transverse section; e.g. asparagus.

Annual Of one season's duration from seed to maturity to death

Annular In a ring or arranged in a circle

Anther The pollen bearing part of the stamens

Apetalous Without petals

Apex The tip or distal end

Apiculate A leaf apex, terminated by a short, sharp flexible point; e.g. *Dalbergia.*

Apocarpous A pistil of two or more carpels which are free; e.g. *Clemetis.*

Appendage Any structure attached to a major part

Arcuately With bent like an arch

Areole The open space formed by an astomosing veins

Aril An appendage or an out growth of the seed coat, growing out form the hilum or funiculus

Arillate With an aril

Aristate A leaf apex, bearing a stiff bristle-like awn, tapered to a very narrow; much elongated apex.

Aromatic With aroma or scented

Articulate Jointed, provided with nodes

Astivation The arrangement of floral parts in bud.

Auricle An ear-shaped appendage or part, usually at the base of leaves or petals

Auriculate A sessile leaf whose basal lobes partially enclose the stem; e.g. *Calotropis.*

Autotrophic Self sufficient about food

Awn A bristle–like appendage

Axil Upper angle between stem and a petiole

Axile Belonging to axis

Axile placentation plancentae bearing the ovules developed from the central axis of a compound ovary, corresponding to the fused margins of carpels; e.g. *Solanum.*

Axillary In an axil.

Balausta A many chambered and many seeded, inferior fruit like the berry. Pericarp is tough with two rows of carpels one above the other bearing seeds irregularly. Calyx is persistent and succulent testa is edible; e.g. Pomegranate.

Basal place-ntation The ovules are a few, reduced to one and are borne at the base of the ovary, the ovules when solitary often filling the cavity, the ovary is unilocular; e.g. Sonchus.

Basifixed Filament attached to the base of the anther; e.g. Mustard, Cassia.

Basilar Attached at the base

Bechic Pertaining to cough

Berry A pulpy, few or many seeded fruit developing commonly from a syncarpus, superior or sometimes inferior ovary; e.g. Tomato, Banana, Guava.

Biannial Plant that lives for two years

Bicarpellary Having two carpels

Bicarpellate Having two carpels

Bifid Cleft into two parts or branches

Bifoliate Two leaflets are articulated to the petiole; e.g. *Hardwickia binnata.*

Bifurcate Divided into two branches

Bilocular With two locules

Biparous [dichasial] A determinate inflorescence in which the main axis ends in a flower after producing two daughter axes of flowers; e.g. *Ixora.*

Bipinnate A twice pinnate compound leaf ,the midrib produces secondary axes on which the leaflets are borne; e.g. Acacia, *Mimosa pudica.*

Biserrate Doubly serrate leaf margin, each tooth serrated again;

Bisexual Having both sexes present and functional in a flower

Biternate Twice divided in to three parts

Blade The expanded part of the leaf

Bract A modified, usually reduced leaf-like structure at the base of the flower.

Bracteate With bract, e.g. *Adhatoda.*

Bracteolate With bracteoles; e.g. *Adhatoda.*

Bracteole Bracts occurring on secondary axis i.e. pedicel of flower.

Branched A stem with many lateral shoots; e.g. ranunculus.

Bulb An underground and reduced stem composed chiefly of enlarged and fleshy leaf bases; e.g. onion, garlic.

Bulbil A small bulb, usually in the leaf axils

Caducous [fugacious] Falling off early, or prematurely; e.g. Poppy.

Calyptrate Resembling a lid-like structure

Calyx The outer or first whorl of flower, consisting of sepals.

Campanulate Bell shaped

Capitate When a large number of sessile flowers arise from a suppressed axis forming a globose structure as in Acacia, Mimosa. It differs from capitulum in the absence of a receptacle.

Capitulum A dense inflorescence comprising an aggregation of usually sessile flowers arranged on a convex receptacle formed by the axis, and having one or more whorls of bracts forming involucre; e.g. Compositae family.

Capsular Like a capsule

Capsule A many seeded dry fruit that develops from a compound, generally superior, one to many chambered pistil and opens in various ways, allowing the seeds to escape; e.g. Datura.

Carcerule A fruit formed of few to many united carpel

Carcerulus A dry schizocarpic fruit developing from a bicarpellary, superior ovary and ultimately breaking into four nutlets; e.g. *Ocimum.*

Carpel A leaf-like organ bearing ovules along the margins, the unit structure of a compound pistil.

Caryopsis A very small dry, indehiscent, one-seeded fruit developing from a mono-carpellary, superior ovary, with the pericarp fused with the seed coat; e.g. Wheat.

Catkin A pandant spike of unisexual flowers found only in woody plants; e.g. *Morus, Salix.*

Caudate Bearing a tail-like appendage

Caudex Non-branched, stout, cylindrical stem, marked with scars of fallen leaves.

Cauline The leaves, which are borne by the main stem only; e.g. Palms.

Cauline and ramal The leaves, which are borne by the main stem as well as by the lateral branches; e.g. Mango, Tamarind.

Chaff A small, thin, dry, membranous bract or a glume

Chaffy Like chaff

Cilia Hairs borne along margins

Ciliate a leaf margin ,bearing hairs on the margin; e.g. *Cleome viscosa.*

Cirrhose Tendrillar and coiled leaf apex; e.g. *Gloriosa.*

Cladode [sp. Stem] It is a phylloclade of one internodes [asparagus] or two internodes [*Ruscus*] only.

Cleft A leaf margin divided in or about the middle into divisions, as palmately or pinnately cleft leaf ; e.g. many ferns.

Climber Plant with thin and long stems, with diffuse branches and special organs of attachment for clings to the neighboring objects.

Climbing stem A weak stem attaching itself to any neighboring object by some special structures and then climbing it.

Clum A jointed stem with solid nodes and hollow internodes

Cohesion The act or state of sticking together

Columnar Column-like, pillar-like

Complete A flower with four whorls of floral parts; pistil, stamen, sepals and petals; e.g. *Solanum.*

Composite fruit Fruit composed of a number of closely associated fruits

Compound corymb A branched corymb; e.g. *Pyrus torminalis.*

Compound leaf A leaf in which the leaf blade is incised up to the midrib or petiole, thus dividing it into two or more segments, called leaflets;e.g. Gold mohur.

Compound spike Axis is branched and the flowers are arranged in a spike-like manner on the branches; e.g. *Amaranthus.*

Compound umbel An umbel with branched axis and the branches bearing the flowers. These are known as umbellules; e.g.*Coriander.*

Compressed Flattened from sides

Conduplicate Folded together lengthwise

Cone A dense and elongated collection of flower or fruits with bracts on a central axis

Connate Two sessile opposite leaves meeting each other across the stem and fusing together; e.g. *Lonicera flava.*

Connective A patch of tissue, which joins the two anther lobes.

Contorted Convolute, twisted

Convergent [parallel venation] Many principal veins arising from the base of the leaf blade converage towards its apex or less parallel manner; e.g. Wheat, Bamboo.

Convolute [ventral] Stipules occurring on ventral side of the petiole. The margins after meeting serve as bud scales; e.g. *Ricinus.*

Cordate Heart-shaped leaf, with a sinus and rounded lobes at the base and ovate in general outline; e.g. Betel.

Cordifolia Leaf of heart-like shaped

Coriaceous [Leaf structure] If a leaf is tough and thick like leather; e.g. *Calotropis.*

Corm A solid, globose, underground stem.

Corn A short thickened underground stem, upright in position in which the food is accumulated; e.g. crocus.

Corolla Second whorl of flower made of petals.

Corona Any appendage or extrusion that stands between the corolla and stamens, or on the corolla; e.g. Madar.

Corymb Indeterminate inflorescence with shortened main axis, in which the lower flowers have much longer pedi-cels than the upper so that flowers are brought more or less to the same level; e.g. Candytuft.

Corymbose Corymb-like.

Cotyledon Seed leaf, the primary leaf or leaves in the embryo.

Creeping A weak stem creeping on the ground, but rooting at the nodes

Cremocarp A dry schizocarpic two seeded fruit developing from a bicarpellary, inferior ovary and splitting at maturity into two mericarps, each borne on a carpophore [prolonged end of the axis]; e.g. *Coriandrum.*

Crenate Shallowly round toothed leaf margin; Hydrocotyle.

Crispate Clured leaf margin, extremely undulate; e.g. *Tagetes.*

Crusiform Shape of cross

Crustaceous Dry, membranous

Culm A jointed stem with solid nodes and hollow internodes.

Cuneate A wedge-shaped leaf i.e., triangular with the narrow end at point of attachment; e.g. *Oxalis corymbosa.*

Cupular Cup-shaped

Cuspidate A leaf apex ending in a long, rigid, spiny point; e.g. Pineapple and date palm.

Cyathium A special type of inflorescence characteristic of Euphorbia, in which a cup-shaped involucre, often provided with nectary, encloses a single female flower [reduced to pistil] in the centre and a number of male flowers [each reduced to a solitary stamen] around it.

Cyclic Arranged in definite whorls; e.g. *Solanum.*

Cylindrical A stem, which is circular in a transverse section; e.g. lemon.

Cyme A broad, more or less flat topped, determinate inflorescence with central flower opening first.

Cymose An inflorescence where the growth of the main axis is soon checked by the development of a flower its apex, and

	the lateral axis which develops below the terminal flower also end in a flower, thus its growth is also checked.
Cymose umbel	Determinate umble inflorescence with central flower maturing first
Cypsela	A dry, indehiscent, one-seeded fruit developing from a bicarpellary, syncarpous, inferior unilocular ovary, with the pericarp and seed coat free; e.g. *Sonchus*.
Cythium	A type of inflorescence characteristic of *Euphorbia*
Deciduous	Falling off along with the petals just after fertilization; e.g. Mustard.
Decompound	a compound leaf which is more then thrice pinnate; e.g. *Coriandrum*.
Decumbent	A trailing stem lying on the ground but with the apex ascending.
Decurant	A sessile leaf with a winged leaf base and the wing extending down the stem so that latter also seems to be winged; e.g. *Lagera pterodonta*.
Decussate	A pair of leaves that stands at right angle to the next upper or lower pair; e.g. *Calotropis*.
Dehiscent [capsular fruit]	Which burst automatically on ripening and discharge their seeds.
Deliquescent	When the main axis in growth is subordinated by more growing lateral branches giving a round shape to the tree.
Deltoid	Delta-shaped leaf; e.g. *Abutilon*.
Dentate	A leaf margin, with sharp spreading, rather coarse indentations or teeth that are perpendicular to the margin; e.g. Melon.
Denticulate	Minutely dentate leaf margin; e.g. *Luffa cylendrica*.
Depressed	Pressed down from the top.
Diadelphous	Stamens united in two bundles by connation of their filaments [anthers being free]; e.g. Pea.
Dichotomous	Forked, two branches from a point
Dicotyledon	Presence of two cotyledons in a seed
Didynamous	With four stamens, two short and two long.
Diffuse	A trailing stem with many spreading branches.
Digitate	Palm-like compound with the members arising from one point.
Dimerous	Two-merous, the parts in two's or multiple of 2; e.g. Poppy.
Dioecious	Having male and female flower on separate plant
Disc	A more or less fleshy development of the receptacle.
Dissected	Divided into many narrow parts.
Distichous	Two ranked
Distinct	Separate
Dithecous	A two celled anther; e.g. Citrus.
Divergent [parallel venation]	Many principal veins arising from the tip of the petiole, diverge towards the margin of leaf blade in a more or less parallel manner; e.g. Fan palms.
Dormant	Not active or growing now but able to become active or to grow in the future
Dorsifixed	Filament attached to the back of the anther; e.g. *Bauhinia, Citrus*.
Dorsiventral	Flattended surface with definite upper and lower surface.
Drupe	A fleshy, generally one seeded fruit with the pericarp differentiated into the epicarp [forms the skin] mesocarp[fleshy and edible] and endocarp[hard and stony]; e.g. Mango, Coconut, almond.
Ebracteate	Without bracts; e.g. *Solanum*.
Echinate	With stout prickle
Eliptical	A leaf, oval in outline narrowed to rounded ends and widest at or about the middle; Guava.
Ellipsoid	Nearly elliptical
Elliptic	Oblong but ends tapering towards both ends.
Elongate	Lengthened, which has become long
Emarginate	A leaf apex provided with a deep notch; e.g. Bauhinia.
Emerginate	With a shallow notch at the apex
Endocarp	Inner skin
Entire	An even and smooth leaf margin; e.g. Madar, Mango.
Epicalyx	whorls of bracteoles developing at the base of calyx, e.g. China rose.
Epicarp	Outer skin or cover.
Epigynous	Used for a flower when the ovary is inferior and other floral organs arise above it; e.g. *Coriandrum*.
Epiphyte	A plant that grows upon other plant, but does not absorb food from them as do the parasites.
Erect	A rigid and strong stem holding itself in an upright position.
Etaerio of achenes	An aggregate of achenes; e.g. Straberry, *Naravelia*.
Etaerio of berries	An aggregate of berries; e.g. *Anona squamosa*.
Etaerio of drupes	An aggregate of drupes; e.g. Rubes.
Etaerio of follicles	An aggregate of follicles; e.g. *Michelia champaca*.
Excerted	Projected beyond
Excurrent	When the main axis continues growth and the lateral branches develop regularly giving a conical appearance to the tree.

Exserted	Stamens longer then the corolla tube, protruding outwards; e.g. Passionflower.
Exstipulate	Stipules absent; e.g. *Ipomoia.*
Extrorse	An anther dehiscing towards the periphery of the flower; e.g. *Argemone.*
Falcate	Sickle-shaped leaf; e.g. *Eucalyptus.*
Fasciculated	With bundle
Fasicle	Bundle
Filament	Thread, stalk of the stamen.
Filiform	A long and slender petiole; e.g. *Ricinus.*
Fimbricate	Fringed, with ciliate margin.
Fistular	A stem having a hollow interior; e.g. bamboo, wheat.
Fleshy [Leaf structure]	A soft and thick leaf; e.g. *Spergula.*
Flexuous	Zigzag.
Floret	Small flower.
Flower	Modified shoot, meant essentially for reproduction of the plant
Foliaceous	Two large green leafy structures; e.g. *Pisum.*
Foliage	Leaf
Foliolate	With leaflets.
Follicle	A dry fruit derived from a superior and one chambered pistil and opening along ventral suture only; e.g. *Calotropis.*
Free lateral	Two free stipules borne on the two sides of the leaf base; e.g.China rose.
Free-central placentation	The ovules are borne on a central column without any septa, the ovary is unilocular; e.g. *Stellaria.*
Frond	Leaf of a fern.
Fruit	It is a mature or ripened ovary.
Fusifom	Tapering towards both ends
Gametes	Unicellular sexual reproductive body
Gamopetalous	When the petals are united; e.g. *Ipomoea.*
Gemosepalous	When the sepals are fused; e.g. Dianthus
Germination	When a seed of a plant starts to grow
Glabra	Without hairs.
Glabrous	A smooth surface free from hairs or outgrowths of any kind; e.g. china rose.
Gland-dotted	Having glands.
Glaucous	Green and shining surface; e.g. *Citrus.*
Globose	Spherical, globe shaped.
Glochid	A minute bristle.
Glume	Dry or chaffy membranous bract.
Glutinous	A surface covered with a sticky exudation; e.g. Tobacco.
Gonous	Angular
Grooved	A petiole provided with a long furrow.
Gymnosperm	Seeds without enclosure of a fruit or seed producing plant which do not produce fruits
Gynandrous	When gynoecium attached with stamens
Gynobasic	Arising from the base of the gynoecium.
Gynoecium [pistil]	The fourth or female whorl composed of one or more carpels.
Gynophore	Stalk of the ovary.
Habit	Characteristic form or bodily appearance of an organism
Habitat	The place where a particular type of plant or animal is normally found
Hairy	Covered with hairs; e.g. *Calotropis.*
Halicoid	Uniparous cyme in which the lateral branches develop successively on the same sides, evidently forming a sort of halix; e.g. *Heliotropium.*
Hastate	A leaf, like an arrowhead in form; but the basal lobes directed outward; e.g. *Rumex hastatus.*
Head	The mass of leaves or flowers at the end of a stem
Helix	A shape like a spiral
Herb	A plant with soft and short stem, height up to 1m.
Herbaceous	A soft, non-woody plant
Hermaphrodite [Bisexual]	A flower in which both stamens and pistils are present; e.g. China rose.
Hesperidium	A fleshy fruit developing from a many carpellary, syncarpous, superior ovary with axile placentation and with endocarp projecting inwards forming distinct chambers, and the epicarp and mejocarp fused together forming the rind of the fruit; e.g. Lemon.
Hilum	Placental attachment scar
Hiruste	a surface provided with rather rough or coarse hairs.
Hispid	A surface, beset with rigid or bristly hairs.
Hollow	Having a hole or empty space inside
Hook climber	A weak stem climbing by the help of recurved thorns; e.g. Bougainvillea, or hook e.g. Climbing rose.
Hydrophyte	Plants living in water
Hypanthium	A cup like receptacle, usually derived from the perianth and stamens, on which are seemingly borne calyx, corolla and stamens.
Hypanthodium	The fleshy receptacle forms a cup-like cavity with an apical opening [ostiol] guarded by scales and bearing flowers on the inner wall of the cavity; e.g. Fig, Peepul.
Hypogynous	A flower in which the ovary is superior and all other floral organs are situated below its level; e.g. Citrus.
Imbricate	Out of the five sepals one is internal, one external and the other three partly internal, partly external; e.g. *Iberis*

	amara, Cleome.
Imperipinnate	a unipinnate leaf with odd number of leaflets; e.g. Rose, *Melia.*
Incised	A leaf margin, cut irregularly, more or less deeply
Incomplete	A flower lacking one or more of the four kinds of floral whorls sepals, petals, stamens and pistils; e.g. *Euphorbia.*
Indehiscent [achenial] fruit	which do not split open at maturity and thus the seeds are liberated only by the destruction of pericarp.
Indicum	Mostly grow in India
Indicus	Mostly grow in India
Inferior	Said of the ovary when it is situated below the perianth.
Inflorescence	a cluster of flowers or arrangement of flowers on floral axis.
Insectivore	A plant which trap the small insects for food.
Inserted	Stamens shorter then the corolla tube remaining included within it; e.g. *Catharanthus.*
Insertion	The act of putting inside else
Internode	The part of an axis between two successive nodes.
Interpetiolar	Two stipules lying between the petioles of opposite or whorled leaves; e.g. Ixora
Intrapetiolar	Stipules situated between the petiole and the axis; e.g. *Tabernae montana.*
Introrse	An anther dehiscing towards the centre of flower; e.g. *Dianthus.*
Involucre	Whorls of bracts
Isobilateral	Having two similar surfaces
Keel	The two front petals, united to form a boat-shaped structure of a papilio-naceous corolla.
Lacerate	Torn leaf margin; irregularly cleft or cut, as in many genara of Ranuncul-aceae.
Lacineate	A leaf margin; cut into narrow pointed lobes,
Lamellate	With linings or filing
Lamellate placentation	The ovules are borne on plate-like lamellae within the ovary. It is a modification of parietal placentation; e.g. *Papaver.*
Lamina	Surface and shape of the leaf
Lanceolate	Lance-shaped leaf, much longer then broad, widening above the base and tapering to the apex; e.g. *Nerium.*
Lateral	Connected with the side
Latex	Milky sap.
Lax	Loose, opposite of congested or compact.
Leaf	An organ of limited growth arising laterally and from superficial tissues of the shoot apex and usually dorsiventral.
Leaf climber	A weak stem climbing by its petiols; e.g. clematis, or leaf tips; e.g. *Gloriosa.*
Leaflets	One part of a compound leaf.
Legume	A type of dry fruit developed from a simple , superior and one chambered pistil and opening along both the sutures; e.g. Peas, beans.
Lenticles	Minute pores on stem and branches
Lians climber	A long woody perennial twiner; e.g. hipatage.
Ligulate	Tongue-shaped, strap-shaped.
Linear	Long and narrow leaf, the sides parallel or nearly so ;e.g. leaves of most grasses.
Lip	One of the parts in an unequally divided corolla or calyx, upper and lower.
Lobe	A segment of an organ.
Lobed	A leaf margin divided into many lobes; e.g. *Ranunculus.*
Locule	Chamber or compartment of ovary.
Loment	A leguminous fruit contracted between the seeded segments separating at maturity.
Lomentum	A dry schizocarpic leguminous fruit, constricted between the seeds to form one-seeded segments, which separate at maturity; e.g. *Acacia,* Groundnut.
Longifolia	With lengthen leaves.
Longitudinal	Going downwards rather than across
Lorate	Strap-shaped leaf, e.g. Vallisneria.
Lyrate	A leaf like a lyre in form i.e. pinnatifid but with an enlarged terminal lobe and smaller lower lobes; e.g. Mustard.
Mamillate	Rough, studded with rounded projections
Marginal	Said of placentation where it is situated along one margin of the ovary.
Marginal placentation	Placentae developing along the junction of the two margins of the carpel in monocarpellary and one chambered ovary; e.g. pea.
Membranous [Leaf structure]	A leaf, which is thin and pliable like a membrane; e.g. *Solanum nigrum.*
Mesocarp	Middle layer of fruit wall
Mesophyte	Plants grow between dried and excess water condition
Modification	A act or process of changing in order to improve it or make it more acceptable
Monadelphous	Stamens united in one group by connation of their filaments [anthers being free] e.g. China rose.
Moniliform	Constricted laterally and appearing bead-like.
Monocarpellary	With single carpel.
Monocotyledon	One cotyledon present in each seed
Monoeceous	Male and female flowers born on the same plant

Monothecous	a one celled anther; e.g. *Ricinus*, China rose.
Morphology	The form and structure of plant and animal
Mucronate	A rounded leaf apex terminated abruptly in a short point; e.g. leaflet of *Cassia obtusifolia.*
Multicarpellary	With many carpels.
Multicostate	A type of reticulate venation, having many principal veins arising from tip of petiole and proceeding upward or outwards.
Multifoliate [digitate]	Five or more leaflets are articulated to the petiole and spreading like fingers from the palm; e.g. *Bombax.*
Multilocular	With many locules.
Multiparous [polychasial]	A determinate inflorescence in which the main axis ends in a flower after producing a number of daughter axes or flowers around. this looks like an umbel but can be distinguished from umbel by the opening of the middle flower first; e.g. *Calotropis.*
Multiple of composite fruit	Fruit composed of a number of closely associated fruits, derived from entire inflorescence and forming one body at maturity; e.g. Jackfruit.
Muricate	A surface with small blunt projections.
Napiform	Of the shape of a beet root.
Nectary	A nectar-secreting gland, often appearing as a protuberance, scale or pit; e.g. Salvia.
Neuter	Not male or female
Nigrum	Black coloured.
Node	A joint of stem where a leaf is borne.
Nodular	With many nodes.
Notch	A V-shaped or circular cut in an edge or a surface
Nut	A dry, indehiscent, one-seeded fruit, developing from a superior, bi-or polycarpellary ovary and in which the fruit wall ios hard, stony or woody at maturity; e.g. chestnut, oak, Litchi.
Oblanceolate	Opposite to lanceolate; a leaf broader at the distal third then at the middle and tapering toward the base; e.g. *Gnaphalium.*
Oblique	A leaf, slanting, the two halves of the leaf are unequal; e.g. leaflets of Margosa.
Oblong	A leaf, longer then broad and with the margin running more or less parallel up to its length; e.g. **B**anana.
Obovate	A leaf reverse of ovate, the apical half broader at the basal; e.g. *Cassia obtusifolia* leaflet.
Obpypyramidal	Reserve of a pyramid
Obreniform	The reserve of reniform , inverted, kidney shaped.
Obtuse	Blunt or rounded leaf apex; e.g. Banyan.
Ochreate	Stipules that form a hollow tube encircling the stem from the node up to a certain height of internode in front of the petiole; e.g. *Polygonum.*
Officinalis	Approved by Government agency.
Offset	A creeping stem which is horizontal, short ,thickened, prostrate branch, producing at the apex a tuft of leaves above and a cluster of small roots below. e.g. *Pistia.*
Operculum	Lid or cover.
Opposite	Term applied to leaves or buds occurring in pairs at a node; e.g. *Ixora.*
Orbicular	Circular or disk-shaped.
Ornamental	Used as a decoration rather than for a practical purpose
Oval	Shape of egg.
Ovary	Ovule-bearing part of a carpel.
Ovate	A leaf with an outline like that of Hen's egg, broader at the base than at apex; e.g. china rose.
Ovule	The body which encloses embryo sac or female gemetophyte and becomes seed after fertilization.
Padate	a leaf margin in which a palmatly lobed or divided leaf of which the two side lobes are again divided or cleft.
Palmate	A leaf margin, lobed or divided into a palm-like fashions; e.g. castor.
Palmately compound	A compound leaf with the leaflets attached at the tip of the petiole and thus seem to be radiating from a common point, like fingers from the palm; e.g. *Cleome gynandra.*
Palmatifid	A leaf margin, cut about half-way down in a palmate form; e.g. castor.
Panical	When axis of receme is branched, it is called a panical; e.g. Gold mohur.
Papilionaceous	Type of the corolla which appears like a butterfly.
Pappus	Peculiar modified calyx of the sun flower family
Parallel venation	The pattern of venation in which the veins run parallel to each other. In this type there are no veinlets and no network is formed.
Parasite	A plant that grows upon other living plant or animal and obtains food its food material from them.
Parianth	A collective term of calyx and corolla when any one or both of them are present.
Parietal placentation	Plancentae bearing the ovules on the inner wall of the ovary and their

position corresponds to the fused margins of carpels and number of plancentae is equivalent to the number of carpels; the ovary is one chambered; e.g. *Argemone.*

Paripinnate a unipinnate leaf with even number of leaflets; e.g. tamarind.

Parted A leaf margin, Cut into quite the base.

Pectinate a leaf margin, comb like or pinnate with very close narrow divisions.

Pedicel Stalk of a single flower in an inflorescence.

Pedicilate Having a stalk; e.g. Dianthus.

Penducle Stalk of an inflorescence or a solitary flower.

Pendulous Hanging from above.

Pentacarpellary Compose of five carpels.

Pentalocular Five chambered.

Pentamerous Five-merous,the parts in five's or multiple of 5; e.g. *Solanum.*

Pepo A pulpy many seeded fruit like berry but developing from an inferior, trica-rpellary, unilocular ovary with parietal placentation; e.g. *Cucurbita.*

Perennial Of three or more season's duration.

Perifoliate A sessile leaf whose basal lobes meet across the stem and fuse together so that the latter seems to pass through the leaf blade;e.g. *Aloe perfoliata.*

Perigynous The floral organ borne and arising from around the ovary and not beneath it; e.g. Peach, Plum.

Perinnial Plant that lives for many years

Persistent Remaining attached in the fruit also; e.g. *Solanum, Datura.*

Petal One of the separate parts of corolla usually coloured and more or less showy.

Petaloid Resembling a petal; e.g. *Asphodelus.*

Petiolate A stalked leaf; e.g. China rose.

Petiole Bearing of leaf

Phylloclade [sp.stem] A green, flattened or rounded succulent stem having many internodes and with leaves either feebly developed or modified into spines; e.g. *Opuntia.*

Phyllode A sickle-shaped petiole flattened like a leaf; e.g. *Acacia auriculiformis.*

Phyllotaxy Arrangement of leaves on stem.

Pilose A surface, thinly covered with long, soft hairs.

Pinna A primary division or a leaflet of pinnate leaf.

Pinnate With pinna

pinnately compound A compound leaf with the leaflets arranged along the sides of common axis, the rachis; e.g. Tamarind.

Pinnatifid A leaf margin, cleft or parted in a pinnate way; e.g. *Asplenium alternans.*

Pinnatisect A simple leaf deeply divided to the midrib in a pinnate manner.

Pistillate A unisexual flower with a pistil.

Pistillode A sterile gynoecium or pistil.

Pistle Gynoecium

Placenta The region or area of the ovary to which ovule or ovules are attached.

Placentation Arrangement of placentae and ovules in the ovary.

Plant A living thing that grows in the earth and usually having a stem, leaves and roots

Plicate Folded lengthwise.

Plumbose Feather-like with fine hairs.

Pod A fruit of legume family.

Pollen Spores or grains borne by the anther.

Pollen sac A part bearing pollen

Pollination Transfer of pollen from the anther to stigma.

Polyadelphous Stamens united in many bundles by connation of their filaments [anthers being free; e.g. Citrus, *Bombax malabarica.*

Polyadelphous Whenstamens are present in many bundles

Polyandrous An androecium whose stamens are free [anthers as well as filaments]; e.g. *Papaver.*

Polycarpellary When carpels are free.

Polypetalous When the petals are free; e.g. Mustard.

Polyphyllous Bearing many leaves

Polysepalous When the sepals are free; e.g. Geranium.

Polystemonous When stamens are free.

Pome A fleshy fruit surrounded by the thala-mus and developing from a two or more carpellary, syncarpous, inferior ovary; e.g. apple, pear.

Pore Small opening.

Porous With small opening.

Prickle Sharp and stout outgrowth on the stem, petioleetc. As in rose.

Prickly With prickles

Procumbent Trailing or lying flat, but not rooting.

Prostrate [procumbent] A trailing stem lying flat on the ground.

Pseudowhorls False whorls.

Puberulous Having fine hairs on the surface

Pubescent Surface covered with soft, short, straight hairs.

Pyramidal Having shape of a pyramid

Pyriform Pear-shaped.

Pyxis A capsule with circumscissile dehiscence; *Plantago.*

Quadrifoliate Four leaflets are articulated to the petiole; e.g. *Marsilea.*

Quincuncial	A form of imbricate where there are five sepals, two internal, two external and one partly internal, partly external, e.g. *Stelaria, Dianthus.*
Raceme	A simple, elongated, indeterminate inflorescence with stalked flowers; e.g. Radish, Mustard.
Racemosa	With recemose.
Racemose	An inflorescence where the main axis does not terminate in a flower, but it continues to grow and gives off flowers laterally in acropetal succession.
Racemose umble	Umble with outer flowers opening first.
Rachis	Axis bearing flowers or leaflets.
Radial	Present at radius
Radical	The leaves, which arise from a reduced underground stem; e.g. Onion.
Ramal	The leaves which are borne by the lateral branches
Raphe	A ridge like structure present on a seed
Receptacle	A more or less enlarged end of the flower axis bearing parts.
Regma	A dry schizocarpic fruit developing from a tricarpellary, syncarpous superior ovary and splitting at maturity into three cocci; e.g. *Ricinus.*
Reniform	Kidney-shaped leaf; e.g. *Centella asiatica.*
Reticulate	The pattern of venation in which the veinlets are irregularly distributed, forming a network.
Retuse	An obtuse or truncate leaf apex furnished with a shallow notch; e.g. *Oxalis corymbosa.*
Rhizome	A horizontal underground stem, distinguished from the root by the presence of nodes and internodes and some times buds and scale-like leaves at the nodes .often thickend and containing accumulated food; e.g. ginger, turmeric.
Rhombate	A leaf, which shape like a rhombus.
Rhombifolia	A plant which leaves shape like a rhombus.
Rootlet climber	A stem climbing by its roots given off from its nodes; e.g. *Pothos.*
Roseous	Like-rose.
Rotund [orbicular]	A leaf blade circular in outline; e.g. Water lily.
Rough	a surface which is somewhat harsh to touch; e.g. *Petrea.*
Rubra	Red coloured.
Rugose	Covered with wrinkles.
Runner	A creeping stem, which is slender, elongated, prostrate, aerial branch with long internodes, creeping on the ground and rooting at the nodes.
Runsinate	A leaf, coarsely serrate to sharply incise with the teeth pointing toward the base; e.g. Poppy.
Saccate	Sac-like, pouch-like.
Sagittate	A leaf, like an arrowhead, triangular with the basal lobes pointing downwards or concavely toward the stalk; e.g. *Sagittaria sagittifolia.*
Samara	A dry indehiscent, one or two seeded, winged fruit developing from a superior ovary; e.g. Acer, *Hiptage.*
Saprophyte	A plant that grows in places rich in decaying organic substances, deriving its nutrition from them.
Scabrous	A surface, feeling roughish or gritty to touch.
Scaly	Small dry scales, usually two in number, borne on two sides of the leaf base; e.g. *Spergula.*
Scandent	Climbing but without tendrils
Scape	A leafless, usually non-branched flowering shoot produced by an underground stem.
Scarious [Leaf structure]	A thin dry and non-green leaf; e.g. *Asparagus.*
Schizocarp	Intermediate between dehiscent and indehiscent.
Schizocarpic [splitting fruit]	Intermediate between dehiscent and indehiscent. The fruit breaks up into one or more seeded units. Sometimes the seeds are liberated only after the decay of pericarp.
Scorpioid	Uniparous cyme in which the lateral branches develop on alternate sides evidently forming a zigzag; e.g. *Ranunculus bulbosus.*
Secund	One sided.
Semi- amplexicaul	A sessile leaf whose basal lobes incompletely enclose the stem; e.g. *Ranunculus.*
Sepal	One of the separate parts of a calyx, usually green and foliaceous.
Sepaloid	Resembling to a sepal; e.g. Date palm.
Sericeous	A surface provided with silky hairs.
Serrate	Leaf margin cut like the teeth of a saw and the teeth directed upward, e.g. China rose.
Serulate	Leaf margin, Minutely serrate; e.g. *Prunus persica.*
Sessile	A leaf without stalk; e.g. *Dianthus.*
Shallow	Not having much distance between the top and bottom
Sheath	Long and tubular structure.
Sheathing	With sheath.
Shoot	The part that grows up from the ground when a plant starts to grow

Shrub Medium size plant, height up to 3m, do not have clear stem

Silicula A dry fruit, much shorter and flattened siliqua containing only a few seeds; e.g. Candytuft.

Siliqua A dry two chambered long, narrow, many-seeded fruit developing from a bicarpellary, syncarpous, superior ovary and dehiscing from below upwards by both the sutures and seeds remaining attached to replum; e.g. Mustured.

Simple fruit A single fruit developing from a single ovary of a single flower with or without accessory parts.

Simple leaf A leaf which may be entire or incised to any depth, but not down to the mid rib or petiole; e.g. Mango.

Slender Thin and narrow, small in amount or size and hardly enough

Solid A stem having a filled interior; lemon.

Solitary axillary Borne singly in the axil of a leaf; e.g. *Cucurbita,* China rose.

Solitary flower Borne singly or alone.

Solitary terminal Borne singly at the apex; e.g. Lily, Poppy.

Solitory Singly.

Sori Sporangium of the ferns present on leaves

Sorosis A fruit developing from spike or spadix in which the flowers fuse by their succulent tepals and axis bearing them becomes fleshy or woody thus forming a compact mass; e.g. Pineapple, Mulberry.

Sorus A cluster of fruiting bodies (spores) of ferns.

Spadix A thick or fleshy spike subtended or surrounded by a spathe; e.g. Maize.

Spathe A large bract subtending an inflorescence, particularly spadix.

Spathulate Spoon-shaped leaf, broad and round at the top and towards the base; e.g. Calendula.

Spike Usually non-branched, elongated, simple, indeterminated inflorescence whose flowers are sessile; e.g. *Adhatoda.*

Spikelet The unit of the compound inflorescence of the grasses ; composed of a cluster of one or more flowers and their associated bracts; e.g. Grasses.

Spinosa A plant with spines.

Spinous A leaf margin, provided with spines; e.g. *Argemone.*

Spinulose Bearing minute spines.

Spiny A surface covered with spines; e.g. *Argemone.*

Spirocyclic Half cyclic; e.g. *Ranunculus.*

Spore A simple, grain like reproductive body of ferns and lower plants.

Spur A tubular or sac-like projection form a bottom, as of a petal and usually containing a nectar-secreting gland; e.g. *Delphinium.*

Spured With spur.

Stamen An individual part of an androecium that produces pollen grains usually composed of anther, connective & filament.

Staminate A unisexual flower with stamens.

Staminode a sterile stamen or a structure resembling stamen and borne in stamina part of the flowers; e.g. *Stellaria.*

Stellate A surface having star-like hairs, radiating branches; hairs once or twice forked are often treated as stellate.

Stem Main axis of the plant; bearing leaf and flower.

Sterile Lacking functional sex organs.

Stigma Terminal part of gynoecium that receives pollen grains.

Stipel Stipule-like appendage at the base of leaflets of a compound leaf.

Stipular With stipule

Stipulate Stipules present; e.g. Rose.

Stipule An appendage on both the sides of basal part of a leaf.

Stolon A creeping stem, which is slender, elongated, horizontal stem, at or below the surface of the ground that gives rise to a new plant at its tip.

Stout Strong, resolute

Striate A petiole marked with longitudinal lines; e.g. *Ficus.*

Strigose A surface with sharp, appressed straight hairs, stiff and often basally swollen.

Strobile Type of spike in which each flower is borne in the axil of a persistent membranous bract; e.g. *Humulus lupulus.*

Style More or less elongated part of gynoecium between the ovary and the stigma.

Sub-alpine Below mountain

Sub-capitate Slightly capitate.

Sub-opposite More or less opposite.

Sub-peltate More or less peltate.

Sub-reniform More or less reniform.

Sub-sessile More or less sessil.

Subulate Narrow and tapering from base to apex.

Succulent [Leaf structure] A fleshy and juicy leaf; e.g. *Bryophyllum.*

Sucker A creeping stem developing from a underground part of the stem but growing obliquely upward and directly giving rise to a leafy shoot or a new plant. e.g. peppermint.

Superficial placentation	Ovary is multilocular, carpels being numerous as in axile type but placentae in this case develop all round the inner surface of partition wall; e.g. Water lily.
Superior	Said of the ovary when calyx, corolla and stamens arise from below it.
Superposed	A pair of leaves that stands directly over a pair in the same plane; e.g. guava.
Syconus	A fruit developing from hypanthodium inflorescence, characteristically having a hollow, pear shaped flashy receptacle; e.g. Fig.
Symbiont	Two organisms living together in such away that they appear to be the parts of the same plant, and are of mutual benefit to each other.
Synandrous	Stamens united throughout their whole length by both-the filaments and the anthers; e.g. *Cucurbita.*
Syncarpous	a pistil of two or more carpels which are fused; e.g. *Melia.*
Syngenesious	Stamens connate by their anthers [the filaments being free to form a cylinder about the style, as in compositae]; e.g. *Sonchus.*
Tap root	A Stout, tapering main root arising from the radical and from which arise smaller lateral branches.
Temperate	Having a mild temperature without extremes of heat or cold
Tendril	A thread-like twining structure or organ.
Tendril climber	A weak stem climbing by its slender, leafless, spirally-coiled structures known as tendrils; *Cucurbita.*
Tendrilar	Stipules modified into tendrils, one on each side of the petiole; e.g. *Smilax.*
Tepal	One of the separate parts of perianth
Terete	A cylindrical petiole being circular in cross section; e.g. *Ipomoea.*
Terminal	At the tip, apical or distal end.
Terrestrial	Of the ground.
Testa	Outer seed coat.
Tetracarpellary	With four carpels.
Tetradynamous	An androecium of six stamens of which four are long and two short.
Tetralocular	With four locules or chambers.
Tetramerous	Four-merous, the parts in four's or multiple of 4; e.g. Mustard.
Texonomy	Science of classing and studying the plants in certain groups
Texture	Overall structure.
Thyrsus	A panicle-like cluster with main axis indeterminate and the lateral axis determinare; e.g. *Liacs*
Tomentose	A surface densely covered with long, soft wool-like hairs.
Torulose	Irregularly swollen at close intervals
Torus	Receptacle.
Trailing stem	A weak stem spreading on ground; without rooting at the nodes.
Transverse	Situated across
Tree	A perennial woody plant with a single trunk, height more then 3m.
Tricarpellary	With three carpels.
Trifoliate	Three leaflets are articulated to the petiole; e.g. *Aegle, Oxalis.*
Trilocular	With three locules or chambers.
Trimerous	Three-merous, the parts in three's or multiple of 3; e.g. *Argemone.*
Tripinnate	A thrice pinnate compound leaf, the secondary axes produce the tertiary axes which bear the leaflets; e.g. *Moringa.*
Truncate	A leaf apex appearing as if cut off at the end; e.g. *Caryota urens.*
Tuber	A much enlarged portion of an underg-round stem provided with buds on the sides and tips; e.g. potato, *Cyperus.*
Tuberculate	With tubers.
Tuberous root	A root of tuber like shape.
Tubular	Tuber like shape.
Turgid	Swollen from fullness.
Twiner climber	A long slender and branched stem, which climbs by twining its body round the support; e.g. *Cuscuta.*
Twisted [contorted]	One margin of sepal overlaps that of the next one, and the other margin is overlapped by the third one.
Umbel	An inflorescence in which the flower stalks of more or less equal length, arise from the same point, like the ribs of an umbrella at the base of flower stalks, there is whorl of bracts forming an involucre; e.g. *Hydrocotyle asiatica.*
Umbellet	With umble.
Unbranched	A stem without lateral shoots; e.g. palms.
Underground stem	A stem lying below the ground and serving for food storage and perennation;e.g. Potato.
Undershrub	Short in height than shrub
Undulate [Sinuate]	Wavy leaf margin,[up and down and not in and out]; e.g. *Polyalthia.*
Unicostate [Parallel venation]	Having only one principal vein that gives off many lateral veins which proceed toward the margin or apex of leaf blade in a more or less parallel manner; e.g. Banana
Unifoliate	A single leaflet is articulated to the petiole; e.g. Citrus.
Unilocular	With single locule.
Uniparous [mono-chasial]	The main axis ending in a flower producing only one lateral branch at a time ending in a flower.

Unipinnate	A pinnately compound leaf bearing the leaflets directly on the rachis; e.g. Cassia.
Unisexual	A flower having only one sex; e.g. *Morus*.
Utricle	A one seeded fruit with a thin wall, often dehiscent by a lid; e.g. *Amaranthus*.
Valvate	Sepals meeting by the edges without overlapping; e.g. *Solanum*.
Velutinous	A surface clothed with a velvety covering composed of erect, straight, moderately firm hairs.
Venation	The arrangement of vascular bundles or veins in a leaf.
Versatile	Filament attached to the back of the anther at a point only, so that the latter can swing freely; e.g. Eucalyptus, Grasses.
Verticillaster	It consists of a series of nodes. At each node there is a condensed dichasial cyme with a cluster of almost sessile flowers arranged opposite one another in the axils of opposite bracts or leaves; e.g. *Ocimum*.
Verticil	A whorl.
Verticillate	Arranged in whorls
Vexillary	Out of the five petals the posterior one is the largest and covers the two lateral petals and the latter in their turn overlap the two interior and smallest petals; characteristic of papilionaceae.
Villous	A surface covered with thickly, long, soft hairs.
Vulgare	With ugly shape.
Waxy	With wax.
Weak stem	`A stem which is not enough strong to keep itself in an upright position.
Whorl	A circle.
Whorled	A ring of leaves, flowers
Woody	A hard stem plant; trees and shrubs.
Wooly	A surface densely covered with soft, long curled hairs looking like wool.
Xerophyte	Plants growing in dry condition
Zygomorphic	Term applied to a flower in which the members of some or all of the flower whorls are unequal. Most irregulars can be divided longitudinally in to two equal halves in only one vertical plane; Pea, *Adhatoda*.
Pyrenes	Seed
Spathe	A large bract usually coloured and enclosing an inflorescence
Succulent	Juicy

Glossary of Medical Word
(Used in this book)

Abdomen	Part of body lying between the thorax and pelvis
Abortion	Expulsion from uterus of the products of conception before the fetus is viable
Abscess	A localized collection of pus in a cavity
Abulia	Loss or deficiency of will power
Acantharsia	Failure to obtain desired purgation
Acidosis	A pathological condition resulting from accumulation of acid
Acne vulgaris	An Inflammatory disease of the skin with the formation of an eruption of papules or pastules
Acroanesthesia	Pain in the extremities
Acroasphyxia	Coldness and paleness of the hands and feet.numbness of finger.
Adaptogenic	One substance which increase adaptability
Adiposis	Obesity; excessive accumulation of fat
Adjuvant	A nonspecific stimulator of the immune response
Adrenergic	Secreting epinephrine or related substance, particularly the sympathetic nerve fibers that liberate norepinephrine at a synapse when a nerve impulse passes
Adultration	Addition of an impure
Agalactia	Absence or failure of secretion of milk
Age vitalizer	To give long life.
Aggravates	To excite; to provoke; to exasperate
Alcoholism	A disorder marked by a pathological pattern of alcohol use
Alexepharmic	A medicine neutralizing poison
Alexeteric	An agent that increase alexia
Alkaloid	Any of a group of organic substances found in plants
Allergy	A hypersensitive state acquired through exposure to a particular allergen
Alleviates	To relive; to mitigate; to allay; to assuage
Alopecia	Baldness, Absence of hair from skin area where it is normally present
Amblyopia	Dimness of vision
Amebiasis	State of being infected by amebas
Amenorrhea	Absence or abnormal stoppage of the menses
Amoebic dysentery	Amebic colitis
Anabolism	The constructive process by which living cells convert simple substance into more complex compounds, especially into living matter
Analgesic	Relieving pain
Anaphrodiasiac	An agent allaying sexual desire
Anaphylaxis	Anaphylactic shock
Anasarca	Dropsy; generalized heavy edema
Anemia	Reduction below normal of the number of erythrocytes, quantity of hemoglobin
Anesthesia	Loss of sensation, or loss of the ability to feel pain
Aneurysm	A sac formed by localized dilatation of the wall of an artery, or vein, or the heart
Ankylosis	Immobility and consolidation of a joint due to disease, injury, or surgical procedure
Anodmia	Lack of Smell feeling
Anodyne	Relieving pain
Anorexia	Lack or Loss of appetite for food
Anorthosis	Failure to achieve penile erction
Anthelmintic	Destroying or expelling worms
Antibactrial	Destroying or suppressing growth or reproduction of bacteria
Antibiotic	A chemical substance produced by a mic-ro organism, which has the capacity to inhabit the growth of or to kill other microorganism
Anticalculous	Suppressing the formation of calculi
Anticholesteremic	Promoting a reduction of cholesterol levels in the blood
Anticonvolsant	An agent that suppresses convulsions
Antidiuretic	An agent that causes suppression of urine
Antidote	An agent that counter acts a poison
Antiemetic	Preventing nausea and vomiting
Antifungal	Destructive to fungi
Antigalactic	Diminishing secretion of milk
Antigen	Any substance capable of inducing a specific immune response and of

	reacting with the products of that response
Antiinflammatory	Suppressing Inflammation
Antilithic	Preventing calculous formation
Antioxidant	Something added to a product to prevent or delay its deterioration by the oxygen in air
Antipediculotic	Effective against lice
Antipruritic	Preventing itching
Antipyretic	Relieving or reducing fever
Antiseptic	Preventing sepsis
Antisialagogue	Counteracting saliva formation
Antispasmodic	Preventing or relieving spasm
Antitussive	Effective against cough
Anuresis	Retention of urine in the bladder or anuria
Anuria	Complete suppression of urine formation by the kidney
Anxiety	A feeling of apprehension, uncertainty, and fear without apparent stimulus, associated with physiological changes (tachycardia, sweating, tremor etc.)
Aperient	A mild laxative or gentle purgative
Aphagia	Difficulty in swallowing
Aphrodisiac	Arousing sexual desire
Aphthae	Small white or red ulcers found in the mouth
Aphthae	Small red or whiteulcers found in mouth
Apnea	Cessation of breathing
Apoplexy	Sudden rupture of blood vessels in the brain with paralysis and unconsciousness
Apozema	Decoction
Appendicitis	Inflammation of the vermiform appendix
Areflexia	Absence of reflex actions
Aromatic	Having a spicy odor
Arteriosclerosis	A group of diseases characterized by thickening and loss of elasticity of the arterial walls
Arteriostenosis	Constriction of an artery
Arthralgia	Pain in a joint
Arthritis	Inflammation of a joint
Aspermia	Failure of formation or emission of semen
Asphyxia	Pathological changes caused by lack of oxygen in respired air, resulting in hypoxia and hypercapnia.
Asthenia	Lack or loss of strength and energy; weakness
Asthenopia	Weakness or easy fatigue of the eye, with pain in the eyes, Headache, dimness of vision
Asthma	A condition marked by recurrent attacks of paroxysmal dyspnea with wheezing due to spasmodic condition of bronchi
Astringent	Causing contraction
Atherogenic	Increase formation of atheromatous lesions in arterial walls
Atheroma	A mass or plaque of degenerated thickened arterial intima, occurring in atherosclerosis
Atonic	Without tone
Azoospermia	Absence of spermatozoa in the semen
Bacteria	A division of the kingdom procaryotae
Bactericidal	Destructive to bacteria
Balanitis	Inflammation of the glans penis
Baldness	Alopecia, especially of the scalp
Baryphonia	Deepness and hoarseness of the voice
Bechic	Pertaining to cough
Benign	Not malignant
Bilirubin	A bile pigment produced by breakdown of haemoglobin from red blood cells
Biological	Pertaining to biology
Blemishes	Deformity or stain
Blennorrhea	Any free discharge of mucus, especially a Gonorrheal discharge from the urethra or vagina; gonorrhea
Blepharitis	Inflammation of eyelids
Breast	The front of the chest, especially its modified glandular structure, the mamma
Bronchial	Pertaining to bronchi
Bronchiectasis	Chronic dilatation of one or more bronchi
Bronchitis	Inflammation of bronchi
Broncho-pneumonia	Inflammation of the lungs
Bruises	An injury in which the skin is not broken but is discoloured due to hemorrhage from the ruptured blood vessels into the subcutaneous tissues
Bubo	An enlarged and inflamed lymph node, particularly in the axilla or groin
Cachexia	General ill health and malnutrition
Calcaneodynia	Pain in the heel
Calculosis	Lithiasis
Candidiasis	Infection of fungi, most commonly involving the skin, oral mucosa, respiratory tract, and vagina
Canities	Grayness or whiteness of the scalp hairs
Cardiopathy	Any disease of the heart
Cardiotonic	Having a tonic effect on the heart
Catabolism	Any destructive process by which complex substance are converted by living cells into more simple compounds, with release of energy
Catalysis	Increase in the velocity of a chemical re-action or process produced by the prese-

nce of a substance that is not consumed in the net chemical reaction or process

Cataplasm Poultice

Catarrh Inflammation of a mucous membrane, with free discharge

Catheter A tubular, flexible surgical instrument that is inserted into a cavity of the body to withdraw or introduce fluid

Chancroid A sexually transmitted disease

Characteristic Typical of an individual or other intity

Cheilitis Inflammation of the lips

Chiasma Poultice

Chickenpox A highly contagious disease, caused by herpes zoster virus

Chloasma Melasma

Chloesterolemia Hypercholesterolemia; an excess of cholesterol in the blood

Cholagogue An agent that stimulates gallbladder contraction to promote bile flow

Cholecystitis Inflammation of the gallbladder

Cholelithiasis The presence or formation of gallstones

Cholera An acute disease, marked by severe Diarrhea and vomiting

Cholesterol A eukaryotic sterol

Cholesterolemia Hypercholesterolemia; an excess of cholesterol in the blood

Cholesterolemia Hypercholesterolemia

Cholinergic Stimulated, activated, or transmitted by choline; said of the sympathetic and parasympathetic nerve fibers that liberate acetylcholine at a synapse when a nerve impulse passes

Chologogue Increase bile flow

Choluria The presence of bile in the urine

Chorea The ceaseless occurrence of rapid, jerky, dyskinetic, involuntary movements

Cinchonism Toxicity due to cinchona alkaloid over dosage

Cirrhosis Interstitial Inflammation of an organ, particularly the liver

Coagulant Promoting or accelerating coagulation of blood

Colic Acute paroxysmal Abdominal pain

Colitis Inflammation of the colon

Colonalgia Pain in the colon

Colonitis Colitis; Inflammation of colon

Colpitis Inflammations of vagina

Coma A state of profound unconsciousness from which the patient cannot be aroused, even by powerful stimulation

Comatose Adjective of coma

Conception The onset of pregnancy

Congestion Abnormal accumulation of blood in a part

Contraceptive Preventing conception

Contraindication Any condition which renders a particular line of treatment improper or undesirable

Convulsion An involuntary contraction or series of contractions of the voluntary muscles

Coryza Profuse discharge from the mucous membrane of the nose

Costalgia Ribs pain

Cough Sudden noisy expulsion of air from lungs

Coxalgia Pain in the hip

Cramp A painful spasmodic muscular contraction

Cryesthesia Abnormal sensitiveness to cold

Crymodynia Pain of cold and damp weather

Cyanosis A bluish discolouration of skinand mucous membranes due to excessive concentration of reduced hemoglobin in the blood.

Cyst Any closed epithelium-lined cavity or sac, containing liquid

Cystitis Inflammation of the urinary bladder

Dandruff Dry scaly material shed from the scalp

Debility Lack or loss of strength; weakness

Deficiency A lack or shortage

Degeneration Deterioration, change from a higher to a lower form

Delirium A mental disturbance of relatively short duration

Delivery Expulsion or extraction of the child and fetal membranes at birth

Dementia An organic mental syndrome characteri-zed by a general loss of intellectual abili-ties involving impairment of memory, judgment

Demulcent A soothing mucilaginous or oily medicine or application

Dengue A infectious, eruptive, febrile, viral disease

Dentalgia Toothache

Dentifrice The substance for cleansing the teeth

Deodorant An agent that masks offensive odors

Depilatory An agent for removing or destroying hairs

Depression A morbid sadness, dejection, or melancholy

Deprivation Loss or absence of parts, power, or things that are needed

Dermatitis Inflammation of the skin

Desiccative To dry

Detoxification Reduction of the toxic properties of a substance

Diabetes Any disorder characterized by excessive urine excretion

Diabetes mellitus A metabolic disorder in which there is inability to oxidized carbohydrates, due

	to disturbance of the normal insulin mechanism
Diabetes insipidus	Polyuria, excessive excretion of urine
Diagnosis	Determination of the nature of a case of a disease or the distinguishing of one disease from another
Diaphoretic	The thing which causes profuse sweating
Diarrhea	Abnormally frequent evacuation of watery stools
Diathesis	An unusual constitutional susceptibility or predisposition to a particular disease
Digestion	The act or process of converting food into chemical substances that can be absorbed and assimilated
Dilution	Reduction of concentration
Dipsesis	Excessive thirst
Dipsosis	Excessive thirst
Diptheria	An acute infectious disease, affecting the membranes of the throat, nose, or larynx, and marked by formation of a grey-white pseudomembrane
Disease	Any deviation from or interruption of the normal structure or function of any body part, organ, or system
Disorder	A derangement or abnormality of function; a morbid physical or mental state
Diuretic	Increasing urine excretion or the amount of urine
Douche	A stream of water directed against a part of the body or into a cavity
Dracontiasis	Guine worm disease
Dropsy	Edema
Dyscrasia	Morbid condition
Dysentery	Any of a number of disorders marked by Inflammation of the intestine, especially of the colon, with abdominal pain, tenesmus, and frequent stools containing blood and mucus
Dyskinesia	Impairment of the power of voluntary movement
Dysopia	Defective vision.
Dysorexia	Impaired or deranged appetite
Dyspepsia	Impairment of the power or function of digestion
Dysphagia	Difficulty in swallowing
Dysphagia	Difficulty in swallowing.
Dysphasia	Impairment of speech
Dysphoria	Disquiet; restlessness; malaise
Dyspnea	Labored or difficult breathing
Dysspermia	Impairment of the spermatozoa, or of the semen, painful ejaculation of semen
Dysuria	Painful or difficult urination
Eczema	A superficial Inflammation of epidermis
Ejaculatio praecox	Premature ejaculation
Ejaculation	Forcible, sudden expulsion; especially expulsion of semen from the male urethra
Elephantiasis	A chronic filarial disease
Emaciation	The condition of being extremely lean
Emaciation	The condition of being extremely lean
Embolism	The sudden blocking of an artery by a clot or foreign material
Embrocation	Fomentation drug
Emesis	The act of vomiting
Emission	A discharge; specifically an involuntary discharge of semen
Emmenagogue	An agent that promotes menstruation
Emollient	Softening or soothing
Emphysema	Over distention and stretching of lung tissue or organs
Emprosthotonos	Titanic forward flexure of the body.
Empyema	Accumulation of pus in a body cavity
Enteritis	Inflammation of the intestine
Enuresis	Bed wetting, involuntary passage of urine at night or during sleep
Ephidrosis	Abnormal sweating
Epilepsy	Episodic impairment or loss of consciousness, abnormal motor phenomena, psychic or sensory disturbance of the autonomic nervous system
Epistaxis	Hemorrhage from nose
Epithema	Any local application
Erection	The condition of being rigid and elevated, as erectile tissue when filled with blood
Erotic	Pertaining to sexual love or to lust
Eructation	Belching; casting up wind from the stomach through the mouth
Eruption	Visible efflorescent lesions of the skin due to disease; a rash
Erysipelas	A contagious disease of the skin and subcutaneous tissue
Erythema	Redness of the skin
Euphoria	Bodily comfort; well being; absence of pain or distress.
Exfoliation	A falling off in scales or layers
Exhaustion	A state of extreme mental or physical fatigue
Exhilarant	An agent enlivening the mind
Exophthalmia	Protrusion of eye balls from the orbit
Expectorant	Promoting expectoration
Exudative	One substance which increase exudation
Fatigue	A state of increased discomfort due to excessive or prolonged exertion
Febrifuge	An agent that dispelling fever
Fermentation	The anaerobic enzymatic conversion of organic compounds
Fetid	Bed smell

Fever	Pyrexia; elevation of body temperature above the normal
Filaria	A nematode worm
Fissure	Any cleft or groove
Fistula	An abnormal passage or commun-ication, usually between two internal organs
Flaccidity	Relaxation, deficiency in muscular tone, weakness or softness.
Flatulence	Excessive formation of gasses in the stomach or intestine
Fluid	Any liquid of the body
Fracture	The breaking of a part, especially a bone
Freckles	A brownish or yellowish spot on the skin
Friction	The act of rubbing
Frigidity	Coldness or female sexual arousal disorder
Frozen shoulder	Adhesive capsulitis
Fumigation	Exposure to disinfecting fumes
Fungicide	An agent that destroys fungi
Furrow	A groove or trench
Furuncle	A boil
Furunculosis	The disease condition of that accomp-anies the appearance of a crop of boils
Galactacrasia	Abnormal condition of the breast milk
Galactagogue	Promoting milk flow
Galactorrhea	Excessive or spontaneous milk flow
Gangrene	Death of tissue
Gargle	A solution for rinsing mouth and throat or to rinse the mouth and throat by hold-ing a solution in the open mouth and agi-tating it by expulsion of air from the lungs
Gastritis	Inflammation of the stomach
Gastroentritis	Inflammation of stomach and intestine
Gastrohelcosis	Ulcer of the stomach.
Gauze	A light, open-meshed fabric of muslin or similar material
Gel	A firm colloid although containing much liquid
Giardiasis	Presence of flagellate protozoa parasite in the intestinal tract
Gingivitis	Inflammation of gingival
Gleet	Chronic gonorrheal urethritis
Gleet	A chronic stage of gonorrhea with mucopurulent discharge
Glossitis	Inflammation of the tongue
Glycosuria	The presence of glucose in the urine
Gonorrhea	A infectious disease of urethra
Gonyalgia	Pain in knee
Gout	A group of disorders with recurrent paroxysmal attacks of acute Inflammatory arthritis
Gravel	urinary calculus
Gynecomastia	Excessive development of the male mam-mary glands, even to the functional state
Halitosis	Offensive odor of the breath
Halitosis	Unpleasant or foul breath
Headache	Pain in the head
Heliosis	Sun stroke
Helminthiasis	Intestinal parasitic worms
Hematemesis	Vomiting of blood
Hematemesis	The vomiting of blood
Hematinic	An agent that improves the quality of blood, increasing the hemoglobin level and the number of erythrocytes
Hematuria	The presence of blood in the urine
Hemihidrosis	Sweating on one side of the body
Hemiplegia	Paralysis of one side of the body
Hemophilia	A hereditary hemorrhagic diathesis
Hemoptysis	Spitting of blood or of blood-stained sputum
Hemorrhage	The escape of blood from the vessels; bleeding
Hemorrhoid	A varicose dilation of a vein of the hemorrhoidal plexus
Hemostasis	The arrest of bleeding
Hepatitis	Inflammation of the liver
Hepatocirrhosis	Cirrhosis of the liver
Hepatomegaly	Enlargement of the liver
Heptotoxicity	Accumulate toxin in the liver
Heredity	The genetic transmission of a particular quality or trait from parent to offspring
Hernia	Protrusion of a portion of an organ or tissue through an abnormal opening
Herpes zoster	An acute, unilateral, inflammatory skin diseases marked by the formation of vesicles in clusters
Hiccough	Sharp inspiratory sound with spasm of the glottis and diaphragm
Hidrosis	Excessive sweating
Hirsutism	Abnormal hairiness, especially in women
Histamine	An amine, found in all body tissues. It induces capillary permeability and lowers blood pressure; contraction of most smooth muscle tissue; increased gastric acid secretion; and acceleration of the heart rate
Hook worm	A nematode parasite in the intestine of man and other animals
Hormone	A chemical substance produced in the body which has a specific regulatory effect on the activity of certain cells or a certain organs
Horripilation	Bristling of the hairs
Hydragogue	Producing watery discharge, specially from bowel

Hydrophobia	Rabies
Hydrostomia	An excessive secretion of fluids in the mouth.
Hydrostomia	An excessive secretion of fluids into the mouth
Hyper lipidemia	Elevated concentration of any or all of the lipids in the plasma
Hypercapnia	An excess of Carbon dioxide in the blood
Hypercryalgesia	Excessive sensivitiness to cold
Hyperesthesia	Increased sensitivity to stimulation, particularly to touch
Hypergalactia	Excessive secretion of milk
Hyperglycemia	Abnormally increased content of glucose in the blood
Hyperhydrosis	Excessive perpiration
Hyperlactation	Lactation in greater than normal amount
Hypermenorrhea	Excessive menstrual bleeding, but occurring at regular intervals and being at usual duration
Hyperorexia	Excessive appetite
Hyperpnea	Excessive respiration
Hyperpyrexia	Excessively high body temperature
Hyperreflexia	Exaggerated reflex action
Hypersalivation	Ptyalism
Hypertension	Persistently high arterial blood pressure
Hyperthyrodism	Excessive thyroid gland activity
Hypertrichosis	Excessive growth of hairs
Hypertrophy	Enlargement or overgrowth of an organ or part
Hypnolepsy	Morbid sleepiness
Hypocholeste-rolemia	Abnormally low levels of cholesterol in the blood
Hypogalactia	Deficiency of milk secretion
Hypogeusia	Abnormally diminished sense of taste
Hypoglycemia	Deficiency of glucose concentration in the blood
Hypomastia	Abnormally smallness of the mammary glands
Hypomenorrhea	Diminution of menstruation flow or duration
Hypomnesia	Diminution of memory
Hypoptyalism	Abnormally decreased secretion of saliva
Hypoptylism	Diminished secretion of saliva
Hyposmia	Decrease in the normal sensitivity to smell
Hyposomnia	Reduced time of sleep
Hyposomnia	Insomnia
Hypotension	Abnormally low blood pressure
Hypothermia	Low body temperature
Hypotrichosis	Deficiency of hairs
Hypourocrinia	Deficiency in the secretion of urine
Hypoxia	Reducing of oxygen supply
Hyptonic	Inducing sleep
Hysteria	Sudden onset of dream states, stupors, and paralysis
Idiosyncrasy	An abnormal susceptibility to an agent e.g. a drug, *Dhatuvaisamya*
Idrosis	Hyperhydrosis
Ignipeditis	Burning pain of sole of feet
Immunity	Security against a particular disease
Impotence	Lack of power; specially, lack of copulat-ive power in the male due to failure to initiate an erection or maintain an erection until ejaculation
Impotentia	Unable to achieve penile erection
Incontinence	Inability to prevent the discharges of any of the excretion, especially of urine or feces
Indigestion	Lack or failure of digestion
Inflammation	A protective tissue response
Influenza	An acute viral infection of the respiratory tract
Infusion	The steeping of a substance in water to obtain its soluble principles
Inhalation	The drawing of air or other substances into the lungs by the nasal or oral respiratory route
Insanity	Mental illness; psychosis
Insomnia	Inability to sleep
Insufflation	The blowing of powder in to a cavity
Ischemia	Deficiency of blood in a part
Itching	Pruritis; provoking the desire to scratch or rub the skin
Jaundice	Icterus; yellowness of skin, sclera, mucous membranes, and excretions due to hyperbilirubinemia and deposition of bile pigments
Jelly	A soft, resilient substance; generally, a colloidal semisolid mass
Juvenile	Pertaining to youth or childhood
Kakidrosis	Foul smelling perspiration
Kerotosis	Any horny growth; such as a wart or callosity
Kinetosis	Car sickness or motion sickness
Lactifuge	Checking or stopping milk secretion
Lactigenous	Producing milk
Lallation	A babbling; infantile form of speech
Laryngitis	Inflammation of the larynx
Laxative	Aperient; mildly cathartic or purgative
Leprosy	A chronic communicable disease, with production of granulomatous lesions of the skin, mucous membranes, and peripheral nervous system
Lethargy	A lowered level of consciousness, with drowsiness, listlessness, and apathy

Leukemia	A progressive, malignant disease of the blood forming organs, marked by distorted proliferation and development of leukocytes
Leukoderma	An acquired condition with localized loss of pigmentation of skin
Leukopenia	Reduction of the number of leukocytes in the blood
Leukorrhea	A whitish viscid discharge from the vagina and uterine cavity
Leukotrichia	Whiteness of the hair
Libido	Sexual desire
Lime water	Prepared and filtered solution of quick lime and water in ratio of 1:100
Lipoma	A benign, soft, rubbery, encapsulated tumor of adipose tissue
Lithagogue	An agent that expels calculi
Lithiasis	A condition marked by formation of calculi and concretions
Lithuresis	The passage of gravel in the urine
Lock Jaw	Tonic spasms of the jaw muscles as seen in tetanus
Lozenge	A medicated tablet or disk; a troche
Lumbago	Pain in the lumber region
Macerate	To soften by steeping or soothing
Malaise	A vague felling of discomfort
Malignant	Tending to become worse and end in death
Mammillitis	Thelitis, inflammations of a nipple
Massage	Systematic therapeutic friction, stroking, or kneading of the body
Mastalgia	Pain in the mammary glands or breast
Mastitis	Inflammation of the breast
Mastodynia	Pain in the breast
Mastoptosis	Pendulous breasts
Masturbation	Induction of orgasm by self-stimulation of the genitals
Matroptosis	Prolapse of the uterus
Meal	A portion of food taken at some particular or fixed time
Measels	Rubeola; a highly contagious viral infection, usually of childhood
Melasma	Sharply demarcated, blotchy, brown macules, usually in a symmetrical distribution on the cheeks and forehead, often associated with pregnancy or other altered hormonal state
Melena	The passage of dark stools stained with altered blood
Meningitis	Inflammation of the meninges
Menometro-rrhagia	Excessive or irregular menstrual bleeding
Menopause	Cessation of menstruation
Menorrhalgia	Dysmenorrhea
Menstruation	The cyclic, physiologic discharge thro-ugh the vagina of blood and muscosal tissue from the nonpregnant uterus
Meralgia	Pain in the thigh
Mercurilism	Chronic poisoning from misuse of mercury
Metritis	Inflammation of the uterus
Metrorrheagia	Uterine bleeding, usually of normal amount, occurring at completely irregularly intervals, the period of flow sometimes being prolonged
Micturition	Frequent desire to passing of urine
Migraine	A symptom complex of periodic heada-che, usually temporal and unilateral
Miosis	Abnormal contraction of the pupils
Moan	To produce a sound expressive of suffering
Morament	Feeble minded
Morbidity	Pertaining to or affected with diseases
Mortality	The ratio of actual deaths to expected deaths
Motility	The ability to move spontaneously
Mucilage	An aqueous solution of a gummy substance
Mucopurulent	Containing both mucus and pus
Mumps	An acute contagious disease of childho-od, involving chiefly the salivary glands
Murmur	An auscultatory sound
Myalgia	Muscular pain
Myasthenia	Muscular debility or weakness
Narcosis	Sleep or general anaesthesia produced by some narcotic drugs
Nasitis	Inflammations of nose
Nausea	A unpleasant sensation vaguely referred to the epigastrium and abdomen, with a tendency to vomit
Necrospermia	A condition in which the spermatozoa of the semen are dead or motionless
Nephritis	Inflammation of the kidney
Neuralgia	Paroxysmal pain extending along the course one or more nerves
Neurasthenia	An obsolete category of neurosis, marked by chronic weakness and easy fatigability
Neuritis	Inflammation of a nerve
Neurodynia	Neuralgia
Neurogenic	Forming nervous tissue
Neurosis	A category of mental disorder marked by anxiety and avoidance behavior
Nictitation	Quivering or winking of the eyelids
Nocturia	Excessive urination at night
Nostril	External opening of nose
Notalgia	Pain in back
Numbness	Anesthesia
Nyctalgia	Pain which occurs at night only

Nyctalopia	Night blindness
Obesity	An increase in body weight with excessive accumulation of body fat
Odontalgia	Toothache
Odonterism	Chattering of the teeth
Odonthemodia	Great sensitiveness of teeth
Odontitis	Inflammation of the tooth pulp
Odontoprisis	Grinding of teeth
Odontoprisis	Grinding of the teeth
Odontoprisis	Grinding teeth during sleep
Oleaginous	Oily; having the nature of oil
Oligohydruria	Abnormally high concentration of the urine
Oligomenorrhea	Abnormally infrequent menstruation
Oligospermia	Deficiency of spermatozoa in the semen
Oliguresis	Scantiness of urine
Onanism	1.masturbation 2. withdrawal of the penis before the completion of the sexual act.
Opisthotons	A form of spasm in which head and heels are bent forward
Orchitis	Inflammation of the testis
Orexigenic	Increasing the appetite
Osteoarthritis	Noninflammatory degenerative joint disease, marked by degeneration of the articular cartilage , hypertrophy of bone at the margins, and changes in the synovial membrane, acompained by pain and stiffness
Osteodynia	Pain in the bones
Otalgia	Pain in the ear; earache
Otitis	Inflammation of the ear
Otopyorrhea	A copious purulent discharge from the ear
Otorrhagia	Hemorrhage from the ear
Otorrhea	A discharge from the ear
Oxytocic	An agent that promotes rapid labor by stimulating contracting of the myometrium
Ozena	A fetid nasal ulceration and discharge
Ozostomia	Bad breath; a foul odor from the mouth
Palpitation	A subjective sensation of an unduly rapid or irregular heartbeat
Parageusia	A bad taste in the mouth
Paralysis	Loss or impairment of motor function in a part
Paraphimosis	Retraction of a narrow or inflamed fores-kin of penis which cannot be replaced
Paraplegia	Paralysis of the lower part of body
Parkinsonism	A group of neurological disorders marked by hypokinesia, tremor, and mascular rigidity
Parturient	Giving birth, by extension
Pectoralgia	Pain in the breast
Peduculosis	Infestation with lice
Pendulous	Hanging loosely; dependent
Penile	Of or pertaining to the penis
Perfrication	Rubbing with an ointment
Pertussis	An infectious disease, marked by catarrh of the respiratory tract and peculiar paroxysmus of cough
Phalacrosis	Baldness
Phalangitis	Inflammation of one or more phalanges
Phallagia	Pain in the penis
Phallitis	Inflammation of the penis
Phallodynia	Pain in the penis
Pharyngitis	Inflammation of the pharynx
Pharyngodynia	pain in the pharynx
Phimosis	Tightness of the foreskin of the penis so that is cannot be drawn back from over the glans
Phlegm	Viscid mucus excreted in abnormally large quantities from the respiratory tract
Phlegmatic	Of dull and sluggish temperament
Phthisis	Tuberculosis
Pityriasis versicolor	A Skin diseases marked by formation of scales
Plague	An acute febrile, infectious, fatal disease
Plantalgia	Pain in the sole of the foot
Pleurisy	Inflammation of the pleura
Pleurosthotons	Bending of the body to one side
Pneumonia	Inflammation of the lungs with exudation and consolidation
Pneumonitis	Inflammation of lung tissue
Podalgia	Pain in the foot
Pogoniasis	Growth of beard in women
Poliomyelitis	An acute viral disease, marked by fever, sore throat, headache, vomiting, stiffness of the neck and back, and paralysis
Pollution	Discharge of semen during sleep
Polydipsia	Chronic excessive intake of water
Polydrisis	Excessive sweating
Polyneuritis	Inflammation of the several peripheral nerves simultaneously
Polyphagia	Excessive ingestion of food
Polyphrasia	Extreme talkativeness
Polysiatia	excessive secretion of saliva
Polytrichia	Excessive growth of hairs
Polyuria	Excessive secretion of urine
Poultice	A soft mush prepared by various substances with oily or watery fluids
Priapism	Involuntary erection of penis
Proctitis	Inflammation of the rectum
Prolapse	The falling down, or downward displacement, of a part or viscus

Prophylaxis	Prevention of disease; preventive treatment
Prostatitis	Inflammation of the prostate
Prurigo	A chronic popular skin disease with intense itching
Pruritus	Itching
Psellism	Stammering
Psoriasis	A chronic hereditary, recurrent dermatosis marked by discrete vivid red macules, papules, or plaques covered with silvery lamellated scales
Psychosis	Any major mental disorder of organic or emotional origin marked by derangement of personality an loss of contact with reality, often with delusion, hallucination, or illusions
Psychroalgia	A painful sensation of cold
Psychrophobia	Extreme sensitiveness to cold
Ptarmic	Causing sneezing
Pternalgia	Pain in the heel
Puberty	The period during which the secondary sex characteristics begin to develop and the capability of sexual reproduction is attained
Pubescent	Arriving at the Age of puberty. Or covered with down or lanugo
Pulp	Any soft, juicy animal or vegetable tissue
Pulse	The rhythmic expansion of an artery which may be felt with the finger
Pyelonephritis	Inflammation of the kidney and its pelvis due to bacterial infection
Pyorrhea	A copious discharge of pus
Quininism	Disturbance of nervous system caused by continuous use or large doses of the Sulphate of quinine
Refrigerant	Cooling; allaying heat
Regurgitation	Flow in the opposite direction from normal
Rejuvenate	To make or become young again
Resolvent	That which causes solution of tissues
Revulsive	Causing transfer of a disease or blood from one part of the body to another, a counterirritant
Rheumatalgia	Chronic rheumatic pain
Rheumatism	Any of a variety of disorders marked by inflammation, degeneration, or metabolic derangement of the connective tissue structure, especially the joint
Rheumatoid	Resembling rheumatism
Rhinitis	Inflammation of the nasal mucus membrane
Rhinocleisis	Obstruction of the nasal passages
Rhinopathy	Any disease of the nose
Rhinophonia	A nasal tone in speaking
Rhinorrhagia	Hemorrhage from nose
Rhinorrhalgia	Nosebleed, epistaxis
Rhinorrhea	A mucous discharge from nose
Rickets	A condition due to vitamin D deficiency, especially in infancy and childhood
Rinorrhea	The free discharge of a thin nasal mucus
Risus sardonicus	A special laughing expression in tetanus
Roborant	Tonic, strengthening
Roborent	Strengthening tonic; renovating medicine
Rubefacient	Reddening the skin
Salivation	An abnormally abundant flow of saliva
Sapphism	Sexual perversion between women
Satiromania	Excessive sexual desire
Satyriasis	Excessive sexual desire
Satyriasis	Excessive sexual desire in the male
Scabies	A contagious skin diseases due to the itch mite
Scar	Cicatrix, a mark remaining after the healing of a wound
Sciatica	Neuralgia along the course of the sciatic nerve
Scotoma	A dark, vanishing picture before the eyes
Scrofula	Tuberculous cervical lymphadenitis
Scrotocele	Scrotal hernia
Seborrhea	Excessive secretion of sebum
Secretion	The cellular process of elaborating and releasing a specific product
Sedimentation	The settling out of sediment or precipitate
Septicemia	Blood poisoning
Sialorrhea	Ptyalism
Sign	An indication of the existence of something; any objective evidence of a disease
Sinus	A recess, cavity, or channel
Smallpox	Variola; an acute, highly contagious, often fatal infectious disease marked by fever and progressive skin eruptions
Snore	Rough, noisy breathing during sleep
Solution	A homogeneous mixture of one or more substances dispersed in a sufficient quantity of dissolving medium
Somasthenia	Weakness of the body
Somatotrofic	Having a stimulating effect on the body growth
Spasmodic	Of the nature of a spasm
Spasmogenic	Producing spasm
Spasmolytic	Producing spasm
Sperm	Semen or spermatozoa
Spermatogenic	Producing semen or sperm
Spermatopoietic	Forming the semen

Spermatorrhea	Involuntary escape of semen, without orgasm
Spermaturia	Seminurea; discharge of semen in the urine
Spleenomagely	Enlargement of spleen
Spondylitis	Inflammation of vertebrae
Spondylosis	Ankylosis of a vertebral joint
Sprain	A joint injury in which some of the fibers of a supporting ligaments are raptured
Sprue	A chronic form of malabsoption syndrome
Sputum	Matter ejected from the trachea, bronchi, and lungs
Stenosis	Narrowing or contraction of a duct or canal
Stimulant	Producing stimulation
Stomachalgia	Pain in the stomach
Stomatalgia	Pain in the mouth
Stomatitis	Generalized Inflammation of the oral mucosa
Stomatodynia	Pain in the mouth
Strain	To over exercise
Strangulation	Choking or throttling arrest of respiration by occlusion of the air passage
Strangury	Slow and painful discharge of urine
Stress	Forcibly exerted influence; pressure
Stria graviderum	Streak or line on lower abdomen of pregnant women
Stupor	Insensibility, unconsciousness
Sudorofic	Promoting sweating; diaphoretic
Sun stroke	A condition caused by excessive exposure to the sun, marked by high skin temperature, convulsions, and coma
Sunburn	Injury to the skin, after excessive exposure to sunlight
Suppurative	Causing or promoting pus formation
Swab	A wad of cotton or other absorbent material
Swelling	Transient abnormal enlargement of a body part or area
Symptom	Any subjective evidence of disease or of a patient's condition
Syncope	A faint; temporary loss of conciousness due to generalized cerebral ischemia
Syndrome	A set of symptoms occurring together; the sum of signs of any morbid state; a symptom complex
Syphilis	A venereal disease
Syrup	A concentrated solution of a sugar, in water, sometimes with a medicinal agent added
Systemic	Pertaining to or affecting the body as a whole
Tachycardia	Abnormally rapid heart rate
Tachyphagia	Rapid eating
Tachypnea	Very rapid respiration
Tachypnea	Excessive rapidity of respirstion
Tape worm	A parasitic intestinal cestode worm
Tenderness	An state of unusual sensitivity to touch or pressure
Tetanus	An acute, often fatal, infectious disease caused by a neurotoxin
Thelitis	Inflammation of nipple of breast
Theriaca	Raw sugar, molasses, treacle
Thread worm	Any long slender nematode
Thrombosis	The formation or presence of a thrombus or an aggregation of blood factor
Thrush	Canddiasis of the oral mucous membranes
Tonsillitis	Inflammation of the tonsils
Topical	Pertaining to a particular area
Toxemia	The condition resulting from the spread of bacterial products or toxin
Tranquilizer	A drug with a calming, soothing effect
Transfusion	The introduction of whole blood or blood components directly into the blood stream
Trauma	A wound or injury, whether physical or psychic
Trichogenous	Stimulating hair growth
Trichogenous	Stimulating hair growth
Trismus	Spasm of the muscles of mastication resulting in lockjaw
Tuberculosis	Any of the infectious disease of man and animals marked by formation of tubercles and caseous necrosis in tissue of any organ
Tumor	Swelling or neoplasm; a new growth of tissue in which cell multiplication id uncontrolled and progressive
Turbidity	Cloudiness, not clear
Tympanitis	Abnormal distention due to the presence of gas or air in the intestine or the peritoneal cavity
Typhoid	Typhoid fever
Ulcer	A local defect, or excavation of the surface, of an organ or tissue
Ulemorrhagia	Bleeding from the gums
Ulemorrhagia	Bleeding from gums
Ulemorrhagia	Bleeding from the gums
Ulitis	Inflammations of gums
Ulocace	Ulceration of the gums
Ulorrhagia	Bleeding from the gums
Ulorrhea	Discharge from the gums
Unconscious	Insensible
Unction	Unguent, ointment
Urethritis	Inflammation of the urethra

Urethrorrhea	Abnormal discharge from the urethra
Urocystitis	Inflammations of urinary bladder
Urodynia	Pain during urination
Urolithiasis	Calculus in urinary system
Urticaria	Hives; a vascular reaction of the upper dermis with slightly elevated patches which are redder or paler
Uvulitis	Inflammation of the uvula
Vaginal laxity	Yoni shaithilya
Vaginitis	Inflammation of the vagina
Vascular	Pertaining to a vessels
Vasoconstriction	Decrease in the caliber of blood vessels
Vasodilator	Causing dilatation of blood vessels
Venereal	Due to or propagated by sexual intercourse
Vermicide	An agent lethal to intestinal parasites
Vermifuge	An agent that expels worms; an anthelmintic
Vermifuge	An agent that expels worms or intestinal animal parasites
Verminosis	Infestation with vermin
Vertigo	A sensation of rotation or movement of one's self
Virus	A minute infectious agent
Viscermegaly	Enlargement of the abdominal viscera
Vitiligo	Chronic pigmentary anomaly of the skin
Vulnerary	Useful for healing wounds
Vulvitis	Inflammation of the vulva
Wheeze	A whistling respiratory sound
Wound	A bodily injury
Zoster	Herpes zoster

Meanings of Hindi and Ayurvedic Words

Aam: undigested or half digested juice extract of food, which acts as poison.

Amla: sour.

Awagahana: tub bath, with medicated water, decoction, Oil or liquid.

Batasha: small round sugar cake.

Bhavana: to soak or make wet some powder with liquid or decoction.

Chapati: *Roti*, a thin cake of unleavened bread.

Charaka: An ancient scholar of Indian system of medicine 'Ayurveda'. 3000 B.C. One of the founder of basic principles of this science, also called father of medicine.

Chasani: solution of sugar.

Chaturbeeja: group of four plants, *Trigonella foinum gracum, Trachyspermum ammi, Carum bulbocastanum, Lepidium sativum.*

Chaturjata: group of four plants, *Cinamomum verum, Cinamomum tamala, Elettaria cardamomum, Mesua ferrea.*

Churna: powder.

Dashamoola: group of ten medicines, *Tribulus terrestris, Solunum surattense,S.ferox, Desmodium gangeticum, Uraria picta, Aegle marmelos,premna corymbosa, Orxylum indicum, sterospermum suaveolens, Gmelina Arboria.*

Dhatu: seven basic material of the body, according to princles of Indian system of medicine, e.g. *rasa* (plasma), *rakta* (blood),*mansa* (flesh), *meda* (fat), *asthi* (bones), *majja* (Bone marrow) and *shukra* (semen).

Dhatvagnimandhya: deficiency of process of forming seven basic material in the body

Ghee: clarified butter.

Gulkand: conserve prepared of rose petals and sugar.

Guna: effect, nature or property.

Guru: substance, who take more time in digestion.

Halava: a typical Indian sweet dish or pudding.

Jawara: small plants of wheat or barley.

Kajjali: well mixed powder of pure Mercury and pure Sulphur.

Kanji: a fermented sour liquid preparation of salt and mustard seeds.

Kapha: anabolism, all mucoidal secretion as synovial fluid, cerebrospinal fluid etc. and all factors who responsible anabolism, or the process by which simple compounds are converted into complex living organized substance in the body.

Kashaya: astringent.

Katu: spicy, pungent.

Kheer: sweet dish of milk and rice.

Khsarasutra: medicated thread, made with latex of *Euphorbia neriifolia* and *Curcuma longa.*

Khsirapaka: medicine boiled in milk.

Kwatha: decoction.

Laghu: substance, who take less time in digestion.

Lakhsa: lac.

Lawana: salt, salinity, comeliness.

Madhur: sweet.

Mridu: emollient.

Murabba: preserved and sweetened fruits etc.

Nasya: snuff, medicine administered by nose.

Pakori: a spicy Indian dish, made from gram flour.

Patal yantra: An apparatus, for obtained oil etc, from seeds or material.

Peya: diluted preparation of rice and water.

Picchala: mucilaginous.

Pitta: responsible factors for catabolism, conversion of complex material into simpler compound for release of energy in the body.

Punsavan: medicine for getting male child, during pregnancy period.

Rasa: taste.

Rukhsa: substance having dry or rough effect.

Sattu: Powder of fried Barley and Sugar.

Shatadhota-ghrita: hundred times washed clarified butter by water.

Sheeta: refrigerant, having cold effect.

Shiro-virechaka: medicine apply by nose and having effect on cerebrum.

Shrotorodha: Occlusion

Siddha- dugdha: boiled milk with medicine.

Snigdha: substance having unctuous effect or oily.

Suji: granulated wheat.

Sukhsma: subtel.

Sushruta: An ancient scholar of Indian system of medicine *'Ayurveda'*. 600 B.C. One of the founder of basic principles of this science, also called father of surgery, also discover plastic surgery.

***Tikhsna*:** pungent.

***Tikta*:** acrid, bitter.

***Trifala*:** group of three medicines, *Terminalia chebula, Terminalia belliarica, Phyllanthus emblica.*

***Trikatu*:** group of three spicy medicines, *Piper longum, Solunum nigrum, Zingiber officinale.*

***Trina-panchamoola*:** Group of five plants, *Desmostachya bipinnta, Saccharum spontaneum, Saccharum bengalense, Imparata cylendrica, Saccharum officinale.*

***Usna*:** thermogenic, having hot effect.

***Vata*:** sense of nervous system and brain.

Vipaka: last effect of a medicine.

***Virya*:** effect of medicine, metabolic property, potency

***Vishada*:** non-mucilaginous.

***Yavagu*:** a concentrate syrup like preparation, made with rice and water, three types- manda, peya, vilepi.

***Yusha*:** a preparation, made from paste of medicine, green gram ant water.

Index to Sanskrit, Hindi and Local Names
According to Serial Number of Plant

Resource Plants of Gums

Usare Revand	*Garcinia indica*
Nadihingu	*Gardenia gummifera*
Ushaka	*Dorema ammoniacum*
Ral	*Shorea robusta*
Mocharas	*Bombax ceiba*
Guggulu	*Commifora mukul*
Bol	*Commifora myrrha*
Salai Gugala	*Boswellia serrata*
Kunduru	*Boswelia floribunda*
Hingu	*Ferula foetida*
Katira	*Cochlospermum gossipium*
Khoonkharaba	*Daemonorops draco*
Vansalochan	*Bambusa arundinacea*
Gandha Biroja	*Pinus roxburghii*

Key Index of Botanical Names of Medicinal Plants

According to Serial Numbers of Plants

(For easy searching of botanical names of various medicinal plants, here is an index. By using this index, we can search any particular plant, included in this book. If someone has forgotten the generic name at the moment and only remembering the specific name, even than, plant can be traced. The names starting with capital letter, have generic name first followed by the specific name, while those starting with a small letter, have a vice-versa sequence. The numeral given at the end of the name is the **serial number** of the plant and **not** the page number of the book)